DATE DUE

DEMCO 38-296

CONCEPTUAL FOUNDATIONS OF SCIENTIFIC THOUGHT

MARX W. WARTOFSKY

Boston University

CONCEPTUAL FOUNDATIONS OF SCIENTIFIC THOUGHT

An Introduction to the Philosophy of Science

THE MACMILLAN COMPANY, NEW YORK
COLLIER-MACMILLAN LIMITED, LONDON

ACKNOWLEDGMENTS

I wish to express my gratitude and indebtedness to the many students in courses and seminars who, by their own efforts to achieve understanding and intellectual mastery, have provided the contexts in which many of my own ideas and forms of presentation have taken shape. Among colleagues and friends, who cannot be blameless for what they taught me but are not responsible for whatever errors and infelicities this book may contain, I wish especially to thank Robert S. Cohen, chairman of the physics department at Boston University and my co-worker in the Boston Colloquium for the Philosophy of Science, whose live sense of scientific inquiry and deep humanism have taught me much, and whose critical reading of portions of an early draft were very helpful; Daniel A. Greenberg, formerly of the physics and history departments at Columbia University, who read the entire manuscript in an early draft; Israel Scheffler, of Harvard University, who read a later draft and whose criticisms and encouragement were invaluable; Abner Shimony, of M.I.T., whose cautions and criticisms helped me to revise the early portions of the book; and to the following, who read portions of the manuscript in various stages and from whose suggestions I hope to have benefited: George D. W. Berry, philosophy department, Boston University; Ralph Schiller, physics department, Stevens Institute of Technology; Thomas G. R. Bower and Charles Gross, psychology department, Harvard University; and Bernard Elevitch, philosophy department, University of Massachusetts at Boston. My editor, Mr. John D. Moore of Macmillan, proved a constant help, as did two diligent but anonymous readers. I wish also to acknowledge the help of my graduate assistants, Mr. Jesse Victor, who prepared the index, and Mr. Richard Beaulieu, who helped read proof.

Finally may I express gratitude and love to my wife and children, who, despite all their best intentions, made this book all but impossible to write. For their disturbing presence, and for their assiduous nonparticipation as noneditors and nontypists, much thanks.

M. W. W.

First Printing

Library of Congress catalog card number: 67-15542

THE MACMILLAN COMPANY, NEW YORK
COLLIER-MACMILLAN CANADA, LTD., TORONTO, ONTARIO

PRINTED IN THE UNITED STATES OF AMERICA

Preface

THE PHILOSOPHY OF SCIENCE IS, as Philipp Frank characterized it, a bridge between the sciences and the humanities. It interprets the concepts and modes of thought of the sciences, and their substantive content, as subject matter for critical reflection and humanistic understanding. In the last half century, in which there has been such a radical transformation and growth of the sciences, the philosophy of science has developed as a many-sided and rigorous discipline in its own right. It has brought to bear the analytic instruments of logical critique and reconstruction, as well as the synthetic effort at philosophical generalization, on the history of science and on contemporary scientific thought. This book presents the philosophy of science in the broad context of these historical, analytic, and synthetic components of the philosophical enterprise. Thus, Part I is concerned with the genesis of science, in common sense and common practice and in the prescientific modes of explanation exemplified in myth, maxim, and technical rule. The roots of scientific knowledge are traced to the ordinary human activities of perceiving, acting, and thinking; and they are traced to the forms and functions of discourse and their development in the origins of criticism and of rational scientific thought in ancient Greek philosophy and science. Part II deals with the methods of science, considering the methodological as well as the epistemological and ontological questions which arise in the contexts of observation, description, classification, measurement, and the use of formal systems and models in science. There follow chapters on hypothesis and experiment, induction, probability, the complex questions of scientific explanation, and the nature and role of laws and theories in science. Part III is concerned with some fundamental concepts of science, such as causality; space, time, and matter; organism and mechanism in the biological sciences, and the issue of reduction; the questions of mind, consciousness, and behavior which arise in the sciences of psychology and sociology; and special questions of content and methodology in the social sciences and history. Finally, the Coda addresses itself briefly to the large question of science, values, and the humanistic understanding, and it attempts to restate the rationale for the broadly genetic-analytic approach of the book.

The use of historical materials, and of examples and illustrations from the various sciences, as well as the reliance on sociological, anthropological, and psychological contexts in the early discussion of the genesis of science, is meant to be self-contained, so that the student or the intelligent layman is provided with the necessary content for the formal analysis embodied in the text. Nevertheless, the vast sweep of contemporary philosophy of science requires that such an introduction of these topics be supplemented by readings in the wide historical and current literature. Therefore, there are extended bibliographical notes for each chapter, in which relevant selected readings are listed and discussed. These should provide a guide to further study, going beyond this introduction in scope, detail, and technical level.

The three appendixes—which provide (1) a case history in the development of the concept of motion from Aristotle to Galileo, (2) a brief account of the development of Greek science after Aristotle, and (3) a note on logical notation used in some portions of the text —are meant to supplement the text; but it is to the largest extent independent of them.

The main emphasis throughout is on the philosophy of science as a philosophical discipline, related therefore to the classic disciplines of metaphysics, epistemology, and logic. Philosophic method is never simply expository. It is critical, analytic, dialectical. Thus, emphasis has been placed on alternative formulations, their arguments and counter-arguments, and on the ongoing criticism which constitutes the stuff of philosophical discourse. It is this dialectic, rather than any set of conclusions, which is central to the text. It is hoped that the reader will enter into this critical spirit and will come not simply to learn about philosophy of science, but to enter into the vital issues as a critic and thinker himself: to appropriate this material as matter for his own reflective understanding; to approach, thereby, that humanistic understanding of science which this work sets forth as its goal.

M. W. W.

Contents

CHAPTER 1
Science and Philosophy: An Introduction

UNDERSTANDING SCIENCE

EVERYBODY KNOWS what science is. That is to say, everybody knows what science does. It experiments; it discovers; it measures and observes; it frames theories which explain the way and the why of things; it invents techniques and tools; it proposes and disposes, hypothesizes and tests; it asks questions of nature and gets them answered; it conjectures, refutes, confirms, and disconfirms; it separates truth from falsehood, sense from nonsense; it tells you how to get where you want to get, how to do what you want to do. The scientist is a man like other men, but also a man unlike other men, for he knows how to do all these things. He has been rigorously trained in a no-nonsense school and has emerged hard-headed, confident, and knowing. There has been combined in him a knowledge of theory and a method by which this theory is effectively applied in practice. The scientist, moreover, enjoys the rare privilege of using his own mind, of practicing the high and lone art of thinking by himself. Yet he belongs to a universal community which speaks a universal language; he is at home in Boston, Tokyo, Moscow, Stockholm, Peking, Buenos Aires, New Delhi, Dakar. For all his individuality his findings, reports, discoveries are subjected to universal scrutiny by his peers, who transcend all barriers of personal interest, all parochialisms of taste, pride, and national view, and critically and objectively assess the new, reconstruct the old. In short, science is a huge success, and the scientist a man marked by success. He is a man who knows, and who knows that he knows.

Now there may be remarked an unsure irony in the way in which all this is described here—unsure, in that it is hard to deny that in fact this is what everyone knows science to be, but it is also hard to deny that anything that good arouses suspicion. It is hard to accept at face value such God-like sureness of purpose and method, such eminence in achievement. It makes us nervous, and some deep rumblings of an ancient sense of *hubris* stir within us. We are equally gratified at the perfection of science and at the flaws it reveals. The scientist's achievement wins our profoundest respect; yet his admission that there are things he cannot explain, the admission of a radical uncertainty at the foundations of his knowledge, or the failure to account "scientifically" for some of the homely things we all understand gives us all a sense of common mortality, a tongue-clucking condescension, a self-reaffirming feeling in the wisdom that recognizes the scientist as a man flawed, like the rest of us, after all.

At the root of our ambivalence there is the feeling that somehow science has paid for its success by enforcing a deep division between the humane concerns, and ordinary traffic of men on the one hand, and naked confrontation with a truth, on the other, before which these concerns pale and become trivial. In older myths the acquisition of knowledge of such a high order as science now represents carried with it the penalty of alienation from the comforts of some felicitous primal state of ignorance. It was a serpent who tempted Eve, and through her, Adam. It was Mephistopheles who bargained for Faust's soul. The scientist, in our popular culture, has been represented as mad, as amoral, or as naively trusting. We seem to recognize in our projected image of the scientists some radical and dangerous compulsion to inquire, to discover, to open Pandora's box. And we are timid. Curiosity, after all, killed the cat. Furthermore, this unbridled revelation threatens the reserves of whatever is hidden in ourselves. We are torn between wanting to know and being afraid to find out, between desire for the power such knowledge brings and repugnance to the awesome responsibilities such power imposes on us all. Our social and cultural institutions, our educational system, our economy all betray the rift. It becomes articulated as one between "the two cultures," the "scientific" and the "humanistic," and we are trapped between what we know science to be—the highest achievement of rational and humane culture—and what we simultaneously fear science has become— an amoral and inhumane instrument which has developed beyond human control, a beast machine without a soul, which devours all before it.

Yet although there are real problems concerning the place of science in our culture, many of the fears, as well as many of the expectations, concerning science are based on ignorance. There is a need to understand science which lies at the heart of our hope for a humanistic culture, for a free and enlightened society. It is a need as great for the scientist as for the nonscientist. Such an understanding alone goes beyond inherited myths, beyond shibboleths, beyond dogmatic and traditional conceptions. It goes beyond them in undertaking a critical and rational examination of the fundamental features of science. It cannot take the mystery out of science, because there is no "mystery" in science. There is only what needs to be understood and studied.

There are two main approaches to the understanding of science. One is the study of science itself. It is the professed aim of our liberal education to provide such study throughout the curriculum, from the elementary school through college. The child is introduced to knowledge of the world around him in his studies. He studies what is known about "nature," "the physical world," "life," "society." He tends to picture what he learns in dramatic form: discrete universes, some populated with dinosaurs, some with stars in picturable constellations, some with ping-pong-ball "molecules," some with such visible wonders of microstructure as those in plant and animal tissue. He realizes form beneath appearance, in skeletal structures, in atomic models of an invisible reality out of which, presumably, the ordinary furniture of the earth is constituted. He is introduced to processes and to their invariant form and sequence and begins to recognize the shape of laws, and the scope of theories. He learns to intervene, experiment, observe, note, and report what he notes. Principles of an abstract sort are exemplified and explained to him in the demonstration experiment. His day-to-day language now countenances such theoretical terms as *energy, force, chromosome, atomic weight, adaptation,* and *gravity.* Concurrently, the ordinary operations of addition and subtraction become more abstract and theoretical as "number facts" replace intuitive counting, and rules replace habits. Abstract entities and abstract operations like "squaring a number," "solving for *x*," and "proving a theorem" join the older pictures and the palpable truths of observation. Mathematics is joined to physical description and to the inferences concerning facts.

Ideally, some such broad spectrum of scientific study is the minimum condition for contemporary literacy. By the time the student has completed his secondary education he has acquired a foundational knowledge of science so great that it tends to be overlooked only because it is regarded as elementary. He has acquired, in addition, for better or for worse, a fairly comprehensive conceptual framework within which the facts, operations, and ideas he has learned are ordered and understood. In the further study of science this framework will be modified and elaborated, but it will never be basically questioned or examined as itself a subject of scientific study, unless a study beyond that of the sciences themselves is undertaken.

Such a study is the study of the conceptual frameworks of the sciences. It is intimately connected with the study of the sciences, because it is within the sciences that such frameworks are operative. But it is just as intimately connected with our nonscientific understanding, with our ordinary notions of the way things are, with what we usually call our common sense. At the very base of science is the impress of its historical continuity with common experience, with common ways of understanding, and with common ways of talking and thinking, for science did not spring into being full grown. It grew by accretion, modification, radical reformulation side by side with tradition and with vestigial concepts. Science has created artificial languages of great rigor and elegance, but it has had to do this speaking our common natural languages and while relating the world as it is represented in our ordinary language and perception to that world of extraordinary language and perception which scientific discourse exhibits.

What such scientific discourse reveals is a conception of the world or parts of it that is often radically different from our ordinary conceptions. The scientist has eyes, ears, and hands like the rest of us, yet what he sees, hears, and manipulates is guided by an inner vision of things often quite different from ours. Where in the ordinary course of things we perceive and cope with the ordinary furniture of the earth—tables, chairs, stars, animals, rain, and other men like ourselves—the scientist studies these in terms of structures, laws, relationships between part and part and between part and whole, origin and development, and change and its ordered sequences. He presses for a reduction of the gross objects and processes of our everyday environment to their elements and to combinations of these elements. His inquiry leads to the formulation of concepts by means of which his different and growing understanding of things is expressed, allowing him to order and communicate the most complex features of his analysis. Such concepts as those of mass, motion, position, time, chemical element and atomic structure, species and adaptation, and society and culture are not bits and pieces of isolated understanding. Rather, they are related to each other, and to a network of concepts by means of which these are in turn understood, to form what we may call a conceptual framework or structure. The work of the scientist—both his theoretical activity and his practical research and experimentation—is guided by such concepts and made systematic by such conceptual structures, so that what he discovers here has bearing on his understanding of what he has discovered there, linked by the network of thought and inference which the conceptual framework provides.

Thus, we may say that the concepts of science are the working tools of scientific thought. They are the ways in which the scientist has learned to understand complex phenomena, to realize their relations to each other, and to represent these in communicable form. Among the most wonderful of those things we consider inventions of science are the concepts of science. They are, in effect, the sophisticated instrumentation, the high technology of scientific thought and discourse.

The lineage of these concepts, however, goes back to the ordinary conceptions of common sense, the ways in which all of us characteristically learn to represent to ourselves and to each other the way things are. To understand science in its relation to common sense and to find here the common roots of the sciences and the humanities is to come to an understanding of science different from that achieved by studying the sciences themselves. We will consider such an understanding as the object of the philosophy of science, and we will define the task of this latter enterprise as the systematic study of the concepts and conceptual frameworks of the sciences. Because the claim here is that such conceptual frameworks are the instruments of scientific understanding, the ways in which the scientist comes to understand the world of his inquiry, we may characterize the philosophy of science as an enterprise in understanding the scientific understanding. And insofar as such conceptual frameworks provide the fundamental shape of scientific thought, or its basic structure, the study of the philosophy of science may be characterized as a study of the conceptual foundations of scientific thought. Such a characterization is admittedly loose, and the limits of philosophy of science are at best vaguely set, as are the borderlines between it and the sciences proper, on the one hand, and the more general philosophical disciplines, on the other. But in this vaguely defined region the substance and hard content will be set out in concrete detail as we proceed. The border areas will concern us not as divisions to be drawn, but as exemplifying the philosophy of science as, in Philipp Frank's characterization, a bridge between the sciences and the humanities.

The relation between science and philosophy therefore concerns not only what science is, or how scientific thought takes place, but the relation of scientific thought to other kinds of thinking—to common sense, to humanistic studies in literature and the arts, and to the extraordinary ways of thinking of the creative artist. Thus philosophy of science provides a link between the two cultures which tries to relate them to each other in some coherent way. Philosophy is nothing if not a dedicated search for coherence, for the synthesis of what we know in one field with what we know in others. Sometimes this enthusiasm for synthesis leads to excess, to fanciful systems and wishful unities of everything-all-at-once which evaporate under critical examination, and are often no more than expressions of scientifically illiterate goodwill and pious hopes for coherence.

Nevertheless, great achievements of synthesis have been hewn out of the rock of rigorous philosophical analysis and construction by scientist philosophers. Such an achievement was Aristotle's, in the ancient world; and in a way which has left its impress on the most advanced contemporary sciences, Plato and Democritus constructed systems of thought which have had profound effect on the most diverse fields of human inquiry. In our own day the natural philosophers Einstein and Whitehead have attempted such broad syntheses.

Our more modest task is to try to understand, or even to try to formulate, the questions that such syntheses would have to answer.

CONCEPTS AND CONCEPTUAL FRAMEWORKS

To put it in a grossly simple way, the concept of a chair is what we understand by *chair*. Thus, the chair standing in front of us is not itself the concept of a chair, nor is the inscription *chair* on this page a concept of a chair. The first is a physical object, usually having four legs, used to sit upon. The latter is an inscription (in this instance in ink on paper) having five letters and belonging to the English language. The concept "chair" is what we take this word to mean, by virtue of which we use it to refer to physical objects like the chair standing in front of us. This sense of the meaning of a word or of a more complex linguistic expression, or of what we understand by the linguistic expression, is therefore distinct from the actual object which the expression names or describes. But it is in virtue of our understanding some such expression to mean this or that, that we would agree as to whether something is a chair or not.

Thus, as soon as we begin to think and to use language to communicate, our activity is concerned with such meaning and understanding. The growth and evolution of our thinking is thus a process of forming concepts and of elaborating the more or less systematic structures within which these concepts are related to each other. But beyond this, once we articulate such concepts we may study these meanings and their relations themselves. That is, we may critically reflect on our understanding and study not simply what our concepts are about but the concepts themselves. In this way we may begin to analyze the relation between our ordinary commonsense conception of things and the scientific understanding.

Our ordinary concepts, at first glance, seem to be quite concrete and practical. Perhaps it is hard to isolate and become critically aware of our most ordinary concepts, for we take them for granted. That (to use one of G. E. Moore's examples) I was smaller when I was much younger, or that the chair is between the table and the wall, or that night follows day is not the sort of thing one spends much time thinking about. Nor does one puzzle over the fact that knives cut, water is wet, and fire burns. Yet all these things had to be learned at some point and our understanding of them established. Our concepts, though they pertain to this or that particular thing or situation, are usually about sorts of things and types of situations. That is, they have a greater or lesser generality, or scope, often ranging over classes of things or establishing the relations of this or that thing to others of its kind. The analysis of this range and of such relations among concepts often reveals to us how systematic our conceptual frameworks are and in what ways our understanding of one concept bears on our understanding of others.

Among our most deeply rooted concepts are those of great generality, which may be said to constitute the basic framework of our thinking. Thus, for example, we have concepts of *hardness,* of *solidity,* of *inside* and *outside,* of *shape,* and of *place* and *being at a place* which are of great generality and apply to many things in our experience. But there is a still more general concept to which these are more or less systematically related (whether we realize it consciously or not): the concept of a *thing.* We also have a general concept of how different things relate to each other. For example, two different things cannot be in the same place at the same time. However, things can replace other things, can come into contact with other things, can be next to, or between other things; things can change and can be changed. On examination, any such general concept as *thing* is seen to be related to other concepts equally general, in terms of which we come to explain or to realize consciously what it is we mean, or what exactly we understand a thing to be. So in conceiving of a thing as being at a place, or being in some relation to other things in "their" places, we appeal to a general concept of space. Moreover, in conceiving of how things act and move and change in relation to other things, we appeal to a general concept of time. In our basic conception of the relation of things to each other we take certain things to be the cause of others, appealing to some general concept of cause and effect, or causality. These are not esoteric, "way-out" concepts, but the ordinary concepts of our ordinary thinking. They represent the way in which we structure the world of our experience in thought. And willy-nilly, whether we consciously try to order these concepts or not, they are related in a more or less systematic way, and such a system of concepts constitutes the common framework within which we make sense to each other and to ourselves. Such a conceptual framework, therefore, is the way in which we rationally order our knowledge. And insofar as our thinking and knowing is intimately tied to our beliefs and actions, such a conceptual framework serves also to order our actions and expectations.

Science has achieved a remarkable rigor in its construction of such a conceptual framework, which goes beyond the ordinary requirements of common sense, common language, and common activity. It has developed the analysis of its working concepts to a very high degree, by the adoption of special languages appropriate to its special subject matters, by the achievement of precision appropriate to such a subject, and by the constant criticism and testing of such concepts against the facts of our experience. But the concepts of scientific work are often highly specialized and are developed in limited domains. The scientist has been able to isolate or abstract certain features of the world for intensive investigation, and he has adapted his concepts to their special use. Yet when he does all this he is a thinking being, like the rest of us, and the general framework of commonsense concepts he has acquired underlies his special conceptual framework. And sometimes what is good enough for common sense is not good enough for the work of science. The physicist's concept of *place* and *thing* and *hard* and *cause and effect* may have developed, under the rigors of scientific criticism and testing, to the point where they are very different from, or even incompatible with, our everyday concepts. Yet the scientist, no less than we, drags the inheritance of common sense, common education, and common language along with him.

Sometimes, his newer concepts replace our older ones, or modify them radically, so that common sense becomes transformed by science. For example, our concept of spatial location, of *being at a place* is, for all practical purposes, clear and adequate. We cannot conceive, for example, that there is anything that is not at some place at a given time, nor could we conceive that something is more or less at a place or that it is at two places at the same time. Yet, on examination, we may dig up problematic aspects of what we mean here. Simply to say that "something" is "at a place" presupposes some clear notion of the boundaries or limits of a thing, as it does a clear idea of a place being "this" rather than "that" place. Our ordinary conceptions fit quite well with the classical physics which made explicit these commonsense notions of position. Yet both the most ancient physics of the Greeks and contemporary quantum physics reveal alternative concepts of *being at a place,* and the history of classical physics itself exemplifies the difficulties in achieving a rigorous and unproblematic conception of position or location. For example, if one conceives of the physical world as ultimately made up of tiny point-like particles which move in a continuous and homogeneous space, do such particles have an "inside" and an "outside"? If they are in constant motion, can one speak of a "place" at which they are at any given "slice" of time, or only of a place through which they are moving, so that they are never really "there," but either arriving or leaving? Or can it be conceived that such an elemental particle can "get" from one place to another without going "through" the intervening places? Can it simply pop up at different places at different times without having a path? Such strange conceptual possibilities strain our commonsense framework severely, yet they are among the conceptual alternatives that theoretical science has been forced to consider. The questions then arise whether such an account of the realm of the very small is incompatible with our ordinary account of medium-sized objects and environments, or whether the two can be shown to be related in a plausible way. Similarly, the conceptual framework which represented the earth as a great body whirling through space in an orbit around the sun seemed incompatible with the commonsense notion that the earth was at rest and that everything else moved around it. That the sun did not really "rise" as it appeared to, but that we rotated into its light seemed equally to strain common sense. When such a conceptual revolution occurs the strains between our (then) ordinary view of things and the one science presents become very severe and a reformulation of the system of concepts becomes necessary.

The same thing happens not merely between science and common sense but within science itself. In modern times one of the sharpest of such conceptual strains appeared when two alternative and apparently incompatible accounts of the phenomenon of light (and of electromagnetic radiation in general) seemed both to be necessary for a full description of such phenomena. One view held that such radiation is a wave or a continuous ray, and this conception explains certain experimental phenomena. Yet there are other phenomena which can be explained only if light is conceived as made up of particles and is therefore discontinuous in its structure. The attempt to formulate a coherent physical picture embodying both of these conditions has occupied theoretical physicists very seriously in recent years and has even persuaded some of them to abandon the attempt at formulating such a coherent picture as a misguided one.

Yet there is a strong inclination to get our knowledge whole, to integrate what we know here with what we know there. Loose seams are aesthetically and intellectually displeasing; man wants not only to do, but to understand. The impetus to philosophical analysis in the interests of conceptual clarity and systematic coherence is too deeply ingrained, especially in the thinking scientist, to permit conceptual inconsistencies and muddles to abide. There is a sense of system and a demand for clarity and for the unity of our thought which go to the roots of our thinking activity, and may very well go even deeper, deriving from the kind of organisms we are and the kind of world we have to survive in. Scientific training and practice sharpen this sense and this demand. In a way, then, the scientist, when he faces the philosophical problems that arise in the conceptual framework of science, is advancing a kind of human activity which goes beyond scientific activity to the very roots of our being—our urge to know and understand.

THE PHILOSOPHIC DISCIPLINES: METAPHYSICS, EPISTEMOLOY, LOGIC

At the outset of this inquiry we shall briefly characterize three major philosophic disciplines and their relevance to science. Among the most basic questions that may be asked are the following: (1) What exists and what is the nature or structure of what exists? (2) How can we know the things that exist and how justify our knowledge-claims? (3) How are concepts related to each other? What is valid inference or correct reasoning? What is truth? Philosophy has concerned itself with such questions in a variety of ways under the general headings of (1) metaphysics, (2) epistemology, and (3) logic. What follows may serve as the barest characterization, for the flesh and blood features of these philosophic skeletons will emerge only when they are seen in the context of the conceptual structure of science itself.

Metaphysics

The driving force of metaphysical thought, both in its classical and modern forms, has been the attempt to get things whole, to present a unified picture or framework within which the wide diversity of things in our experience could be explained on the basis of some universal principles, or as manifestations of some universal stuff or process. Thus, the very origins of philosophy and science, in the Greek colonies in Ionia in the sixth century B.C., grew out of physical speculation as to how the multiplicity of things and kinds in nature came into being, out of some primal stuff or out of some primal activity or motion. Such explanations in terms of some unitary principle concerned the coming into being of the natural world and as such represented a prescientific and speculative form of cosmogony. It derived in great part from myths and religious accounts of creation, but it differed sharply from these in attempting to give an explanation in terms of natural and impersonal forces, instead of supernatural personifications of gods and spirits.

The corollary of this speculative cosmogony is the cosmological speculation on the structure of the world. It asks such questions as, "What is everything made of?" "How can one account for the diversity of things in terms of transformations of an initial and elementary stuff, or of a few such elements—typically, air, earth, fire, and water—or as constituted of combinations of bits of elementary stuff?" It should be clear from this that the earliest metaphysics already adumbrates the sorts of questions which later come to be typical of physics and chemistry—that is, questions concerning the structure of matter.

With Plato and Aristotle the earlier physical speculation or natural philosophy passes over into an explicit analysis of the principles of explanation themselves—that is, to a consideration of the kind of thing one is asking when he asks for such unitary and universal explanations. The question on what there is becomes transformed into a question concerning the rational principles by means of which the manifold complexity of things known and experienced could be comprehended. By *rational principles* the Greek metaphysicians meant something like what we have described as the most general concepts in terms of which anything could be understood. "Anything" presumably leaves it open as to what particular things may be chosen as objects of understanding. But here is the peculiarity and the force of metaphysics: the underlying assumption is that anything in the universe has features that it shares with everything else. There are therefore universal features of all that exists or universal principles of understanding existence which comprise the most basic subject matter of critical, reflective thought, of what could therefore be called "first" or "primary" philosophy. Thus Aristotle conceived of this subject matter as a science of first principles and spoke of it as a science of Being in itself—that is, not as particular sciences of this or that form or aspect or division of Being, such as biology, physics, psychology, or politics (about which he wrote separate treatises), but about the presuppositions or ultimate principles in terms of which any of the other sciences could come to be studied and rationally comprehended.

The history of metaphysics is a history of the criticism of concepts of such a universal or general sort, and of the attempt to formulate systems of such concepts in which the relations between them would be explicit and would follow canons of logical consistency and coherence. We might summarize this by defining *metaphysics* as "that enterprise in the formulation and analysis of concepts which undertakes a critical and systematic inquiry into the principles of Being, and the origin and structure of what there is."

Now, except for its extreme generality and its vagueness when stated in this form, this could very well be a broad definition of the enterprise of science. One classical criticism of metaphysics is that it states its questions in such a form that they are answerable only by the sheerest speculation, without evidence or justification by means of concrete, empirical, scientific inquiry. A more generous version of this criticism is that metaphysical questions remain merely speculative until they can come to be reformulated as scientific questions, answerable by means of hard, experimental research, and therefore testable by scientific means. But there is another view which regards such systematic critical and speculative thought as a part of science: namely, that part which serves as the most general conceptual framework within which scientific hypotheses and theories come to be formulated. Metaphysics serves therefore as a source of ideas, as a guide to the systematization of different parts of scientific thought. Such pervasive characteristics of the scientist's commitment as the notion that nature is uniform, that scientific laws are nonlocal or hold equally in all parts of the universe, that nothing comes into being out of nothing (the earliest formulation of so-called conservation principles), or that nothing happens without a cause —all these, although they are not themselves the sorts of things whose truth can be tested by experiment, are nevertheless underlying regulative, or heuristic, ideas in science. That is, they form the basic world view of the scientist, the deep structure of his way of thinking, and constitute his (perhaps unstated) beliefs about the nature of things. As such, these metaphysical ideas regulate or guide the scientist with respect to the kinds of things he will regard as important or plausible. The critic of such a sanguine view of metaphysics would hold that instead of guiding the scientist, such vestiges of mythical and poetic imagination lead him astray, or worse yet, strait-jacket his thought within rigid and dogmatic frameworks.

In summary, the sorts of questions which concern metaphysics may be sorted out thus: If the question concerns the structure of what there is, the way in which things are put together in the world, we may call this "cosmology" or "structural metaphysics." If we ask what the origin of things is, how or why they come into being, we may call this "cosmogony." This concerns questions or characterizations of the origin of things in terms of some principle, or ground, or originative cause or purpose, in classical views. If we ask what kind of stuff or what sort of entities constitute this structure or have this origin—that is, if we ask "what exists" in respect to some ultimate characterizations of existence—for example, we might say "everything is matter in motion," or "everything is made up of discrete packets of energy," or "everything is either a physical object or a non-physical idea in some mind"—then we may call this study concerning what exists "ontology." We may, on the other hand, ask a very different sort of question, not about the structure or origin of things, nor about what exists, but about what this or that system of thought or language asserts or takes to be the case with respect to such questions. We may therefore be giving a description of the metaphysical beliefs or commitments of some group of people or some community of shared beliefs and meanings, and thus concern ourselves not with what exists but with what is said to exist by this group. This may be called "descriptive metaphysics."

Epistemology

Science is a way of knowing about the world, as it is also a body of knowledge. It may be characterized in terms of a process of inquiry, of a quest for truth. And we may characterize it also as that structure or body of accumulated and established truths or truth claims which such inquiry has generated. A set of basic questions arises concerning the status of such knowledge and such claims: What does it mean to say that one knows or that one is justified in believing this or that? What are the means by which such knowledge is acquired? What difference is there between initial conjectures and hypotheses and those we hold to be confirmed? What role does sense perception play in the acquisition of knowledge? How is thinking related to such perception? What role does inference play in the genesis of knowledge claims? Among alternative, incompatible claims how does one choose? What serves to warrant or justify belief, on the one hand, and to discredit or controvert it, on the other?

The analysis of such questions may be called "epistemology," or the "theory of knowledge." Its relevance to the scientific enterprise should be clear on general grounds, because science itself is both a way of knowing and a body of knowledge claims. The specific relevance of epistemology to philosophy of science concerns the instrumentalities for the acquisition and validation of scientific knowledge, the special aspects of the scientist's ways of coming to know. Thus, the role of observation and experiment, of description and classification, the role of inference or reasoning in science, the nature of hypotheses and the role of models, laws, and theories, the conditions and characterization of scientific discovery all concern the ways in which scientific knowledge is acquired and established, and thus also the ways in which some of the claims of science may be critically tested, refuted, and discarded. The quest for truth entails also the disposition of falsity. In this sense science is a critical, nondogmatic enterprise subjecting all its claims to test and criticism. Broadly conceived, the conditions of generating and testing the knowledge claims of science fall within the province of the epistemology of science. And in this sense our major concern in this book with the methodology of science may be characterized as an epistemological concern.

Logic

Some of what we know or claim to know seems direct, or immediate, intuitively certain, self-evident, and incontrovertible. Sensations or feelings of pain or hunger; convictions concerning one's self-identity; the belief that the same thing cannot be in two different places at the same time or that the whole is greater than any of its parts; or the belief that if some statement is true, it cannot at the same time be false in the same respect—all of these seem to be matters of certainty, either of sense or feeling, or of belief, or as is sometimes said, certainties of thought or reason.

Yet much of our knowledge, and perhaps most of it, is indirect or mediate knowledge, or knowledge by inference. Insofar as inference "moves" from one statement taken as a premise to another which we say "follows" from it as a conclusion in an argument, the "moves" we thus make constitute what we ordinarily call "reasoning" (or what an older usage called "ratiocination"). We may certainly be said to do our own "internal" reasoning, as when we say we think something through to a conclusion. But much of our reasoning takes external or public form. Our inference procedure is exhibited to plain view in some language. We give reasons, argue, show, prove, demonstrate in such a way that we suppose any other reasonable (or "rational") person should end up with the same conclusions we have arrived at, given the same premises and the same rules for moving from premises to conclusions. This articulate and explicit inference therefore has its embodiment in some language, and this language is both public and common, in the sense that idiosyncrasies and ambiguities are delimited so that a community of speakers share features of the language in common and can communicate with it. We then may speak of a universe of discourse which such a language exemplifies, and within such a universe, of the universality of the rules for the formation of proper, "grammatical" expressions, and for correct inference.

The hope for such an ideal and universal language, in which all rational beings or members of the community of discourse would share common rules and common commitments to the validity of inferences made in accordance with these rules, seems a hope for an ideally rational community. There would be universal agreement, presumably, concerning the conclusions that anyone would reach by correct or valid inference procedures; and upon common acceptance of the truth of the premises of any such argument, there would be a common acceptance of the truth of the conclusions. Such a broad vision of an ideal rationality pervades the history of logic. Leibniz conceived of it as a *mathesis universalis,* a universal mathematics which would settle all arguments unequivocally and by common consent to the rules of the game.

The more modest hope is that the analysis of proper or correct inference leads to a clarification of our knowledge, a clear articulation of the reasons and arguments by means of which we justify our beliefs. This concerns, then, a science or a rational theory of inference, or as it is sometimes called, a science of deduction. Such a science is sometimes characterized as a formal science, because it has to do not with the content of this or that argument, but with the form of the argument, or the form of the inference.

A part of logic, then, is the analysis of the forms of correct inference. Another, related part concerns the matter of definition—of making our meanings precise and showing how concepts are related to other concepts, or how one concept is defined in terms of another. This is the task of establishing, in fact, that common language which the ideal community of discourse shares, and of eliminating or delimiting vagueness and ambiguity. Beyond this, the use of formal systems in the sciences introduces a major philosophical issue: What is the relation between logic and reality, between the form of inference, of proof and demonstration, and the truth of things? In other terms, this raises the question of what the relation is between a linguistic system, or a system of concepts, or a theoretical model in the sciences and the reference of such a system or model to things outside the language.

The force of this concern may be seen when it is raised with respect to the so-called universal language of science, mathematics. Mathematics may be taken to be a formal system of inference (or a set of such systems) which deals with abstract entities and abstract operations upon them. Now one may take such a system as an abstractive representation of the concrete operations of counting, collecting, arranging sets of things in some order with respect to such properties as size or numerousness. The "formal system" may then be taken as the most abstract or general representation of such properties and relations in the real world, which affords us the most economical and systematic way of talking about them. Mathematics, however, may also be considered as an "uninterpreted" system of inference, in the sense that its terms are not taken to stand for anything at all outside the system itself, and the system itself is taken as a "purely formal" or ideal construction. There are difficult questions and alternative views in the philosophy of mathematics concerning such formal systems, which we cannot begin to deal with here. But the question arises, "How is it that deductions in a formal system, e.g. in arithmetic or geometry, have application to the real world, to the relations among physical properties of things?" How may numerical relations in a formal deductive system be mapped on the physical operations of measurement, i.e., how do we assign numbers? What correspondence is there, if any, between the formalism of mathematics, or the inference procedures of logic, and the facts of science which are stated or systematized in this form? A host of questions are now raised concerning the status of that knowledge we acquire by means of inference. In the flush of success of the mathematical description of the physical world, in the seventeenth century, Spinoza could express the correspondence of thoughts and things as an identity: "The order and connection of thoughts is the order and connection of things." In effect, our construction of a rational conceptual representation of the world corresponds to the way the world is, because reason, which is exemplified in mathematical reasoning, also exemplifies world structure itself. Such a conviction, that the world is rationally and mathematically ordered, is of the sort we have previously discussed as metaphysical, and the philosophy of logic often borders on such metaphysical conceptions. Furthermore, to the extent that logical analysis of inference and definition bears on the status and the validity of knowledge claims formulated by means of inference, such analysis also bears on the epistemological questions we have raised, and especially on the question of truth.

Perhaps the most basic philosophical question one may ask about logic, if one conceives of it as a science of valid inference and of the precise definition of the terms used in inference, is the question concerning what it means for something to be a "correct" or "valid" inference, or a "proper" definition. For this alludes to the norms or criteria of logic itself, and to the status of its rules. Are they conventions decided upon by fiat, simply postulates that we may change at will? Do they derive from the character and structure of natural languages themselves, from the very conditions of communication? Are the rules simply justified as instrumentalities which help us to get where we want to get, therefore as "good transportation" or "inference tickets" between the way stations of scientific thought? Or do they in fact reflect the order of reality itself and therefore give us a true representation of its basic structure?

In this preliminary sketch we can do no more than raise questions such as these, in order to characterize the typical concerns and the general boundaries of logic, metaphysics, and epistemology. These are not entirely discrete, but related philosophic disciplines which overlap at many points. For example, if we examine these questions from still a broader view, it becomes clear that certain fundamental concepts of science are logical concepts, that some of these logical concepts bear on epistemological questions about the nature and justification of our knowledge, and that, moreover some of these logical-epistemological questions bear directly on metaphysical questions. Concepts like *necessity, possibility, probability, existence, identity;* others like *class, individual, element, set, group;* and the general concepts of relation, such as *part-whole, class-member, order, substance-attribute, thing-property, genus-species, essence-accident;* and such logical-linguistic relations as *naming, referring, abstracting, denoting, meaning* all play a role in criticism and concept-formation in the sciences.

These three interrelated disciplines of philosophy have a rich history of rigorous critical inquiry. All three have profoundly affected the history of science and have been profoundly affected in turn by the history of science. The fuller understanding of science, which the philosophy of science purports to achieve, draws upon and is guided by what has been achieved in these disciplines. It is hoped that it contributes to them as well in its inquiry into the conceptual foundations of scientific thought.

ARE THERE PHILOSOPHICAL QUESTIONS IN SCIENCE?

Having said all this, it may appear paradoxical to add that one of the basic questions for philosophy of science is whether there are philosophical questions *in* science. One may argue, for example, that although questions concerning ontology, epistemology, or logic arise out of scientific thought, they are not in themselves scientific questions and are not to be resolved by the methods of science. On the other hand, it may be claimed that all scientific questions are "ultimately" philosophical, or rest on philosophical presuppositions, or assumptions, which thus form the foundation of scientific thought itself. Or at the very least it may be claimed that science helps to resolve what were once considered to be distinctively philosophical questions by translating such "perennial" and perennially undecidable questions into good, clear, decidable scientific questions.

Here a distinction suggests itself between different sorts of questions in science: There are questions with which the scientist deals as a working scientist in his particular field—for example, "What is the specific gravity of molybdenum?" "What are the compounds of mercury?" or "What accounts for the strange behavior of superconductors?" None of these questions involves any of the questions ordinarily called philosophical. Instead, these seem to be demands for straightforward, matter-of-fact answers. But there plainly are questions of another sort, related to these, which seem to be more broadly theoretical, such as, "What is the ultimate structure of matter?" or "Can the origin of life be explained strictly in terms of physico-chemical interactions?" or "Is light to be described as wave-like or as particle-like, as a combination of these two, or in some entirely different way?" Such questions seem to bear on the way things are ultimately put together, what may be said to exist, and how nature is to be conceived. There are also questions concerning scientific judgment: "What passes for a proper experiment?" "How does experimental evidence confirm or disconfirm a hypothesis?" "How do laws in science function in scientific inference and prediction?" In this range of questions matters of the method of scientific inquiry and the justification of scientific belief arise—in short, questions concerning the nature and validity of scientific knowledge. There is still another kind of question which arises concerning the formal systematization of a field of inquiry (for example, the periodic table of the elements, the matrix form of wave mechanics, or the classificatory schemes of families, genera, and species in botany and zoology). And there is the still more complex formal systematization when two or more fields of inquiry are related to each other by means of a unifying explanation or formal model, as for example in electromagnetic theory or in the relation of geometrical optics to quantum mechanics. Here are raised questions of the formal or logical structure of scientific theories.

Now these aspects of scientific thought seem to be *in* science if anything is. Although the scientist at work on specific problems may not be explicitly concerned with such questions in the abstract, as a theoretician within his science he cerainly copes with them as a set of questions to be concretely answered in his inquiry. Thus, they constitute, in their practical embodiment, the stuff of day-to-day scientific inquiry.

Yet if one examines these sorts of questions in their general form, as questions concerning what exists, concerning the acquisition and justification of scientific knowledge, concerning the logical structure of science and the nature of scientific inference, then these may be seen to be akin to the characteristic philosophical questions discussed earlier. To the extent that such questions are treated not simply in the concrete contexts of actual scientific practice but are abstracted for reflection on the nature of scientific knowledge, these are no longer questions *in* science, but questions *about* science. To put it another way, they are not so much questions of scientific theory as questions concerning a theory of science.

A theory of science which deals with the substantive and methodological questions which arise in science may indeed lie outside the day-to-day practice of science. Yet it is enmeshed in the very way in which the scientist regards his work and his universe. The scientist, like the rest of us, drags the unformulated and inexplicit heritage of common sense with him into his work, as he drags the inchoate inheritance of metaphysical, epistemological, and logical formulations which have become imbedded in his science in its historical development. It may well be the case that this uncritical and uncriticized heritage may hobble him with hidden and unrecognized dogmas; and it may well be the case that the forms of thought thus appropriated may also serve a heuristic function, guiding the scientific imagination along the unexamined and little understood paths of discovery. At crucial points in his activity it sometimes happens that the reflection on such questions of method and substance, or the reflective critique of the concepts of science become necessary to the advance of a science, to the reformulation of its fundamental ideas. At such times the working scientist may well become a philosopher of science. He may be a very bad one, if he is philosophically naive or uncritical. Or he may achieve the philosophical distinction of a Descartes, a Newton, a Leibniz, a Planck, or an Einstein, who all helped to reshape not only the conceptual frameworks of science but the fundamental concepts of philosophy as well.

The question as to whether there are philosophical questions in science thus already involves us in the characterization of science, in reflection on the nature of scientific questions—which is to say, it is a philosophical question. It does not have a simple answer but involves us at the outset in analysis, in reasons and arguments, in that critical dialectic which is the lifeblood of philosophy.

In the course of this study we shall group the characteristic questions about science into two major classifications: (1) those having to do with the procedures and methods of scientific inquiry and (2) those having to do with the world view of the scientist, within the framework of which he practices these procedures. The first of these we will call *methodological* questions, and the second *substantive* questions. The first will deal with such concepts and practices of science as observation, measurement, hypothesis and experiment, confirmation and disconfirmation, induction and probability, forms of scientific inference, the general nature of formal systems and their empirical or descriptive interpretations as representations of the facts and as instruments of inquiry. We will then examine typical structures or patterns of scientific explanation and the nature of laws and theories in science. The discussion of the function of laws and theories raises substantive questions concerning the concepts of lawfulness and causality and the status of theoretical entities. This leads us to the consideration of those fundamental concepts which delineate the frameworks within which scientific inquiry proceeds and which often affect methodological considerations as well: the concepts of space, time, and matter; of life; of the relation of the mental to the physical; of mind and behavior; and finally of society and history.

The aim of this study is not simply to consider one after another the various questions and subject matters of philosophy of science, but to realize in the course of these considerations some humanistic understanding of the sciences and of the scientific enterprise. What such a humanistic understanding entails will concern us explicitly in the concluding section of this book. But the context of such an understanding will concern us at the very outset, before we cope with the matters of method and substance which characterize contemporary science, for such matters do not suddenly appear, just as science did not suddenly appear. Its roots in the common understanding, in the ordinary ways of knowing, and in fundamental human activities bespeak the humanism of science, not in some vaguely ethical sense, but in the practical sense of science as a distinctively human enterprise. Thus, our concern in the succeeding chapters is with the genesis of science and its foundations in ordinary human activity, in perception, in common sense, and in the prescientific ways of knowing, out of which science arose.

PART I

The Genesis of Scientific Thought

CHAPTER 2
Science as Human Activity

THE REIFICATION OF SCIENCE

SCIENCE IS A HUMAN ACTIVITY and has its roots in the ordinary human capacities we all share. As homely and obvious as this truth is, its significance often gets blurred in many of our definitions of science and in our attitudes toward it.

A common and generally correct view of science is that it is an organized or systematic body of knowledge, using general laws or principles; that it is knowledge about the world; and that it is that kind of knowledge concerning which universal agreement can be reached by scientists sharing a common language (or languages) and common criteria for the justification of knowledge claims and beliefs. We think of science as universal and of scientific truths as independent of time, place, and circumstance. Such truths we take to be objective, in the sense that they are true apart from and independent of anybody's happening to know them or believe them. We have a strong commonsense belief in the existence of such truths, as for example when we say, "No one has yet discovered the truth about *X*" (whatever *X* may be). This presumes that something is true, whether anyone knows it or not. We also think of science and of scientific truth as cumulative, as having an independent existence, over and above the life span of particular scientists, and even of particular scientific communities. Thus, we conceive science to be continuous, autonomous, objective, universal, and its truths to be timeless and nonlocal.

This is an important view concerning the objectivity of science. Yet in one interpretation of such an "objectivist" view, science comes to be taken as some transhuman or superhuman essence, as an entity in itself, or a "thing" apart from the matrix of human conditions, needs, and interests in which it originates and develops. There is a danger which lies in this reification of science. The continuity of science with common sense, of scientific activity with fundamental human activities, of scientific understanding with the common understanding is broken. Practically, this reflects itself in the isolation of the scientist from the rest of the human community, in the assignment of science to some transcendent priestly class which dwells apart in its preoccupation with its own esoteric mysteries. Nor is this simply an imagined possibility. For the divorce of some scientists from their roots in the human community has produced a serious social crisis in our own culture.

This problem is not to be solved by piously decrying the isolation of the scientist, or by attempts to drag him from his "ivory tower" back to earth. For in much of his work the scientist requires the isolation and the insulation which permit him to pursue the inquiry into truth in a fully autonomous way, free from the pressures and influences of extrascientific concerns. This is not therefore an argument for getting the scientist out of his laboratory or his study and "involving" him in something vaguely conceived of as "humanity." Rather, we need to reframe the question so that scientific work itself can be seen as essentially human and in a high good sense, humane. For this purpose we have to consider what the foundations of scientific activity are in human activity of the ordinary sort and we have to establish the actual continuity which exists between science and ordinary life. We have also to consider what is distinctive about science, not in the sense that science transcends human activity, but in the sense in which it is itself a distinctive and unique human activity different in crucial ways from other human activities. If the question is approached in this way it will be seen that science represents one of the highest achievements of humanity, not something which stands outside it.

STRUCTURE AND FUNCTION: APPROACHES TO THE STUDY OF SCIENCE

The definition of science as "an organized and systematic body of knowledge" characterizes science from the point of view of its structure. But science is also an activity, an ongoing process of inquiry, whose description in structural terms alone is inadequate. In this latter sense we need also to characterize the functions, the modes of activity, the typical procedures of science with respect to the ends or purposes they serve.

We may make this distinction clear by an analogy. One may study vertebrate organisms from two different but related points of view—anatomically and physiologically, or in terms of structure and function. The first focuses on the skeletal and tissue structure of the organism, on the description of the parts and of their structural relation to each other. For this purpose, dissection is an eminently suitable method. On the other hand, one may want to study the life processes of the organism, e.g., its metabolic rates, its feeding, sleeping, and reproductive habits, and so on. Plainly, anatomical dissection is not adequate to this end. We may of course infer, from anatomical structure, certain functional features of the organism. From specimens of jaw and tooth structure, digestive tract, specially adapted digging or probing organs, we may hypothetically reconstruct what a typical diet would be; from the structure of its body and appendages we may reconstruct what its mode of locomotion would be and what sort of terrain it is probably suited for. Yet this requires the joint knowledge of physiology and anatomy. Both methods are required then, and both are mutually enhancing. It would be detrimental to biological science to ignore one in favor of the other, although in practice the scientist may pay attention to only one at a time for purposes of sustained study and deeper specialization of knowledge.

The point of the analogy is that science has not only a structure, but a function; it is not only a body of knowledge whose anatomical structure we may investigate, but also a complex of activities and functions directed to some end. In its development science is more like an organism than like a dictionary, with entries under appropriate headings, or a watch, with isolated parts which may be disassembled and reassembled.[1] Analogies, of course, are only initially helpful in suggesting what one ought to pay attention to. This one suggests that in order to understand science, it should be considered functionally as well as structurally, i.e., in terms of its characteristic activities, its aims, and its development.

In this spirit we will be concerned in this and succeeding chapters with the genesis of scientific thought and knowledge, with its evolution from its foundations in ordinary human ways of knowing: in perception, in common sense, in the prescientific ways of knowing characteristic of earlier modes of explanation. Finally, in this first section we will deal with the ways in which ancient Greek thought formulated the framework in which science came to be a distinctive and unique way of knowing, and the ways in which Greek science and philosophy set the mold for modern science.

[1] For a discussion of the analogy of organism and mechanism with respect to physical science, see Pierre Duhem, *Aim and Structure of Physical Theory* (Princeton, N.J.: Princeton University Press, 1954), pp. 187–88.

THEORETICAL KNOWLEDGE AND PRACTICAL KNOWLEDGE

There is a common distinction that is drawn between theoretical knowledge and practical knowledge, between knowledge as inquiry for the sake of understanding, and knowledge as an instrument or a guide to successful practice. If knowledge of the latter sort seems to be connected with our immediate (or even long-range) interests or concerns, then knowledge of the former sort may be characterized as disinterested (not in the sense that it holds no interest for us, but rather in the sense that such an "interest" is not directly tied to practical needs). We all know the natural curiosity of children, expressed not only in their direct questions (the classic ones in this context are "Why is the sky blue" and "Why is the grass green"), but also in the play activities which are such "disinterested" explorations, experiments, adventures, inquiries of a naive sort into the nature of things. Some theorists have speculated that such spontaneous and disinterested play is actually highly practical, because in this way children come to know how to manipulate objects, develop their motor skills, and become socialized, in "games" which are really preparations for adult life. But whatever the cunning use to which Dame Nature puts childish play, the play and the curiosity it exhibits cannot be said to be "practical" in the sense of meeting any direct and immediate interests that demand action. Therefore, such activity is often characterized as "spontaneous," "undirected," and "free." (Of course, once the child is in school he is directed to be spontaneous, in periods assigned to "free activity"!) But such spontaneous and relatively impractical activity is also characteristic of much of our adult behavior. If I am asked, "Why do you want to know why the sky is blue," and I answer, "Just for the sake of knowing," or, "Because I'm curious," then I assert that my knowledge is not for the sake of something else, but is for its own sake.[2]

Traditionally, the kind of knowledge pursued for its own sake, out of the desire to know, has been called theoretical, in contrast to the kind of knowledge whose main function is its use in practice. This distinction goes back to the Greeks, especially to the Athenian philosophers of the fifth and fourth centuries B.C. One historical thesis traces it to the separation of head and hand in ancient Greece,[3] that is, to the separation of the functions

[2] For discussion of recent psychological research on such behavior in animals and children, see H. Fowler, *Curiosity and Exploratory Behavior* (New York: Macmillan, 1965), and D. E. Berlyne, "Curiosity and Exploration," *Science*, **153**:25–33 (July 1, 1966).

[3] See Benjamin Farrington *Head and Hand in Ancient Greece* (London: Watts & Co., 1947), and also his *Greek Science*, rev. ed. (Baltimore: Penguin Books, 1961). See also John Dewey, *Reconstruction in Philosophy* (Boston: Beacon Press, 1959), Chapter 1, for another version of this view. It has been contested (by Cornford, for example in "The Marxist View of Ancient Philosophy," in *The Unwritten Philosophy* (Cambridge: Cambridge University Press, 1950), pp. 117 ff.

of theoretical explanation and practical know-how, in the separation of man's practical activity (i.e., his production of the goods and necessities of life) from his theoretical activity (i.e., his rational reflection on his practical activity, and on the nature of things).

This distinction between theoretical and practical knowledge traditionally came to be regarded as a distinction between "higher" and "lower" kinds of knowledge. This derives in part from the fact that only a leisured group could devote itself to theoretical knowledge for its own sake, and such a leisured group has historically been a privileged group in most societies. The social status of the theorist thus carries over into the status of his activity, and theory begins to acquire the connotations of "purity," "ideality," "higher perfection" which surround this privileged social status. The divorce from practical activity becomes a sign of this privilege. Something done for its own sake is regarded as higher than something done merely for the sake of something else; the instrumental or practical value of the latter is a "lower" value than the intrinsic value of the former, by analogy to the hierarchical relation between the master and the servant. The servant does what he does for the sake of the master, and not for his own sake; the master is not bound by such service for the sake of another but pursues his own ends. He is "free," whereas the servant is "bound." Theoretical activity comes to be regarded then as "free" activity; practical activity as "bound" to the "practical" service which it performs for some higher end. It is valued, then, only instrumentally, insofar as it subserves this higher end. Whatever the social contexts in which such distinctions arise, it is plain that the reflection, the time to think required for critical intelligence and theoretical thought does call for a certain distance or detachment from the press of practical immediate action. In this sense the leisure, which historically was the prerogative of a socially privileged group, is in fact the requirement for theoretical activity. Such "free" activity is also "pure" in the sense that it is not mixed with immediate practical concerns and is pursued for its own sake. The immediate concern is not for the application of such theoretical conceptual understanding for the sake of successful practice, but for the satisfaction of a disinterested curiosity, or of an "impractical" aesthetic preference for getting things whole or well ordered.

We recognize this distinction in the use of the terms *pure science* and *applied science*, where the former is defined (as, for example, by N. Campbell) as "a branch of pure learning which aims at intellectual satisfaction." For all their distinction, however, it is plain that these two aspects of our knowledge are closely related. Theory receives its stimulation, its richness, its content from practice; practice becomes more than blind imitation, repetition, instinct, or animal habit, by means of intelligent reflection and by the formulation of rules and rational principles to enlighten and guide practice. Thus, it has often happened that such theoretical knowledge, which is presumably far removed from the immediacy of practical life, has had astounding and unexpected practical import. Purely theoretical and formal considerations in scientific thought have had consequences which have revolutionized not only ways of thinking, but the very foundations of our ordinary day-to-day existence as well. The relation of conceptual revolutions in science to technological revolutions in society is a striking feature of modern history, although one that is taken for granted. Sometimes it is clearly the case that a scientific revolution, a radical reformulation of the conceptual framework of science and of its methods of inquiry, is the result of some rapid technological advance. Thus, for example, the development of engineering, of manufactures, and of techniques for the control over nature in ancient Miletus, in the sixth century B.C., may have provided the framework in which the first philosophers turned from mythical to physical theories to explain the nature and origin of things. Thus also the introduction of gunpowder into feudal Europe from China and the revolution in military technology which this introduced may have brought about that host of physical inquiries which had to do with metallurgy, chemistry, the analysis of projectile motion, and the mechanical arts of fortification. On the other hand, the Milesian nature philosophers also inherited a rich conceptual tradition from Greek religion and mythology, and from the cross-fertilization which a wide commerce and trade with other nations around the Mediterranean and across the land to Babylonia provided. The natural philosophers, alchemists, mathematicians, and metallurgists of late feudal Europe also inherited a rich tradition of practical arts and speculations, which had much to do with how their theories were formulated.

The concepts of science thus derive from a great variety of contexts: technological, cultural-religious, social, political, economic. Sometimes the key to a historical revolution in science is something as seemingly unimportant as a notation (e.g., numerical notation and the introduction of zero into the number system); sometimes something as directly practical as the demands of military technology, or as specific as the demand for a theory to explain the practical principles of navigation. Sometimes it is as random and personal as the demand made by the Chevalier de la Méré of Pascal that he consider games of chance in terms of mathematical analysis of probabilities. Personal quirk and historical need both play their role in the development of scientific concepts. What has remained a striking fact is that apparently disinterested and abstract theoretical inquiry has led to the wider understanding of the way things work in practice, and in this way to the transformation of disconnected rule-of-thumb practices into wide-ranging rational systems for prediction and control.

The sort of knowing activity which science represents certainly involves the efficacy, the power of this knowledge as an instrument of human use, for control over nature. It also involves the satisfaction of a desire for understanding, a curiosity which seems idle in practical contexts. We have suggested that the desire to know for its own sake may be seen to have a remarkable affinity to the function of science as a guide to successful practice. One may conjecture therefore that knowledge of truth is itself a means by which the human species enhances its existence and succeeds at the task of surviving. Thus the instrumental function of science (how it "pays off") and the cognitive function of science (the disinterested pursuit of truth) may not be as sharply distinct as they are sometimes represented.

KNOWLEDGE AND SURVIVAL

The acquisition of knowledge—both practical and theoretical—is a characteristic activity of the human species. We might imagine that, like T. H. Huxley's Saturnians, we are scientific observers from another planet. We might then want to know how this characteristic activity works in the economy of species life and how it came to evolve. Following the lead of the evolutionary biologists, we may consider the broad thesis that knowing activities, and the special sort which involves reasoning, have evolved from precognitive responses and adaptations to an environment and that they are the product of natural and cultural selection, in the sense that they have survival value for the human species.

The special advantage man is supposed to have over other forms of life is his special and critical intelligence or his reason. What distinguishes him, in Aristotle's phrase, is that he is a rational animal. This rationality may be considered as the refined adaptive instrument of species survival. If man fails to survive as a species, we may then say (if there are any of us left to say it) that this critical intelligence, this rationality, as far as it went, was insufficiently adaptive to changes in human environment—including not only the biological environment but also the cultural and historical changes in that environment which man himself created. Therefore, in this respect, rationality may be only one special adaptation, suited for one fairly short and atypical set of cosmic circumstances. All this presupposes that the sense and meaning of human activity of whatever kind, and therefore of that uniquely human activity of rational thinking, depends on how it enhances continued human existence, how it helps to assure species survival. Now many other things may be true about rational knowledge, and about man's *raison d'être;* but it also seems clearly to be the case that rational knowledge (and scientific knowledge, in particular) is a main instrument of human adaptation, and hence, of survival. The hope is that scientific knowledge, as the mode of adaptation and of human control over nature, may also be a major instrument of human self-control, by means of rational intelligence. Such rational self-control, such clear knowledge of our own nature is that ideal of human self-knowledge, the fulfillment of the imperative, "Know thyself," which the Athenian philosophers spoke of. It is, as they already knew, the condition of human freedom.

THE ROOTS OF REASON: HABIT FORMATION, INTELLIGENCE, AND ADAPTIVE BEHAVIOR

If we are concerned to show that science has its roots in ordinary ways of knowing and if we commonly understand science as the archetype of rational knowledge, then how shall we relate reason to such prerational functions as sense perception, habit formation, or even instinctive or native behavior?

One of the earliest systematic formulations of this question was made by Aristotle. As noted, Aristotle defines man as a rational animal; that is to say, in a more perverse formulation, that man is a scientific animal. This view is clearly set forth in the opening passages of Aristotle's major work on the foundations of scientific thought (the *Metaphysics*) and it is cited here almost in full, for it gives a remarkably fresh and clear presentation of key questions concerning the relation of scientific knowledge to ordinary ways of knowing.

> Human beings are naturally curious about things. For example, we like to use our senses, especially the sense of sight, for the sheer joy of perceiving, and not only for the fulfillment of day-to-day needs. One of the greatest pleasures we have is to gaze upon an object, not only when we intend to use it in some way but even when we are not studying it with any practical purpose in mind. This is because sight, more than any other senses, enables us to perceive and to distinguish things most clearly. The ability to perceive is an innate characteristic of all living beings. Some of them remember what they perceive and are therefore more intelligent and better able to learn than others which cannot remember. . . . Animals function by reacting directly to images they perceive, and also by remembering; occasionally, they can even use their memories to learn from experience. Man however makes use of skills and rational thought, and constantly uses his memory to learn from experience. . . . Skill is acquired by generalizing from a number of specific experiences which have already been understood to other similar cases. An unskilled man, relying exclusively on his experience, knows that a particular treatment helps Callias, and Socrates, and other particular people when they are suffering from a particular ailment; but the mark of a skilled professional is the knowledge that a particular treatment helps all those suffering from a particular ailment—for example, that one treatment helps all those suffering from severe colds, that another helps all those suffering from acute indigestion, and that another helps all those suffering from a high fever.

As far as practical consequences are concerned, there seems to be little difference between an unskilled amateur relying on his experience and a skilled professional—except that experienced people are generally more successful than people who have mastered theory but have not yet practiced what they have learned . . . someone who has mastered the theory but has never practiced the profession and who knows general principles without ever having come face to face with an actual case often turns out to be an unsuccessful practitioner, since after all is said and done a doctor has to cure patients.

Nevertheless, it is generally held that knowledge and understanding can be found in a skilled professional sooner than in one who relies on experience alone, and that the former is on a higher intellectual plane than the latter, since we think that intellectual achievement results from true knowledge. This general opinion is due to the fact that the skilled professional knows why he is doing something, while the man who relies on experience alone does not. The latter knows what he is doing but not why he is doing it. . . . In short, the reason we esteem skilled professionals more than common workmen is that we associate intellectual achievement with an orderly grasp of theory, and with an understanding of the reasons of things, rather than with continual involvement in the practical aspects of things. . . . Furthermore, we do not usually identify intellectual achievement with the use of the senses. True, sense perception is the principal means of acquiring information about particular events, but the senses alone can never give you the reason for anything. Our senses, for example, can tell us *that* fire is hot, but not *why* it is hot. . . . What people call intellectual achievement is universally associated with a knowledge of the elements that go into explanations of things and of the fundamental concepts on which all things depend. . . . It is clear, then, that true intellectual achievement comes from a knowledge of the fundamental concepts on which a given subject rests and of the elements necessary for a complete explanation of that subject."[4]

The striking thing about Aristotle's approach is that he traces ordinary human ways of knowing back to their animal origins. This is not to say that he had a conception of the evolution of human capacities from animal origins, but rather that he saw that there was something common in the two. What it is that animals and men share is sense perception and memory. Aristotle wants to show what, beyond these common capacities, distinguishes men from animals. He does not take this to be intelligence, because he thinks animals are intelligent also. That is, they can learn from experience and bring past experiences to bear in the regulation of behavior. But man is capable of something beyond intelligence: he is capable of

[4] Aristotle, *Metaphysics,* Book A, 980a–982a. I have used here the excellent new translation of Book A by Daniel E. Gershenson and Daniel A. Greenberg, in *The Natural Philosopher* (New York: Blaisdell Publishing Co., 1963), Vol. II, pp. 5–9.

reason. Reason therefore goes beyond the mere recognition of similarities and differences from one case to the next. That is, it goes beyond being able to operate successfully (which is practical skill required for the existence of any organism) and involves knowing the reasons why things operate as they do. Such a knowledge is defined by Aristotle in terms of being able to explain why something operates as it does. Thus, rational knowledge is knowledge of what explains things rather than knowledge that things operate in a certain way.

Such rational knowledge involves what Aristotle calls "fundamental concepts," or principles of explanation, and such principles go beyond the particular and finite set of instances given in experience and are instead universal. This means that if such explanatory principles are true or adequate, they would apply to all instances, both those already experienced (which they would presumably explain) and those to be experienced (which they would presumably anticipate). The practical function of such rational knowledge is therefore the anticipation of experience—being able to foresee and therefore being able to consider actions before they are undertaken, with a view to their anticipated outcomes. The importance of this is that action is no longer blind, not merely a response to a given situation. Rather, it is deliberate. Aristotle emphasizes past experience as the basis for such deliberation and for the choice among actions to be taken, for without previous experience of similar situations there would be no basis for judging that one rather than another choice of actions would be more successful. We would be reduced to simply acting randomly or instinctively. Yet with only previous experience of similar situations, we would be limited to reacting on the basis of habit alone.

Such "habits" would involve patterns of action and therefore recognition of certain patterns in experience, because like responses would be given to like situations. Memory would serve to help establish such patterns by linking similarities of past occurrences with present ones. And such behavior, based on habituation, would therefore be intelligent, because trial-and-error learning could take place: remembrance of past failures would serve to inhibit the repetition of such previously unsuccessful reactions and stimulate experimentation with new ones. Such trial-and-error learning would, over a period of time, establish optimal habits for given situations. Wide fluctuations in response to similar situations would be minimized, and a mean approximation of optimal responses would then become reinforced as a strong habit.[5] Optimal habits, for Aristotle, are those suited to the "nature" of the organism, so that "right activity" is that which is in

[5] In his writing on ethics (the study of what constitutes the good for man, and consequently, the study of those actions which would make for a good life), Aristotle develops a theory of such an optimal mean and how it is to be achieved (or learned) through experience. In other words, he attempts to provide a theory of how good habits are achieved. [Aristotle, in fact, makes a point of the fact that the etymological root of the term *ethics* (*ethike*) is *ethos,* which means *habit.*]

accordance with this nature. But unless there is some independent way of knowing what this nature is, how is one to know whether or not an activity is "in accordance with nature"? It might appear, then, that Aristotle's account is empty, or viciously circular. However, Aristotle suggests an experimental criterion for determining what is and what is not in accordance with an organism's nature. When the organism is functioning optimally (that is, when it is operating or acting in such a way that its existence, growth, or normal development is assured) it experiences pleasure. When it is not functioning optimally, it experiences pain, symptomatic of the impending disorganization or threat to the existence of the organism. Pleasure then reinforces the favorable sorts of activity, as pain inhibits the unfavorable ones, and learning takes place as habits of avoidance and attraction are established. According to Aristotle, then, the way any organism "finds out" what its nature is, or finds out what constitutes successful operation, is by experimentation in its actions and by the regulation which pleasure and pain afford in developing habits of action. Thus, organisms have a "natural (or innate) tendency" to maintain themselves and to grow or mature by adapting to or assimilating experiences in a favorable way. This tendency is manifested in the "natural" responses to an environment which an organism exhibits, in its avoidance of what is painful and its search for what is pleasurable.

There are notorious difficulties in this formulation. For example, the argument is circular if what is painful is defined in terms of what is avoided, and what is pleasurable is defined in terms of what is sought. Yet there is a commonsense view contained here which it seems hard to repudiate: namely, that our observations of animals or plants or men seem to lead to the generalization that there exist what we may call "survival mechanisms" or "adaptive mechanisms." Living things in general seem to be adept at overcoming odds, avoiding dangers, fighting off threats, adapting to changes in environments, or seeking favorable environments which enhance the chances for survival. We tend to explain such survival mechanisms in terms of natural selection. The adaptive behavior of an organism, its ability to learn by trial and error, we say is the product of an evolution in which such learning mechanisms gave biological advantage to organisms and species which possessed them and thus were selected out for genetic survival and transmission. But such adaptive behavior proceeds without any foresight by the organism of possible outcomes, and certainly without any knowledge of the reasons for the success or failure of any of its actions, or habits of action. Such behavior is then either instinctive or blindly empirical, simply the establishment of patterns of response to patterns of stimuli. It is reactive rather than creative activity and is plainly not yet rational.

Nevertheless, such adaptive behavior already presupposes ways of ordering experience, ways of sorting and selecting with respect to some optimal state, which are already built into the structure of organisms.

PERCEPTUAL STRUCTURES: THE ORDERING OF EXPERIENCE

If our perception were constituted of nothing but the agglomeration of millions upon millions of unique and separate discriminable characteristics of one or another sense modality; if the sensory field were strewn with countless and unordered colors, shapes, textures, sounds, feels, flavors, smells, tickles, it would be inconceivable how we could come to order such sensory debris. But perception is already selective and the organization of the sensory field is a primary feature of the perceptual process.[6] Furthermore it seems to be the case that such perceptual ordering gives survival advantages to organisms, in terms of the economy and efficiency which such abstractive selection affords. In effect, generalization of responses to perceived patterns of experience, of like responses to like situations, is habit formation. And we may say that such habit formation and learning derive from mechanisms of trial and error into which there are already built criteria for success. For example, in the instinctive approach and avoidance behavior of newborn animals, innate perceptual recognition of appropriate shapes and sizes serves to help the neonate to distinguish food from nonfood, safety from danger, all of which counts toward successfully surviving through the first days of life.

Thus, to the obvious question, "What function does this perceptual ordering have for the organism?" the answer which suggests itself most readily is that it is a means whereby the organism is able to fit its actions to its environment. That is, it permits ordered action with respect to meeting the survival needs of the organism. The ordering of experience becomes an instrumentality of success in action, and it is such success in

[6] The crucial nature of perceptual selection becomes clear when we consider, for example, a complex and highly specialized organ like the human eye, and only one feature of visual perception, like color vision. There are estimated to be over 7 million colors that the eye is capable of perceiving as different. Yet none of us becomes so overwhelmed at this profusion that ordinary action and decision is blocked. See, for a discussion of this, J. S. Bruner, J. J. Goodnow, and G. A. Austin, *A Study of Thinking* (New York: John Wiley & Sons, 1956), Chapter 1. The authors write, "were we to utilize fully our capacity for registering the differences in things and to respond to each event encountered as unique, we would soon be overwhelmed by the complexity of our environment. . . . Such discrimination capacities . . . if fully used, would make us slaves to the particular . . ." (p. 1). What saves us from drowning in a sea of particular discriminations is that we have some way of selecting and ordering them, of singling out only certain of these as relevant or attention holding. The degree of specificity of this ordering and organization, even at the primary level of the peripheral sense receptors, and at the primary stage of infancy of the organism, goes far beyond what Aristotle could have suspected, as evidence from recent research in the physiology and psychology of perception suggests. See on this the bibliographical references to the work of Huebel and Wiesel; Lettvin and Maturana; Fantz; and Bower. The extent and significance of this selectivity and organization was the insight of earlier Gestalt psychology.

action which has survival value for the organism. We may also surmise that over the generations, a good deal of this "success" is genetically selected in terms of the statistical privileges which favorable genetic traits have in being passed on. Thus proclivities to successes of a certain sort become inherited characteristics by the workings of genetic selection (from what geneticists colorfully call the "gene pool"). We may call these "instincts," or we may call them "inherited dispositions" or "innate capacities." In any case, recent research gives good evidence that the propensity to order experience is a characteristic of the genetically inherited structure of organisms.

PERCEPTION, ABSTRACTION, AND CONCEPT FORMATION

Our ordinary perception, like that of all animals, already operates abstractively; that is, it sorts out for attention, recognition, and generalization some, but not all of those features of different situations which may be said to be alike or similar in some respect. Thus, when psychologists of perception talk about perceptual generalization or stimulus generalization or pattern recognition, they allude to perceptual behavior in which various items are grouped in terms of certain criterial features or properties in which they are similar or alike. The pigeon, conditioned to respond to a shape or a color, then responds to a variety of items different in other respects but alike in that shape or color (or in some feature of it which the pigeon notices but which may elude us). Though some experimental psychologists would call this sort of perceptual generalization the formation of a concept by the pigeon,[8] it is not clear what it would mean to attribute "concepts" to such an organism. It would be difficult to assign a "conceptual representation" to the pigeon, except by way of analogy or metaphor; and in any case we would not claim that this was yet a concern with conceptual *reasons* or *explanations,* though it is clearly a case of ordering experience.

The "abstractions" which perception achieves at this level, we may say, are not yet detached from the actual perceptual situations themselves, nor are they represented in some explicit symbol apart from direct responses to environmental stimuli. Perceptual "abstraction" is at best a way of operating within perceptual experience, in actual perceptual situations. Memory and imagination take us a step beyond actual, relatively

[7] See, for a summary of classical and recent views on this topic, Anatol Pikas, *Abstraction and Concept Formation* (Cambridge: Harvard University Press, 1966), esp. Chapters 1, 2, 5, 6.

[8] For example, see R. Herrnstein, "Complex Visual Concept in the Pigeon," *Science,* **146**:549–551 (Oct. 23, 1964).

direct perceptual involvement. In effect, we detach the perceptual image from direct outward sensory or motor activity. Thus imagination and memory provide a kind of isolation from the flux and press of sensory discrimination and response. But both memory and imagination are still tied to the direct imagery of sense perception, even when this imagery appears in fanciful or distorted form. The memory image, or the imagined image, may be vivid or faint, vague and confused, or clear and distinct; but it remains bound to the sensory qualities of colors, shapes, sounds, feels, smells, and so on.

A different sort of abstraction entirely concerns the representation of these features of sense perception symbolically, or by means of a code. This possibility appears with the use of a language, in which perceptual features are symbolized, and not literally re-presented. Thus, the word *red* is not red, nor is *square* square. It is argued, by analogy to this symbolic representation in language, that perceptual processing in the nervous system likewise transforms sensory properties into an electrical or chemical "code," for the nerve impulse which triggers our recognition of red or square is itself neither red nor square. The difference is that in the human use of language, the symbol system itself becomes detached from the direct perceptual situations it represents. Furthermore, in its freedom from representation in terms of sensory imagery, a language system is capable of greater independence from perceptual experience than is either memory or imagination. (However, as is trivially clear, the communication of such linguistic symbols is by means of sense perception—speech must be heard, writing seen, and so on.) In the development of language, the abstraction from contexts of direct outward perceptual or motor activity proceeds to the point where we operate with, or manipulate symbols instead of things. The word and the sentence replace the perceived thing or situation, so that this symbolic linguistic abstraction achieves a certain autonomy from the contexts of direct sense perception and action.[9] This representation of perception and of direct outward activity by means of symbols, and the formation of a system of such symbols in a language thus achieves an abstraction of an entirely new sort. We have in effect, an abstract symbolic model of experience, whose elements may be manipulated by thought and whose scope is not bound either to direct perception or to the sense imagery of memory or imagination.

[9] See H. Werner and B. Kaplan, *Symbol Formation* (New York: Wiley, 1963), for an account of this development of what they call "The autonomy of the linguistic medium." This is a stimulating view of the developmental approach to the relation of thought and language. See especially Part I, Chapter 4 and Part II, Chapter 13. See also Roger Brown, *Words and Things* (New York: The Free Press, 1958), for an introductory account of psycholinguistics. A full range of articles on this is in *Psycholinguistics—A Book of Readings,* ed. S. Saporta (New York: Holt, Rinehart & Winston, 1961).

ADVANTAGES OF CONCEPTUAL ABSTRACTION

What advantages are there in such conceptual abstraction, which the symbolism of language affords? In summary fashion, we may suggest six such advantages, and then suggest how rational thought and theory become possible on this basis.

(1) *Conceptual representation in a language is economical.*

Perhaps the most obvious feature of the use of symbols to represent things, events, or processes is the economy of representation. Words denoting objects, once they are abstracted from the perceptual situation of pointing to or naming present objects, may be taken to denote nonpresent objects, and classes of such objects, or all objects of a certain sort or having certain properties. Linguistic abstraction may also embody a rule of action, expressing in symbolic, communicable form directions for complex performance of the sort that would otherwise require long practice and learning to acquire, by means of imitation or habit formation. Although acquired skills, technology, attitudes, and beliefs can be transmitted from one generation to the next, by repetition and example, the transmission of such cultural information is by the use of language. The human brain, with the acquisition of language, becomes adept at storing both organic memory (i.e., memory of perceptual and motor activity) and verbal memory, with its enormous increase in range, abstraction, and information. The ability to communicate, the sharing of concepts, thus gives rise to a community of shared meanings and practices that are no longer limited to genetic inheritance and the relatively slow process of genetic biological evolution. Rather, the spectacularly rapid process of cultural evolution becomes possible, as conceptual abstraction and the medium of symbolic representation work their economies on the acquisition, storage, transmission, and use of information.

(2) *The detachment of the conceptual representation from direct perception and action permits the reflection on ends and means and introduces the possibilities of judgment and rational choice.*

In the conceptual abstraction, past experience and future outcomes may be represented independently of direct perception and action, that is, not bound to direct, outward perceptual and motor activity. This permits a relatively "free" or detached manipulation of the elements of past experience and future anticipation, insofar as they are represented in the inward "space" of conception. One may therefore talk of a model or abstract representation of human actions, an enactment in thought, so to speak, in which "rehearsals" of alternative courses of action may take place without the commitment to direct action, and without its consequences.

The advantage of such an imaginary enactment of alternatives is that it provides the opportunity for a choice among alternatives based upon reflection. But such reflection, if it is not to be idle, requires a basis for choice, with respect to the ends-in-view of the purported action (that is, "end-in-view" both in the sense of the anticipated outcome of the action and of its goal or what its outcome will serve) and also with respect to the means by which such ends may successfully be achieved. Thus, the possibility of reflective examination of the relations between ends and means arises only with the development of a conceptual representation of action. The objects of such deliberative choice are no longer perceptual images, but abstract judgments; further, such choices are no longer simply governed by instinct or habit, but now may be determined by conscious reasons. In short, the possibilities of rational judgment and rational choice are now open.

(3) *The conceptual model is time-binding.*

In the "real time" of events and actions in the world, what is past is past, what is future is not yet, and (profundity of profundities) only the present is present. In memory, the past is somehow "preserved" in some memorative image, as in imagination we can construct hypothetical past and future states, or even imagine the present as other than it is in our direct or actual perceptual experience. (As when we fantasize in the present tense; "I am now conducting the Boston Symphony. . . .") Thus memory and imagination provide the means whereby past and present are represented "now," in the "internal time" of our consciousness. But such reconstruction of the past or projection of the future is bound to the concrete representation of memorative or imaginative imagery—i.e., in terms of the concrete, particular elements of perceptual representation. The schematic representation of past-present-future relations, in some conceptual "now," abstracts from such perceptual imagery and presents us with an abstract model of time relations or sequences. Manipulation of alternative time relations or sequences thus abstractly represented can proceed free from the conditions of "real time." In reflective consideration of a conceptual model of time relations or sequences, there is a suspension of outward activity: reflection turns inward and constructs a time-sequence model freed from the conditions of outward action. Obviously time "presses on" even while we think, so that as we ordinarily say, we need "time to think," or the relative leisure in which the suspension of direct outward activity is possible. If we could not "stop to think," then of course reflection would be impossible. But our abstract model of time sequence is freed from direct reaction to outward stimuli, in "real" time, and can represent alternative time-binding sequences of past-present-future for critical reflection.

(4) *Implicit habits or learned patterns of action become explicated as rules or plans which can come under conscious scrutiny and criticism.*

A pattern of action, or the kind of ordered response which is learned by trial and error, implies a rule; that is, there is some description of the pattern which may be stated in a universal way, as applying to all instances of the pattern. But an implicit rule, or one which is simply embodied in behavior of a certain sort, is not an actual rule, in the sense that such rule-like behavior might be in accordance with a rule, but it is not governed or regulated by the rule. Our usage points to a distinction between the kind of behavior which is law-like and that which is rule-like. Rules may be broken; laws, as laws of nature, may neither be "broken" nor "obeyed." They simply are the way things behave. Furthermore, one use of "rule" (e.g., "As a rule, I get up at seven") suggests that rules describe what is usually, but not necessarily always, the case.

But following a rule or acting on a rule means more than simply embodying a rule. It means acting in a certain way because of the rule, and such action requires the explicit formulation of such a rule. The formulation of a rule of action therefore requires its explicit representation in some language or in some symbolic form. Once the rule becomes explicit in this way, a new element enters into the regulation of our activity. This new element goes beyond habit (which may also be said to regulate our activity, as an acquired pattern of response, or a disposition to respond in a certain way in given situations). An explicated rule regulates activity in terms of conscious anticipation of ends-in-view, and by conscious direction of means to attain these ends. For example, if the rule is "Cross only on green light," then the performance of an action which is governed by this rule, and is not simply in accordance with it accidentally (as when I happen to cross on a green light without noticing either the light or the rule), is one whose "end" is to cross only on green light. Kant, in speaking of rules, put it even more stringently: the "end" of the action is to act for the sake of fulfilling the rule, to obey the rule because it is a rule. Thus, obedience to a rule or governance by a rule is itself ordered by a second-order rule, e.g., "rules are to be obeyed." In such a case, there is conscious self-regulation by a rule. In Kant's phrase, our action then becomes "free," i.e., self-determined or autonomous. And in his view, such action is rational, or dictated by our reason; thus only rational action is free.

The activities which are regulated in this way are therefore no longer either instinctive or innate responses to certain classes of stimuli, nor are they habitual responses learned through trial and error. They are symbol-directed or rule-governed activities. Insofar as such symbols or abstracted conceptual "rules" may be said to govern our activities, these rules now constitute a new and different kind of activity, which is a response not merely to the perceptual field, but to the linguistic field in which such rules become explicit. We behave, act, respond with respect to linguistic expressions, which we ourselves have created. Words, sentences, commands, questions, descriptions, expressions of a wide linguistic variety come to constitute a domain of meanings to which our responses become educated. We not only make symbols, we use them. Furthermore, we use them self-directively, and this is of the greatest importance. For now there emerges a kind of human activity which is not only pattern-directed, by habit, but is directed by our own constructions of rules.

This in itself might be nothing more than the kind of signal-directed behavior of animals, who do regulate themselves, and others of their species by effective signals, e.g., of warning, command, danger, discovery of food, mating signals, and so on. And it is very likely that language develops from such vocal, gestural, or other sorts of regulative signals. However, with the explicit formulation of rules, something is achieved beyond this. The rules themselves can now be scrutinized, reflected upon, adapted, improved, accepted, rejected. The judgment that some action is or is not in accordance with the rule, as a reflective judgment, now becomes possible, and explicit criticism of the rules can take place. The effect of this is multiplied in a spectacular way when one considers that such critical reflection becomes the activity of a whole community, and potentially of the whole species. That is, the critical and corrective scrutiny of such rules, once they are formulated in the public and communicable form of language, takes advantage of the manifold experience of a whole community of rule-using organisms; the breadth and depth of the rule contexts is hugely enlarged, across space and time. The time-binding aspect of language brings the preserved past experience even of no-longer surviving members of the community to bear on the formulation and reformulation of such rules. And communication of such rules across space, in the network of communication which language makes possible, enormously extends the domain of application. From local there develop nonlocal rules. The patterns of experience and action to which such rules apply and by which they are tested can be derived not only from the limited experience of one individual, or even from the lifespan of one community, but from the continuing experience of the whole species, insofar as communication by means of language across time and space is possible.

Such rules, formed in the crucible of a common language and a common experience, constitute a large part of what we call common sense—the minimal set of directive concepts by which a community regulates its practical and everyday activity—and also provide the matrix for that critical common sense which develops into science.

(5) *Explicit rules of contradiction and consistency emerge with the development of rational discourse.*

A regulative feature of rules which bears on the development of rationality is the function of rules of discourse. The development of explicit rules of contradiction and consistency in discourse is a special and relatively late development, having originated in ancient Greece. Yet such rules seem implicit in certain common features of ordinary experience. Suppose that there are two alternative courses of action with respect to a given end-in-view, and suppose further that they are mutually exclusive. For example, to get to Chicago from New York, one may go either by train or by plane, but one obviously cannot go by train and by plane on the same trip, or at the same time. This kind of choice runs through much of our ordinary activity. There is a pattern common to all such actions which may be abstracted and formulated in symbolic terms. In the conceptual representation of such alternatives, in language, this may be formulated in a rule of discourse, explicitly. Thus, if we assert *X*, we cannot also mean to assert not-*X*. The explicit rule would be something like, "Either *X* or not-*X*, but not both," or, "One cannot assert both a statement and its negation, in the same respect."

What enters here is the whole notion of assertion and denial in linguistic discourse, and with it, the notions of truth and falsity. With two such mutually exclusive statements, or with a statement and its denial, we cannot assert both, because we cannot say that both are true together. One or the other must be true, but both cannot be true.

Such a rule is highly abstract, and although it may derive from patterns of action, it does concern discourse. It introduces and regulates that kind of symbolic activity which we may call argument, the activity of reasoning in the explicit form of a language. If our assertions and denials are ordered systematically and the whole system of assertions is subject to this rule—which is the rule of noncontradiction—then contrary assertions like, "It is the case that *X*," and, "It is not the case that *X*," cannot both appear in this system as true expressions. If there are no such incompatible assertions in the whole system of assertions, then the system is said to be consistent.

This is a slightly formal version of a homely and commonsense belief concerning truth. But it is only by the explication of the rules of noncontradiction and consistency that rational criticism of argument becomes possible. Indeed, the very rule of noncontradiction itself may then be scrutinized critically, as it has been by some logicians and philosophers. Rational criticism then may be seen to depend on the explicit formulation of our concepts and rules, so that in this form they become objects for critical reflection.

(6) *Explanation or understanding the "why" of things rests on knowledge by means of concepts.*

The use of concepts and rules is the sign of a symbol-using organism that may be said to be intelligent in a human way. The reflection on these rules and concepts themselves is the sign of a critical intelligence, of an organism which may be said to be rational. Rationality then is dependent upon the use of concepts but requires more than such use; it requires reflective activity in which the concepts and rules are themselves the objects of scrutiny and criticism. The experience ordered by concepts, the knowledge acquired by the use of concepts may in fact have the advantage of educating us to anticipate that things will happen as they do. Understanding why they happen as they do, and being able to offer an explanation, requires the further reflection on the concepts themselves which marks a rational intelligence, and the beginnings of theoretical scientific inquiry.

CHAPTER 3

Prescientific Ways of Knowing

THE CONTINUITY between scientific knowledge and ordinary ways of knowing could lead one to the erroneous conclusion that all knowing activity is scientific. The discontinuity between scientific and ordinary ways of knowing could lead one to the alternative conclusion, equally erroneous, that science has nothing to do with ordinary ways of knowing. The genesis of scientific thought in the intelligent human action which uses concepts, and in the rational human understanding which reflects on concepts, leads to a more qualified conclusion than either of these two. All science is knowledge by means of concepts, but not all knowledge by means of concepts is scientific knowledge. When we are weaned from our mother's milk and begin to acquire a language, concept formation is already well under way; and when we ask our first questions about the use and meaning of concepts or terms ("How can grandma be a mother if she's a grandma?") reflection on concepts has already begun. Such conceptually ordered knowledge may indeed be the requisite for the development of science, and the child may thus have the capacity to become a scientist. But most of the knowledge acquired in this way is clearly not yet scientific knowledge. In considering the genesis of science we need to distinguish nonscience from science. But beyond this, we need to show how certain ordinary ways of knowing form the distinctive matrix in which science could arise; how, in this sense, certain patterns and modes of thought are prescientific. In particular, we want to suggest how theoretical explanation and the formulation of laws derive from prescientific contexts.

At best this is a complex and difficult task, for it requires a reconstruction of the modes of thought, and of the culture and technology of prescientific societies. As such, this is the task of the historian and the anthropologist. But the philosopher of science, concerned with the genesis and the character of scientific thought, may offer a speculative reconstruction of such prescientific ways of knowing, drawing on the evidence of the social scientist and the historian. Such a reconstruction is not concerned with the particular development of this or that ritual, or myth, or technique, but with the forms such patterns of thought and action exhibit, and with the ways in which these forms leave their trace on the typical forms of scientific knowledge. Thus, in this chapter we will be concerned with the nature of prescientific explanation as it bears on the genesis of theories and laws in science.

WHAT SCIENCE IS NOT

(1) The most obviously questionable use of the term *science* is that which applies it to quackery, fakery, and to systematized superstition. For the price of a pack of cigarettes one can buy such treatises as "The Science of Numerology," "The Science of Dreams and Prophecies," "The Science of Astrology." There is a healthy common sense which marks all such pseudoscientific quackery as "superstition," that is, as irrational belief, based on wish-fulfilling fantasy or fear, with no foundation in actual knowledge. Yet what are now regarded as superstitious beliefs at one time played a role in the development of science. Were these beliefs superstitious then as well? Certainly. But they were not anomalous then as they are now. They were not mere superstitions, but attempts to explain the mysterious, the awesome, the terrifying, and the wonderful within the conceptual framework of an earlier age.

The prototypes of scientific explanation are often hidden from our view because we tend to write them off either as ordinary common sense or as products of ignorance and superstition. A universe peopled with gods and demons, evil and good spirits, magical powers, incantations, spells and rituals, mystical words and numbers by means of which one could control events and actions, black magic and white magic, secret rites, taboos, tricks and potions to make one loved, fertile, or feared, to make the crops grow, ward off the evil eye, fool the gods, or blind one's enemies—the catalogue of superstitious belief is as long as it is colorful. But its significance is not that it was a symptom of man's ignorance, but that it exemplified man's attempt at explanation, and at control over nature. That such attempts at explanation became ritualized and institutionalized, that they became socially sanctioned and enforced rules of operation and requirements of belief, says something about the nature of sociocultural development, for the stage of such superstitious belief is a universal one in widely disparate societies, and the modes of such belief are strikingly similar in otherwise unrelated cultures.[1]

(2) There is another sort of knowledge which, although it does not pretend to the name *science,* is significant in the genesis of scientific thought. It is the sort which gets expressed in proverbs, folk sayings, and rules of thumb: "Red sky at night is the sailor's delight, red sky in the morning, sailor take warning"; "Better to lose with a wise man than to win with a fool"; "Easy come, easy go." Such folk wisdom as concerns human experience, and such craft wisdom is the distillation of the manifold experience of generations. The laconic expression of this sort of knowledge serves to imprint it readily in the mind, and the use of analogy relates it to other contexts, extending its scope and application. In such expressions some regular relation among things in common experience is asserted. The most general form in which one may paraphrase many such sayings is, "Whenever . . . then . . . ." ("Whenever the cat's away, then the mice will play.") Such expressions embody in economical and graphic form well-observed uniformities in the experience of whole communities. They have the form of inductive generalizations, but also the genius of real discovery. They strike us therefore by their aptness and scope, and by their revelation, in explicit terms, of truths of which we were already dimly aware.

(3) Finally, there is a popular misconception that expresses itself in our common usage, and contains a half-truth: One may know how to drive a car or a nail, or how to build a bridge or a tunnel, or how to run a poultry farm. Popular usage often labels such know-how, such mastery of technique or of rules of operation, as "science," as in "the science of bridge building," "the science of poultry farming," or even "the science of driving a car." There is the weight of tradition in this usage, as there is also the testimony of etymology. The word *science* after all derives from the Latin word *scientia,* which comes from the plain, everyday verb *scire,* which means "to know." In German, for example, the link to ordinary "knowing" is equally close to the surface, for *science* is *Wissenschaft,* from the verb *wissen,* which means "to know." Yet it seems to be an abuse of the modern connotations of the word *science* to use it concerning all knowledge. And it is at best a queasy use which characterizes any skill or technique whatever as a "science." One way to avoid this is to refer to skills and techniques, in the operative sense, as "arts." (So, for example, we talk of the "medical arts" or the "manly art of self-defense," or the "art of teaching," and arguments rage as to whether history is an art or a science.) But it

[1] See, for example, Sir J. G. Frazer's *The Golden Bough—A Study in Magic and Religion,* abridged edition (New York: Macmillan, 1963), for a fulsome account of such transcultural similarities.

would be a dogmatic purism which did not realize the relation of well-ordered skills and techniques, perfected and systematized over years of practice, to the development of science.

We have discussed three sorts of knowledge here: (*a*) that of explanation in terms of some imaginary powers or beings, (*b*) that of generalizations from experience, and (*c*) that of rules of operation or techniques of a well-ordered sort. None of these ways of knowing fit comfortably within the scope of what we should want to call scientific knowledge. Yet all three provide prototypes of the forms of scientific knowledge, and all three have had a major role in the development of science. They are all attempts to order experience in some way, to achieve control over an environment, and all use the medium of symbolic formulation in one or another sort of language.

Because each of these represents a prescientific way of knowing, any genetic account of the development of science out of ordinary ways of knowing would be incomplete without an examination of the form and the function of these modes. Further, because science does not spring suddenly forth but develops as a distinctive way of knowing only through a long and difficult process, any attempt to mark off sharply the place at which science emerges from prescientific modes of knowing is bound to vulgarize and distort in the name of clarity. Science is long-aborning, its origins and development are complex and sometimes obscure, and it carries within it the signs of its travail. Just as the boy can be recognized in the man, the childhood of science and its origins in prescientific ways of knowing leave the trace of its earliest forms and methods of thought in modern science. Such prescientific ways of knowing may therefore also be considered *proto-scientific* ways of knowing. The capacities for the growth of science are already indicated here. Let us turn then to a more schematic formulation of what it is in these three ways of knowing that exhibits this protoscientific form. Let us also see what rudimentary forms of scientific thought emerge in each of these modes.

MYTHOPOEIC THOUGHT: ANTHROPOMORPHIC AND ANIMISTIC EXPLANATION

Origins, Reasons, and Causes

Among the earliest forms of explanation is that which accounts for the phenomena of nature in terms of human and personal actions and purposes, or pictures natural forces as living, conscious, and intentional. The poetic and dramatic imagination refashions the awesome, the striking, and the unusual in our experience in the concrete imagery of human action and feeling; and the myth serves to evoke in us an intimacy with nature, a way of feeling at home with the unknown both in the natural world and in ourselves. Such mythopoeic reconstruction of experience certainly bespeaks the creativity of the human imagination, the free aesthetic inventiveness of the human mind; but it functions too as explanation, as a way of understanding and accounting for what otherwise would remain obscure, threatening, and uncontrollable.

If we may be permitted a speculative reconstruction of how such an instance of explanation may arise, our claim for this function may become clearer. We imagine the terror of some ancient man in the face of natural disaster or catastrophe, say of an iron-age man facing a thunderstorm, with lightning striking with wild energy from the sky. We imagine further that in this instance the lightning strikes a great tree, which falls in flames close by. The brute reaction is fear, unreasoning and instinctive, urging flight, or striking with such terror that only paralysis or hysteria ensues. Given nothing but brute animal reaction, nothing more can be done. Yet the traumatic experience is remembered and refashioned by the imagination. The incipient philosopher asks, "What is the lightning? Where does it come from? Why has it struck near me?" This is already to go beyond brute fear and to think: to hypothesize that the lightning, which comes from "up" and comes "down" is somehow like things which fall or are thrown; and to look for origins, reasons, causes which will give some satisfying account of the phenomenon. For example, the question may be, "Why did it strike near me? Why here and not there?" To admit that it strikes randomly is to be constrained to the helplessness of brute fear. To conceive of it as striking for a reason, however malignant, is already to conceive the lightning as something akin to other things which occur for a reason. Now reasons, by analogy to human reasons, entail purposes: "for the sake of . . ." or "with the end in view that . . ." What is hurtful or damaging or terrifying occurs because or for the reason that it hurts, or damages, or terrifies. Such a "reason" is intelligible, in human experience. One hurts or damages by way of retaliation: evil for evil done. The *lex talionis*—an eye for an eye—is woven into the earliest records of human action. The hurt is therefore interpreted as a punishment or as a return for some previous hurt done. In any case, some way of accounting for the "reason," in terms within the understanding of human action, has been provided. Further yet, "What is the lightning?" It is bright and fiery, hot because it causes flame, yet unlike fire, more definitely shaped. It is an object of a sort, a close analogy to which, in the experience of the iron-age man, is molten metal, which suggests the technique of working metals; and the technique further suggests the practitioner and the instruments of his craft. The lightning comes from on high, it is delivered for a reason—therefore directed, or thrown—and the thrower works the metal, presumably in a forge, fashioning it as an instrument of purposeful retaliation.

Why all this imaginative construction? Out of some innate desire to embroider, to picture, to make up stories? Perhaps, but it is not an idle desire, but a vital need. The brute reaction of fear in the face of the unknown gives way to purported knowledge, of the origin, the reason, the character of the lightning. There is nothing to do in the face of such a force if there is no way to conceive of what to do. Yet the conception of the unknown in terms of well-known and intelligible characteristics now suggests a way of dealing with this phenomenon, by some kind of reasoned action. If the hurler of thunderbolts is angry, then anger can be propitiated either by discovering what it was that caused the anger and making good the fault or by offering some substitute to appease the anger, by way of sacrifice (thus also making good the fault by substitution). Or, in the worst case, if the malignant being is an enemy, one deals with him as an enemy: by calling forth to battle one's "own" gods, the enemies of one's enemies (our population on high grows larger) or by threat, or retaliatory action. Fear for fear: frighten the enemy off using his own means, make noise, or give fearsomeness a face (as in primitive masks) and make it ugly enough that it will frighten even such an enemy.

There are alternative modes of adaptation to one's brute fear, but all have this in common: the natural event is objectified in the form of a personal event, with a personal doer who therefore will respond to personal modes of reaction. Nature is conceived by analogy to what human beings have experience of: their own motives, reactions, purposes, desires, and fears. Fear is given shape (as purposes, motives, desires are also given shape) and in effect, one frightens off or propitiates one's own fear, now that it has objective and intelligible form. All events in nature are conceived under the form of willed events, and the doers of these events enact them as *dramatis personae*. The elements of conceptualization and imaginary construction take on the form of a story, full of actions, intentions, and outcomes. But the event is no longer a brute event, and the reaction no longer a brute reaction. It is understood, and the reaction is deliberate. Frankfort describes it thus.

> For the ancients natural phenomena were regularly conceived in terms of human experience and that human experience was conceived in terms of cosmic events. . . . The world appears to primitive man neither inanimate nor empty but redundant with life. . . . Any phenomenon may at any time face him, not as 'It,' but as 'Thou.' In this confrontation, 'Thou' reveals its individuality, its qualities, its will. . . . The whole man confronts a living 'Thou' in nature; and the whole man—emotional and imaginative as well as intellectual—gives expression to the experience. All experience of 'Thou' is highly individual; and early man does, in fact, view happenings as individual events. An account of such events and also their explanation can be conceived only as action and necessarily take the form of a story.[2]

[2] Henri Frankfort, et al, *Before Philosophy* (Baltimore: Penguin Books, 1949), pp. 12–15.

Such instances also show prototypical notions of causation. A striking example is that of the widespread "devil theory" of disease. In some prescientific society some deadly disease takes its course. The symptoms (in our terms) are high fever, extreme physical fatigue, spasms of trembling, an inability to retain food. Sheer hopelessness and helplessness would remain at whatever instinctive sympathetic actions might be undertaken, such as offering food and drink, or consoling, or caressing—actions not far removed from animal response. There is also the traditional folk medicine, the administration of whatever herbs or mixtures medicinally found to be effective in like cases in the past. But none of this early medicine remains merely an application to relieve symptoms. There is also involved the quest for an explanation of the disease, which follows the course of questions of the sort: "What is it? Where does it come from? What makes it happen? Why has it occurred in this instance?" These are protoscientific questions, and the answers, for all their apparent naiveté to us, are protoscientific answers. The disease is conceived in terms of some origin, a means of transmission, the agency of its present effect, and also in terms of an intelligible reason as to why it should have occurred in this instance. If the symptom is fever, then the cause is some fiery substance, or something that has the capacity to make things hot. If the symptom is trembling, then there is some power which causes the trembling; if strength is sapped, then there is something that uses up the strength. It seems to us, perhaps, that in each case this merely restates the symptom twice. To say that something is hot seems equivalent to saying that something has been made hot. But in the very common sense which imputes this relation there is already the conceptual formulation of something as the *cause* of something else. Clearly, this empty formulation that there is a cause for each symptom is in itself insufficient as a guide to action, because it is too vague. The concreteness required to direct action demands a concrete and specific characterization of this cause, which then admits of being acted upon in a certain specific way. Again, the mythopoeic imagination supplies the concrete imagery of causation in the form of something known: not familiar as such but possessed of familiar properties. The disease which causes pain and death is thought to be, like lightning, malignant and is attributed to a personal agency with personal and particular motives. The motive may again be construed as punishment for some wrong done, or enmity. The mode of action of this causal agent is, to all appearances, from within the body of the victim, causing outward symptoms as reactions to actions. The cause is moreover invisible, although clearly envisionable. On this reconstruction some evil or malignant personal power is thus taken to be the cause and retaliation or punishment is the motive. The attempt at control over such a power is, in the first place, an attempt to determine what sort of thing it is and why it acts as it does. Then a conceptually directed mode of response is possible. Incantations, purgings, frightening noises, masks ugly enough to scare the demon, propitiatory offerings alluring enough to distract him (her, it), sympathetic re-enactment of the victim's suffering in order to draw off the activity of the demon into another body—all these "magical" and "superstitious" ways of acting are nevertheless ways of acting directed by deliberate thought upon some hypothetical entity taken to be the cause of the disease.

The mode of thought which conceives such ways of acting is largely characterized by imaginative analogy. It explains what is unknown in terms of an imaginative construction of some causally efficacious entity which in key respects is like something already well known; in short, it explains by means of a model. The formal features of this disease-causing agency may be characterized: (1) it is an entity, or a thing of some sort, (2) it acts upon other things directly. The most common feature of experience which is here conceptually formulated in the model is that of causal relation. But there are many alternative models of this causal relation. For example, one may seek the origin of this demonic agent. One may seek to characterize the way in which it operates, as for example, by direct contact or by some intermediate agency. Thus, the disease demon may not operate directly, but by means of a verbal curse or by means of a copy or apparition of itself—a substitute, so to speak—or by means of some other person whom it has taken over as an instrumentality for its purposes. But such curses, or apparitions, or surrogate instruments are themselves taken as things—for example, words and images are taken as objects, which themselves act upon other things, and may in turn be acted upon. Thus, word magic, voodoo, dream apparitions, witches, pictures, and signs are all taken as causal agencies, for each of which specific modes of response, or ritual methods, develop.

In summary: In anthropomorphic and magical explanations, as in the myths concerning the god of the thunderbolt, or in the so-called devil theory of disease, there is already a protoscientific conceptual framework. If sickness is caused by an evil eye or a vengeful spirit, then we have not merely a description of the disease in terms of its symptoms, or even the more sophisticated account of its stages of development, but also an account of its etiology—i.e., of the reasons for it. We have a conceptual framework, constructed by the human imagination, which presumes to explain the observed facts in terms of some hypothetical cause. This cause is conceived, in mythopoeic terms, as some personal, concrete agency, and not in abstract terms as a "principle"; but like the "principles" of a later stage of explanation, this cause, as "spirit" or "demon" or "god" is invested with all the properties necessary to explain why something happens, in terms of something else already known, which is similar or analogous in its formal characteristics. Thus, "spirits" are not mysterious, but familiar: they are "evil" or "vengeful"; they enter through the nostrils or through the ears or through some other opening in the body. They can be frightened or propitiated; in short, they are imaged after familiar things. In some cases they cannot be directly observed and are recognized only by their effects. But in other cases there is a firm belief that they can be observed, and in the hysterical imagination they are "observed," and then they turn out to look like humans or animals in some grotesque fantastic version.

Our own feeling that such "observation" is merely the product of hallucination or hysteria is already the critical reflection of a more advanced theory of observation, conditioned by the development of science. But even our own usage retains the sense of observation which unconsciously draws on an accepted conceptual framework, as when we say we "observe" the collision of elementary particles in a bubble chamber, or "observe" the earth's rotation during a sunrise. The conceptual framework of mythopoeic explanation "observes," within that framework, with much the same sense of warranted certainty, so that whole communities have a common standard or a common convention concerning what the various demons, devils, and gods look like when they are purportedly seen.

Physical Principles of Explanation

The rejection of mythopoeic explanation, in terms of such imaginary personal entities, is closely related to the first instances of physical explanation. The context of this revolutionary move in the development of scientific explanation is not simply intellectual: myths were not rejected simply because they suddenly appeared foolish to a rational and critical thinker. Rather, the conditions for the growth of rational critical thought are closely tied up with the conditions of the rejection of myth, which are of a social and political as well as of an intellectual sort. Myth and magic served not only as modes of explanation but also as ideologies and methods of social control. Thus the priests in whose hands the administration of magical powers were lodged also constituted by this means a privileged and socially powerful ruling group, in many early societies. The kings whose right was sanctioned by descent from the mythical gods, whose powers and dominion they inherited as well, often used mythology as an ideology of state rule. As Francis Bacon realized when he said, "Knowledge is power," the presumed knowledge of the priestly guardians of the myth carries with it respect for their presumed power.

The process of social change, in which priestly ruling classes and theocratic priest kings were overthrown or their power curtailed, included the acquisition of new modes of explanation, which proceeded with the acquisition of new techniques and methods of control over nature. This development in ancient Greek thought and history is too complex and problematic to be examined closely here. But the upshot is that with such social and technological changes, and with the growth of new modes of explanation, the mythopoeic and magical models were radically transformed. Instead of personal entities, with motives of an anthropomorphic sort and with the physiognomic characteristics of a *Thou,* physical principles conceived of in terms of familiar natural substances began to function as independent means of explanation. Thus, instead of malignant personal spirits or devils as causes of disease, explanation was sought in terms of the balance or imbalance of physical substances in the body (for example, the four so-called humours: blood, yellow bile, black bile, and phlegm, or in terms of natural "elements" or "principles": the hot, the cold, the dry, the wet). Explanation of natural phenomena also replaced willful gods with such "elements": water, air, fire, earth, or combinations of these. Yet what is significant for the model of explanation is that the formal characteristics of mythopoeic explanation were not abandoned but transformed. Explanation in terms of origins, causes, and reasons and the construction of hypothetical entities whose nature or form of action explained natural phenomena was preserved. Physical theories replaced anthropomorphic and magical theories, but the profound conceptions of causal relations among things in some way which could be intelligibly conceived, already provided the mold for these newer forms of explanation.

One of the earliest of these physical speculations proposed that all things are water. Now it is not clear whether this means that all things are made of water, originate from water, or are different forms of water (as, for example, ice and steam are). But whichever of these alternatives one chooses, critical questions can then be raised as to how the variety of observable things are "made" of water, or what it means to say that they "originate" from water, or in what sense they are "forms" of a single stuff. "Being made" or "being constituted" suggests some sense of being put together; but if there is only one fundamental stuff, what is it that is being "put together"? "Originating from" means, somehow, coming into being out of, or being given birth to (by analogy to the familiar "origination" of living things, in the relation of parent and offspring). But then, what is water that it can "originate" or "give birth to" the variety of things in the world? In one sense, we can say "life comes from the sea," echoing an ancient metaphor. But what we ordinarily mean is that the sea provides food for life or that the sea "gives birth" to the life in it, in the metaphorical sense that water provides the medium in which such life arises and develops; or even in the more general sense that living things need water to stay alive. Again, "forms of a single stuff" suggests that this stuff undergoes transformations and that although it changes its "form," it remains the same stuff through all these changes.

None of this is yet precise; all of it is metaphorical, vague, or merely suggestive. Still, questions such as these are the result of a radical departure in human thought. They exhibit a critical and reflective intellect, an attempt to encompass the whole range of natural phenomena under a single or unitary principle of explanation. *Principle* here also seems to mean two things, not yet clearly distinguished: on the one hand, the "principle" seems to be a physical stuff or matter of one kind, out of which all things are constituted. On the other, *principle* seems to mean a way or a mode of explanation, showing how the variety of the things of our acquaintance, or the variety of our conceptions of them, is related to some overarching concept or idea which orders them in an intelligible way—that is, in a way which makes us feel we understand these relations. The notion of such an ordering principle (i.e., a principle of explanation) leads early Greek philosophy and natural speculation to the formulation of the notion of an intelligible or rational principle not just of our thought, but of the world itself. We can thus understand the world by means of such an ordering principle because the world is itself ordered by such a principle. The world, in short, is intelligible in its very nature, or is rational in the very way that it is.

This sort of speculation goes beyond the nature-philosophy or physical speculation which explains in terms of water, air, or fire, or in terms of such "physical" principles as hot, cold, dry, or moist. Instead it considers the form or order of things. If "stuff talk" is the earliest form of physical speculation, then "form talk" is the earliest form of metaphysical speculation. The two are not clearly distinguished in early Greek philosophy, which talks both of such physical "principles" as water or air and of such formal "principles" as the *logos*—the intelligible order or form which makes all things knowable to reason.

The move from the concrete imagery of anthropological and magical explanation, in terms of human agencies and motives, to physical explanation, in terms of natural "stuffs" of one sort or another, still preserves the concrete perceptual reference to things seen, touched, heard (or imaginatively visual or pictorial, as demons are). All talk of "invisible" spirits still conceives them in the imagination with pictorial properties, but the move to metaphysical explanation in terms of so-called intelligible principles now leaves nothing to the imagination. For such principles cannot be pictured, though they can be thought. Such explanatory principles are, in effect, highly abstract concepts no longer bound to perceptual imagery. Yet there is a continuity through all these modes of explanation. In all of them some entity (whether concrete and picturable or abstract) is conceived to exist, whose "nature" or whose mode of activity is such that it accounts for the natural phenomena. Here lie the beginnings of theoretical explanation.

GENERALIZATIONS OF EXPERIENCE: DESCRIPTIVE LAWS

The previous section dealt with imaginatively conceived entities whose "nature" or way of acting underlay the outward appearances of things, and thus explained these appearances. But there is a prior requirement for such a formulation. If an entity of the sort just discussed has a "nature," then presumably this nature remains the same, if it is to serve as an explanatory device. The demon that causes trembling does so in victim *X* just as in victim *Y*. There is some regularity in the action of whatever it is that is taken to be the cause of the disease. The angry god that acts retributively has, as his "nature," retributive action. The physical elements which explain the variety of things have as their "essential" or unchanging natures certain qualities, as *fiery,* or *earthy,* or *watery.* The underlying conception of such agencies, or causes, or principles is their regularity or uniformity of action.

This has its roots, as many inquirers have shown, in the way we talk, in the features of linguistic use, in which naming and referring to the "same" thing twice presumes a certain identity in both cases. The concept of "same" underlies the possibility of using the "same" name for the "same" thing, and of preserving identity of reference. But what underlies this linguistic use, developed as one among the earliest of our language habits? It would be odd to claim that language is somehow "given" in this form, that this is the *a priori* "nature" of language and that therefore this ultimately explains how the concept of "same" arises. Rather, it seems more reasonable to suppose that the patterns of experience which occur at the prelinguistic level of perceptual and motor activity already prefigure this linguistic concept. The habit formation discussed earlier already involves the implicit use of some such idea of "same," if memory is to do any connecting of past and present. Thus, in the behavior of animals, down to the lowest living organism, there exist selective nonrandom patterns of response to stimuli. Patterned behavior already bespeaks some principle of selection, and some way of "recognizing" similarities in different situations. This "recognition," at some prelinguistic and preconceptual level, is what we mean by "habit," or perhaps by "instinct."

The form of such habits is something of the following sort: "Whenever *X*, then *Y*," or, "The class of *X*-stimuli or *X*-situations evoke *Y*-responses." Once there is a linguistic or symbolic articulation of this form, explicit conceptual formulation may replace the implicit patterns of behavior. What was a habit of response becomes a formula, in the explicit form of language. The implicit generalization which a habitual pattern of activity involves becomes an explicit generalization of experience, because now experience is not merely enacted, in concrete responses to stimuli of certain sorts, but is abstracted in a linguistic description or representation, and may then be reflected upon. The simplest sort of such generalizations may be that which associates a thing with some of its properties. Thus, for example, in the common knowledge of a food-gathering society, identification and classification of edible fruits, berries, and roots associates certain recognizable visual features with edibility, others with inedibility. Most of us learn quite early that green apples make you sick, that green bananas are not ripe for eating, and that green tomatoes are better left to turn red. Greenness, unripeness, and inedibility are associated in some general fashion, which seems to go beyond the particular instances of those unripe fruits already experienced, because it suggests what to do in any future case as well. The utter practicality of such commonsense notions seems to be devoid of any formal idea of laws or rules. Yet there is an important feature to all such inductive generalizations—(that is, generalizations made on the basis of a usually large number of particular instances which exhibit a certain regularity and uniformity in the association of certain properties, such as greenness and unripeness, in the example). That feature may be called pairing, or simply associating with each property or quality of an object some other property or quality which is taken to go with it, as a matter of course. The phrase *matter of course* means here *in general,* or *in agreement with past observations or experiences.* But simply making a list of such pairs as happen to turn up in particular instances would not yet yield a generalization. It would simply give a report or a collection of data about the given instances. Making such a list may have some intrinsic interest, of course; it may satisfy the extraordinary propensity we have to record, to preserve the notable things we remember beyond the capacity of any one man's memory. But even such chronicling of past events is selective. And when the chronicle is used to teach a lesson, or point a moral, it takes on the form of a generalization. Thus, in recounting the experiences of the day, the food-gatherer may regale his listeners with a tale of how many green apples he tasted and found inedible. But the point of the story is, "Don't eat green apples!" And the generalization involved here goes beyond the specific green apples already found to be inedible. It suggests that any green apple will have the same characteristic inedibility, or that greenness of apples and inedibility go together in all prospective instances.

If one were to extend the association to bananas and tomatoes, and then further to fruits in general, the generalization would be, "All green fruits are inedible," and this would plainly be false (as it is also false about apples, some varieties of which are green when ripe and edible). Still, the tendency to generalize from a limited number of instances lies very close to the sources of our natural habit formation and is reinforced by the way in which we develop linguistic habits, using abstract class names for sets of things with common properties. Such hypothetical generalizations come easily to us then, and we are prone to anticipate the recurrence of familiar associations.

Over hundreds and even thousands of years of refinement and modification, the set of common generalizations of experience begins to constitute a hard core of almost unshakable beliefs, so widely tested as to appear finally as practically self-evident. We find such beliefs in folk sayings and in the very fabric of our language. Who, for example, would reasonably doubt that, "What goes up must come down," or "Where there's smoke, there's fire," or, "A stitch in time saves nine"? What is interesting about such generalizations is that they operate at more than one level. On the one hand, they are literal, in that we recognize the reference to actual "ups" and "downs," actual fire and actual stitches. But the literal events also have a metaphorical interpretation, which interprets them as maxims concerning human affairs. This connection between natural events and human events (as between actual smoke, and the telltale "smoke" of the metaphor), and between technical maxims and moral ones (as between the tailor's stitch and the connoted early remedy for human woes) exhibits an important feature of prescientific thought: namely, that the order and regularity of nature which serve as the dependable basis for necessary human activities are somehow akin to the need for orderly regulation of human life if it is to be dependably dealt with. This in itself would be an interesting but only marginal point in this context, unless it had bearing on prescientific modes of explanation. Its bearing is that the descriptive generalizations from experience are merged, in prescientific thought, with prescriptive rules and imperatives, such as are characteristic of human regulations and laws. Let us make this more explicit.

Empirical generalizations, of the green-apple sort, are clearly instances of practical knowledge. The prescription (or proscription) that our green-apple generalization bears is the imperative, "Don't eat green apples!" If we take a more complex generalization, though still of the same type, we can see broader consequences of this apparently innocuous connection between generalization and imperative. Suppose the pairing now takes place between a complex observation of a certain astronomical configuration (e.g., certain patterns of stars hitherto not visible in this year make their appearance near the horizon of the night sky) and an agricultural fact (e.g., optimal planting time). Let us imagine that these two facts have to this point remained unrelated, that optimal planting time has hitherto been arrived at by a dating method relying on certain nonastronomical facts, such as annual flooding or the nesting of a certain species of bird. But now the correlation is established between the annual appearance of a certain constellation above the horizon as evening begins and the annual events which mark optimal planting time. The formula, "Whenever . . . then . . ." now is seen to hold for these pairs of events, but perhaps in no more than a descriptive way. The two happen to occur together, and an inductive generalization emerges concerning the proposal that they always do or the expectation that they always will. But insofar as the second element in the pair is a human action, essential to survival—namely, planting—the association takes on the character of an imperative: "When the constellation X appears on the horizon, then you are to (should, must, are commanded to) plant seed." The first element of the pair now bears a prescriptive relation to the second, and all the characteristics of an imperative human law or rule of behavior are transferred to this pairing generalization. The social group that has special knowledge of the stars may turn out, on this account, to be a law-giving group, prescribing when and in what manner the life activities of the agricultural community are to take place.

The summary point about this prescientific mode of knowing is that the inductive empirical generalization which derives from the deeply practical sources of habit formation itself, becomes formulated conceptually as a law. The most general form of such a law is a universal and abstract formulation of the sort, "Whenever . . . then . . ." ranging over instances past and future. But the form of such a law, in its barest descriptive version, is closely associated with the practical imperatives of such law-like knowledge. And such imperatives lend the character of prescriptiveness to the law, giving it the character of human imperatives of the sort exemplified in rules and laws of a society. Such laws presume a lawgiver, a purpose of human weal, and an instrument of punishment for disobedience. These moral characteristics are easily transferred to the bare pairing criteria which govern empirical generalizations, as human affairs and natural events are conceived under one general family of concepts. Man is conceived as the world in small, his individuality and his society a microcosm whose projection in nature at large gives the macrocosm. Natural laws find their ultimate interpretation in the fulfillment of human purposes, as human laws find their sanction in the grand necessities of nature's order.

LEGISLATIVE RULES, TECHNICAL MAXIMS, AND NORMATIVE LAWS

The third sort of prescientific explanation derives from common human practice, much as the first two do, but takes its form more explicitly from technical practice and from societal laws and regulations. Much of human activity has to do with the production of the means of life, and consequently, with the ways in which such production is organized and its techniques preserved and transmitted. We know from the study of ancient cultures and from their artifacts that there is great uniformity within a culture in basic methods of production of the tools and instruments of economic life. For example, the classification of stone-age implements depends often on determining the techniques by which they were produced. The characteristic shapes, formed by flaking or chipping, or the characteristic techniques of weaving baskets mark off distinctive cultures, or periods within a culture. In effect, one of the anthropologist's instruments in the classification and dating of artifacts is his reconstruction of the rule of production or technique which an artifact exhibits. We know from the study of ancient societies that such rules often become legislative, that they are often treated in ritual fashion, that a way of production is taken to be the "right way," and that the proper sequence of steps in the production of an implement becomes closely associated with the ultimate efficacy of that instrument in use.

With the specialization of toolmaking and with division of labor the toolmaker's craft becomes an almost religious activity, and its regulations become ritual injunctions: "Do it this way and no other!" Laws for the regulation of society are in this sense closely akin to such technical rules, and the necessity for proceeding in a certain way—the "right way"—acquires moral and religious overtones. Religious rite and magic are, in fact, techniques for the control over nature and over the human nature which conceives nature to be in its own image.

Techniques of work are also strictly regulated and ritualized, and the reason is not hard to see. For in the collective work which involves many people doing the same thing in unison, or in a common rhythm, uniformity of action is a prerequisite for successful operation. Sea chanteys and work songs in our own recent past, as well as those dance rituals of the hunt or of war which still exist, give evidence of this sort of aesthetic regulation. Similarly, the medieval guild rules for production of cloth or implements of daily use show the legislative character of such rules. Any craft has its successful and sanctioned modes of operation, and it is these that the apprentice learns as rules when he learns the craft. Technology proceeds by recipe and by the preservation of traditional techniques, for by this means the culture is able to transmit from one generation to the next the cumulative operational know-how it has acquired. (Innovation, of course, becomes difficult under these circumstances, and novelty and free experimentation are restricted, sometimes fatally.) All this seems clearly to suggest the relation between such technical rules and the legislative regulations we recognize as laws, by which social institutions are preserved. The organization of technique is itself a social institution of great importance, and in early societies such as those of Egypt and Babylonia the priestly class merged its ritual and religious functions with hegemony over technical knowledge. Science and mathematics become sacred possessions, in such a context, just as "right ways" of operation are, because the two are intimately related. The relation of theoretical knowledge (e.g., astronomy and of mathematics) to practical technical regulation (e.g., planting and reaping or measuring land areas) becomes a function of a special group, whose institutional role is ensured by its sanctity and its direct connections with the powers and agencies that work for human weal and woe.

It is tempting to speculate that the ritual "necessity" of doing things in a certain approved way, if they are to turn out right, is at least one of the sources of our concept of necessary truth, of that truth which cannot be conceived to be other than it is. There are clearly other sources, such as the (related) exercise of political authority and the experience of unchanging physical sequences and irresistible physical forces in nature. The force of tradition, made rigorous by the explicit formulation of rules, and the sanctification of these rules by myths of their divine origin, calls for absolute belief in this "right way." Such "right belief" or "orthodoxy" thus comes to connote *necessary* belief. Such beliefs are not acquired from practical experience, in this context, but are handed down from one generation to the next as received doctrine, and as *a priori* truths. In such a tradition of cultural transmission, such beliefs and such "necessary truths" as are objects of such beliefs appear entirely self-evident. To question them is to question the whole fabric of technological organization and training, and indeed the whole social structure and system of values which founds itself on such orthodoxy. The meanings of words themselves are enmeshed in this social-technical fabric, so that the linguistic formulations of such beliefs, the definitions of terms in such a linguistic framework become ritually fixed. One practical reason for such fixed meanings becomes clear when we consider that originally much of this body of knowledge and rules gets passed down in an oral tradition, by repetition of the same account in precisely the same way. The efficacy of such ritual repetition, in practice, is that it preserves a certain accuracy; the copy is less likely to differ widely from the original if the very technique of transmission requires a formal and careful ritual performance.[3]

In short, rules easily become fixed and become distinctive entities with a necessity of their own. They become legislative and not merely descriptive accounts of how to operate. They take on the form of normative laws, prescribing right and wrong ways of acting. Ethical rules and technical rules, rules of art and of morality are in their origin closely related; and these, because of their intimate connection with social and political rules both in substance and in form, take on the character of imperatives, whose observance is sanctioned and whose violation is punished.

The significance of such prescientific formulations is that they carry over into scientific thought the concepts of legislative necessity, or normative law, and of divine sanction. In the history of early science such conceptions dominate and give direction to much scientific and theoretical explanation. Science sets out to discover the "right way of working," which is taken to be an imitation of the "divine way" of working (or in another interpretation, "nature's way" of working). The true craftsman imitates nature's mode of operation, and by this imitation works in conformity with nature. The guarantee of his successful operation is therefore the knowledge of this

[3] The evidence of the accuracy of such transmission is striking, whenever there is occasion to investigate a contemporary instance. Indian chants and prayers, for example, are repeated for hundreds of stanzas, on different occasions, with remarkable fidelity both in the music and the words, in cases where alternative performances have been tape-recorded and compared. The human capacity for such ritual repetition also shows itself strikingly in the pathological cases of compulsive behavior in which exactly the same sequence of events or acts must be repeated; and the role of repetition in learning of the ordinary sort underlines the centrality of this technique at the very beginnings of our knowledge, and of our learning the use of a language. (Reading a story to children for the fifteenth time is a good test of this ritualism: among the very youngest, who do not yet read, any slight variation in a word or even in an inflection calls forth protests about "not doing it the right way.")

divine or natural "way." The relation between right action and true knowledge, or orthodox belief, is seen to be an essential relation: one is not possible without the other. This is a mode of thought common to religious observance, ethical action, and technological operation. This conflation of religion, ethics, and early scientific theory is a commonplace of early science. The normative law, the canonized rule, the technical maxim are set up as ideal forms to be emulated in practice, as limits toward which right operation or action will tend.

The idealized entities of anthropomorphic explanation are still figurative, personal. Rules, maxims, and laws are already removed from such picturing by a major step: they are linguistic expressions, imperatives sanctioned by the gods, spoken in everyday speech or in ritualistic holy language, but spoken nevertheless. Abstraction enters with the very articulation of such rules and normative laws, in a language, for the word itself becomes holy, the ritual formulation is itself endowed with regulative power, the commandment itself becomes the verbal image of the divine will.

Yet such a language need not be explicitly verbal. A rule may be implicitly given in a model. The flaked point which shows no signs of use may have served as the model for the toolmakers. The implicit (or explicit) direction is, "Make it like this one." A diagram or a picture, as part of the sympathetic magic which transferred the properties of pictures to those who "participate" in them (by making them or by observing them), may also have served as a model ("Do it in this way!") Descriptive records, in the stylized pictographs of American Indian deer-skin paintings or in Sahara Desert rock paintings, constitute a history of past battles and hunts. But there is a normative art as well, a record which exemplifies ideal relations and carries the power of the imperative, as in totem poles and in ornamental scarification, which also serves to mark degrees of rank or sexual status (e.g., virgin, wife, chief, and so on). These are rules of behavior in pictorial form. They suggest or command that things be done in a certain way if certain results are to be achieved, that certain actions and relations are permitted and others prohibited.

The symbol itself is considered to have a directive power, and its efficacy is connected with its right use. The same animism which gives canoes "eyes" and assures the efficacy of a weapon by rituals of purification now attaches to the embodied rule. The formulation itself becomes a normative entity, and the notion of obeying the embodied rule or of violating it is overlaid with moral and religious attitudes. The embodied rule becomes a sacred thing with its own independent status. The violation of such a sacred rule, even if it is a technical rule for a way of working or operating, is tantamount to violating a moral, social, or religious law. Because the whole community has a stake in the right operation of this rule, the whole community is taken to suffer from such violations, and the balance can be set right again only by punishing the violator. In this way rules of operation become hypostatized. Insofar as they are taken to represent the right way of working, or nature's own way of working, or the mode of operation of a divine necessity, violations of such rules become violations of nature or of the gods. The outcome, as it bears on the development of later scientific thought, is that such linguistic entities are taken to express or to represent laws of nature (or divine laws), and the force and necessity of such laws is taken to be characteristic of the necessity of the rules themselves. Legislative rules of "right" human operation are taken as expressing laws of natural operation, and these laws themselves are taken to embody right and therefore necessary relations.

The history of early science exhibits the use of word magic, granting to verbal formulations a certain efficacy in getting things done. Incantations, spells, "secret formulas" were thought to give the user a certain power over natural events. And the reason is not far to seek. These ritual formulations are after all the "secrets" which embody nature's own rules. So-called sympathetic magic operates on things because things "obey" the magic formula, and they obey it because their very "essence" or "nature" is given in the formula. This notion, of the revelation of some essence of nature in a formula, though it is here reconstructed in its animistic and mystical form, plays a large role in the development of science and concepts of natural laws.

We have thus considered three prescientific modes of knowing: (1) anthropomorphic explanation, (2) inductive generalization, and (3) technical rules. In each case certain fundamental patterns of explanation become formulated in their earliest way: In the first, explanation in terms of imaginary or hypothetical entities that are assumed to exist and whose "nature" or properties account for otherwise inexplicable natural phenomena; in the second, generalization of patterns in experience or action, explicitly formulated in what are prototypes of descriptive laws; and in the third, prescriptive or normative formulation of laws, in which these laws themselves are considered to have a certain necessity and a divine or extrahuman status, an objectivity transcending local human purposes. The wider concepts of a developed science, concerning theoretical explanation, empirical or descriptive law, and notions of natural necessity and determinism, which we shall consider in later chapters, are already contained in their germinal form in these prescientific ways of knowing.

There is, however, a need to consider the most general features of the ordinary ways of knowing, apart from their formulation in the explicit patterns we have examined here. What these all share at the root is the soil of common sense, which remains unarticulated, not yet formed into the explicit patterns of myth, maxim, and rule, but immediately relevant to the widest contexts of human experience and practice. In this sense, common sense is not superseded either by these prescientific patterns of explanation or by science except as the contexts of ordinary and universal everyday practice themselves are superseded, as the demands of curiosity or wonder or the needs of technology go beyond the limits of common practice and common understanding.

Common sense is elusive and is uncommonly hard to characterize. Yet there are features of it which bear directly on the genesis of science and help to illuminate, by contrast, the unique nature of scientific thought. What concerns us then is the transition from common sense to that deliberately critical and systematic mode of thinking which marks the beginnings of philosophy and science.

CHAPTER 4

From Common Sense to Science: The Remarkable Greeks and the Origins of Criticism

COMMON SENSE

MUCH OF OUR KNOWLEDGE is practical know-how. It concerns in an eminently down-to-earth way how things are to be done, how ends are to be achieved, how one is to act in usual situations. Such "common-sense" knowledge is common in that it is what *anyone* would be expected to know. Thus it constitutes a body of homely and ubiquitous truths that are scarcely articulated for critical reflection, because they are so pervasive and well entrenched in our practical speech and behavior. True, much of this is expressed in the literature and religion, in the myths and morals of a people, as well as in its store of technical maxims, as we have seen in the discussion of prescientific ways of knowing. Yet the commonsense content of this heritage becomes assimilated in such a way that it becomes part of the tacit understanding: its "truths" are obvious, taken for granted, and unreflective, although they are embodied in linguistic form and expressed in the ordinary language of men as proverbial saying, or turn of phrase, or home remedy. Even here common sense is so intertwined with common usage that its expression is elliptical, and much of it is contained in what is called the idiom or the genius of a language (e.g., in such elliptical phrases as, "There he goes again!" "What did you expect?" or "It's about time!").

The characteristic of such commonsense knowledge is that it is neither explicitly systematic nor explicitly critical; that is, not all parts of it are brought to bear on all other parts, nor is there a conscious attempt to regard it as a consistent body of truths. Yet it has a rough-and-ready wholeness, as the common property of a culture, as the set of dependable expectations concerning what everyone ought to know about the common and basic activities of everyday life. It thus ensures dependable anticipation in matters of human action and assures against unanticipated surprise. Its functions in making common work and social life possible, in delimiting randomness and danger in action are inestimably important.

Common sense is not so changeless or universal as not to vary with contexts and historical periods. The common sense of one generation sometimes turns out to be the nonsense of the next. It was once common-sensical to close the windows against the noxious night air; now it is common-sensical to keep a room well ventilated at night. Yet throughout these variations there would seem to be some universal contexts, some characteristic human situations which cut across differences of time, place, and circumstance, and thus some commonsense universals appropriate to all contexts. It is a favorite game of comparative anthropologists to seek to establish or disestablish such pervasive common features. "Universalists" find such common traits in widely divergent societies and speculate about the "universals of human nature." "Relativists" delight in exploding such claims to universality by discovering exceptions and counterinstances. Yet some low-level commonsense attitudes and beliefs do seem to prevail everywhere, or at least give the *prima facie* appearance of doing so. Nowhere is it accepted practice to try to walk through solid objects, and everywhere there is some cautionary version of, "Look before you leap." As widely divergent as are the customs regarding the treatment of strangers, it is safe to say that in every society, there is some maxim about not trusting everybody, and some obligation to trust somebody.

This is the rub, for such formulations are so wide and vague that any number of alternative interpretations would fit them. As in the practice of "proof-texting," wherein justification for opposite conclusions may be found by citing suitable chapter and verse in the Bible, one may find commonsense support for opposite sorts of actions. Thus, one may urge caution with, "Look before you leap," and encourage risk taking with, "Nothing ventured, nothing gained." The commonsense conclusion to be drawn from such apparently opposite counsels may be, "Nothing in excess." But the definitive characterization of an action as being of this sort remains ever a matter of "good, sound commonsense judgment," for which there is no specific.[1] Tradition and the consensus of all mankind may sometimes be ap-

[1] The advice of a cook of my acquaintance, on how to reproduce an especially savory dish, is to "add just *a little too much* vinegar."

pealed to in support of such judgments. But here too we are left with either a practical maxim or with a vicious circularity: Rely on the best judge to give the soundest judgment. The practical maxim gives a clue to the nature of common sense, for the "best judge" is the one with the widest experience. And common sense is clearly the product of wide and long experience. It may be said to be the evolved adaptation, at the most practical level, to the human environment. Its adaptiveness bespeaks its strong survival value, and on some evolutionary views, it is as refined and important an instrumentality of human species survival as is protective coloration or social organization among some animal species.

In defense of common sense, one may say that it is slowly and carefully formed and is effectively tested in areas of the widest common experience, that its core has been perhaps a million years in the making, and that it is the condition for sociability and for community in the practical matters of living and working. But although it may be the soil out of which science grows, it is not scientific, in that it is not the subject of conscious, reflective criticism. It may be adaptive by the workings of the "criticism" of experience, over long periods of time. But because it is so tacit and unexplicated in the ordinary way of our commonsense beliefs, it seems closer to habit than to conscious thought. It is often mistaken, even in practical situations, false with respect to matters of fact and too vague to be adequate as a guide to action in special and new situations. Its fixity in the face of change has suggested to some critics and defenders that it is close to instinct. The first philosophical defenders of common sense, the so-called Scottish commonsense realists, such as Thomas Reid and Dugald Stewart, considered the fundamental beliefs of common sense to be natural instincts with which we were fitted to get along in the world. For example, the belief in the existence of an external reality independent of our knowing it was seen by these theorists of common sense not as a philosophical generalization, nor as something acquired by experience, but as a native instinctual belief unassailable by doubt.

This is, instincts aside, a fair description of the character of common sense. The commonsense belief is held, in all unself-conscious good faith, to be indubitable. The very challenge of such a faith is seen as either inconceivable or as a clear mark of the irrationality or downright idiocy of the challenger. Thus, C. S. Peirce characterized common sense as by its very nature *acritical,*[2] and this is where common sense, for all its inductive breadth and strength, parts company with scientific thought and philosophical analysis, which are by their nature critical. And it is the emergence of this criticism, as crucial in the transition from common sense to science which will be the concern of the rest of this chapter.

[2] C. S. Peirce, "Critical Common-Sensism," in *Philosophical Writings of Peirce,* ed. J. Buchler (New York: Dover, 1955), pp. 290–300.

FROM COMMON SENSE TO THE CRITICISM OF CONCEPTS

Common sense may give the rule or the guide to action, but leaves vague the method of its application. It depends for this on "good sense" or "sound judgment"; and, as we know by common sense, no amount of education or sheer talk will guarantee such sound judgment. We say it depends on "experience," on having come to know or to recognize such judgment in practice. The commonsense method for ascertaining good sense is to point to some model or paradigm and to urge imitation. Thus much of our education in judgment is said to come from good example, and this is like the use of exemplary models in the technological contexts discussed earlier. The instruction is, "Make it like this," or, "Do it in this way"; and the answer to the upstart's question as to *why* it should be made or done in this way is, "Because that's the way it's done," or, "Because that is the right way to do it."

Yet once such implicit rules by example or explicit maxims become articulate, they may themselves become the objects of judgment. The criticism originally leveled by the master at the performance or the product of an action by the apprentice—e.g., "This is a bad arrow you made," or, "That was a poor kill you made"—may now be explicitly concerned with failure to follow a rule, or following a bad rule—e.g., "You didn't follow the instruction," or, "The rule you followed is wrong." The transition seems slight, if a transition at all, but attention has shifted from the performance or the production to the rule or the judgment which governed it. The criticism now goes beyond the criticism of practice itself and is instead leveled at the linguistic formulations and the concepts which describe and prescribe this practice. The criticism of rules and judgments now supersedes the criticism of experience, as mere common sense passes over into critical common sense—from the use of commonsense concepts to their critique, to the reflection upon them which distinguishes practical intelligence from rationality.

This brings with it a train of *formal* considerations, as to the validity and consistency of commonsense judgments. Common sense itself may be said not to be aware of "incompatible beliefs" or "inconsistencies" within its own structure, precisely because it is so largely tacit. Such incompatibility becomes apparent only upon critical reflection. But such reflection therefore requires some notion of systematicity, of how the various proposals of common sense bear on each other, of how one concept relates to another, or of how one judgment entails another. What further needs to be made explicit are such systematic criteria as consistency and noncontradiction. For such criteria to be relevant, for such criticism to be at all possible, the content of common sense needs to be articulated as a system of discourse, i.e., an explicitly formulated system of linguistic expressions in some relatively permanent form, which may be inspected and is publicly available.

The most important difference between science and common sense lies in the explicitness and the refutability of the scientific proposition and in the aim of science to be consciously and deliberately critical as a matter of course. The conditions of criticizability are, minimally, that the object of criticism must be articulated sharply, as an object of conscious reflection, no longer tacit. But what is it that constitutes such an object of criticism, or what can come to be criticized in this way? It cannot be merely experience itself, for experiences are simply *had.* To be critical *of* experience requires that it be formulated in such a way that it can become an object of reflection. Minimally, then, such experience has to be remembered or recollected. But this is not enough, for to recall an experience is, in some sense, to re-enact or relive it. But "lived through" experience is uncriticizable, as such. However, recounting or describing an experience is no longer a case of simply having it. The public formulation in a language becomes the object of critical and public reflection, for now questions may be asked about the experience as it is described in overt linguistic form. Once language becomes the explicit vehicle for the communication of information about experience, of attitudes toward it, of attempts to explain or order it, criticism becomes possible. Questions concerning the meaning of the utterance, how it is to be understood, whether it is true or false can then be asked. And the answers themselves are once again objects of the same critical reflection, the same inquiry into meaning and truth.

The concepts and the judgments expressed in language thus become the subject of explication—of making explicit the largely tacit and unarticulated content of commonsense knowledge and usage. This analysis of concepts and of the systematic frameworks in which concepts are related to each other is one source of philosophy. We may say that, in part, philosophy is that explication of common sense which makes it the object of sustained and systematic reflection and which forces us, therefore, to consider what it is we take ourselves to know and to mean and to believe in the ordinary way of common sense. The philosophical concern with language is not the linguist's concern, although how language is structured, how it comes to mean, and how it changes, may bear on philosophical questions. Rather, philosophy is the critical approach to the thought content of language, and to the way in which articulation in a linguistic form shapes and is shaped by this thought content. Thus it supersedes common sense, being about common sense rather than another form of commonsense knowledge itself. In this way it is detached from the immediate practical concerns of common sense, whose object is workaday decision and action itself, but it is the critique of the concepts which govern this practice, or of the beliefs which are embodied in it.

In this sense philosophy is criticism. But we have seen that a large part of man's thought is concerned with more than commonsense matters. Beyond the short-term periphery of everyday activity there are speculative and theoretical questions concerning the why and wherefore of things. These too may be questions of human weal and woe, of practical consequence in the larger and long-term economy of human life. But they are questions of such great abstraction and vast generality as only language makes possible. The very formulation of questions of this scope has as its condition that conceptual abstraction which language affords. Thus, where common sense, oriented toward the specific and the concrete, may ask, "What is good or right in this instance, or in instances of this sort?" or, "Where does this or that thing come from?" speculative inquiry generalizes in such a way that the questions are of a qualitatively different sort: "What is *the good* or *the right* in human life? What, in general, makes anything good or any act right?" or, "Where does *everything* come from? What is the origin or the beginning of *all* things?" Once articulated, such questions themselves become objects of critical reflection: What does the question mean? What sort of answer does it call for? How would one go about deciding between true and false answers to such questions?

Here, then, is another sort of subject matter for philosophical criticism, but for that criticism which has the dual task of explication and analysis, and of theoretical construction. For such questions do not admit of answers derived from commonsense observation and practical knowledge, although they may be reconstructed by generalization from such knowledge. Rather, what is asked for is a hypothesis which transcends common experience and is yet bound by the constraints of what the common understanding finds plausible: something which reason applauds but which perception and common practice do not deny or find absurd.

The tension between theoretical construction and common sense, between hypotheses framed to answer the questions of the speculative intellect and the plain facts of everyday know-how and observation thus gives rise to a criticism of a more complex sort. For our purposes, in examining the genesis of scientific thought, this is crucial. For it marks the radical transformation of acritical common sense into critical, rational scientific thought. It is not accidental that the earliest instances of philosophical speculation and criticism and the earliest instances of rational natural philosophy are one and the same. For science and philosophy have a common ancestry: on the one hand, the matrix of tacit commonsense knowledge, and of the prescientific formulations of myths, technical maxims, and social rules; and on the other, that reflection and criticism which the objective form of language makes possible. Out of this amalgam the Greeks fashioned a conceptual revolution so profound, so decisive in its impress that the main features of scientific thought—what we here call its conceptual foundations—retain to this day the features of that mold.

In completing this brief introductory account of the genesis of scientific thought, from its foundations in ordinary ways of knowing, in prescientific patterns of explanation, in common sense and the advent of criticism, we turn now to a characterization of some of the major features of Greek philosophy and science.

THE BACKGROUND OF GREEK SCIENCE AND PHILOSOPHY

The background of myth, law, and technical practice provided the systematic frameworks within which philosophical criticism and speculation on the nature of things developed in that flowering of thought in ancient Greece which gave birth to rational science. In addition, Greek wisdom-literature, embodying the refined commonsense precepts of ethical and political life, and Greek art with its remarkable sense of form and order, were the ready materials for philosophical analysis and generalization.

Greek mythology embodied a roughly systematic account of how the cosmos came into being and how it was ordered, as well as an implicit set of prescriptions and models for human behavior. In common with all cosmogonical myths it conceived of cosmic origin and development by analogy to human experience, and the relations among the gods expressed the imaginatively and anthropomorphically conceived relations among elements in the natural world. From an original chaos and the strife of the early generations of the gods for dominance, there emerged an order of things arranged according to an overarching law whose necessity was unshakeable. The laws of men and the features of social order all found their embodiment in the structure of myth: the division of territory, the hierarchy of powers, the punishment for transgression were all seen as proceeding according to law, and the equity of the earliest forms of human justice was expressed in the sense of right balance and proportion, the harmony which law produces out of strife and which pervades the mythical accounts. Here, then, was the prototype of a systematic account of the reasons for things, a prescientific theoretical explanation in terms of hypothetical entities.

Furthermore, law making and the codification of laws proceeded rapidly in the volatile conditions of political unrest and change. The Greek city-states introduced and experimented with a variety of governmental and administrative forms. In Athens, in particular, the codification of the laws by Draco (in 621 B.C.) and the law reforms of Solon (in 594 B.C.) provided that heritage of public, explicitly formulated, and systematic law that is one of the prototypes of systematicity and law in philosophy and science.[3]

The flowering of Greek art—in particular, the interrelated arts of music, poetry, and drama and the plastic arts of architecture and sculpture—and the high level of technological activity which developed in the Greek colonies in Ionia, particularly in the great port city of Miletus, filled out this rich and complex background. The arts embodied an aesthetic ideal of great depth which pervaded much of Greek life. In art, as in life, the Greeks sought to bring together the elements in some ordered, unified, and

[3] The extent of this legal production can be gauged by the fact that Aristotle surveyed the constitutions of 158 different city-states in Greece as a preliminary study to his writing of the *Politics*.

harmonious way, and the ideal of a well-ordered life was represented in the ideal of a well-ordered art. Balance, symmetry, right combination of elements constituted the good in art, as they also constituted the good life and the well-ordered state. Justice in the affairs of men was conceived as the achievement of harmony, the integration of the various parts of a whole, each acting according to its "proper" or "appropriate" nature toward the end of an ideal unity. Injustice, by contrast, was the strife engendered by the violation of the natural or proper order of things. The myths of origin mirrored this profound sense of "right ordering": the *Cosmos* was produced out of an original *Chaos* by this ordering or right proportion. The inchoate rationalism of the Greeks already expressed itself in the notion that an original formlessness, a swarming confusion of disordered things, could be brought under some unifying principle of order. Poetry and drama showed forth the ordered structures of discourse. In the representation of events and actions language itself was seen to be capable of mirroring the patterns of human experience and of natural events in a way which could be understood and which explained the sense and meaning of these patterns.

The Greek delight in language, in the sheer sound of words, in storytelling, and in debate was perhaps the central experience out of which rational criticism developed. The story, which is such a central experience for all peoples and the primary introduction to the community of discourse for the young in every society to the present day, had an inordinate attraction for the Greeks. That one could fashion comprehensible structures with words, that all could share in this common intelligibility, this *Logos,* that talk could communicate truths, laws, feelings, commands, that it could effectively regulate and direct human action—all this struck the Greek mind as a revelation. It was taken not simply as a revelation about discourse but as a revelation about the very nature of things which such discourse could communicate. Talking, thinking, doing formed aspects of one reality, and language could express the order and the nature of human life and of the world. Thus, man could come to understand his world and himself by representing it in his art and his discourse. The secret of the world's intelligibility was also the secret of the intelligibility of art and language: form, structure, well-ordering.

THE BIRTH OF RATIONAL SPECULATION AND THE ORIGINS OF NATURAL SCIENCE

Given this background of myth, art, and law, the first attempt to give a natural or physical explanation of how the world came into being and what constituted it was that of the Milesian natural philosophers, the founders of philosophy and physics, who flourished in the great Ionian commercial colony of Miletus in the sixth century B.C. The major thesis which marks off this school from the earlier background of religion and myth is that it attempted to explain the origin and structure of the world of our experience entirely in terms of natural causes. This is not as simple as it sounds, for the term *nature* does not have a clear and definitive meaning. The Greek term which we translate as *nature* is *physis* (φύσις), whence this group of thinkers came to be known as the *physiologoi,* or "inquirers into nature." The most important methodological thesis of the *physiologoi* was that the variety and multiplicity of things was ordered by a unitary principle, or derived from some unitary stuff, so that this variety could be explained genetically as having evolved from this underlying material stuff or process. What was attempted, in short, was a unified theory of the universe—of its coming into existence, its structure, and its processes of change and transformation, on the basis of physical principles alone.

These natural philosophers (sometimes called the pre-Socratics because their mode of thought dominated until Socrates introduced a radical departure in Greek philosophy) formulated a series of alternative cosmological hypotheses as reasoned speculations concerning the nature of things. But especially significant for our account is the fact that these were not simply alternative constructions. Rather, they developed in the course of criticism, each representing an attempt to overcome the inadequacies or inconsistencies of the preceding one. What emerges is a dialectic—a process of conjecture and criticism—which marks off this mode of thought from acritical common sense and myth. The first of these natural philosophers, Thales, proposed that everything "came from" or was "made from" water. The reasons for this speculation are fairly clear, though it seems naive to us at this distance. Water is the source of life, in several senses: all living things seem to originate in or from some watery source, and water is a necessity for all living things. In addition, the process of human birth itself suggests this watery origin, and the Greeks already knew about the amniotic fluid in which the fetus develops. Water is also capable of transformation from the liquid to the gaseous and solid states, and it is completely plastic, formless in itself yet capable of taking on any shape. Many cosmological myths envision the earth as resting on water, or as surrounded by water (as one might expect in river or maritime civilizations).[4] Thus this "naive" speculation may be seen in its context as a reasonable one. The dependence on water for the very sustenance of life, the observation of the watery origin of living things, the transformability and plasticity of water, its presence in the widest variety of things as a constituent all suggested to Thales that water was the one "stuff" out of which all things came to be or were constituted. Although all this is formulated in earlier myths, it is the nonmythical form of Thales' conjecture that is new. The succeeding attempts to explain the nature of things by some common unifying principle or stuff continued in this spirit, as nature myths were replaced by such natural speculation.

[4] The earliest cosmogonical myths already exhibit this fundamental notion, in many instances, as in the "precreation" Egyptian god-figure *Nūn,* who represents the primor-

When Anaximander, the second of the Milesian philosophers, supplanted Thales' conjecture with the notion of an *indeterminate stuff* as the origin of all things, it was by way of criticism of the adequacy of Thales' explanation. Anaximander conceived of this origin in a boundless and qualitatively indeterminate stuff with an inherent motion. This stuff—"the indeterminate" (τὸ ἄπειρον, or the *apeiron*)—gives rise to the elements, which are separated out (or separated *off*—interpretations vary) from it by this inherent whirling motion or vortex. Thus the elements themselves come to be (or "grow" or are "given birth") out of the original motion or self-activity of the indeterminate. Thales' conjecture of water, as a qualitatively determinate origin, is thereby rejected by Anaximander. Rather, he sees the qualities or elements, as paired opposites (hot-cold, wet-dry) and as themselves coming into being by means of some process or motion. (In "stuff" terms, these qualities are the standard four elements of early accounts: fire, air mist, water, and earth) The "separation" of these elements is natural, or "according to necessity," in Anaximander's terms, and is therefore conceived of as "just." But the things in the world are mixtures of these elements, or mixtures of opposite qualities, and this mixture is "unjust." In the Greek context this injustice is the "strife of opposites" which must ultimately be set right. Things in the world are therefore, at best, impermanent mixtures of the elements whose dissolution is inevitable, just as in the Greek view, justice is inevitable. As Anaximander is said to state it, the elements, in encroaching on each other in the mixture, "pay penalty and retribution to each other for their injustice according to the assessment of time." Thus change is the inevitable working of a retributive justice, in the dissolution into their primal elements of the mixtures which make up things. Change in the world is the coming into being and passing away of things, by combination and dissolution.

The richness of Anaximander's physical concepts may not be immediately apparent and we may not properly appreciate the conceptual advance here,

---

dial waters, or the self-begetting progenitor-god *Atum,* who arises out of the primordial waters to create a *Cosmos* out of *Chaos;* or more strikingly, in the first sustained cosmogonical myth of the Babylonians, the *Enuma Elish* (written in Akkadian, about the middle of the second millenium B.C.) in which the earliest stage of the universe is described as a watery chaos, a mixture of three "principles," *Apsu* (sweet waters), *Ti'amat* (sea waters), and *Mummu* (probably clouds and mist). (See, for a fuller account, Frankfort, *Before Philosophy* (Baltimore: Penguin Books, 1949), pp. 183 ff.) Silt separates from the waters and is deposited (represented as the birth out of the watery chaos of the two gods *Lahmu* and *Lahamu*), and thus the generation of the primal elements of a Cosmos is begun. The origin of nature is anthropomorphically represented in the birth of gods. When Thales articulated the first "natural" cosmogony, he may very well have been indirectly drawing on Egyptian and Babylonian sources in myth, or he may have been deriving his principle from the early Greek version (itself possibly related to these other sources) which spoke of "Okeanos, begetter of gods" or "begetter of all," as Homer describes it in the Iliad. See G. S. Kirk and J. E. Raven, *The Pre-Socratic Philosophers* (Cambridge: Cambridge University Press, 1957), p. 15. See pp. 11–19 for fuller discussion on *Okeanos*.

because the concepts first formulated here have become so ingrained in our present commonsense views that we fail to note them. In modified form they are present in much of contemporary science, and we may summarize them schematically.

1. The notion of an activity or original motion whereby origin and transformation proceed, and the notion of how this motion operates (as a whirling motion which separates out original elements from the indeterminate).
2. The notion of *element,* and the notion that things in the world are combinations or mixtures of such primary elements.
3. The notion of constant change in the world, that things are impermanent mixtures and that change proceeds by combination and dissolution of elements.
4. The notion of the indeterminate as a ground, or origin, and as a unitary field or process which contains in itself all the elements necessary for world formation.
5. The notion of a legislative necessity operating through time; that is, the notion of an overarching lawfulness in nature.

The natural philosophers who followed Anaximander in turn criticized his views, proposed alternative ones, or elaborated and refined the earlier ones. Of great significance is the thought of Anaximenes, who was Anaximander's contemporary and his companion. At first examination, Anaximenes' view seems to be a reversion to Thales' sort of explanation; instead of water, Anaximenes proposes that *air* (or *air mist*) is the one stuff out of which everything is made. The significance of Anaximenes' proposal is that it is closely tied to both natural observation and to the technical knowledge of the time. The Greek conception of air was that it was a damp or dark mist. Anaximenes, in rejecting Anaximander's *indeterminate,* introduces several ingenious explanatory considerations in favor of *air* as the primal stuff. First, it may be visible (as in mist, or in the further "condensation" of this air mist as clouds) or invisible (the transparent atmospheric air). But when it is compressed, as in breath or wind, even this invisible air may be felt. Thus air has various phenomenal appearances, as it is more or less *compressed,* or *condensed* (literally, "made more dense"). Under still greater pressure, then, air becomes earth-like or even rock-like. When it is rarefied it becomes lighter and, as in the case of evaporation or of fire, it rises. Thus condensation carries it down and evaporation carries it up. (Why clouds "float" then remains unaccountable.) The analogy to technical processes is made by Anaximenes in accounting for the formation of clouds, which he says are produced by an operation of compression, like that of *felting.* (Felt was one of the products of Miletus, and the felting process, in which fibers were soaked thoroughly, then heated and compressed to form the felted cloth, was well known.)

Anaximenes thus provides not only a unitary "stuff" capable of transformations, but also suggests the mechanism of this transformation by means of the natural processes of condensation and rarefaction, derived from the common experience and the technical skills concerned with pressure variation and from the observation of evaporation and condensation. Thus Anaximenes is the first to draw explicitly on a technological model, in which technical knowledge and human means of control and manipulation of nature become the sources of explanatory analogies.

REASON AND FORM: THE *LOGOS*

Whereas the Milesian *physiologoi* offered unitary explanations of the origin and nature of things in terms of some material "stuff" or process, two other Ionian philosophers introduced an alternative emphasis on the *form* of things as their unifying principle. Xenophanes is principally known for his open attack on the anthropomorphism of myth. As in the earlier monotheisms of the Jews and of the Egyptian pharaoh Ikhnaton, Xenophanes proclaimed that there is but one God, "in no way similar to mortals either in body or in thought." This *One* which Xenophanes called "God" is formally similar to the "one stuff" of the Milesians. But it is not a material stuff. Rather, it is a being which "remains in the same place, moving not at all . . . (which) shakes all things by the thought of his mind." Here is a radical departure from the formative notions of the Milesians, whose principles of world formation were in terms of some physical process—motion, the vortex, compression, combination and dissolution. These are replaced by a "mental" ordering, by means of "thought." If to understand the world is to render it intelligible to thought, then the nature of what is understood (i.e., the world) is taken to be *like* the nature of what understands it, or how it comes to be understood (i.e., in thought). There are strong elements here of the older framework of sympathetic magic, in which like acts on like, and this continues to pervade much of the later physical speculation. But Xenophanes fixes on the nature of thought as the model of natural reality itself, as its underlying unity or form, as the *One* which underlies the being of all things.

Heraclitus, who develops this notion of an underlying formal unity, proposes a radically new way of explaining the nature of things. Instead of taking the elements or some one thing as the ultimate origin of all things, he takes the process of change itself as ultimate. Thus, there are no elements nor any single element which constitutes all things, but rather a "flow" or "flux," a constant process of change and transformation. The so-called elements or things in the world are therefore nothing but "aspects" or "moments" or "phases" of this continual change. What is radical here is that this seems contrary to our ordinary notion of *thing* which underlies so much of our commonsense view of the world. "Things" are relatively permanent and have an identity. But in Heraclitus' view, if the changing "flux" is fundamental, things are only stages in this change and are completely transient. In the flux everything is coming into being and passing away continuously, and in this sense, a "thing" both "is what it is" and "is not what it is," for in this continuous change, self-identity is at best transient, for everything is constantly being transformed into something else.

This opposition between "what is and is not" is conceived by Heraclitus as a "strife of opposites," and all things are transient unities of these opposites. Whereas Anaximander also saw in the "mixture" of elements a strife of opposites, and regarded this as "unjust," Heraclitus regards it as "just," as the way things are by nature. He says, "All things happen by strife and necessity," and metaphorically, "War is father of all and king of all." Aristotle reports Heraclitus' views thus, "Heraclitus rebukes the author of the line, 'Would that strife be destroyed from among gods and men': for there would be no musical scale (*harmonia*) unless high and low existed, nor living creatures without male and female, which are opposites."

Given this eternal and necessary internal opposition in things, how then does Heraclitus see the unity of nature? This, he says, is not apparent to view, for the appearance of things is that they are many, discrete, and separate. But this appearance is not the way they actually are. The reality underlying these appearances is the unity of this constant change and transformation itself, which operates by necessity or law. This, he says, is hidden to the ordinary view. "The real nature of things is accustomed to hide itself," and, "An unapparent connection is stronger than an apparent one." What appears to the senses is not wrong or mistaken in itself, but it needs to be understood as revealing something more fundamental. On the one hand, he says, "The things of which there is seeing and hearing and perception, these do I prefer," but also, "Evil witnesses are eyes and ears for men, if they have souls that do not understand their language." The perceptual world is therefore a "language" which requires understanding, but it is reason or the mind which "reads and understands" this language. Thus, to all appearances, things have their "own" identity, yet at the same time they are constantly changing. In his most famous fragment, Heraclitus says that we do not step twice into the same river. The flux, being continuous, is never the same at two instants, and Heraclitus uses fire as an example to characterize this flux as an ever-moving, ever-changing process. "All things are an equal exchange for fire and fire for all things, as goods are for gold and gold for goods." Yet through this transformation there is the unity which renders the changing world more than a random process. The reason which grasps this unity is itself the common currency, in terms of which all things are exchanged for all things. This reason, or *Logos,* which in Heraclitus' striking phrase "steers all things through all things," is the measure or the lawfulness of the flux. The flux is therefore ordered and by virtue of this order can come to be understood. The world is intelligible because it is lawful. And the reason which can know the world as intelligible, or rational, is the same reason which constitutes this intelligibility. Knowing and the known are alike, therefore, and when I speak truly, my speech merely exemplifies the inner, hidden reason, the *Logos,* which is the very nature of the world itself, as it is of my knowledge of the world.

The conception here is difficult, but extraordinarily important in the development of science. The sharp distinction between appearances and the underlying reality, between what is known to the senses and what is understood by reason expresses that tension between sense and reason, between observation and theory which characterizes much of the history of science. The analogy to human discourse is evident throughout the work of Heraclitus. The term *Logos,* translated here as *reason* comes from a root which means "to tell" or "to recount," as when one tells a story. The "story" is what is understood in common by the community of speakers of a language. Thus, though stories differ in content, and sentences differ from each other in the infinite varieties of language, there is the underlying *Logos,* the shared meanings of a community of discourse, the unified base of rational comprehension which underlies the very ability to communicate. The various common metaphors which allude to "The Book of Nature" or "The Language of Nature" are in the spirit of Heraclitus' analogy between discursive understanding and natural knowledge. The unity, the structure, the comprehensibility of one's native language becomes the model for the unity, structure, and comprehensibility of the world itself. Despite the constant flux and transformation (which like the activity of thought appears to be fleeting, volatile, never twice the same) there is the underlying unity of the *Logos* which ensures comprehensibility.

In related ways Xenophanes and Heraclitus emphasize the underlying unity and form in nature, as of the same sort as the unity of rational thought, and thus knowable to reason. What appears to the senses as *many* is ultimately *One;* thus the senses without reason are deceptive.

The fullest development of this theme of the unity of Being comes with a philosophical school which was the first to make explicit the logical conditions of rational knowledge and to formulate the principle of noncontradiction as fundamental to reason. These were the *Eleatics,* principally Parmenides and Zeno of Elea. Their views were antithetical to those of Heraclitus, though their emphasis, like his, was on the formal unity underlying appearances. They argued that if Being is One, then change or transformation is impossible, and the appearance of change is the deception of the senses. In their view, change means motion, or change of place of a body. But if such motion is to take place, then something has to move from a place where it is to a place which is empty. *Empty* connotes a place where nothing is; but in the Eleatic view, if there were an *empty* and a *full* (i.e., if empty place or void *existed*), then Being would not be One, but Two. But *empty* of any thing means non-Being, and Being cannot both exist and not exist. This sounds very much like a language game one might play with children: "What's in the box?" "Nothing." "If I take Nothing out of the box, what's left?" "Nothing." "If I put Nothing back in the box, what will be in the box then?" "Nothing." The term *Nothing,* like *non-Being,* permits the kind of confusion which ensues when one thinks of "Nothing" as itself a kind of "thing" or "existence." Parmenides argued thus: "That which is-not cannot be conceived, nor can one utter it," and further, "That which is spoken and thought must necessarily *be* . . . but it is not possible for *nothing* to *be.*" At best this is a difficult formulation, if not simply confused. But the sense of it seems to be this: If there is no non-Being, there is no place where non-Being "is," and so there is no empty or void place. But if no void, then no motion from place to place, and if no motion, then no change, no transformation, no flux. Moreover, there can be no *many,* but only *One*—a single, seamless unity that is changeless and eternal, a "block universe." Because we plainly see and experience variety and plurality, this perception is delusive or in error, for it would require of reason that it countenance a contradiction: namely, that Being both is and is not.

The radical methodological conclusion here is that the criterion for reality is thought, or rational discourse, as in Heraclitus. But the criterion for this rational discourse is noncontradiction. Parmenides, in this peculiar way, is the first to state the principle of noncontradiction in explicit form. But he makes it both a principle of thought and of Being, or *what is.* In effect he imposes on the conception of reality the condition of rational discourse: what cannot be stated without contradiction cannot be. He asserts the fundamental logical principle of noncontradiction as, at the same time, an ontological principle. The truth of things is discoverable by rational thought, and by this alone, and must be in accordance with its principles. In the tradition of a later philosophy, this asserts the identity of *thinking* (i.e., of rational thought) and *being.* What is real is rational and what is rational is real.[5]

[5] Zeno of Elea, a follower of Parmenides, developed Parmenides' form of argument in the form of the so-called *reductio ad absurdum* proof. Zeno's famous "paradoxes" attempted to prove, by this means, that motion was impossible, that there could not be many things, but only one, and that there could be no void, but only a plenum. The proofs start with the assumption (as a hypothesis) that what is to be *dis*proved is true. Then, by logical inference, it is shown that this premise leads to two mutually contradictory conclusions, both of which are inescapable if the premise is assumed to be true. The conclusion from this, in the proof by *reductio ad absurdum,* is that the premise must therefore be false and that its contrary must therefore be true. This method of proof has had a notable career in logic and mathematics, as have also the paradoxes he introduced, which are based on the notions of infinity and infinite divisibility of a continuum. Zeno may be said to have introduced the formal method of logical proof into philosophy.

ATOMISM: ELEMENTS AND COMBINATIONS

One of the most fundamental concepts of physical science grew out of the critique of Eleatic philosophy. It is a concept whose development reveals clearly the relation between conceptual foundations and their elaboration in scientific thought. It is the concept of atomism, first developed by the Greeks, and reconstructed in one or another form down to the present day. It is perhaps wrong to talk of *the* concept of atomism, because there is a family of atomistic concepts, deriving from different sources and "cross-breeding," as it were.

The immediate source of the concept is in the notion of elements, or elementary stuff, which by combination yield the variety of things in the world. These elements, it will be remembered, were originally conceived in terms of perceptual qualities (hot, cold, wet, dry) or as their correlated stuffs (fire, air mist, water, earth). In the early versions of atomism it seems clear that these elements were thought of as corporeal, but the notion of spatial extent of a quality, or its spatial location, was only diffusely conceived. Rather, it was the combination of these elements which formed the ordinary spatially bounded and localized things, or bodies which are physical objects in the world, rather than qualities.

Into this rather indistinct conceptual framework there entered two distinct atomistic traditions, one of which we may characterize as physical, the other as mathematical, although this oversimplifies the matter. The first, following the Milesian tradition of natural philosophy, faced the problem of conceiving the combination of elements in a distinctively spatial way, as the combination of bounded, corporeal elements or physical bodies. In this tradition Empedocles accounted for the combination of elements by envisioning differing proportions of the four original elements, in combinations which "filled up" all of space. Space thus remained a *plenum,* as with Parmenides, but one with internal variation in the distribution of the qualitative elements. Empedocles' model for this plenum is awkward, for he has not resolved the problem of how motion of elements or changes of proportion of the mixture take place in a plenum. Thus, he says the elements "run through one another" (which is difficult to conceive). Each of these elements is itself changeless and permanent, like the Parmenidean *One,* but there are four, and change does take place, as in Anaximander's "mixture," by combination and dissolution in varying proportions of these elements.

The division of the *One* into an infinite plurality of elements carries the fragmentation of the Eleatic unity to the extreme. In the scheme of Anaxagoras, the last of the nature philosophers in the Milesian tradition and the first philosopher to reside in Athens (during the reign of Pericles in the so-called Golden Age of the fifth century B.C.), there are infinitely many kinds of elements, as well as infinitely many elements. For every quality existing in the world, there is an element. Moreover, in his spatial or corporeal conception of these elements, he says that they may be infinitely divided, or cut up, so that "there is no smallest part of what is small, but there is always a smaller." The stuff which constitutes things is therefore an infinitely divisible stuff, and these cuttable elements are therefore, too small to be detected as the division proceeds to the infinitesimally small. Yet even though there is no smallest element, the infinitely small still has magnitude, because it can be cut in half and thus constitutes some corporeal body in space. The still stranger suggestion (which has an element of the Heraclitean "exchange of all things for all things") is that the things in the world, which we perceive, are made up of combinations of *all* the infinite variety of kinds of elements. What we take a thing to be is determined, therefore, by the numerical preponderance of one kind over another. Thus Anaxagoras says, "There is a portion of everything in everything." Coming into being and perishing are therefore characteristic of combinations, but not of the constituent elements of these combinations, so that elements are eternal but their mixtures are transient. He says, "The Greeks are wrong to recognize coming into being and perishing; for nothing comes into being or perishes, but is rather compounded or dissolved from things that are. So they would be right to call coming into being 'composition' and perishing 'dissolution.'" Thus with Anaxagoras, the seamless unity of the Parmenidean *One* is fragmented into an infinite plurality, so that it would seem that in this physical plurality there is no residue of either the material or formal unity of earlier thought.

Yet the form principle of Xenophanes and Heraclitus makes its appearance here too, and unity is reasserted by Anaxagoras. To give order to this physical plurality he postulates something which stands outside this physical mixture but which controls all things in their mixture and combination and is the source of motion or activity, of all the changes in the physical world. This something is itself pure and unmixed, not constituted out of anything else, and is a self-active essence which in effect orders the plurality and is the active agency of that change by combination and dissolution which produces the world of our experience. This something Anaxagoras calls *Nous,* which is ordinarily translated as *mind,* although it is not clear exactly what he meant by it. He talks of it as "having knowledge of all things," and also as "being where everything else is too, in the surrounding mass and in the things that have been either aggregated or separated." In the tradition of the Heraclitean *Logos* or Xenophanes' God, *Nous* is the intelligible principle that is somehow in the world, but not of it; its form aspect rather than its "stuff" aspect. This introduces a duality into nature of active form and the pluralistic matter which is ordered by this form.

These physical speculations in the direction of atomism were supplemented by a mathematical tradition, which formulated atomism in a structurally more elegant way. In this tradition of Pythagoreanism the elements were not taken as physical entities which could be perceived or felt, but as conceptual entities, the objects of thought. The conceptual entity central to the Pythagorean philosophy is *number*. In effect, they said that all things were number, or to put it in a less opaque way, all things are constituted as numerical relations or ratios. The ultimate structure or being of anything is therefore its mathematical form. The sense of this theory depends on the conception of number which the Pythagoreans held. As in the combinatorial views of Anaximander and Empedocles, all things are constituted of elements. Unlike Anaxagoras, the Pythagoreans established a limit to the divisibility of things. But if things are constituted of number, then the limit of this number, conceived as a magnitude, is the monad, i.e. the *unit,* or *one,* out of which magnitude is itself constituted. In Pythagorean conceptions of mathematics, arithmetic and geometric notions are not yet clearly distinguished, and the unit is therefore conceived simultaneously as the geometrical point. Such a "one" or point-unit is therefore the element, combinations of which constitute the structures of the world. The geometric point is conceived of as that which cannot be "cut" any further, into parts, so that it is an indivisible unity, itself not constituted out of any more elementary units. Because it cannot be "put together" or "taken apart," it is changeless or immutable. Thus, it has no magnitude in itself, or is not yet itself number, but rather is that which generates number, in the Pythagorean view. (Arithmetically, then, the Pythagoreans took *two* to be the first "number," rather than *one.*) The interpretation of physical being as ultimately geometrical being brings with it the notion of an "uncuttable" element, then, or what in Greek was called *atomos* (literally, "uncuttable"). This *atomos,* or *atom,* is the unit element out of which the Pythagoreans generated their conception of the world. Thus, the geometric "line" is generated by two points, the "plane" is generated by three points (generating the "simplest" plane figure, the triangle), and the root solid—a pyramid of triangular base— is generated by four points. "One," therefore, by combination, i.e. by addition of "ones," generates number, arithmetically. The point-unit, by the geometric analogy, generates lines, planes, and solids. This conception of the universe as a geometric construction, which is so fundamental a notion in the development of physical science, is first clearly formulated by the Pythagoreans.

Thus number revealed the true nature of things beneath their perceptual appearances. World structure was in reality relation between numbers, or *ratio.* This *ratio* was conceived of as both the arithmetic relation between positive integers and the geometric relation between magnitudes, which stood to each other in the ratio of such positive integers. The intelligibility of the world of our experience was therefore the intelligibility of its underlying mathematical structure, which could be grasped only by reason. The world was comprehensible to that reason which could know number; the world thus was quite literally, *rational.*

The great crisis in Pythagorean thought was the discovery of the irrational, and in this context it can be seen why this is so. By use of the Pythagorean theorem (which was, by the way, already known to the ancient Egyptians in a practical way, and for which it appears the Babylonians already had a mathematical proof) it can readily be shown that the diagonal of a square is a so-called incommensurable length. That is, if we take the sides of the square as unit magnitudes, or as magnitudes expressed by integers, then the diagonal cannot be expressed as a ratio between two integers and is therefore "irrational." (When the sides of the square are unit magnitudes, the diagonal is the irrational $\sqrt{2}$.) It is not too far wrong to characterize this "irrational," in Pythagorean terms, as a "crazy number." For within the context of Pythagorean rationalism, this "irrational" destroyed the perfect mathematical structure thus far envisioned and threatened the whole Pythagorean world picture. A traditional legend has it that a member of the Pythagorean brotherhood (Hippasus of Metapontum) was expelled, or perhaps even drowned at sea, for revealing to those uninitiated in the Pythagorean cult the terrible "secret" of the "irrational."

The Pythagorean development of the notion of atoms as elemental point-units finds its physical expression in the atomism of Leucippus and Democritus (and in its elaboration by their later followers Epicurus and the Latin poet Lucretius). This required an argument against the Eleatics, for the existence of the void or of empty space. If there were separate, indivisible atoms, as little physical bodies, then such bodies were spatially bounded. The atoms constituted the "full" space; but between the atoms there was void, through which the atoms moved by means of their inherent, or "natural," motion. Thus, the world is made up of moving atoms and void. Things are combinations of these atoms, and these combinations happen not by the intervention of some unifying agency or mind, but by chance, as the atoms "swerve" and bump into each other and get hooked up. The mechanical nature of this view is clear from the account which Democritus gives of the "hooks" which the atoms must have, in order to join together, and its forthright materialism is equally clear from the absence of any formal or mental agency guiding the atoms. Their motion is taken to be inherent. Certain chance combinations persevere for longer times than others, so that the world is in constant change. But this change reduces to nothing but motion of the material atoms in space.

In keeping with the geometric thinking of the Pythagoreans, Democritus conceived of different kinds of atoms having different sizes and shapes. (He added, however, the dynamic property of weight.) All the perceptual qualities—hot, sweet, sour, rough, cold, and so on were accounted for by the shape, size, and motion of these atoms. Thus, the "fastest" atoms were small and round, and these were the "fiery atoms"; even thought itself and visual perception were accounted for in terms of this motion of atoms. Thought, being "swift" and able to go "through" things, was therefore taken to be constituted of such "fiery" atoms. Moreover, this whole construction proceeded in terms of invisible, hypothetical entities—thought constructs—the argument for which was that this hypothesis gave a rational account of natural phenomena and of world structure. It was thus the last of the great rationalist-materialist world hypotheses of this early period of natural philosophy. This Greek atomism was thus the culmination of the tradition of natural speculation which gave rise to philosophy and physical science. It can be seen as the outcome of the arguments and criticisms which developed concerning the indivisible *One* of the Eleatics, the pluralism of Empedocles and Anaxagoras, and the mathematical atomism of the Pythagoreans. The further development of this atomistic materialism, the sharp critique of this natural philosophy which arose among the Athenian philosophers, the great systematic and critical analysis of Plato and Aristotle, which followed, can be understood most clearly when the fundamentals of this earlier Greek development are themselves clear.

RATIONALISM AND EMPIRICISM: THE GROWTH OF ATHENIAN PHILOSOPHY AND SCIENCE

What we have examined thus far is the development of speculative constructs of great breadth and imagination—world hypotheses which proceed on the basis of rational conjecture and criticism. There is implicit in many of these philosophies a concern with methodological and epistemological questions—with what the relative warrants are which sense and reason provide for our knowledge of things. The explicit turn toward such a rational criticism of the foundations of our knowledge itself takes place in Athens. The tension between the rationalist and empiricist emphases, between reliance on the evidence of the senses and reliance on the arguments of reason, gives rise to the most thorough and elaborate critique of knowledge and belief in the history of philosophy. The nature of common-sense knowledge is itself examined, as is that of scientific knowledge. A flowering of scientific observation, research and theory goes hand in hand with the criticism of the very methods of observation and theory. Here too are elaborated all those substantive concepts of science with which we shall deal later: causality, determinism and law, space, time and matter, motion and change, the nature of life, the nature of thought, the mind's relation to the body, and so on. The first institutional organization of scientific research begins in Athens, with the founding by Plato and Aristotle of what were in effect research institutes. Plato's *Academy*, as it was called, lasted continuously in Athens for over 900 years; Aristotle's *Lyceum* lasted continuously for some 600 years, in Athens and then in Alexandria. Their impress on the development of science was decisive, both with respect to the quality of their conceptions and to their institutional longevity.

But we begin this account of Athenian philosophy and science with two modest figures: one, a gadfly, a constant talker who so upset the Athenians with his questions about the homely things of their acquaintance and the cherished dogmas of their belief that they ended by putting him to death; the other, a doctor concerned with diseases and their cure. The first is Socrates, the second Hippocrates.

The Socratic Reformation in Philosophy: The Dialectic Method

The development of the art of rational analysis, of that conscious and deliberate criticism of concepts which seeks out the presuppositions, the hidden assumptions, the structure of an argument itself, is indebted to a philosopher who disdained natural speculation and addressed himself instead to the conscience and the rationality of his fellow Greeks. This philosopher was Socrates. His impact on scientific thought is not ordinarily appreciated, because his concern seemed to be mainly with ethics and with the critique of common discourse and belief. His method of criticism is called *dialectic,* which may be loosely translated as "the art of argument"; but its connotations go deeper, and the method itself is exemplified in the so-called Socratic dialogues of Plato.[6] The technique of dialectic consists in drawing one's opponent in argument into explicit recognition of the contradictions which his beliefs or his arguments entail. Such criticism cuts to the bone of argument, by means of cross-questioning which elicits the grounds or premises for stated conclusions, and by this explication makes the subject aware of the inconsistencies or the consequences of his belief, or makes him conscious of his ignorance. Thus the dialectician defends no favored position, but objectively seeks to expose all positions to the same rigorous rational analysis. As such, this is the method of criticism par excellence, the origin of that self-conscious critical reflection on common sense which we discussed earlier. Socrates' method is thus the method of articulating meanings and knowledge claims for the sake of critical test, of sharpening and explicating formulations so that they stand in the bright glare of reason and become fit subjects for critical analysis.

The method itself may have its roots in the most common methods of coming to know something. As a contemporary philosopher of science, Karl Popper, has pointed out, dialectic is akin to the method of trial and error. Popper goes further, in saying that, "If the method of trial and error is developed more and more consciously, then it begins to take on the characteristic features of 'scientific method.' "[7] The thrust of such a

[6] Notably, The *Crito, Phaedo, Apology, Euthyphro, Laches, Lysis,* and *Charmides,* among others. The term *dialectic* has its root in *dialogue* (from the Greek verb *dialegein,* which means "to discourse or discuss with another person").

[7] Karl Popper, "What Is Dialectic?" in *Conjectures and Refutations* (New York: Basic Books, 1962), p. 313.

method is negative: it is said to "eliminate" those theories which do not stand up to testing. Similarly, Socrates' method of dialectic is negative. He does not propose solutions to the problems he raises, but rather shows that, once they are examined critically, proffered solutions are often unacceptable to reason. The positive content of this dialectic is its insistence on rationality, on open and conscious criticism of everything with a view to consistency and clarity. Thus, Socrates addresses himself not to the natural speculations of world origin and the structure of reality, but to the warrants of our knowledge and belief in the most ordinary contexts of human social and political life. His is then the paradigm of that critical common sense we spoke of earlier. But here is its connection with the growth of scientific thought, for the same critical reflection which Socrates imposes on questions concerning such common matters as courage, piety, obligation, death, and the fear of death is now ready to be imposed on questions of a speculative-theoretical sort concerning the nature of things. We saw that the development of natural philosophy exemplified such an implicit and sometimes explicit critique of prevailing or antecedent theories. With the refinement and explication of this critical method Socrates sharpened the instrument of rationalism, introducing into subsequent science and philosophy standards of intellectual rigor which still obtain. Socrates' student, Plato, employed this method as well, but with a primary view to the construction of rational hypotheses, as well as to their criticism. The clearest example of the impact of the dialectic method is in Plato's work. He is that rarity among systematic philosophers who has devoted a major work (the *Parmenides*) to the fundamental criticism of his own formulations.

Empiricism: Hippocrates and the Test of Experience

In contrast to the emphasis on sheer intellectual criticism, Hippocrates, in emphasizing empiricism, insisted on the test of observation, and on the practical application of theories. Much of Greek philosophical theory alludes to and derives from the practical arts and technical skills. In a sense, Socrates is also empirical, in his constant reference to common experience in his analogies and his arguments. In the development of such skills as medicine, careful observation and empirical classification served to tie theoretical formulations closely to practice. Plausible theories, in this context of applied science, are not enough. The nature of practical applications provides a constant, if loosely organized, context for testing against experience. The great body of such empirical science in the fifth and fourth centuries B.C. in Greece was the so-called Hippocratic corpus—some seventy works dealing with medical practice, with diet, with anatomy, and with the classification of plants and animals. Hippocrates, the "father of medicine," who codified much of the work of this school, directly criticized that science which was based on plausible theories and which deduced its conclusions concerning nature and man from *a priori* principles or postulates. He writes, in *Precepts,*

> One must attend in medical practice not primarily to plausible theories, but to experience combined with reason. . . . I approve of theorizing if it lays its foundation in incident, and deduces its conclusions in accordance with phenomena. For if theorizing lays its foundation in clear fact, it is found to exist in the domain of intellect, which itself receives all its impressions from other sources. . . . But if it begins not from a clear impression, but from a plausible fiction, it often induces a grievous and troublesome condition. All who act so are lost in a blind alley.

Hippocrates, in inveighing against *a priori* speculation, pronounces the essential thesis of empiricism: "The intellect receives all its impressions from other sources." On the basis of such a view, all that can be established as scientific truth about the world depends on sense perception. Observation thus becomes crucial for science, not merely incidental. But organized observation for the purpose of testing and validating scientific theory is not merely looking and seeing. Rather, it is ordered observation, in two senses: (1) It is the ordering of *what has been observed,* establishing relationships; this is classification. (2) It is the ordering of the *activity of observing,* not only in the sense of looking for certain things, but in the additional sense of *arranging* for certain things to be observed, by artifice. This *artificial* ordering of observation is experiment.

One standard view of Greek science and philosophy has it that the Greeks failed to develop experimentation and observation, relying too much on *a priori* speculative construction and on the test of rational criticism rather than the test of experience. That is, the Greeks were not empiricists. The intimation is that science proper does not develop until the so-called experimental method is introduced (on such accounts, usually by Francis Bacon or by Galileo). The error of this view is partly one of ignorance of the rich empirical work in Greek science, as exists, for example, in the Hippocratic corpus. But more importantly, this error is one of interpretation. For the whole intent of Greek speculation in natural philosophy, and even more clearly in ethics and political theory, is to give an account of the appearances, of the empirical data, of observation. The failures of *a priorism* arise when theoretical or speculative arguments are not submitted to the test of their empirical adequacy. But this concerns the complex matter of what such adequacy is, what is to count as observation or as evidence for or against some point of view. If one reconstructs the Greek context sympathetically, or even if one relies on one's own commonsense level of experience, then the most speculative of the Greek theories may be seen as an attempt to order and explain the world of common sense. The reliance on "plausible" theories touches another nerve of the issue of explanation, for plausibility is linked with frameworks of conception. What Hippocrates insisted on was careful observation, due attention to the readily available empirical data of ordinary perception, and the test of successful practice in curing and alleviating disease. A "merely" plausible theory, in his view, was one which stopped short at an *a priori* hypothesis. The degenerate forms of rationalism may indeed evidence such unbridled speculation and dogmatic adherence to the constructs thus devised. But Plato and Aristotle, the masters of rational system building in Athenian philosophy, and their students in the *Academy* and the *Lyceum,* who founded the modern sciences of physics, biology, geography, astronomy and who pursued mathematical investigations of high originality and sophistication, were never mere *a priorists.* Given the tension between rationalist and empiricist emphases in scientific theory and practice, they coped with this still-fresh problem in ways that we still recognize in contemporary science.

PLATO: THE WORLD OF FORMS

We have seen how, in the theories of Heraclitus, Anaxagoras, and the Pythagoreans, ultimate reality is taken to be the underlying form of things. Thus, what we see, touch, or hear is only the outward *appearance* of this underlying reality. The world of appearances which the senses deliver to us is therefore at best a copy of this reality and at worst a blurred image or an inadequate approximation of it. Though sense perception may be our first mode of access to this reality, or the imperfect means of our acquiring knowledge of it, it is finally the rational intellect which comes to know the way things really are and which can give an explanation of the world of appearance.

The elaboration and systematization of this point of view is due to the greatest of Socrates' pupils, Plato, and this view may, in general, be called *idealism,* because it takes what is ultimately real to be the "ideas," or forms, beneath appearances, and takes these to be immaterial entities which do not themselves exist "in" in the world of sense perception, but underly it. The world of appearances is changing, a passing image of the real world of forms, which itself is changeless and eternal. The notion that such a changeless ideal reality is perfect and that its image is imperfect lends a normative or valuative aspect to Plato's view, for by the very sense of the terms, the *perfect* is better than the *imperfect.* Yet, as in Pythagorean notions of mathematical structure, here is that conception of laws of nature or natural principles which are themselves immutable, but are revealed by the rigorous rational analysis of experience. This conception is at once recognizable as the Platonic aspect of much of scientific thought, and it played a major role in the scientific theories of Galileo and Newton, as well as those of contemporary physics.

Such a view seems to introduce a dualism, a conception of two worlds, real and apparent, and of two sorts of knowledge, rational and empirical. Plato's system is, in large part, an attempt to relate these to each other in some rationally plausible way. Thus his researches and theories are concerned with the ontological or metaphysical aspects of this claim, and also with the epistemological problems to which it gives rise. For he is not satisfied merely to leave the two unrelated, but to see one as the "shadow" or the "image" of the other, to see the world of forms as somehow exemplified in the world of appearances, or to see the variety and multiplicity of the perceptual world as somehow "participating in" the well-ordered and unified world of forms. The difficulty and complexity of this formulation may be seen from the evidence of Plato's own long-term struggle to give it a coherent formulation and to test its explanatory power in applications to various realms, such as cosmology, physics, astronomy, ethics, politics, and grammar. As already noted, he even dedicates a major work to the criticism of its flaws.

One crucial difficulty in Plato's formulation concerns the claim that the form or the ultimate reality, of things exists (or "subsists") apart from its exemplification in the world of appearances; thus, even if the physical world did not exist, the forms would continue to *be,* because the world comes into being and passes away, whereas the forms are eternal. Thus, the mode of existence of these forms is problematic and suggests a mode of ideational existence, as in some sense "meanings" or "truths" may be said to "exist."

Thus, one might ask, "Would the gravitational law be true even if there were no world of which it held true?" One way of formulating this would be to say that such "truths" are "necessary truths," which would hold for all possible worlds. But certainly the gravitational law may well be a contingent truth, holding of a universe of this sort only. But then one might ask, "Is the sum of the squares of the sides of a right triangle equal to the square of the hypotenuse?" And this, it would seem, would be true whether or not there "existed" triangles. So that one might say, "If anything is a right triangle (suitably defined), then the Pythagorean theorem is true of it." The claim here is that this would be true in all possible worlds. The question of the status of such statements or of such "truths" we shall discuss in a later chapter. But it is to the "existence" of such immutable truths that Plato addressed himself, attempting to formulate a theory in which the relation of such truths to the world of experience or of knowledge could be made clear.

Plato's applications of his theoretical framework to natural science show his debt to Pythagoreanism. In his cosmology he introduces the duality of form and matter and hypothesizes as the means of mediation an active force, or *demiurge,* which imposes the order of the ideal forms on a recalcitrant and formless matter, which serves as the "receptacle" for these forms. In his physical theory, which reveals the strong influence of Pythagorean mathematics and some of the atomistic notions of his older contemporary, Democritus, he sets about to construct the universe on a mathematical model. Like the Pythagoreans, Plato takes the triangle as the "simplest" plane figure and as the basic element of his construction. He postulates two "basic triangles" (the "half-square," or isosceles right triangle, and the "half-equilateral," or 30°–60°–90° triangle) and proceeds to construct, by combination, the "basic solids" from these plane figures. He hypothesized further that the "basic solids" were the five regular convex solids, interpreting these in turn as the physical elements—fire, air, earth, and water—and what he called "cosmos."[8] Now the fanciful nature of this hypothetical construction may strike us as naive or strange. Yet it is close to the tradition of mathematical physics which constructs its models as mathematically formulable structures whose properties are then interpreted in such a way as to account for physical properties. Thus, though Plato certainly could not have intended anything of the sort, our contemporary models of crystal structure, as well as our models of atomic structure, are in this tradition of mathematical-geometric construction. Similarly, Plato's theory exhibits that demand for economy, for the assumption of the most minimal number of elements needed to account for the variety and profusion of natural phenomena, which becomes an ideal in scientific theory construction. In Plato's own view the construction is at best a hypothetical construct, plausible because it is satisfying to reason, and to that deep aesthetic sense of regularity, systematicity, and simplicity which pervades so much of Greek thought. It is an attempt at a theoretical construction of what *would* explain appearances, given the current framework of the four-element theory, if these elements are now interpreted in a geometric-mathematical way. The fifth element was itself to have a notable career in astronomy, connoting in its later forms that "quintessence" (literally, "fifth element") which distinguished the realm of the so-called celestial spheres,

[8] These five regular solids were already known to Greek mathematics, and it was known as well that there were only five. These are the tetrahedron, the cube, the octahedron, the dodecahedron, and the icosohedron; all of these except the dodeca-

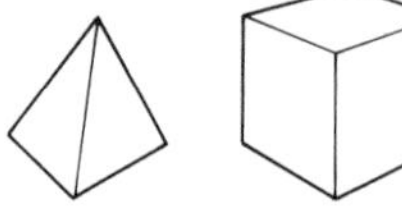
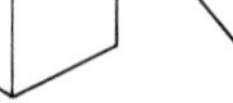
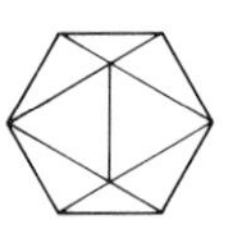
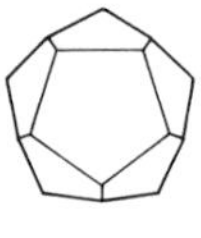

hedron are constructible out of Plato's "basic triangles." (The dodecahedron requires for its construction an isosceles triangle with each of the base angles double the vertical angle, i.e., a 72°–72°–36° triangle.)

or the heavens, from the terrestrial sphere constituted of the original four elements.

We may thus mark in Plato's thought criteria derived from Socrates' rigorous critical rationalism, the standards of logical and mathematical consistency, and the commitment to the consequences of rational analysis. But there are also criteria of another sort: a certain taste and predilection for that which is simple and symmetrical. The notion that this kind of "perfection" was the hallmark of true reality, of the ideal forms, was an appeal to the economy of thought as against the profusion and variety of the world of sense perception and feeling. The ordering of this profusion meant the reduction of variety to some original elements, to principles which would order and explain the sensory world of appearances by revealing its hidden and underlying real structure.

ARISTOTLE: FORM, FUNCTION, AND MATTER

Plato and Aristotle are closely related to each other in fundamental ways, sharing common problems and a common framework for their solution. But the emphases differ, sometimes sharply, so that the terms *Platonist* and *Aristotelian* sometimes connote mutually exclusive and antithetical views. One major difference is that Aristotle does not hold that the ideal forms exist in any way apart from their embodiment in actual things and processes in the world. However, for Aristotle, as for Plato, it is reason which comes to know these forms. In Aristotle's view, the forms are not abstract universals subsisting in some Platonic realm beyond the sensible world, but are the forms of things and of their patterns of action, which the mind elicits by abstraction from sense perception. Thus, the form of anything is at the same time that which makes it what it is, or the kind of thing it is—which "individuates" it as that distinctive thing and not something else. It is also what the mind comes to know when it has knowledge of the nature of a thing.

In most ordinary uses of the term *form,* we carry over the Platonic and atomistic associations of form as a configuration, or spatial arrangement or shape—a geometrically conceived notion well expressed in atomism, in which all qualities are determined by the shape and arrangement of the atoms. *Form* has another connotation in Greek thought, already exhibited in Plato but emphasized by Aristotle. In this other sense, it is the characteristic mode of activity of anything, the *way* in which it operates or functions. Thus, the "form" of man, or what "individuates" him distinctively as a member of the human species, and distinguishes him from all other kinds of things, is described by the definition of man as a *rational animal.* This says nothing about his structure or his appearance, in terms of the spatial configuration of his parts, but rather describes the essential pattern of activity which is uniquely human. Aristotle's vast systematic scheme, which encompasses and helps to delineate the whole range of science, is an elaboration of this functional approach and is an attempt to apply it in such diverse fields as physics, astronomy, biology, psychology, politics, ethics, and aesthetics.

In Aristotle's view, the knowledge of anything, if it is rational knowledge and not merely perception (i.e., if it is scientific knowledge) is a knowledge of characteristic modes of activity, insofar as these are typical of this or that *kind* of thing. Scientific knowledge is therefore not knowledge of particular things, but of things of a certain kind. To know a thing is to know what its class characteristics are, what properties it shares with all things of its kind. By virtue of this, we come to know that it is this kind of thing and not another. The characteristics or properties which make any thing *this particular thing* are thus not common characteristics, not *essential* to its classification as to kind; and such characteristics are therefore called *accidental.* Thus, for example, having four legs, a tail, and an elongated head are essential characteristics of horses, but being brown or dappled or having a wound on the right foreleg is accidental.[9] Such accidental characteristics are not the subject matter of scientific knowledge, therefore, but of sense perception, which takes particulars as its objects. Scientific knowledge is of universals, i.e., of "forms" in this sense of characteristics which hold for all members of a given class.

On this basis, Aristotle develops the principles of classification, which he takes to be an ordering of "real kinds," or of the embodiment of a formal universal in all the individuals which belong to a class. For example, if a particular thing is soluble in water, then it is an individual of the class of all things soluble in water. Now this seems painfully obvious and empty, for if any particular thing were not soluble in water, we would say that it lacked the distinguishing class characteristic which marked it as the kind of thing we were talking about. In effect, it would necessarily follow that if something were *of* a certain kind, it would have the class characteristics of that kind of thing, which seems to come to the tautologous statement that anything of a certain kind is a thing of that kind. Aristotle was led to examine the form of such arguments in which things are asserted to have certain class characteristics, and he reconstructed the logic of such arguments as a formal logic of classes. The form of the argument goes something like this:

All things of the kind *K* belong to the class *C*
The individual thing *T* is of the kind *K*
Therefore, *T* belongs to the class *C*.

[9] Some of the difficulties of the relativity of this distinction between essence and accident, or its dependence on frameworks of consideration, are immediately obvious here. For there may be a class of brown horses, or of horses with wounds on their right forelegs; or in a Platonist view, there may even be a so-called unit class, whose sole member is the one and only horse with a particular set of properties. This is discussed later in Chapter 6, pp. 151–152.

The classic example of this form of reasoning is familiar: "All men are mortal. Socrates is a man. Therefore, Socrates is mortal." An argument of this form is called a *syllogism.* Aristotle developed the formal analysis of such arguments, which seem little more than an explication of common sense. But he showed the advantages of formalization, abstracting the general argument *form* from the content of particular arguments and showing that the validity of the argument was based on its form alone. The logic which develops from this analysis is often called the *class calculus.* As logical form, therefore, it is empty of content in the sense that it seems to give us no more knowledge about the things involved than we already had (and this is characteristic of deductive arguments in general, not peculiar to the class-calculus). If we know that Socrates is a man, then of course we already know that he is mortal, because being mortal is one of the things we mean when we say that someone is a man. Such knowledge is of course not empty, because it depends on acquaintance with the facts about life and death. The assertion that, as a matter of fact, all men are mortal, stated as the major premise of the argument, is thus not simply a matter of definition, for one might make the empirical claim that some men or a particular man is immortal and one would have to establish as a matter of fact that there was such a man. Or one might argue, on classificatory grounds, that such an individual is therefore not a man at all. Still, the method of classification, of the assignment of individuals to classes on the basis of essential or universal characteristics shared by all members of a class, is not itself a way to acquire matter-of-fact knowledge about things, but rather a way to order what we have already discovered to be the case. It may seem that merely ordering things already known adds nothing to what we know about them. But if the ordering makes such knowledge explicit, if it reveals explicitly what the relationships are among the things we know, then this explicit awareness of these relationships, which may be said to be contained implicitly in our knowledge but is not yet subject to conscious awareness and reflection, is itself "new knowledge" in this sense. Thus, such classificatory analysis not only orders our knowledge, but systematizes it; that is, it reveals how different parts of our knowledge are related to each other and leads to inferences of a logical sort which lead us to test our knowledge by observing new facts which bear on it.

Thus, in Aristotle's view we come to know universals by the activity of reasoned experience, by observation of particulars from which we abstractively infer that they are individuals of a certain kind, members of a certain class. The philosophical or metaphysical aspect of this view is that the *matter* which is given in sense perception of particulars is never without *form,* and this form is never given except in relation to or by means of the sensible matter which is thus "informed." Formless matter or matterless, disembodied form are therefore *conceptual* limits and do not exist as such, except as objects of thought or conception. The further philosophical elaboration of this view relates it to the functionalism we spoke of. For anything in the world is a process in time, in which its form is realized in its pattern of activity. Its natural history, therefore, is the history of the *actualization* of its natural *potentialities,* the process of "normal" or "natural" development of that kind of thing. Matter as such is the potentiality, the raw stuff through which this actualization or realization of form takes place; but what actualizes such matter is the form. Pure form, without matter, would thus be "pure actuality." It would not be the *process of becoming* this or that kind of thing, but would rather already be the pure "kind" or "ideal form" which Plato spoke of. Pure matter, without form, would thus be "pure potentiality," or absolutely nothing in particular. These limits exist only as limits of conception. Pure form or "pure actuality" would subsist changelessly as an object of pure thought, or as Aristotle says, "Mind thinking itself." Pure matter or "pure potentiality" would likewise be a matter of conception only, as that metaphysical "prime matter" which Aristotle posits as the requisite eternal and vacuous stuff, which can be neither created nor destroyed but which bears the absolute potentiality for becoming anything whatever. Thus, in Aristotle's view, such matter is eternal, neither coming into being nor passing away, and in this sense there is no "beginning" of matter, but simply a process of coming into being and passing away of individuals which are unities of matter and form. The study of natural science is therefore the study of the "becoming" of things, their life history; and this is conceived by Aristotle as a passage from potentiality to actuality.

This change is conceived of not simply as change, but as directed change or development, as the natural form or pattern of activities of any kind of thing is realized. The characteristic pattern of activities of a kind of thing is that activity which is "in accordance with its nature."[10] This "nature" is therefore what is fulfilled in the course of a thing's "normal" or "natural" development, or in its "right functioning," and thus comes to be spoken of as the "end" (or *telos*) to which such activity tends. The embodiment of the form in a thing of a certain kind is therefore the embodiment of this "end," as a *program* so to speak, in accordance with which natural activity and growth proceeds. This "embodied end" (*entelechy,* from *telos*) is thus the object of scientific knowledge of a thing's activities or natural functioning, because it is in carrying out of such "programmed" activity that a thing's form is revealed to reasoned experience. Thus, we see or perceive merely the parts of a thing's activity; on the basis of such observation, the rational understanding conceives or forms a concept of the innate form or "essence" which such activity reveals. Natural science is the study of these

[10] A thing's "nature" is therefore its "essence," its "natural form," or (in older translations) its "virtue." This term has a complex sense in Greek philosophy, and we give here Aristotle's emphasis. The more general connotations are of a thing's "excellence" or "prowess" or "fit activity," and in Homer, for example, it means "manhood" or "valor."

activities, their classification, and sequence, in order to arrive at a rational reconstruction of the whole pattern and its character. Such activity is sometimes spoken of as the "motion" or "change" from state to state which perception grasps in observing things in nature. The intellectual grasp of the overall pattern of such "motion" or patterned activity is not concerned simply with an account *that* things happen in a certain way, but with an explanation of *why* they do. Thus, Aristotle's analysis introduces both descriptive categories or frameworks within which the analysis of this change of state takes place. Thus, he talks of four species or aspects of the genus *motion:* alteration (or change of quality), increase and decrease (or change of quantity), coming to be and passing away (becoming or development), and change of place (or locomotion). The theoretical construct which explains all of these as aspects of change is the passage from potentiality to actuality, the realization of the form of a thing in its life process or history. Because Aristotle postulated this form not simply as the formal pattern or the "program" which described a thing's activities, but as the activity of carrying out this program, of operating "for the sake of" the fulfillment of the programmed form, this suggests a kind of patterned energy operating in things which is regulative and directed toward an end. Explanation of a thing's characteristic activity is thus in terms of such "ends" built into and constituting the very nature of a thing, and its processes of coming to be. The various sciences are studies of this characteristic "motion" with respect to different sorts of things. Physics, thus, is the study of this activity with respect to physical bodies in space, as biology is the study of such "motion" in the behavior and growth patterns of organisms (whose characteristic is that they are self-moved, whereas physical things have their source of motion from without, or with respect to their "natural location" in space). Ethics too is the study of this "motion" or characteristic activity with respect to human interaction.

This type of what we may call teleological analysis is distinctive of much of Greek thought, but is most fully elaborated in Aristotle's functional approach. These concepts dominated much of scientific thought in every field for over twenty centuries, and their mark in the history of science and in contemporary issues in science and philosophy is very clear, as we shall see in subsequent discussion. Whereas Pythagoreanism and Platonism stressed concepts of structure, Aristotelian science stressed concepts of function. The geometrician is replaced by the biologist, who sees all natural processes by analogy to those of organisms, which start from seed, grow and develop in a certain pattern, behave in a characteristic way, eventually mature as their potentialities or capacities for development are (normally) realized, then begin to degenerate and die. The change from state to state is conceived by Aristotle as a complex movement in which different aspects may be distinguished by the analysis of thought, as the mind comes to rationally comprehend the universal forms or patterns of such processes.

This is what a rational or scientific analysis of experience reveals, or in Aristotle's terms, these are the *intelligible reasons* which the mind grasps in coming to understand and to explain nature's way of operating.

THE CONTINUITY OF GREEK SCIENCE AND CONTEMPORARY SCIENCE

What is of import here, in this account of the development of scientific thought, is the role of dominating concepts in all these particular sciences. The very shape of scientific formulations is not simply determined by looking and seeing, nor merely by some neutral activity of thinking things through. The manner of thought has its styles, and individual geniuses leave the imprint of their idiosyncratic mode of problem solving or of concept formation. But there are also fundamental concepts which establish the framework and sometimes set the limits of scientific work. The dichotomy between sense and reason, between practical application and contemplative theory affects the character of Greek science in many ways. Thus the way in which the Greek scientists conceived of the role of observation and experiment, the way they conceived of the nature of their scientific models, their notions of space, of time, of matter and form, of motion and change were largely conditioned by more fundamental notions they held concerning the nature of things. In the formulation of such fundamental concepts as that of the constitution of things by combination of elements; of the elements as irreducible and immutable units; of geometric form and symmetry as ideal models of reality; of the underlying rationality and unity of the structure of things; of the distinction between the ideal realm of changeless forms and the terrestrial one of growth, change, and plurality; of the concept of the ultimately real nature of things as their form or as their directive patterns of activity—in all of these formulations one sees the operation of deep structures of thought upon the particular formulations of astronomy, physics, biology, mathematics. In many instances these deep structures serve as a guide to highly theoretical conceptions of great systematicity within particular sciences. In others, these same notions serve to limit and distort the explanations of the world of experience, in favor of some *a priori* commitment on nonempirical grounds—religious, aesthetic, traditional, social. In these deep and fundamental conceptual structures, more is at work than the mere impress of perceptual experience. Human wishes, hopes, fears operate there, in a subterranean way, as do taste and feeling. It is not as if experience were some pristine and virginal gift waiting to be accepted. It too has to be sought; and the manner of seeking often has much to do with what it is that is received.

The "experience" of the Greeks derives from that same complex matrix of common sense that we have earlier discussed and that we in large part still share with them. This permits us to understand how even those conceptual formulations which we now regard as false could have been reached and could have seemed plausible. This continuity makes historical understanding possible. It also makes possible that comprehension of the development and critique of concepts which permits science to supersede the common sense of an era and to reconstitute our experience in a new way.

Contemporary science still operates within the conceptual frameworks of matter and form, of structure and function, of laws of change and development. Like the Greeks, we postulate theoretical entities to explain the phenomena, and like theirs, our science has a deep sense of the underlying mathematical structures of the physical world. Like them, too, we are not satisfied merely to acknowledge these pervasive deep structures of our thought, but are prone to assess them critically, to pursue that rational analysis of what we mean and what we understand, which is the true and broad sense of philosophy. But also like the Greeks, we are even in the flush of our rationality haunted by the irrational, by the mysterious and the unfathomable. Their supreme intellectual vitality saw this as a challenge to reason, not as an invitation to despair. This makes them vividly contemporary, for although our science has far outstripped theirs in the content of our theoretical understanding and in the scope of our control over nature, it is profoundly continuous with theirs.[11]

[11] See Appendix B for an account of the growth of Greek science after Plato and Aristotle.

PART II

The Methods of Science

CHAPTER 5

Observation

OBSERVATION AND EMPIRICAL SCIENCE

AMONG THE APPARENTLY innocuous statements that are bound to start a philosopher talking fervidly is this one: "Our knowledge of the world is acquired by means of experience." It surely seems unproblematic to say that what we know about an external reality, what science comes to know about nature, is in some clear sense the product of our experience of this nature by means of sense perception. To claim otherwise would seem to consign us to the absurd (or perhaps interesting) conclusion that everything we come to know is somehow already laid out in our minds, that all that is required is some proper means of eliciting this *a priori* knowledge. The philosophical discussion concerning the sources of our knowledge rarely goes so far as to assert that *all* of our knowledge is empirically gained or that none of it is. Yet the polar positions in epistemology which tend toward these alternative emphases, which may generally be characterized as empiricism and rationalism, do offer plausible arguments for the relative importance of what is acquired from experience as against what we contribute by way of the mind's own organizing capacities and its so-called innate ideas. These distinctions carry over into philosophy of science, in its consideration of the rational and empirical elements in scientific thought.

The distinction is sometimes made in philosophy of science between formal science and factual science. The former is that study concerned with so-called formal systems or calculi, in logic and mathematics, which are linguistic systems of deductive inference, the elements of which are either formal or abstract terms, defined within the system, or "primitive" undefined terms, with respect to which all others are defined. Thus, the x's and y's of our algebra and logic are empty of content unless they are interpreted to refer to this or that. That is to say, they are empty of factual content or of reference to experience or to the external world ("outside" the language). By contrast, factual science is said to deal with the concrete content of experience, with concrete reference to the external world, with the facts of nature and their description in some language. Empirical science has to do with the facts as they come to be established by actual observation, measurement, experimental interaction with objects, events, and processes in the world.

The distinction is not meant to assert that there is no formal inference in empirical science or that there may not be empirical sources of formal science (as, for example, in formal geometry, which has its roots in the empirical practice of earth measurement, or in formal arithmetic and number theory, whose sources are in the ordinary practices of counting and collecting). But what is counted as distinctive about the empirical sciences is that they depend on sense perception, on observation, on reference beyond the linguistic system in which the findings and inferences of the sciences are formulated. The alternative emphases of rationalism and empiricism are on the extent to which our knowledge about the world relies on this evidence of the senses, as against the operations of the mind and what it can come to know by sheer reasoning, which yet pertains to knowledge of the world.

This relation of sense and reason is a central question in epistemology, but it is also a central question in philosophy of science, for it focuses on problems of the status and validation of scientific knowledge, and on the nature of its dependence on observation and experiment. All would be much simpler if observation itself were as simple and unambiguous a process as it appears. In our ordinary experience, observation is transparent; that is, when we "look and see," we are not simultaneously aware that we are looking and seeing. In practice, we rely on the veridicality of our sense perception unless it becomes problematic, so that illusive or delusive perception, once we are aware that something is wrong, startles us and is not accepted as a matter of course. But fuller reflection on observation and on its conditions—on how it functions as grounds for empirical knowledge claims, on its relation to interpretation and to inferences made from its evidence—involves us quickly in basic questions of the epistemology of science. It is to such questions that we will address ourselves in this chapter.

THE PLAIN FACTS OF OBSERVATION

The plain facts of observation seem plain enough. We see what we look at, and what we look for. Or things impose themselves on us willy-nilly, getting themselves observed by us, calling attention to themselves. Yet we are fooled or mistaken often enough. What we took to be a figure in the gloom turns out to be a shrub. The automobile unaccountably sliding backward next to us at the stoplight finally reminds us to step harder on the brake when we realize it is we who are moving. Distinctions or discriminations among unfamiliar objects often elude us at first, and later seem perfectly obvious, as when we learn a new alphabet (say Russian, or Chinese, or Arabic): the unfamiliar marks look jumbled, some not clearly distinguishable from others, and their order seems inaccessible. Then, with familiarity, we observe distinctions with ease, and wonder at the trouble we had at first. Looking at so-called ambiguous figures or hidden figures, we stare and stare; then, with the "click" of illumination, the face hidden in the trees, or the rabbit-like aspect of the apparent duck, becomes clear and distinct. Yet we were looking at it all the time without seeing it. The plain facts of observation thus have to account for an equally plain fact: What we observe is largely a function of intent and context, and depends to a very great extent on frame of mind, attention, on what we know to look for. Much of this escapes us. Sleight-of-mind takes over for us, working efficiently and transparently until we run into trouble, until we discover that we are deceived.

We do not need to look to the extraordinary cases of illusion and error to realize that observation concerns more than meets the eye. For consider the sorts of things we are wont to say we observe: We observe the sky, and that it is blue; we observe that it is getting dark, or that it is night; we observe the pen on the table, the hole in the wall, that Sam is shorter than Jack but taller than Philip; we observe the way a person talks or that he is getting angry; we observe that a button is missing, that the room is empty, that nothing has changed since we left; and we observe sunsets and sunrises, eclipses of the moon, and atomic disintegrations taking place in bubble chambers. Thus, in general we may be said to observe things or types of things, objects, events, processes, qualities and changes of quality, states of affairs, relations among things, and even absences or lacks.

A quizzical physicist may try his hand at one-upping my plain statement of a fact of observation, when I assert, "I see the sky." "Not at all," he says, "what you are *really* seeing is the refracted light of the sun as the photon stream enters the layers of the upper atmosphere. You then go on to interpret this, in your common-sensical way, as 'seeing the sky.' " Not about to be one-upped, I may reply, "What I see is the sky, just as what you see is the sky. Then *you* go about interpreting this fact of observation in terms of refracted light and whatnot. The interpretation is yours, not mine." Each of us makes a claim to what is "really" being seen and what is derivatively being interpreted. The appeal in both cases is to some bare fact to which the interpretation eventually may be reduced. In a court of law the witness is asked not to interpret, but to give the plain facts of observation: not what he heard told, nor what he saw some event *as,* but the unvarnished and bare facts of observation. The assumption in all such cases is that in perception something is given, and given in an unmediated or direct way.

THE IMMEDIATELY GIVEN: SENSE DATA AND KNOWLEDGE

There is, then, a demand to get to rock bottom, to the zero level of observation, to the indubitables of hard and unmediated sense experience, unspoiled by judgment and thus veridical because it cannot be other than as it is apprehended. This raw datum, immediately given in experience, then becomes subject to the processing which the perceptual system, or the mind, works on it; it is the input upon which we then proceed to operate, arranging and interpreting it and drawing conclusions. This bare evidence of the senses, what they directly report, is in such a view presumed to be the *sine qua non* of empirical knowledge. It is ultimately what our scientific knowledge is about; all the rest is interpretation, inference, construction. Once processing begins, once we go beyond merely having the experience, or once we say what it is we see, the virginity of this immediate experience is lost.

This view in epistemology which regards sensation as the primary stuff of knowledge and as the original and primitive element of perception has a long philosophical history. It is associated with the earliest formulation of empiricism: "There is nothing in the mind that wasn't first in the senses," and in its modern form derives from the British empiricists of the seventeenth and eighteenth centuries, principally Locke, Berkeley, and Hume. In its contemporary form, it has been elaborated as the so-called sense-datum theory primarily by English philosophers, such as G. E. Moore, Bertrand Russell, C. D. Broad, H. H. Price, and A. J. Ayer. There are great difficulties in this view and it has been vigorously criticized in contemporary philosophy. But it emphasizes a significant distinction between sensing—which we may take as a basic organic activity at the level of the surface receptors of a percipient organism—and perceiving—which presumably involves some higher integrative activity, in which the sense data are taken as the "evidence" for the perception of some thing or object constructed out of these data by perceptual activity. The sense data are typically conceived of as qualitative impressions: color patches, shapes, tones, sensory qualities of hardness, softness, smoothness, and so on, whereas perceptual objects constructed out of these data are ordinary tables, ice cubes, cabbages and kings, the ubiquitous pennies which though round "appear" elliptical, and sticks which though straight "appear" bent in water. Thus, by this view, we are said to *sense* sense data but to *perceive* tables and pennies. Observation concerns the objects of perception, for we do not "observe" sense data. By this version, then, the immediate givens of experience are never "observed" but "had." Russell distinguished between these two sorts of knowledge as knowledge by acquaintance (of the directly had sense data) and knowledge by description (of the now attenuated constructions we put upon them).

Furthermore, sense data seem irretrievably private. They may be had but they cannot be shared: what's mine is mine and what's yours is yours. And the difficulty which this places upon characterizing them as "knowledge" of any sort is that we think of knowledge as prospectively public, expressible in a language common to a community of percipients and testable in some public or intersubjective way. It would seem then that one certainly could not use sense data as the basic reference for scientific knowledge, which must be public and shareable. Still a suitably public character for sense data might be arranged within a psychological theory about them. For example, one could say that there is a language of sense data which is public and scientific, namely, an account of the sensory structures of human beings and of sensory laws. Thus physiology may give an account of the common, inherited species structures of vision, touch, taste, smell, hearing, as psychophysics may approach the formulation of laws governing the relation of physical stimuli to sensory responses. We may then claim that, at this level, sense data are held in common in similar situations, because the structures of response are themselves common, or species, structures, and not individual and unique. Even if there is uniqueness in each person's particular sensory configuration, all are alike enough so that we may speak of a common mode of sense experience. This is a rather plausible and commonsensical view for there certainly seems to be sufficient similarity within the normal range of sensory experience to permit us to get along as though this were a common world of such experience. On such grounds, one might adduce a common universe of shared sense experience. But this is a far cry from the philosophical analysis whose focus is on the immediacy, the uniqueness, and the utter primacy of sense data.

At any rate, our concern for the role of observation in the acquisition and validation of scientific knowledge could not rest with an ultimately private revelation in the way of sensory felt qualities. It would seem to require instead that we separate what we mean by observation from the postulated case of immediate sensory experience, and tie it instead to perception and the objects of perception.

THE OBJECTS OF PERCEPTION

What is perceived is not a sense datum, then, but some object, situation, relation, or state of affairs, something which is recognized or taken to be of a certain sort. For perception is not bare or immediate, but involves a degree of recognition of the objects of perception as this or that sort of thing. This is not to say that "unrecognizable" in the sense of unfamiliar objects may not be perceived. In fact, as common sense suggests and experiment has shown, the unfamiliar alerts us and we are prone to notice and pay attention with heightened interest when something novel and strange is introduced into our perceptual field. Conversely, the utterly familiar may escape our notice, for though it is clearly recognizable as this or that once we are asked to notice it, we ordinarily take it for granted. Still, some degree of recognition is a condition for something to be an object of perception at all, and even the unfamiliar object has certain perceptually recognizable features—say, some shape or color or even something as vague as "presence"—though we may not be able to identify it. Such a weak sense of "recognition," which we may distinguish from recognizing something to be this or that explicitly, involves taking what we perceive to be "something." When we fail perceptually to achieve even this, we may be said not to perceive at all. The untrained observer looking at a slide under the microscope may in fact not perceive what to the trained observer is perfectly clear. A similar event occurs when our attention is called to something which had we paid attention in the proper way, or within the proper framework, should have been perfectly obvious to us.

The situation we have been describing is surreptitiously linguistic; to perceive something seems to come to saying to oneself or to someone else, "This is so-and-so or such-and-such." So intimately tied to the framework of language is our perception that our identification of things and properties of things in the language may in effect influence what we see and fail to see. Language may thus be said to teach us perceptual discriminations we might not otherwise make, and lead us as well to overlook others. Just as the trained musician can hear differences in pitch or in harmonic interval that the layman may fail to hear even when his attention is called to them, so too the speaker of a language may be trained or attuned for certain perceptual discriminations. The relation of language to perception is so intimate that it often takes the artist to separate the two and force us back into perceptual naiveté, to recapture a linguistically ingenuous perception for us and shake us loose from the accustomed framework of language which leads us to see things as being this or that.

Perception, at least at the level of the speaking adult, is therefore always the incipient assertion that something is the case. When we move from casual scanning to looking at something, or looking for something, thus to that more attentive focus of observation proper, then our observation statements are the explicit linguistic assertions that something is the case. Observations themselves are of course not statements, but may be expressed by statements. Such statements, then, are assertions, and the objects of such statements are the *purported facts* of observation. Thus, the expression of an observation, that is, the explicit statement of it in some language, is a claim that some proposition P is true.

OBSERVATION STATEMENTS AND THE ANALYTIC-SYNTHETIC DISTINCTION

We thus have a class of expressions which we may call observation statements or observation sentences. But how shall we tell whether a given expression belongs to this class? What criteria shall we use for determining that some expression is an observation statement? If the language of empirical science is to be characterized as in some sense and to some extent constituted of such statements, how shall we distinguish them? For certainly there are some statements which are not observation statements and whose truth and falsity does not rest on their agreement with empirical matters of fact. For example, if one were to say "There are four prime numbers greater than 1, between 1 and 10," it would indeed be odd to claim that this asserted a fact of observation. Rather, we would say that its truth or falsity depends on the *definition* of "prime" and of "number." Similarly, if one announced "All four-sided figures are quadrilaterals" or "all regular polygons are regular," it would clearly be absurd to go about observing quadrilaterals or regular polygons to find out whether as a matter of fact these statements were true or false. Likewise, if one asserted, "All red roses are red roses," or, "It is raining here and it is not raining here at the same time," it would be misplaced scientific zeal to make observations to determine the truth or falsity of these statements.

In the case of the quadrilaterals, *four-sided figure* is what *quadrilateral* means, and because we take these expressions to be synonyms, and interchangeable, making observations to find out whether all quadrilaterals were indeed four-sided figures would be equivalent to checking on whether all four-sided figures were indeed four-sided. The statement would be true by virtue of the meaning of the terms. In the regular polygon case, also, what is asserted about the subject ("All regular polygons") in the predicate ("are regular") is already contained in the subject, so that nothing new is being said about the regular polygon that is not already in the meaning of the subject term. These expressions then are not "facts of observation," but of analysis of the accepted meanings of the terms. Such meanings may be fixed by stipulation, by definition, by universal usage, and in these contexts expressions that are true because of the meaning of the terms are seen to be so by inspection of these meanings, or by analysis. They are, in general, called analytic statements, because they are true or false on analysis or inspection of the statements themselves and do not require matter-of-fact observation or experience of the external world. "All red roses are red roses," states an identity, and "It is raining here and it is not raining here at the same time" states a contradiction, and we say that the first is logically true and the second logically false. If one were to substitute variables or place-holders for the content terms in these statements (i.e., "red roses," "it is raining"), so that the formal structure of the statements could be given as "All x's are x's" and "x and not x" we would say that these statements had the same truth values (i.e., "true" or "false") for any interpretation of the variables, or for any content terms put in the places held by the variables.[1] The first is always true, independent of interpretation, and the second always false, on the grounds of the logical form of the statements. Such statements are generally called tautologies, being always true or false *vacuously,* by virtue of their logical form alone, and thus logical truths or falsehoods, empty of content.

Such analytical statements and tautologies are plainly not observation statements then. Insofar as they do not depend on experience or observation for their truth or falsity, they are generally called *a priori* statements, and this class of statements may be called *analytic a priori* statements. In discussing these distinctions, Kant, in *The Critique of Pure Reason,* considered that all statements which were not analytic (i.e., true or false on inspection) were synthetic—that is, what was asserted about the subject in the predicate was *not* contained in the subject of such statements. All knowledge of matters of fact or knowledge about the world was of this sort, he claimed. For example, the assertion, "the sun is 93 million miles from the earth," is such a statement, for it is not part of the meaning of "sun" that it is 93 million miles from the earth. Thus there is more in the predicate than is contained in the meaning of the subject term. Our knowledge of this "more" must thus come from something beyond inspection of meanings. When it comes from experience, from perception or observation of the world, from natural inquiry, Kant calls it knowledge *a posteriori,* in contrast to *a priori* knowledge. In general, then, such truths as are based on knowledge about the world gained by experience and observation are called synthetic *a posteriori* truths. Kant held, further, that there were some truths about the world, therefore matter-of-fact truths, which could be known by pure reason, *a priori,* and were not contingent upon observation and experience, but were necessary truths of reason. Thus, they were not simply analytic, but synthetic; yet they were not *a posteriori* but *a priori* truths, truths of reason alone. Such truths he called therefore synthetic *a priori* truths, and his examples of one type of such truths are mathematical truths—e.g., $7 + 5 = 12$—which he claimed are not analytic (because the concept "12" contains "more" than is already contained in the concept "7 + 5"); yet such truths are *a priori,* following from pure reason or from our mathematical intuition. This difficult concept of synthetic *a priori* truths, which have reference to the world or to matters of fact and yet are known *a priori* without dependency on observation, has occasioned much discussion in the history of philosophy, in mathematics, and in philosophy of science, but we shall not pursue it here.

[1] Thus, if I replace "red roses" with "green emeralds," or with "chess-players over 40," or whatever, the logical identity "All x's are x's" has the same truth value (T), and similarly with the contradiction, whose truth value is always (F). On truth values, see Appendix C.

Our former distinction between formal and factual sciences may be elucidated further in this context: The formal sciences are those which deal with analytic *a priori* statements, and only these. The factual sciences deal with synthetic *a posteriori* statements, whose truth and falsity depend on observation and experience. Scientific inference may make use of the formal sciences, i.e., pure mathematics or logic, as instruments of reasoning, or, as Carnap calls them, "auxiliary calculi," but what makes science empirical or factual is that its content is dependent on the facts of observation as these are expressed in observation statements.

But note that although this analytic-synthetic distinction appears to solve our problem neatly, by dividing all statements which are either true or false into those which are analytic and those which are not, it really leaves unsolved, because untouched, the problem of determining what characterizes an observation statement as such. The negative condition, that it is not analytic or tautologous, does not give us such a characterization; at best, if we take observation statements to be members of the class of nonanalytic statements, this yields a logical or formal truth, namely, that statements which are nonanalytic are nonanalytic, and therefore, if they are either true or false, depend on something else for their truth or falsity. Thus if we define an empirical science as one which contains observation statements in its corpus, we are saying no more than that empirical science is empirical unless we further characterize such statements. Surely, an empirical science appears to contain many statements which are nonanalytic but which we do not ordinarily take to be observation statements. These are then members of the class of synthetic statements, but are not themselves observational in any clear sense that we have yet established. For example, if we say that the speed of light in a vacuum is 2.99792×10^8 meters per second, it is not clear in what sense *this* fact is "observed," though it seems perfectly clear that it is a purported fact about the world and that it *depends* on observation. But what exactly does it depend on, in "depending on observation"? Is the speed of light in a vacuum observable, as such? Is the fact that it is 2.99792×10^8 meters per second an "observable fact?" If we say, instead, that it "depends on" observation, what are the observables which it depends on? Would one want so wide an interpretation of observation that all synthetic statements would be observation statements, no matter how "theoretical"? Or would one want to claim, in a modified way, that observation statements and theoretical statements are simply distinguished by matters of degree rather than of kind, namely, that all observation statements are more or less "theoretical," and that all theoretical statements are more or less "observational" along some continuum without sharp distinctions? Or shall we depend on some appeal to the common understanding which takes "observation" to have to do with ordinary seeing, hearing, touching? This raises questions which the analytic-synthetic distinction does not even touch. What we require then is some criterion of observation which determines for us what observables are, or what it is that observation statements are about. Any view going beyond the commonsense view of observation involves a theory of how our factual knowledge is acquired and what it is about. In short, any such view involves epistemological questions.

EPISTEMOLOGICAL THEORIES AND THE CRITERIA FOR OBSERVATION

We will consider what *observation* and *observable* mean in four alternative formulations: (1) realism, (2) phenomenalism, (3) the analysis of ordinary language, and (4) linguistic pragmatism, or the "alternative languages" approach. The first two are classic epistemological theories, and the last two are typical of recent attempts to reframe epistemological questions in terms of the use of language. Thus, the realist and phenomenalist views share a common approach: that the criterion for observability is to be dealt with by means of a theory of knowledge, in which certain entities are theoretically defined as observables. The ordinary language and pragmatic approaches both appear to eschew epistemological theories and instead focus on how a community of speakers uses the terms *observation* or *observable,* or on which of the alternative ways of talking about observation is best suited for given tasks of communication and description.

Realism and phenomenalism, as theories of our knowledge of the external world, propose different sorts of entities as the objects of knowledge. The realist would argue that what we know and what we perceive exist independently of our knowing and perceiving, and that the objects of knowledge and perception are things in the world. The "direct realist" would say that the material objects and properties of the external world are directly known, that we perceive them as they really are. A representative realism, such as Locke's, for example, would hold that our knowledge of the external world is indirect, by means of the direct impressions or ideas which are caused in us by real objects. So-called critical realism emphasizes the role of interpretive and critical judgments of perceptual evidence as our warrant for knowledge of the external world; but it sees this interpretive activity as mediating a knowledge which yet remains knowledge of an independent reality. Phenomenalism, by contrast, speaks of external reality as at best a warranted construct, or a hypothesis, and therefore not known, as such, but inferred from the direct objects of knowledge, which are sense impressions, or "appearances" (therefore the term *phenomena*). *What* they are appearances of is a matter of constructive inference by the mind operating on the "bundles of sense data." The phenomenalist would typically argue that what we can know is the way things appear, but not the way they are in themselves, for as such they are unknowable—the best we can do is make more or less plausible conjectures or hypotheses. The radical phenomenalist might even argue that belief in the existence of "things" or "the external world" is at most a good bet—a belief induced in us by habituation or because it pays off; we may *believe* that things exist beyond or beneath the appearances in perception, but we cannot *know* that they do. The external world then is a construct of imagination or belief, but is not the object of knowledge or perception.

A question concerning the relation of the perceiver to what he perceives arises in such theories. On one account, the so-called spectator theory, the perceiver is taken as a passive recipient of ideas or sense impressions or stimuli from the external world which act upon him (or his mind or sense organs). In Locke's account the mind is taken as a blank tablet (*tabula rasa*) upon which experience writes. Perceptual or mental activity consists in the arrangement or rearrangement of this passively received input, according to the structure of the mind, or by means of its "natural operations" (e.g., the "association of ideas," or the "natural disposition" to associate things which resemble each other or occur together or contiguously in space or time) Perception is passive in the sense that it does not go out soliciting impressions or ideas but takes what it gets, so to speak; it is nevertheless active in terms of the "mental operations" by which these received ideas are ordered.

Another view regards the mind or the perceptual apparatus as fully active, doing the selecting, the probing, the searching, and determining the order of what is perceived from an indeterminate and inchoate domain of possible perceptions. The perceiver brings to perception certain *a priori* forms in terms of which alone his perception may take place. The perceptual apparatus is a scanning and filtering device, and only that can become an object of perception which fits the perceiver's *a priori* framework, which he imposes on an otherwise undifferentiated perceptual field. Whatever the "real" objects are which may be hypothetically conceived beyond the scope of these forms or frameworks, they are perceptually unknowable; they are, in Kant's terms, "things-in-themselves" (*Dinge-an-sich*) and not "things-for-us." If the mind has any knowledge of such things, it is not by means of perception, therefore not empirically or by knowledge of phenomena, but rather transcendentally, going beyond what can be learned from experience, and thus *a priori.*

An alternative approach to such epistemological questions is by way of linguistic analysis. Instead of adducing a theory about what sorts of entities are observables, whether sense data, or material objects, or appearances, linguistic analysis sets out to describe how the term *observe* is used or what it is taken to mean by a community of speakers. In one such view, so-called ordinary language is taken to be the clue to what *observation* means. In another such view, the advantages of certain usages for certain purposes are examined: an ideal language especially constructed for the purposes of science is seen to provide the preferred scientific use of the term *observable.*

On analysis, it turns out there are many uses of *observe,* some of them related in a family way, but some not so. For example, *observe* is taken to mean things like *see, touch, taste, smell;* that is, it is associated with the terms characteristic of sense perception. Yet it may also mean *understand* or *rationally comprehend,* as in, "We observe that the period of the precession of the ecliptic is 26,000 years," or, "We observe that the English kings were constrained to a policy of limited autocracy." Certainly these are not the sorts of things one could see or smell. Similarly, *observe* is used in the sense of *noting that* or *being of the opinion that,* as in, "He made the observation that things were going worse than had been expected." In these cases, the meaning and scope of *observation* depends on contexts of use. To specify such uses, we might ask what sorts of entities the verb *to observe* takes in various contexts. Thus, in the first case *observe* is used only for the class of visual, tactile, or aural objects, where the paradigms for such objects are given by, "I *saw* a red ball," "I *touched* the rough table," but not by, "I *saw* I had nothing to gain by staying," or, "His plea *touched* my heart." Interpreting this differently, only terms denoting physical things may be taken to be objects of the verb *to observe.* (Thus I cannot be said to "observe a holiday" in this sense, nor can I "observe God," unless I take God and holidays to be physical objects.)

In short, the class of observation statements will be determined by considerations of the ordinary use of *observe,* or by its use in specified contexts. There will be no "essential" or theoretical definition of observability apart from this report on or description of the "ordinary" uses. If therefore the community of physicists uses *observe* (among themselves) for such "objects" as atomic disintegrations or fluctuations in a magnetic field, then such "objects" are observables in this framework. It may be objected that this is a special, and not an ordinary, use—that is, a use common to all speakers of a language—but then the question simply seems to be one concerning the scope or size of the linguistic community. For a large part of the English-speaking community, it is not problematic to talk about "seeing an eclipse"; yet for a large part of the medieval Chinese community, "seeing a dragon devouring the sun" might have been just as unproblematically observable. Furthermore, the objection that both communities were really seeing the same thing—namely, a dark disk passing over a bright one—but seeing it *as* two different things, on interpretation, simply becomes a claim that in still a third linguistic community, talk about "dark and bright disks" replaces "eclipses" and "dragons" as observation language.

Such a relativization of observation language to contexts or to linguistic communities suggests the fourth of the approaches we will consider, which we may call the pragmatic or methodological approach. Such a view refuses to offer epistemological judgments concerning what "really" are the objects of perception: material objects in the external world, phenomena in some subject's awareness, or strange entities like sense data. In this view, the questions arising out of epistemological considerations concern what really exists, or what can be truly known, and these are ontological or metaphysical questions lying outside the scope of determining how "observation" shall be used. This is a practical problem: what is the best way to use it in various realms of discourse or scientific inquiry.

Phenomenalism and realism do offer real alternatives here, but not in their classic epistemological form. Rather, the choice between alternative phenomenalist or realist frameworks is a choice among alternative *linguistic* frameworks. Is it useful or appropriate, in certain contexts, to talk in a way which countenances phenomena or sensory appearances as the references to which "observation" reduces? Or does it better suit a scientific inquiry to talk in terms of physical objects or things? Language is taken to be an instrument, and the choice among alternative languages is made on the basis of which serves a particular function best. For practical everyday purposes, it may indeed be the case that the commonsense realist "thing-language" is most suitable; it may be the best adapted and slowly evolved instrumentality for dealing with practical commonsense contexts. But for theoretical purposes, we may demand that our language be more consistent, rigorous, or economical than is demanded by everyday practice. Scientific inquiry and the community of scientists will specify (explicitly or otherwise) what these special needs and interests are, and scientific discourse exemplifies such special uses of language in its introduction of technical definition, its standards of description, its use of devices of classification, measurement, and mathematical inference.

On the pragmatic view, the philosopher of science, insofar as he is a theorist of the language and logic of scientific discourse, may attempt to reconstruct the language of science in an ideal way, delimiting ambiguity and introducing formal logical rigor and precision. Such reconstructed languages, whether in the phenomenalist or the physicalist-realist mode of speech, are proposed therefore as the refined instrumentalities for the analysis and reconstruction of scientific discourse. If successful, such a program of reconstruction will offer the prospect of a linguistic and methodological unity within science, since languages, like the rest of scientific instrumentation, will be standardized as scales and oscilloscopes are.

No language, therefore, is intrinsically "observational"; rather, this depends on what one chooses to be the observation terms or predicates. In the formal system of the reconstructed language of science, there is of course the "auxiliary calculus," the logical structure of inference and definition, but the empirical content of such a language is determined by what one chooses as observation terms and how one characterizes the operations or processes which such terms will denote. For all the empirical content of the language will ultimately be reducible to observation statements, that is, expressions containing the observation terms and referring to concrete operations denoted by such terms. The so-called theoretical terms of a science which have empirical import will have it by being attached to observation terms; they will be "reducible to" or "interpreted by means of" such terms.

Thus, determining what are observables may be reduced to the question of choosing the so-called basic predicates of the reconstructed language. For example, if one chooses as basic predicates such "phenomenal" terms as *red, heavy, hot, loud,* and such "phenomenal" relations as *longer than* or *brighter than,* then this fixes such terms as denoting the observables for that system. The only question is whether the theoretical terms of a science may somehow be reduced to these, and thus tied to observation as stipulated. On the other hand, one may choose terms of physical measurement as the basic predicates, so that everything would in principle be reducible to such predicates as measured distances, time intervals, or measurements of mass, or of electrical charge.

It is on pragmatic or instrumental grounds, according to this view, that one chooses among alternative languages—on grounds relating to the methodology of science, involving what scientists do when they observe, measure, etc. Nor does one simply choose among prevailing languages, which may have developed haphazardly in the history of science; rather one constructs artificial languages, ideally reconstructed languages, choosing the terms and even the logical structures best suited to scientific frameworks.[2]

What appears as an utter relativism concerning "observation" thus has certain constraints. Although someone may choose anything at all as his basic or observation predicates, in practice the choice is not haphazard. When scientists talk about observing something, the context and the operation have been delimited by the culture of science, just as when observing is spoken of in common usage there is a consensus on what this means and how it is done. The mystic may claim to have observed the face of God in his private revelation; and in delirium, someone may perfectly sincerely claim to observe figures and objects which we take to be hallucinatory. Yet we do not take these as the normal cases of observation, though we may grant that to the person involved, all the features of normal attentive perception or observation were present. The reason is that we take observables to be common and public; we begin with the expectation that what we see is what anyone would see if he were looking; and thus we take observation to be constrained by the check of reference to public objects. Even the phenomenalist does not claim that his observation is private, but rather that, although his sense data or appearances may be matters of his individual perception, the inferred constructs he derives from them will be public, communicable, and in this sense open to check by others. The alternative is solipsism: the theory that all experience is

[2] This program of "logical reconstruction" grew out of the impetus of the logical positivist movement, and its vision of the "unity of science," and is exemplified principally in the work of Carnap, Hempel, Frank, and Feigl, among others. This "unity of science" is interpreted as a unity to be achieved in the *language* of science, on the grounds of such logical reconstruction. The central notion of "reduction" to basic predicates will be discussed more fully later in this chapter and in Chapter 13.

private and unshareable, and all that can be vouched for is the individual's present experience. In this view, the only thing he can know is that he exists when he is aware of his own experiences: all else exists derivatively, by virtue of his thinking it, or being aware of it. (Such a view, said Schopenhauer, is more in need of a cure than a refutation; but as a theoretical consideration, it has played a major role in the philosophical discussion of perception.)

The public quality of observation (What we might facetiously call the communism of the observable, where no property is private and all is commonly owned; and where the maxim holds: "From each according to his ability, to each according to his need"), this open availability to all comers, is then a criterion which excludes certain experiences, such as revelation or hallucination, from being observational. Beyond this, it seems, no other constraints are definitive. Still, this, like the criterion of non-analyticity for observation statements, is a negative one, and the impulse to give a positive characterization of observability, which we have seen in epistemological theories, is strong. We want our observation statements to be tied to facts, to be true or false by virtue of their reference to the way things are. In short, we want a way to break out of the shell of language, and to establish some connection between what we say there is and what there is.

OBSERVATION AND REFERENCE

Observation statements have factual reference. But how does one take a piece of language, or an utterance, and make it refer? Having worked our way from the operations and processes of observing to the expression of such observation in a language, we want now to see how the words get back to the things, how what we put on paper or utter in speech gets linked with what goes on outside the language. The problem is not simply to relate my own expression to my own experience or perception; I presumably am aware of what I mean to refer to when I make an observation statement. Rather, it is a matter of establishing this link in a public and communicable way. The solution is already embedded in the statement of the problem, however, for the very language in which the statements are made is by its nature a common language, one which I learn in a community of speakers and which evolved as a means of communication. How then could it be otherwise than common? Furthermore, the world of facts to which the language refers, or which it represents, is taken to be a common world, and not my private construction. That I take it to be common and objective is the mark of my rationality, and of my acceptance as a member of the community of rational beings who share this world view with me. Thus, everything in the culture operates to socialize me in these respects, linguistically and ontologically. The world I choose to take as the common one and the language in which I describe it all encourage this sense of the objectivity of my reference, for it is precisely these which my community of language and of actions reinforces in me (and, for all I know, for which I may be biologically fashioned).

The question therefore is not whether observation statements refer to objective facts. This is definitive of observation statements. Rather, the analysis concerns how this is achieved, how this process itself may be descriptively and theoretically reconstructed. What constitutes the context for the reference of observation statements is a framework of familiar neighborhoods and familiar ways of talking. But how do they become familiar?

Analysis proceeds by simplification. It seeks the primitive elements out of which complexes are constructed. Here too, it seeks rock-bottom reference, some exemplification of the simplest, most unencumbered mode of using language to refer. Analysis finds it in *ostension,* i.e., in linking an utterance to an object or a state of affairs by pointing. The simpleminded account of ostensive reference runs like this: I utter the word "table" and I point to a table, so that my utterance is taken as indicating or naming the object; or there is established in the mind of my listener and watcher an association between my utterance and what I am pointing at. This is simpleminded on several counts. First, it is clear that before this could take place, the notion of pointing or indicating has to have been established. It is not primitive, as simple home experiments with pet dogs and infants will show. Second, what *I* have in mind when I point may not be what you are looking at, when you follow my indication. For the reference of fingertips is opaque, nor would needle-tipped pointers increase clarity or precision of reference here. I point to an ashtray and say "ashtray" to someone who presumably does not know what the word means. Assuming he understands pointing, and follows my fingertip instead of admiring my outstretched arm, he may yet take me to be pointing to an innumerable number of features in the area of my fingertip or in the direction it indicates. I may have said "yellow-colored" or "ashes in the tray" or "round" or "five inches across"; my language learner, not knowing any of these words, can hardly know which of these properties or objects to look at, or which of them I have in mind.

Story has it that an Australian settler, seeing a strange hopping animal for the first time, asked an Australian aborigine what animal that was. (He knew the language well enough to ask the question, of course). The native answered, in his own language, "I don't know," the expression for which in the native's language is "kangaroo." The moral is clear, but the normal situation is not that bad. We do not acquire our first or native languages as if they were our second languages. As native speakers of our own languages, we do not ask questions about a "foreign" language when we learn to speak. Learning to speak is tied up with the whole apparatus of naming and pointing, of uttering sentences and getting responses, and of giving responses to uttered sentences; it is also, on some present accounts, tied up with the genetic apparatus our species has for acquiring a language. Thus, modes of reference are not simply the emasculated reconstruction we have given of ostension, which is easy to pick apart because it is simpleminded and abstract, but must instead be inordinately rich and complex in their operation. Thus, ostension surely works somehow, for we do learn by having things pointed out and exhibited to us; but the model of ostension must therefore be richer and more complex than the simple one given above.

Using a statement to refer to something outside the language, to something perceivable or observable, thus presupposes a framework in which the notion of reference is already embedded. Perhaps this is acquired by learning: by the eliciting and reinforcement of appropriate responses to utterances, so that we come to behave as we are expected to by our teachers. The evidence that you have understood what I have said, in a referential context, is that you do what I would expect you to do if you had understood. If I point and say, "Open the door," and you in fact open the door, and if this response is reliable, and not idiosyncratic or haphazard, I take it that you not only understand what I mean, in some private sense of comprehending the meaning in your mind, but also can act appropriately with respect to what I am referring to. However, I may train a monkey or a dog to act on command, and yet would not assume that the animal had "understood" my linguistic utterance in a linguistic way, but only that he took the utterance as a sign or a cue to perform in the way he had been trained. Appropriate response then seems too impoverished a criterion for the characterization of referential use of language. Furthermore, if observation statements are only rarely as simple as, "There is a table in the room," or, "You are walking into the wall," it would seem impossible to give a characterization of "appropriate responses" for the complex cases, at least in simple behavioral terms. When the scientist says matter-of-factly and observationally, "In properly prepared sections of the cell bodies of neurons, Nissl granules appear in the cytoplasm as fine basophilic granules which are usually grouped in dense clumps," by what appropriate response would he know that his reference had been understood? Presumably by behavior that would proceed as if this were in fact the case, or such that it set about finding out whether it was the case. The test of "understanding" might well be, as in the case of exam questions, an explication of the meaning of the statement by means of other statements within the language. For example, the question might be "Where would one expect to find Nissl granules?" and the answer would require no more than "observation" of the original statement. If observation statements could be determined to be such simply by virtue of intralinguistic reference to other statements, then indeed the matter of reference to the external world would be in a bad way.

The argument for the reduction to basic predicates that we alluded to earlier is precisely an argument for reduction to predicates that have so-called operational definitions, that can be unambiguously linked to overt behavior of a certain sort or to easily determinable appropriate responses. Thus, though the complex observation statement cited above may have no simple appropriate response, the reduction claim is that the crucial terms which make it an observation statement do have such references to overt responses readily recognizable, even if by way of a chain of so-called co-ordinating definitions or reduction sentences, which lead from the complex theoretical formulation to the basic predicates. A "properly prepared section" of a neuron presumably is something one has learned to achieve in the practical training of the laboratory, and the criteria for which one may have learned to recognize in terms of "basic" perceptual features of color or shape or the intactness of certain parts. "Dense clumps" is an appeal to commonly recognizable features, though the discrimination between "dense" and "not-dense" clumps in a microscopic display may be something one has been trained especially to recognize. "Basophilic" also may be interpreted or reduced to the chemical test for "affinity to basic dies" which has recognizable features of a perceptual sort which one has been trained to recognize, and for which one has been taught to test.

The reference of observation statements is then tied to more or less complex frameworks, within which such reference may be tested. Knowing how to test the reference of such statements is knowing under what conditions of one's own observation such statements would be true or false. What makes such a test presumptively objective, is that one's own conditions of observation are taken to be those which anyone else could reproduce. The observation statement is thus an open appeal for experimental verification or falsification: a proposal of means of warranting that truth conditions have been fulfilled, or a claim that things really are a certain way. The observation "It is raining now" has as its truth condition the fact that it is raining now. The means of ascertaining whether in fact such a condition has been met, and that the statement is therefore true, involves the set of observations which, in the framework commonly accepted, are taken as evidence that it is raining now—in this case, "seeing the rain," "getting wet," and so on. In the special scientific case, the truth condition for "There is an alpha-particle passing through the cloud chamber," is that there is an alpha-particle passing through the cloud chamber. What we take to be evidence for this fact is established by the complex framework of theory and instrumentation, which interprets a string of water droplets of a certain length and a certain curvature as the effect of just such an event. What makes this a case of observation is that reference to alpha-particles is operationally determined in this instance by an apparatus constructed for *visual* display; that is to say, the "basic predicates" of cloud-chamber talk, insofar as it involves observation terms, are the terms of visual perception and measurement: *string of water droplets, length, curvature.*

Sciences differ, then, and different inquiries within a science differ in what will be taken as the appropriate reference of observation statements. But it is in terms of such context-defined observation that one decides whether the statements are true or false, whether the purported facts of observation are facts, whether things outside the language are the way the linguisitic claim says they are.

THE SHIFTING OBSERVABLE: THEORETICAL FRAMEWORKS AND OBSERVATION

What is observable, in the pragmatist view, is what a community of speakers and inquirers takes to be observable. The predicates appealed to as the means of establishing whether truth conditions have been fulfilled, as the empirical test or warrant of truth-claims, therefore determine the observation language for a framework of inquiry. This serves to relativize the notion of observation with respect to current scientific usage, or the different usages of different sciences. It also serves to take the question of what is empirical out of the classic epistemological framework, which is concerned to establish whether sense data, or physical objects, or other sorts of things are the objects of perception. Surely, all observation is perceptual; but this gets us into a vicious circle, for it does not tell us what *perceptual* is any more than it tells us what *observational* is. The way out of the circle would seem to be an appeal to the common understanding of these terms, or to psychological theory which examines how perception takes place. But each of these in turn constitutes a framework which adduces certain predicates as perceptual or observational, leaving us relatively (and relativistically) no better off than we were before.

The good sense of common sense urges us to use common understanding as a base from which we depart and to which we return. But even common understanding changes, often under the influence of changes in the scientific understanding, and in scientific uses of "observable." "Seeing an eclipse" is a case in point, for not until the theoretical framework which took eclipses as something other than mythical events had developed could one talk observationally about "seeing eclipses." We know that our perceptual apparatus, in terms of its physiological structures and capacities, has not changed in this time; yet to delimit perceptual apparatus to physiological description is once again to enter into a theoretical framework in which perception and observation are defined in terms of the basic predicates of that framework.

If we are to talk about scientific observation, about the observables of science, we can at least begin by talking about what it is that scientists take themselves to be observing, with the meanings understood by scientists or the concepts used in the sciences, in what are taken to be observational and experimental contexts. The pragmatic test is whether the observational or descriptive language guarantees reference to the satisfaction of the scientific community, and whether it delimits ambiguity to the extent that scientists are able to communicate. In the pragmatic view, then, there is no holy or ultimate or essential sense of "observation" which supersedes this, or to which the scientist must conform. If in fact it turns out that scientists have chosen and still do choose as observation terms those which cluster around the common-sense notions of sense perception, then this fact is no more than a cultural artifact, since what observation "really is" is not an epistemological but a methodological question. On the other hand, if the reference of "observable" shifts radically within scientific frameworks, this also connotes only that for the purposes and interests of scientific inquiry a different instrumentality has been adopted. For example, for common purposes descriptive or observational predicates for color, such as "red" or "reddish-orange" might do perfectly well to elicit the appropriate responses or the expected discriminations. For physical investigation, however, one might want to know wave-lengths where the observation language is in terms of physical measurement predicates. Thus, "7000 Å" may replace the term "red" for these purposes, as an observation term. We might insist that on inspection, the physicist has not "observed" a wavelength of 7000 Å but rather a line on a line spectrum and a numeral inscribed on a scale where this line appears. But with similar justice, the scientist may insist that when we report that we observe red, we are "really" observing light at 7000 Å, which *if* it were exhibited spectrographically would then show up as a line on a scale. We may argue further that "seeing a numbered line" cannot under any circumstances be construed as a case of "seeing red," but only some other things—lines, numerals—which are, within the framework of scientific inference and instrumentation, taken as evidence for the presence of light of a certain wavelength. Thus, what is "really" observed is *interpreted* within that framework as "seeing red," but only in this derivative sense. But again, one could argue that the common-sense framework, or that of ordinary use which takes "red" and "lines" and "numerals" as the characteristic objects of "direct perception" merely substitutes, for its own needs and purposes, basic predicates of a different sort than those which are required for the frameworks of scientific observation.

On such a relativistic view of what constitutes "observable," and therefore what sorts of predicates will be taken to name a statement as an observation statement, observation and observability turn out to be framework-dependent. What this comes to, in the way of a linguistic pragmatism, is that any predicates whatever may be taken as basic predicates if, in some conceptual framework, or in some context of linguistic use, such predicates are taken as *uninterpreted for that framework*. The one "real" framework of observation proper becomes steadily more elusive the further such an analysis proceeds. For on a logical reconstruction of what distinguishes observation from interpretation, the so-called basic-predicates are merely those which function as primitive terms or undefined terms in a given framework, and are simply those in terms of which all the other descriptive or content terms are defined or interpreted. Thus, what happens to be taken as "observable" already specifies a framework in which such observables serve as the primitive terms, as the place where the empirical buck-passing stops.

The appeal to some "immediately given," which we dealt with earlier in the discussion of sense-datum theories, itself becomes one among a number of alternative theoretical frameworks in which to consider the question of observation. The epistemological theories, whether realist or phenomenalist, are then seen to be philosophical arguments in support of one rather than another observation language. In the pragmatist view these are reduced to recommendations that, for one or another purpose, it is better to speak in terms of observing physical objects, or sense data, or appearances, or qualities, or something else. Questions of epistemology or of ontology thus become transformed into methodological questions, depending on practical considerations or on the expediencies of scientific inquiry.

We may consider this dependency on a framework in terms of an analogy, taking the "basic predicates" of the observation language as the raw material offered up to inquiry for interpretation. "Raw data" or "raw experience," like "raw material," are considered raw with respect to some framework. Raw material for the publisher is paper and ink; for the paper manufacturer, it is wood pulp, rags, chemicals. Raw material for the tree from which the wood comes is water, sunlight, nitrogen, phosphates in the soil. If we pursue the publisher, in a metaphorical vein, he may admit that his "ultimate" raw material is water, sunlight, and soil (and sweat and tears). In this mood he may enjoy the rustic metaphor and concede that in the long run, dust we are and to dust return. But his accounts list bills payable to the paper manufacturer and not to mother nature. So the framework of his activity as a publisher delimits the relevant items he will take as "raw" or "basic." Similarly, the scientist's accounts are payable to the scientific community in a specified coin; and like money in an exchange economy, his basic terms are those to which all the others may be reduced, by the transformation which translates all goods into cash values.

The monetary metaphor runs very close to the bone of the reduction question. For purposes of facilitating exchange, the scientist may pay his accounts not in coin, but in legal tender or by check. That is, he may not have to reduce all his descriptive content to the basic "penny predicates," but may use his credit in the community or the established means of exchange in the "theoretical" language—what we may call "banknote predicates"—because everyone knows that the conversion from note to coin may always be performed, simply and effortlessly. This notion that theoretical terms in a science, like *atom* or *magnetic field* or *basophilic*, may be reduced, or translated, or interpreted, and turned into basic coin leads us finally to the outcome of the argument for reduction to basic predicates. For basic coin is valued simply by the convention that permits one to exchange other things for it. It has no character other than the methodological, and one cannot make claims for its intrinsic value, but only for its instrumental value. What establishes this value for it is the whole *system* that underwrites the exchange—the monetary system and the public agreement that upholds it. To make the metaphor explicit then is to see that what upholds the status of "observables" as coin of the realm is the theoretical system whose acceptance confers the credit which such observables enjoy. We may, if we like, claim that science as a whole constitutes such a credit system, and that *observable* is therefore the index of the whole framework of science, or of the standard beliefs of the scientific community.

But if the sense of *observable* shifts from one to another framework, it may also be seen that the frameworks of science also shift, historically, so that the standard "observables" of one period are either augmented or replaced by those of another, as the "standards of credit" themselves change. Aristotle depended much on common observation as the raw material which his theoretical system had to account for; but he counted very little on what we would call measurement in the strict sense. Galileo's observation language presumably used measurements of distances and times (albeit by instruments crude by our standards), assigning numbers to physical magnitudes. We exemplify this sort of classification of the sciences by means of their observational criteria, distinguishing the "exact sciences" (those which depend on quantitative measurement and the use of mathematics) from the "inexact sciences" (which on this sanguine account rely on "qualitative" distinctions, or are "nonquantitative" or merely "descriptive"). Such choices of basic predicates—say, of numbers or of classes or of qualities—is once again relative to requirements, and "exactitude" itself may be such a relative requirement. (As Eddington once said, you don't need a razor to cut butter.)

The notion of measurement itself undergoes changes, so that what distinguishes so-called direct or fundamental measurement from indirect or derived measurement becomes a function of what is theoretically conceived as "direct" and "indirect." By means of x-rays, we may be said to directly observe internal bone and tissue structure; yet it is only by a theory of the instrument that the x-ray photograph may be said to be a "picture" of an otherwise unobservable structure. But the same thing may be said of so unproblematic a case as that of the ordinary photograph, the subject of which we commonsensically have no trouble in recognizing, even though it is two-dimensional instead of three-dimensional, is on a much smaller scale, may lack color, and so on. When the results of x-ray photography become so esoteric that we "take a picture" of, say, crystal structure, by means of x-ray diffraction, we tend to say that we are not observing crystal structure, but only visual evidence which may then be interpreted according to theory as crystal structure. By contrast, when we look through a microscope, what we see is "really there." In the one case, it may be argued, observation is wholly indirect, and "reading" the photograph depends on a body of theory to support inferences from the data, whereas in microscopy we are "looking directly at the evidence." Yet to use the microscope as an instrument of pathology, to consider whether what is "seen" is pathological tissue and use this data as evidence for or against some diagnosis—all this requires not simply a theory of the instrument, but a complex theory which interprets the smudges and squiggles on the microscopic slide as pathological evidence. On such a view, then, nothing is *evidence* except in some framework of interpretation, and examining varicolored smudges and squiggles through an eyepiece is not yet a case of examining cellular tissue for pathological evidence. The untrained observer will not "observe" such evidence, any more than will the untrained observer of x-ray diffraction photographs. Thus, what may be taken as observable depends on the background, the theoretical expectations and understanding of the observer, and the theory of the instrument which leads one to interpret clicks, or undulating lines, or squiggles, or shadows as this or that.

Having established the framework-dependence of observation, one may again insistently ask, "But aren't you really observing clicks, lines, squiggles and shadows, even though you take them to be evidence for something which admittedly is theoretically enmeshed, like 'radioactivity' or 'pathological tissue.' Shouldn't you then, in principle, report your observations as what they really are?" The reply may well be, "If you insist on talking that way, and if it makes you feel more securely anchored to the world of common-sense perception, then go ahead and interpret what I say in these terms. But this is not my observation language, as a scientist. My theoretical language *is* my observation language, and in the community of scientists, it would be as redundant for me to talk about 'squiggles' as it would be for you to talk about 'two-legged,' 'long-haired,' 'interestingly curved,' and 'high-voiced,' every time you wanted to say 'girl.' "

Without resolving this question, we may say that observation is not casual scanning but a conceptually-ordered search for evidence. For sheer "data" to be evidence already presupposes that such data will function in some framework of inference. Blind collection of data is, on several grounds, probably impossible, for even at the minimal levels of perception there is some selective framework already operative. Certainly, at the level of scientific observation what we call "observation" and what we call "inference" are indissolubly bound together. Observation in science, as Charles Darwin said, if it is to be of any use, has to be for or against some view. The point of observing is not merely to collect and sum up observations, but to search for and reveal some order among the facts. The shifting "observable" thus shifts with the interests and purposes of inquiry and involves our outcomes with our intentions. Yet we do not simply see what we like or wish to see, nor is our observation simply a function of expectation, for then the objectivity of science would be radically jeopardized. The upshot seems to be not an abandonment of objectivity, but a certain modesty. The plain facts of observation are nowhere so plain as they may at first have appeared to a naive view. But the aim of scientific inquiry is to reestablish, by more sophisticated means, the empirical function of observation as the test of our claims to knowledge of the external world.

CHAPTER 6

Formal Systems, Models, and the Representation of Facts

SCIENCE, ORDER, AND INFERENCE

SCIENTIFIC INQUIRY is not simply a matter of amassing facts, nor is science a dump heap of accumulated facts. Insofar as science is rational and critical, it is an attempt to order the facts of observation, to represent them in some coherent, systematic way in the articulate structure of a language. Therefore, much of science begins where observation leaves off and, as we have seen, much of science concerns what goes on before observation begins. Observation itself is not free of frameworks, and proceeds within one or another prospective order, already disposed to take *this* as a case of *that*. Thus, observation never yields passive data to the scientist but rather implicates him in inference, in reasoning, in the cut and fit and match which mark his enterprise as systematic and rational. Such a rational science is not simply concerned with "knowing the facts," but with reasoning from them, and indeed with reasoning *to* them as well.

The means to this intellectual activity of scientific thought is the representation of the facts in some model, some abstract construction in a language within which relations among the facts are made explicit, and within which the form of such relations may be expressed. Such a conceptual and linguistic abstraction becomes a means of operating with the surrogates or tokens which are taken to represent the facts and their relations, instead of operating with the facts themselves; it substitutes the manipulation of symbols for the manipulation of things and events, reflective inference for direct action and intervention in the world of facts. In effect, such a representation is a map on which the campaigns and forays of science are planned, carried out in imagination, and then put to the test, as predictions of what will happen when the map is used as a guide to practice and experiment. The purposes of such a map are therefore practical: it is a guide to action, an instrument for the rational direction of practice. But, as with all maps, the intentions and motives of its formulation may be largely aesthetic, the fit and match of parts and the coherence and elegance of the whole becoming ends to be achieved for their own sake, or for the sake of that distinctive intellectual and aesthetic pleasure which well-ordering affords us. In this chapter we will be concerned with the ways in which such mappings of the world of our experience are made, with the nature of representation in a language, with models and formal systems in general and how they operate to give us a rational reconstruction of the structure of our empirical knowledge.

REPRESENTATION, ABSTRACTION, AND ORDER

In a recent article the scientist S. S. Stevens writes, "Science, that curious hurly-burly of intellectual probing, makes progress to the extent that its models succeed in mapping the universe on paper."[1] Such mapping requires some tokens or marks, some set of inscriptions which will be taken to represent features of the world itself. This set of inscriptions we may take as a code or language, which we learn to read and understand through some system of coordinating it to what it stands for. The most familiar of such mappings is that most general all-purpose map, our ordinary spoken and written language. By means of language we represent the world on paper and in our spoken discourse. Whatever other functions our language serves, e.g., in its expressive or evocative uses—it serves as our means of describing the world, of making assertions about matters of fact, in the public and objective form of inscription and utterance. There are of course other ways of representing what we know or believe to be the facts, as by pictures or diagrams or by the various artificial symbolic systems man has developed as artifacts for representation. These range all the way from the ritual and social symbols of rank or kinship-relation—totems, ritual scarification, special dress, or modes of speech—to the highly systematic and abstract notations used in the sciences, such as the schematic notation of molecular structure and chemical interaction used in chemistry or the "languages" of mathematics and logic. All such "languages"—we shall call all such modes of representation languages in this generic sense—have certain common features. We shall examine three such features here: *reference, abstraction,* and *structure.*

[1] S. S. Stevens, "Quantifying the Sensory Experience," in *Mind, Matter and Method: Essays in Philosophy of Science in Honor of Herbert Feigl,* Paul Feyerabend and Grover Maxwell, eds. (Minneapolis: University of Minnesota Press, 1966), p. 218.

Reference

Insofar as a language has a representative function, its marks or tokens are taken to stand for things outside the language. That is to say, the language has somehow to refer beyond itself. The scheme of reference may ultimately depend on the ostensive definitions of the basic terms of the language, assigned by relatively direct pointing and uttering. We saw in the last chapter how such ostension already raises problems of relative clarity or opacity of reference; but such a way of connecting words or linguistic tokens to things seems necessary as the minimal condition for reference. It may be that the scheme of reference is not simply the primitive operation of pointing and labeling but is so systematically implicated in the whole framework of a language that "simple" reference is already a framework-dependent and complex operation. But without some way of delivering itself from the bounds of sheer "internal" relations to other parts of the language, no part of a language will be able to denote anything outside the language.

The condition for reference then is that some mark or token in a language be assigned to something beyond the language; thus a relation must be established between two things (that is, a "binary" relation between x and y) such that x refers to y. But if a language is constituted of tokens which are taken to be its terms or expressions, then it is the relation of *being taken to be an expression in some language L* (by some user of the language) which confers linguistic character on an otherwise nondescript set of physical marks on paper or sounds. In one classical scheme of language, the relation between entities in a language and entities outside the language to which they refer is taken to be a *ternary* relation rather than a *binary* one (that is, a relation among three things rather than between two), which may be expressed as: S takes x to be a linguistic term or expression which refers to y (or more simply $R(S, x, y)$, where S takes x to refer to y, and the use of something as a means of referring bestows linguistic character on it, with S as some speaker or user of the language and R as the ternary relation of reference).

The following elements, then, are found in such a scheme: there are, of course, the tokens and the things outside the language with which they are coordinated; but there is also the interpretation or the scheme of coordination or the mapping which assigns tokens to things. Thus, the physical token or mark *bird* is in one sense nothing more than the inscription of a certain shape on paper. Its reference to the real bird flying in the sky is made through an interpreter who takes this mark as a sign for that thing. (One might also argue that to take the inscription as a "physical mark on paper" entails some framework of interpreting entities as "physical objects," so that what is at issue are alternative frameworks of interpretation, physical and linguistic). The view that marks or tokens have no essential or intrinsic relation to what it is they are taken to be signs of asserts that such assignment or designation is conventional; that is, it is the convention of use for a certain purpose which interprets physical marks as signs, and this is a matter of choice or convenience. On the other hand, if one extends the metaphor of *language* and talks of the *language of nature,* then certain physical features or properties in nature may be taken as *natural signs* of others, or as nonconventional representations. For example, we say "clouds are a sign of rain," or, "fever is a sign of illness," taking these natural signs as symptoms, or as properties which we learn are naturally associated with certain others. Such symptoms we do not take to be conventional, or matters of choice. In an extension of this sense of *natural,* we may also take the view that names of things in "natural languages," like English or French, evolved in the course of development of languages, are not simply conventions, in the sense of arbitrary assignments, but have become "naturally associated" with their objects. Such a view, however, may easily lead to confusion between such "natural associations" as that between rain and clouds, and the artifacts which man has created and evolved for his use, as means of reference.

If we take the ternary relation of reference as holding among a sign, its reference and the interpretation which makes the assignment, we may take this interpretation as the meaning of the sign. If one proceeded in this way, the reference of a sign would be distinct from its meaning. It might appear that if a sign had no reference it could hardly be assigned a meaning, for then, how could one know what it was a sign *of,* if it were not a sign of *something*. However, this formulation leads to difficulties. In a language, there are many signs—say, terms or expressions—for which there is nothing which exists to which the sign may be said to refer. Yet such terms or expressions may be perfectly meaningful because we *understand* what they mean. For example, such names as the "Mock Turtle" (from *Alice in Wonderland*), or such descriptions as the "forty-seventh president of the United States," or the "present king of Utopia" fail to refer to anything which exists now or existed in the past. We may say that *Mock Turtle* "refers" to a fictional character in a book, and then be involved in the problems of fictional existence, or say that if there is a forty-seventh president of the United States in the future, then the description *will* refer to him (or that it already does, tenselessly). But barring such exotic senses of "exists" as fictional existence or future existence, we may say that there are no entities outside the language to which such expressions refer (or, in the case of future existence, no way to know whether or not they do). Yet the meaning of these expressions is clear; we all *understand* what the expressions mean, apart from the question of whether or not they refer. We therefore distinguish between meaning and reference. The traditional distinction is made in terms of *connotation* and *denotation,* connotation being what we understand by a term—some mental conception or intralinguistic "sense" or "meaning" that the term has, which has also been called its *intension*—and denotation being what the term refers to outside the language—some extralinguistic entity, which has been called the *extension* of the term.

One way of saving reference, even for those expressions of a language which are about things that do not exist, is to regard all such expressions as having the *same* extension, although they may have different intensions. Thus, the "Mock Turtle" and the "present king of Utopia" are said to refer to the empty set or the null set, i.e., to the set or the class that has no members. In this sense, these expressions have identically the same reference as, for example, the "man who is 30 feet tall" and the "two-digit number larger than 99." It is quite clear that we can conceive of a man 30 feet tall, and that we understand the expression; it is another question whether we can conceive of a two-digit number greater than 99. This would lead us into an analytic falsehood or contradiction, for by the definition of 99, in the ordinary number system, it is the largest two-digit number. In any case, by such a method one may clearly distinguish meaning from reference.

However, from another viewpoint which eschews introducing such "mental" entities as concepts of things or meanings as intensions, it might be argued that the meaning of a term is the way it is used, or the behavior which it elicits, reducing meaning to "verbal behavior" and defining it by "reducing" the intensional contexts to appropriate verbal responses to linguistic stimuli, thus making the account of meaning a psychological or behavioral one. Two terms will then be said to have the "same" meaning only to the extent that they call forth the "same" responses or exhibit in this way that they are in fact *taken* to mean the same thing, and may be substituted for each other as synonyms. There may be some cases in which two terms are taken to have different meanings but in fact refer to the same thing. The common example, introduced by Frege, concerns the terms *evening star* and *morning star*. These may, at one time, have been taken not only to mean different things—as they still do—but to refer to different objects, that is, to two different "stars," before it was known that both names refer to the same body, the planet Venus, in different contexts. Reference then seems to have to do with the truth and falsity of statements concerning matters of fact; for although *morning star* does not mean the same as *evening star,* it is false that *morning star* does not refer to, or denote, the same body as *evening star*.

Reference then concerns the extension or denotation of the signs in a language, and thus is the crucial aspect of representation. A representation of the facts fails when the facts are not as represented. But however the distinction may be drawn between reference and meaning, it also seems clear that if the meaning of expressions in a language were not clear, we would have no way to know what in fact would fulfill the conditions of reference, or of failure to refer. For example, unless we understood the meaning of the term *snow,* we could not know under what conditions the statement, "It is snowing now," would be true or false. However, simply knowing the meaning of the term would tell us nothing about the truth or falsity of the statement on a given occasion. As we have seen, it is true only of analytic statements that their truth or falsity can be determined by inspection of their meanings alone (see p. 105). What we require in a representation of the facts are therefore synthetic statements, those which depend for their truth or falsity on their reference outside the language to matters of fact.

Abstraction

Representation in a language may require no more than the assignment of labels to things, or tagging. Thus the purpose of representation, in a restricted context, may be no more than to give each thing a unique label, as a means of identifying it as that thing and no other. The condition for such unique representation of individual things is, simply, that no one label be assigned to more than one thing, i.e., that no two things have the same label and no two labels be assigned to one thing; and to avoid confusion we may require that no label remain unassigned. Such a unique one-to-one mapping of things and their labels is in effect an assignment of proper names to everything. Such a mapping would fail in its purpose of unique identification if two things had the same proper name, since it would be ambiguous which of the two was being identified. Thus, for example, when two people have the same proper names, we then specify certain other features (e.g., birthday, parents' names, address, photograph) to distinguish individuals from each other. In this sense of identification, a proper name "represents" an individual, just as a license plate "represents" the car to which it is assigned.

But even license plates and proper names do more than simply label unique individuals, for they are related to systems of *classification* in which the names themselves are linked with classes of things to which they belong. A license plate not only uniquely identifies a car, but identifies it also as a member of a class of cars, namely, those registered in a certain state. Similarly, a given name is conjoined with a family name, to mark the individual as a member of a given family. Such a classification is made in terms of certain properties that all members of a given class share in common. The family name connotes that all members of the family have a common ancestry, and the state license plate, that all the cars bearing it have been registered in that state.

In the representation of facts in science, such identification and classification represent the basic requirements of description. We want, on the one hand, to be able to refer to specific and unique instances of this or that; but beyond this we want to classify such instances as being of a certain kind, sharing properties with others of that kind. The purpose of scientific inquiry is never simply to identify unique instances but to discover relations or patterns among the facts, to order them or to link them to each other in some intelligible way. Thus, our mode of representation has to be able to distinguish between what is alike and what is different in some set of observations. But likeness and difference, as the basic distinctions upon which observation rests, involve likeness or difference *in some respect,* or *in a certain property,* as when we say *x* is more like *y* than *w* is like *z,* which singles out the respect in the comparison. Therefore, the representation of likeness and difference is always *abstractive;* that is to say, in considering likeness or difference, we choose or abstract some property or properties in making these distinctions, and we ignore the rest. If we did not abstract in this way, the initial step of identification and classificaton would be impossible. For everything is like everything else in an infinite number of respects and different from everything else in an infinite number of respects. Representation therefore embodies that same principle of selective confrontation which we have characterized in observation, and which has its roots in the very selectivity of our perceptual apparatus. Thus, representing the facts always connotes representing them abstractively, severely delimiting the respects we will take to be relevant or the properties which will hold our attention, and ignoring all the others. Such representation involves, therefore, a choice of *parameters,* a severe abstraction of those and only those properties of things which we shall choose to observe or measure. Thus, for example, in the representation of motion in physics, consideration is restricted to motion as change of place, and the parameters for the description of such motion are distance and time. Similarly, in classifying physical characteristics in some survey, we may use such parameters as a person's height, weight, age and blood type, and entirely ignore his political opinions, his hair color, or his name, identifying him simply by some anonymous label or number.

The question arises: If abstraction so severely delimits the scope of our attention as to ignore most of the properties which things have, how can we know that we are not thereby eliminating parameters that are crucial or decisive to our inquiry? If scientific description of the facts is focused on only certain parameters determined by the needs and interests of our research, may it not be that our needs and interests are parochial ones in the universe, and that our narrow-minded pursuit gives us only that slice of the facts which enters into such a pragmatic perspective? The answer is that we cannot know that we are not so severely circumscribed, or that ours is anything more than a worm's eye view; and, further, that science operates within these limits. But this situation is less desperate than it appears in such a drastic formulation. If we take science to be an instrument for successful prediction and for rational control of the environment, then this purpose is served in coping with the limited set of facts or properties which do catch our interest or which are singled out by the practical delimitation imposed by this or that problem. On the other hand, if we take science to be at the same time an inquiry into truth, an attempt to get at the real nature of things beyond the limitations of practical interest and instrumental perspectives, then abstraction serves this purpose as well. For it makes explicit precisely what the parameters are which we do choose to consider, and permits or even suggests to our inquiry that we consciously introduce others to test the limits of purported relevance. We thus enlarge the scope of our inquiry precisely by becoming consciously aware of its limits, and by refusing consent to the dogmatism which takes part for whole. The classical philosophic view which says "knowledge is limitation" (or in Spinoza's phrase, "Every determination is a negation") thus expresses this twofold function of abstraction: delimiting the scope of inquiry and sharpening its focus, so that it may be pursued thoroughly and in depth; and articulating for us the critical Socratic maxim which urges us to know that we do not know, to be consciously aware of our ignorance.

Structure

Every language or mapping has its own structure, its own systematic relationship among its parts or elements, which we may generically call its grammar or syntax. The structure of English, for example, concerns the syntactic form of its sentences, the formal relations of noun phrase and verb phrase which underly all its well-formed expressions. We may abstractly represent this structure, taking a language itself as a subject of inquiry and representation and thus mapping a language by means of a more abstract one. The distinction is made between a language taken as an object of representation and the language in which one represents it, or talks about it, as between an *object language* and a *metalanguage*. Thus, even when I talk about the English language in English, the reference of my "talking about English" concerns the linguistic entities and the relations among them in the English language. For example, if I use the language in its ordinary referential way, then the term *dog* is taken to refer to a four-legged animal of the canine species, that is, to a dog. However, if I take the term *dog* itself as the object, I may then refer to it as, for example, a three-letter word in English, or a noun, and denote it by a name. (The usual convention for names of terms in a language is to give the term, or expression, in double quotes as "dog," and the name of this term or expression in single quotes, as 'dog.' Thus, 'dog' is the name, in the metalanguage, of the term "dog" in the object language.) Clearly, what I denote by 'dog' does not have four legs, and what I denote by "dog" does not have three letters. In this way, I may represent linguistic entities and the structure of a language itself by means of a metalanguage. As in all representations, mapping a language requires symbols (in the metalanguage) which will be taken to refer to things outside the metalanguage and in the object language. Abstraction operates here as well, as when certain properties of sentences are chosen for mapping and others ignored, and when sentences are classified in terms of the properties which they share in common. Again, there are infinitely many properties which sentences share, but only certain of these are relevant to the given inquiry. Among these, we may characterize two properties of sentences in a language: their syntactic structure or grammatical form and their semantic aspect or meaning (and on some accounts, their reference as well). Syntax will therefore have to do with the well-formedness of sentences in terms of what is and what is not grammatical, or according to the formation rules for sentences of that language. Semantics will ordinarily have to do with the "dictionary meaning" of terms and expressions in the narrower context of lexicography, or with a broader concern with questions of synonymy and of significant sequences or strings of sounds or inscriptions, thus with sameness of meaning and with meaningfulness within a language. We may distinguish between syntactic and semantic aspects of sentences in the following examples:

1. The boy kissed the girl tenderly.
2. The girl slapped the boy furiously.

1′. The girl was tenderly kissed by the boy.
2′. The boy was furiously slapped by the girl.

Sentences (1) and (2) are clearly different in meaning, or semantically dissimilar; yet they are alike in grammatical form or syntactic structure, as we may see by "parsing" the sentences, that is, by representing them abstractly in terms of their syntactic properties.

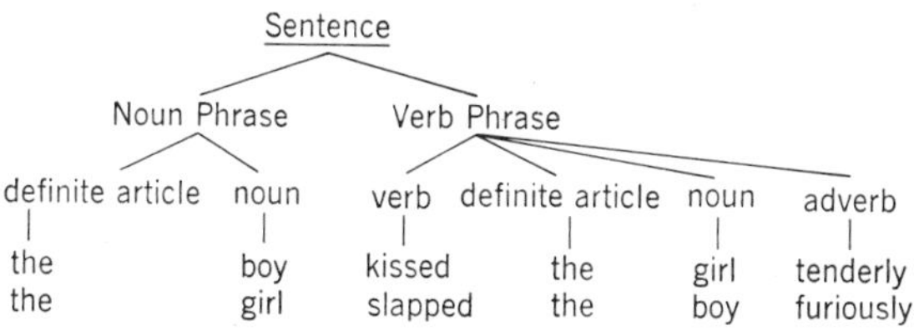

Fig. 1

Sentences (1′) and (2′) are also different in meaning and alike in structure. But (1) and (1′) are alike in meaning, as are (2) and (2′), though these pairs are superficially dissimilar in structure. We may see, however, that, "The boy kissed the girl tenderly," is simple to map onto the variant, "The girl was tenderly kissed by the boy," by means of a rule, so that the two structures (1) and (1′) may be seen to be alike, in terms of some "kernel" sentence of which they are mappings. The rule which would transform (1) into (1′) is therefore a *transformation rule,* and in this case it would be the rule for the active-passive transformation, which we may represent simply by the abstract model: "*a X*'s *b*" → "*b* is *X*'d by *a*" (with suitable refinements for past tense, and for position of the adverb). Such a syntactic representation abstracts from the meaning of the various sentences and concerns only the formal structure in terms of such "parts" or syntactic functions as *noun, verb,* and so on. Even in the case of a nonsense sentence like, "The crabbage slimped the trackle fluviously," we may recognize the same structure as in (1) and (2) and effect the transformation to the structure of (1′) and (2′)—"The trackle was fluviously slimped by the crabbage." Things are never as simple as they are made out to be in examples, of course, and the whole matter of mapping the structure of sentences in a natural language is fraught with difficulties. But the point is that such an abstract representation of the structure of a language may be given no less than an abstract representation of the facts and their relations in the domain of any science.

The set of rules for the formation and the transformation of sentences in any language, where "sentence" will be used generically for any well-formed and complete expression in that language, we will call the syntactical rules. The rules for the assignment of terms to their referents, or to what it is they designate, we will call semantical rules. If such syntactical and semantical rules can be made explicit, we may be said to have a *theory* of the language, by means of which we can then sort out grammatical from nongrammatical, and meaningful from nonmeaningful sentences.

If we take this as a general approach to languages of any sort, and not only to natural languages, this becomes an inquiry into the abstract structure of such languages, and an attempt to give an abstract representation of their form. We often start such an inquiry with instances of what we take to be well-formed terms or expressions, and then try to devise the rule of classification which will sort these and only these well-formed terms or expressions from those which are not well-formed. Thus, we recognize that the term *happy* is well-formed, but that *c6¢g″+yt8* is not. (The minimal rule is apparent: only those tokens which are letters of the alphabet may be used to form words in English.) Similarly, we recognize that the expression, "Quickly in saw the doggedly green up," is not well formed grammatically. In the language of mathematics, we recognize that "7 + 5 = 12" is a well-formed expression but that "= 7 5 +" is not. Similarly, we recognize that, in the ordinary arithmetic, "9 − 6 = 3" is "grammatical," in the sense of being in accordance with the rules of subtraction but that "3 − 9 = 6" is not. Here one may argue that mathematics is conventional, and that one may devise the rules in any way one likes, as long as one is consistent about it and does not devise rules which lead to contradictions. In terms of a purely formal system of marks or inscriptions, one may indeed play such a game—or invent it—as an exercise in formal construction. But the constraints on arithmetic are that we ordinarily take it to be a system dealing with number properties, i.e., an *interpreted* formal system, in which there is a scheme of interpretation or assignment of the reference of the signs to properties or operations outside the language. Thus, in the purely syntactic system, we may take "3" or "6," or for that matter "*" or "#" simply as shapes to be manipulated according to rule but without an interpretation. In this way we may construct an artificial language as an uninterpreted formal system, using certain inscriptions and sequences of them in accordance with invented formation and transformation rules. But if I assign a meaning to the shape 3, and take it as a conventional name for the number three (or, in terms of our previous distinction, take '3' as the name for "3," and "3" in turn as referring to some physical or magnitude property of sets of things in the world), then such an interpretation fixes the formal system as a map of some domain. The fit of the map to what it maps may then be judged for its adequacy in preserving invariant the relations which obtain among the facts.

Given some empirical domain in science, we represent it by means of a language. This is what we started with. We may now see that the features of reference and abstraction make such representation possible; but what we do, ultimately, is to map structures on structures: the structure of the language on the structure of the facts. What the abstractive representation preserves, then, is the form of the relation among facts. The relations among the appropriately chosen elements or terms in the map have the same formal properties as those among appropriately chosen elements in the domain of reference of the map.[2] We say then that the map and what it maps are *isomorphic,* or have the same form. The map is abstract, however; as we have seen, it singles out only certain properties as relevant, only certain parameters as significant for the inquiry. In this sense, its isomorphism is always delimited. It is not a duplicate of its domain, in the sense of preserving all the features in the represented domain, for then the representation would be a duplicate of what it represents. The map would in effect *be* the terrain if it were identical in all its features; or at least would be the twin of its terrain so that we could not tell one from the other. But with respect to a delimited set of properties, or of relations among the facts, the map may give a one-to-one or point-for-point representation, and may therefore be isomorphic in this respect, just as the parsing diagram of the sentences in the earlier example provides a point-for-point mapping of the

[2] "Appropriately chosen" is intentionally vague here, for a simpleminded view of mapping may require, for example, that for each "word" taken to be an element of a sentence, there should be something in the mapped domain which it "pictures." Thus, for the words "the," or "a" (as definite or indefinite articles), there would have to be *the*'s or *a*'s in the world, in a point-for-point mapping. See the bibliography for relevant discussions on the so-called picture theory of language.

features of syntactic structure of the sentences given, and of as many other sentences as can be devised which share these syntactic features, however different such sentences are in other respects. It remains to give an account of how such isomorphism is revealed, in terms of the invariance of the formal properties of the relations in the map and in the domain which it maps.

MAPPING THE DATA: INVARIANCE AND RELATIONS OF ORDER

The object of research is to discover laws, or invariant relations which hold between the facts of observation and measurement. The ordering of the facts is the means whereby the scientist is able to realize such relations in an explicit way, and to test law-like hypotheses which assert that some relation holds universally. But if, as we have said, there is an infinity of relations among things, or an infinite number of properties which things share with each other, we may say that some relation or other, or a plethora of them, is revealed in any set of data. For example, the relation among the data of some inquiry may be that they were all gathered by Scientist *X* between 2 A.M. and 4 A.M. on the morning of September 9, 1956. Or the order among the data may be taken to be the sequence in which they were reported in a laboratory notebook. Among the possible parameters of observation and measurement, an inquiry will fasten on only a few, and the data derived from observation of such parameters will be mapped in only one or a few of the possible ways of mapping the data.

The problem of selectivity, of choice of parameters and of mappings, intrudes upon the ostensibly simple matter of finding out what the facts are, but even more on the task of ordering them in some way. For if the business of science is, in great part, the discovery of laws of universal scope, then a mapping of the finite set of observed instances needs to be more than a listing of these data, as in a grocery or laundry list. What we want the mapping to do is to exhibit relations in such a form that invariance or law-likeness will be revealed. Thus, what we require in our representation of the facts is the abstract or formal structure or ordering in terms of which such invariance may be stated, at least among the observed instances. For some ordered pairs of numbers, such as (1, 1), (2, 4), (3, 9), (4, 16), which represent the data of measurement on two parameters, we want to be able to give the invariant form of this relation, or give the second number in each pair as a function of the first. (In this instance, for example, we want for each pair (x, y) to give y as a function of x, i.e., as $y = x^2$). If, on such a mapping, we hypothesize that this relation between the observed parameters is invariant, then we predict that this same invariance will hold in instances to be observed in the future, and we test the adequacy of our formulation against such future instances. But now, the map is not simply a representational device but a predictive one as well. It constructs a model of the data within which inference may be carried out and predictions made, so that the map or model serves, in effect, as an inference machine. The choice of ways to map the data is guided by this purpose. The means of representing the data, the language of the map, should therefore have a structure within which such inferences may be made.

In the preceding example, the inference system is that of arithmetic, which permits us to compute or calculate one value of the pair, given the other. On the standard graphs used to represent data, inference is by extrapolation or interpolation of a finite set of data, transforming a discrete set of "points" on the graphs into a curve which maps an infinity of points. The languages used to map the data may therefore be characterized as calculating devices, or *calculi,* whose internal structure is such that transformations or "moves" from one statement to another may be made in accordance with a rule, as the move is made from the premises ($y = x^2$ and $x = 5$) to the conclusion ($y = 25$). Such rules of calculation, as this one or the rule for active-passive transformation of sentences in English, are often implicit, or are learned as practical procedures or as algorithms. However, a theory of the language and of the inferences or calculations that may be made in it will explicate such rules, or construct an abstract model which maps these rules in such a way that on interpretation they yield the same "outputs" for "inputs," the same transformations that obtain in the modeled domain.

In this context we want a theory of relations which will give an abstract and highly general account of them, and of the inferences which may be made in such a language of relations. We also want an account of invariance, that is, a characterization of how the formal properties of a relation remain invariant under transformations. An example from projective geometry may make this clear. If we take a given shape—say the capital letter *A*—then we may make any number of projective transformations of this shape in which the relation among all of its parts remain invariant, if we specify the relation as a certain order among the points on the lines which make up the shape, apart from considerations such as length or curvature.[3] That is to say, through the transformations any point will remain in the same relations of order to the other points in which it stood in the original shape. A simple and familiar transformation is the mirror image of *A*; another is the projection of *A* through a lens which inverts it to *∀*. Similarly, a projection of *A* which increases its size retains the invariance or constancy of the relations among its parts, as does also a slanting of *A* as in italics, or even a rubbery version of *A*, which turns straight lines into curves or squiggles,

[3] This is a nonmetric or topological transformation, and is presented simply intuitively here. To specify the "relations of order" which remain invariant under such a transformation can be a very technical task.

as in *A* or in *A*. Our perceptual recognition of such invariance through transformations has to do with the classic perceptual constancies of shape, size, distance, etc. For example, we recognize the shape of the object represented in Fig. 2*a* to be the same as the shape of the object represented in Fig. 2*b* though the retinal images are different, and thus take rectangular tables to be rectangular even when we are not suspended directly above them. Perspective transformations thus give us rules for invariance through transformation. However, there are linguistic invariances of the same sort

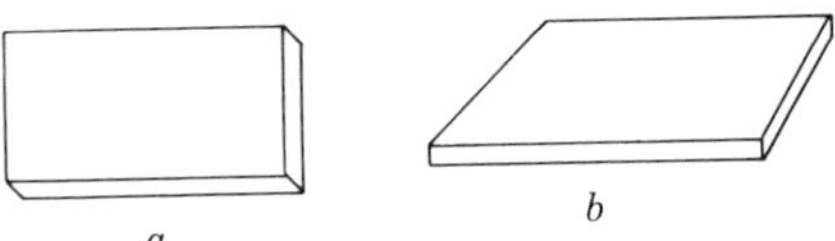

Fig. 2

which retain the formal properties of relations invariant through transformations. For example, the "mirror image" or right-left transposition of the terms of a mathematical equality preserves the invariant relations between the terms of the equality (e.g., "$7 + 5 = 12$" is preserved in "$12 = 7 + 5$"). If we abstract from the two instances of relation (1) "If John is taller than Phil and Phil is taller than Sam, then John is taller than Sam," and (2) "If Sybil is the sister of Susan and Susan is the sister of Serena, then Sibyl is the sister of Serena," then we see that the relations *taller than* and *sister of* have the same formal structure which remains invariant in both instances. If we mapped this formal structure abstractly, using variables (x, y, z) for the terms and R for the relation, the structure would be (3) "If xRy and yRz, then xRz."

The notion of invariance may be seen to have an extraordinarily wide application when we consider the range of transformations in which invariance is preserved in a variety of contexts. A photograph, for example, transforms a light input into a chemical reaction in an emulsion, which is transformed by processing (developing the negative, printing the picture, enlarging, etc.) into the finished picture. Through these transformations, certain properties of the photographed object—shape, dark and light, color—are mapped abstractively so that the picture preserves certain of the relations among these properties invariantly. Certain other properties of the object are of course lost in the transformation, such as its three dimensionality, its weight, and so on, since these are not transmitted by reflected light. Similarly, the recent photographs of the surface of Venus converted reflected light from the planet into a code of radio signals, which mapped such properties as relative positions of the segments of the photograph and varying intensities of the light at each mapped segment. The signals thus preserve certain relations invariantly through the transformation: *camera-*

lens image to signal, and the signal received is then "decoded" by the inverse of this same transformation to reproduce the camera-lens image in a photograph. The mapping into signals involved a transformation of the light-input into sets of numbers, the numbers in turn representing a code for the various parameters of position and intensity of light.

In general, every mapping is a transformation whose object is to preserve certain relations invariant. Every process of encoding and decoding is a transformation of this sort, in effect "scrambling" an input or a message by means of some transformation and "unscrambling" it by the inverse of that transformation. The transformation effects a mapping of some set of relevant properties of its object, or of relations among its parts. Thus, a translation from one language to another is such a transformation, and the "good" translation is the one which retains certain relevant properties of the original invariant through this transformation.[4] When we translate operations of measurement into numbers or one numerical language into another —e.g., translating our ordinary decimal or ten-digit numeral system into a binary code using only 1, 0 and position—we again preserve the number relations invariant through the transformations. The study of the order or the relational structure of some domain by means of a representation of it is thus closely related to the matter of preserving invariances through transformation.[5]

[4] One such relevant property, in translating natural languages, is obviously the *sense* of the original (though defining what we mean by the "sense" is rather difficult; we may mean the "spirit," or even the "style," or more simply, some recognizably similar meaning). The sorrows of mechanical translation derive often from failure to preserve invariance through transformation (or translation), as in the following example. The English sentence, "The spirit is willing but the flesh is weak" was translated by computer into Russian, by means of an English-Russian translation program, or a "dictionary" which we may call T_{er} ("Translation: English to Russian"). To check on invariance, the Russian sentence thus derived was translated back into English by the "dictionary" T_{re}, which should have yielded the original English sentence or something close to it. The retranslation of the original came back as "The whiskey is good but the meat is rotten." Artificial languages are constructed to avoid such ambiguities and mistranslations by strictly delimiting or disambiguating the meanings of terms, or deliberately impoverishing the language and fitting it to special purposes. The representation of natural languages by means of artificial languages, i.e., by abstract representations of their structure and meaning, is difficult if one wants to retain the richness, intricacy, and ambiguities of natural languages, but such mappings have proceeded quite far in sophistication and subtlety in recent years.

[5] A common model for such mapping, derived originally from engineering and from information theory and current in the computer sciences, is the so-called "input-output" model or "black-box" model. The three elements of such a model are (1) an *input,* (2) some *transformation,* and (3) some *output.* In experimental research the data are "input data" and "output data"; e.g., in psychology, the observations or measured data of stimulus and response, or in physics, initial measured values and terminal values for some set of parameters (e.g., a given input energy and a given work output in some mechanism). The so-called black box is the actual mechanism or organism which effects the transformation, whose "internal" operations may be

The question then becomes: What types of ordering or relations are typical of the mappings of data which scientists make? How do these reveal invariant relations, and how are these invariances preserved through the transformations of mapping? How do such mappings lend themselves to the making of inferences? To consider this further, we will examine some of the typical relations of order in science, and how these may be abstractly or formally represented.

We will briefly characterize such relations of order here, and treat them at length in the chapter on measurement. In general, we may order things by classifying them, by assigning them to the same class as all other things sharing a certain property or set of properties; and as we have seen, we may order classes with respect to each other. A typical and standard form of relating things of a certain kind to each other is to rank-order them in terms of some property which they share in common, as we order minerals with respect to hardness or estimate such sensory qualities as loudness or brightness or sweetness with respect to intensity. We measure, in terms of unit intervals or multiples of some unit interval, such magnitudes as length or time or quantity. In our equations we order in terms of equal ratios or of proportional equalities, pairing a change in magnitude of this with a change in magnitude of that. Thus in our physical laws we relate changes in distance to changes in time, increases or decreases of volume to increases or decreases of pressure and temperature. We say, for example in the Boyle-Marriotte law for gases, that pressure and volume are "inversely proportional," and that both "vary directly" with temperature. Galileo's law of freely falling bodies gives the distance of fall as a "function" of the time, varying with the square of the time. Or in psychophysics, we say the Weber-Fechner law gives the relation of stimulus energy to sensation as a "logarithmic function," whereas in Stevens' law the subjective magnitude estimation is given as a "power function" of the stimulus-energy. We represent such relations by means of tables, charts, graphs, equations, all of which map the relations among the data on paper in some abstract representation.

---

unknown but whose description may be given by a mathematical function which maps inputs onto outputs, as numerical values corresponding to the measured values. Norbert Wiener calls such a functional mapping an "operative image," as against a "pictorial image," which is a "picture" or description of the actual mechanism "inside" the black box. He sees this operative image as the more fundamental description of the two. (A wry version, which pertains to the physiological mechanisms or brain mechanisms that transform inputs into outputs, speaks of a "pink box," no less opaque than the black box.) Such a functional description of the relation between input data and output data is therefore a mathematical model of the data, which is isomorphic with the measured values of the parameters and is an abstract mathematical representation of the observed relations among the facts. Such a model is "phenomenological" (or "phenomenalistic") in the sense that it simply accounts for the observed data, without introducing theoretical entities ("inside" the black box) to explain the observed relations.

The means of representation grow apace, and the sophistication of the logical and mathematical models increases, as more and more powerful instruments of analysis and more and more sensitive ways of eliciting the order among the data are developed. But just as we abstracted the formal properties of relation in the linguistic example, we may abstract certain formal properties of order which are highly general and may be interpreted in the widest variety of contexts.

Relations

We may generalize the notion of relation, taking a relation as holding between two things or among three or more things, whatever they are. Thus, taking as examples of relations between two things ("binary" or "dyadic" relations) such instances as *father of, larger than,* or *included in,* we may represent the terms which stand to each other in such relations as variables (x, y, z) or as constants (a, b, c), and the relations themselves by capital letters, e.g., F for *father of*, L for *larger than,* and so on. Relations among three things ("ternary" or "triadic" relations) or among n things ("n-ary" or "n-adic" relations) may be represented in the same way. When a relation holds between x and y, we say that "x bears the relation R to y," which we may represent as xRy. Alternatively, we may take the relation as a predicate which holds of an *ordered* couple $\langle x, y\rangle$ or an ordered triple $\langle x, y, z\rangle$ or an ordered n-tuple, where $\langle x, y\rangle \neq \langle y, x\rangle$ and $\langle x, y, z\rangle \neq \langle y, z, x\rangle \neq \langle z, x, y\rangle \neq \langle x, z, y\rangle \neq \langle y, x, z\rangle \neq \langle z, y, x\rangle$ etc. Relations may be defined in terms of classes or sets (in certain systems of logic, as shown by Wiener and by Kuratowski) if we take the binary relation as the class or set of ordered couples $\{\{x\}, \{x, y\}\}$. For example, *father of* may be defined as the class of ordered couples $\{\{x\}, \{x, y\}\}$ such that x is the father of y. By extension, a ternary relation is the class of ordered triples and an n-ary relation is the class of ordered n-tuples. The importance of the ordering is that a relation which x bears to y may or may not be borne by y to x. For example, *father of* is not borne both ways, whereas *next to* is. The notation "$\langle x, y\rangle$" is used for *ordered couple,* where the ordering is by position (first, second). The alternative (introduced by Kuratowski) "$\{\{x\}, \{x, y\}\}$" obviously is independent of position, because the sets $\{x\}$ and $\{x, y\}$ are ordered by differences in membership.

The generality of this notion of relation is that it may be seen to apply as a formal representation to all the cases of ordering or relations among the facts which we sketched in the previous section. Thus for ordering in terms of more or less or of equality, we may use this same notation (as we ordinarily do in mathematics, where, for example, "x is greater than y," "x is smaller than y," or "x equals y" are represented, respectively, as "$x > y$," "$x < y$," "$x = y$," and where the relation "x is greater than or equal to y" is represented as "$x \geqslant y$."

If we examine instances of such relation, we see that there are characteristic types of such ordered relations which we may then define. For example, the relation *father of,* if it holds from one individual to another, does not hold from that other to the first. Symbolically, "if xFy, then not-yFx." Such a relation we say is *asymmetrical.* On the other hand, a relation like *equals,* if it holds from one individual to another, also holds from that other to the first, or "if $x = y$, then $y = x$."[6] Such a relation is *symmetrical.* There is yet another case, for example, if we were to say that John is either taller or the same height as Phil. Here the relation is "either taller or the same height"; it is neither symmetrical nor asymmetrical and *is called antisymmetrical.* Its (somewhat peculiar) definition is that a relation R is antisymmetrical whenever "if xRy and yRx, then $x = y$" holds of it. The arithmetic relation $\leq$ ("is smaller than or equal to") is antisymmetrical. Further, if we take a relation like "greater than," we may see that "if xGy and yGz, then xGz." Such a relation is called *transitive.* All the relations of degree which are analogous to this one, e.g., *taller than, heavier than, older than,* are likewise transitive. So too, all relations of equality, e.g., =, *is the same age as, has the same name as,* are likewise transitive, as are certain relations in which the equality is implicit such as *sibling of* (*has the same parents as*), and so on. An intransitive relation is one which does not fulfill this condition. Thus *father of* is intransitive, because if x is the father of y, and y is the father of z, x is not the father of z. *Immediately precedes* is another such intransitive relation, as is *immediately succeeds.* Thus a relation is intransitive if whenever xRy and yRz, then not xRz. Our definitions are thus

1. Symmetry: If xRy then yRx.
2. Asymmetry: If xRy then not-yRx.
3. Antisymmetry: If xRy and yRx, then $x = y$.
4. Transitivity: If xRy and yRz then xRz.
5. Intransitivity: If xRy and yRz then not xRz.

The additional relations of *reflexivity, irreflexivity, connectedness,* and *strong connectedness* will be introduced in the next chapter, as needed. The additional cases bearing on symmetry [where neither (1), (2), or (3) hold] and on transitivity (nontransitivity) may be ignored for our purposes here.

A standard way of representing these relations, using the notation of symbolic logic, is the following: the individual variables x, y, z are said to be members of the set A (or belong to the set A), which is represented by the symbol for set (or class) membership "ϵ" ("epsilon"). The symbol,

[6] "Is identical with," for which the symbol "=" is also used, is a special case of *equals,* but its conditions are stronger. We may say, for example, that A and B are equally endowed with ten fingers, though we do not mean that they both have identically the same ten fingers. We may say, of course, that they have identically the same *number* of fingers.

"$\rightarrow$" represents the conditional or material implication, which we will render as "If-then," so that "$x \rightarrow y$" reads "If x, then y." Biconditional implication or equivalence, in the sense "if and only if," is given by "$\leftrightarrow$." The connective "and" is given by " $\cdot$ " and "either-or" in the inclusive sense of "and/or" is given by "V." To signify universal quantification, that is, where what follows the quantifier holds for any instance of it, the term "(x)" (read "for any x"), is prefixed to the expression over which it operates, so that, for example, "$(x)(y)(xRy)$" reads "For any x, for any y, xRy." A full discussion of these logical connectives, their truth-table definitions, and quantification can be found in most introductory logic texts, and will be foregone here. (See the brief account of logical notation in Appendix C.) Our relations may then be represented in one standard way as

1. Symmetry: A relation is symmetrical in the set A if and only if $$(x)(y)(x \in A \cdot y \in A \cdot xRy \rightarrow yRx)$$
2. Asymmetry: A relation is asymmetrical in the set A if and only if $$(x)(y)(x \in A \cdot y \in A \cdot xRy \rightarrow \text{not-}yRx)$$
3. Antisymmetry: A relation is antisymmetrical in the set A if and only if $$(x)(y)((x \in A \cdot y \in A \cdot xRy \cdot yRx) \rightarrow x = y)$$
4. Transitivity: A relation is transitive in the set A if and only if $$(x)(y)(z)((x \in A \cdot y \in A \cdot z \in A \cdot xRy \cdot yRz) \rightarrow xRz)$$
5. Intransitivity: A relation is intransitive in the set A if and only if $$(x)(y)(z)((x \in A \cdot y \in A \cdot z \in A \cdot xRy \cdot yRz) \rightarrow \text{not-}xRz)$$

We will use this form in introducing the relations of reflexivity, etc. in the next chapter.

We say that one mapping of a relation is isomorphic with another when the two relations have the same formal properties. Thus, the relation *next larger than* and the relation *next older than* are isomorphic, because both are asymmetrical and intransitive. Both of these are isomorphic with the series of ordinal numbers, that is, with the sequence of "first, second, third . . ." which we will say are related to each other as "successor of" (or "predecessor of"), and thus we may map relations like *next larger than* or *next older than* by means of the ordinals.[7] That is to say, we may rank-order all the members of the set of the relation by assigning the ordinal

[7] This is true of individuals only if for each position *next larger than* or *next taller than,* there is uniquely one individual. If there are several of the same size or age, then the ordinals may be said to uniquely map *classes* of all individuals of the same size or age (whether there are one or more members in such classes), so that any number of individuals may be assigned to each unique ordinal position. With respect to such equivalence classes, the ordinals would give a one-one mapping; but with respect to the individuals where there are more than one in some class, this would not be an isomorphic or one-one mapping, but a many-one mapping, or a homomorphic mapping, more than one individual being mapped onto some (or all) of the ordinals.

numbers as labels. But if we do this, then there must be a member of the set of *next larger than* who is the smallest, or who is not larger than any other member, and who will be "first in line," since such a condition obtains for the ordinals—that is, there is a first number. If there were no smallest member of the set of *next larger than,* then the isomorphism with the ordinals would fail.

Suppose that we take the three sets of things:

1. All those which stand in the relation *next larger than,* including one smallest member, or one which is not larger than any other.
2. All those which stand in the relation *next taller than,* including one shortest member, or one which is not taller than any other.
3. The set of ordinal numbers which stand in the relation *successor of,* such that every member of this set is the successor of some number, except the "first," which is not the successor of any number; and such that no two numbers have the same successor, i.e., every number has exactly one successor in the set. We will take the ordinals as 0, 1, 2, 3, . . . , where 0 is the "first" number.

It may be intuitively clear that these three sets of things in these relations are isomorphic to each other, that there is a formal structure of the relations which is the same in all three cases. In effect, we may match the members of set (1) by the members of set (2) and match both by the members of set (3), and preserve the ordering relations invariant. But consider that, as in matching the number of people in a room to the fingers of both hands, (1), (2) and (3) would then have to have the same number of members, or the isomorphism would fail. We may show that in set (3), although there is a first number, there cannot be a last number, for there would then be a number which had no successor, and we specified that in that set every number has one and exactly one successor. Therefore, the isomorphism or one-to-one correspondence of the members of (1), (2) and (3), in the given relations, would be preserved only if in (1) there were no largest member and in (2) no tallest. If there were, then (2) and (3) would be isomorphic not with (3), but with some finite subset or part of (3).

This does no more than to state our intuitions about correspondence, and about ordinal numbers. We may go a step further however, and say that *if* the conditions of (3) were met in (1) and (2), then all three would be *models or mappings of some formal theory* which stated in abstract terms the relations of order exhibited in all three cases. We are led to consider a more abstract question underlying much of what we have discussed thus far in talking about representation, namely, the question of formal theories and their models.

THEORIES AND MODELS: FORMAL SYSTEMS AND THEIR INTEPRETATIONS

A clarification of usage is necessary at this point, to avoid a confusion sometimes introduced in discussions of this topic. Thus far, we have talked about the representation of some domain of facts as a mapping or a model of that domain, so that "map" or "model" is taken to be the abstractive representation of formal structures revealed in the mapped or modeled domain. This is the current usage in the natural and social sciences, and derives from the common-sense metaphor in which maps and models are the *derived* or representative versions of something taken to be the original. The relation is therefore one between *original* and *copy,* and is most often taken also to be one between *concrete* and *abstract.* In the case of things like scale models (say, of ships or airplanes), the models are concrete enough, or just as concrete as what they model. In representations in some language, which we have been concerned with, we say the linguistic model is abstract, the symbols standing for certain "concrete" things in the world, or for the "facts." However, our use of *abstract* was methodological rather than dependent on intuitions concerning abstractness and concreteness. The model was taken to be "abstractive" in that it singled out for representation only certain properties or relations taken to be relevant, and not all of the properties of the objects modeled.

Now if we recall for a moment the earlier discussion of the Platonic and Pythagorean theories and, in general, the Greek notions of underlying formal structure, we may see that one can invert the usual sense of *model.* For Plato, the "real" subsisting realm was that of the forms of things (or the "ideal forms"). The world itself was not modeled by these forms, but was modeled after these forms; that is, the world of perception was an embodiment of these ideal forms, or in Plato's own metaphor, a copy of the forms, so that the forms (as ostensibly abstract entities) were the originals. Similarly, the Pythagoreans from whom Plato derived saw the world as essentially *number*: underlying the perceptual appearance of things were the mathematical structures *of which the world of perception was a mapping or a model.* This Platonist-Pythagorean inversion of the ordinary sense of mapping thus makes what we would ordinarily call the world of fact or the concrete world of our perception itself a *representation* of the forms or formal structures, instead of seeing these forms as being the abstract representation of the world of fact.

This Platonist usage dominates the mathematical and logical disciplines which treat of the formal structures we are discussing. Therefore, in the ensuing discussion, the model is taken to be the "concrete" embodiment, or in methodological terms, the interpretation of a formal system. Such a purely formal system is therefore an uninterpreted formal system, in itself. In terms of our former distinction, it is a purely syntactical system, dealing with the formal structure of a set of entities taken to constitute the system. In a linguistic or symbolic system of this sort, these entities are taken to be the uninterpreted terms or primitives of the system. All other terms are "reducible" to these, or are explicitly defined in terms of these. The primitive terms are therefore undefined, though we may talk about them abstractly as "individual terms," "predicates," "class terms," "relations," or "operations." For example, we may take the inscription "[**o**]" as connoting an undefined operation, "**o**" on the undefined terms "[" and "]." We may also talk about these entities (as we are doing now) in a metalanguage (as we are doing now). But until we give a semantic interpretation of "[," and "**o**" and "]," the formal system in which these terms occur is not itself *about* anything. If we assign the meaning "number" to "[" and "]," and the meaning "multiplication" to "**o**," then we may be said to be mapping the formal system onto arithmetic, or giving it an embodiment. The arithmetic would then be the *model* of the formal system (or *a* model of it). Thus, if we work one way—as we have until now—by giving an abstract representation of the structural properties of a domain of empirical inquiry such a representation goes in the direction of *formalizing* that domain. (We shall see that this requires more than simply an abstractive representation, but also a scheme of inference in the representation.) However, when we work in the other direction, we may start with a purely formal system in the sense indicated, and discover or establish a mapping or a model of this formalism in the empirical domain. Thus, in this discussion the uninterpreted formal system, or the formalization of some domain, will be called a theory, and its interpretation, or embodiment, will be said to be a mapping of that theory onto some domain, or a model of the theory.

Given this introduction, we see that an abstract formal structure which may be mapped onto the relations (1), (2) and (3) of the previous section (*next larger than, next taller than,* and *successor of*) is a theory of which (1), (2), and (3) are models. Thus to be a model in this sense is to be a mapping of some theory. Further, for a given range of theories—the only ones we will be concerned with—any model of that theory is isomorphic with any other model; i.e., they are alternative mappings of the same theory, and preserve the relations set forth in the theory invariantly through transformations. They are all, in effect, perfect translations of the same abstract text or core structure. The Platonic metaphor may be seen in all this, for all the perfect copies of some original—say, for example, all the satisfactory etchings taken from the same plate—are alike in structure, or isomorphic with each other.[8] However different such models may be from each other

[8] It is difficult to give a satisfactory general account of isomorphism beyond this introductory explication of our intuitions of "same structure," without getting involved in the technical rigors of set theory and group theory, which I will not presume to do. However, we may say generally that two relation structures are isomorphic if there is a one-to-one function f which maps one on the other. For example,

in other respects, in the relevant respects of the formal structure they are the same, or constitute a class of models equivalent in these properties, any one of which could then be used to *represent* any of the others in this respect.

Suppose now we wanted to represent the order of the set of *next larger than* and *next taller than*. If we can find that both these sets are, in their relation structure, isomorphic with the set of ordinals, then we may use the ordinals to represent the order of these other two relations. In practice, then, we may line up people in a group in size place, each except the first taller than the preceding one, and then represent this order by assigning numbers, from a finite subset of ordinals placed in one-to-one correspondence (having same number of numerals as there are people in the group). If we further assign a name to each number, identifying the person to whom the number has been assigned, we then have a representation of the set of people arranged in order of height, by means of the numerals assigned to their names. We may do the same with a set of blocks of different sizes, each except the smallest larger than some other, and so on with all relations which are isomorphic with the ordinals (or in these cases, with some finite subset of them).

But what we want now is a formulation of the theory of which (1), (2), and (3) are models. Furthermore, we want the theory as a formal *system,* one in which inferences may be carried out. In effect, we want to formalize the models, or construct the formal theory of which the models are models. For beyond rank ordering, there are other operations we want to perform in the representation, which we shall take to hold as well of the domain represented. That is, we want a theory which will theoretically support the computations we perform in the representation, by making explicit the formal conditions that permit us to take computations or calculations in the representation as holding for the represented domain. In short, we require a theory which will set forth the conditions under which a representation and what it represents may be said to be isomorphic. Such a theory does not *determine* that a mathematical or symbolic representation of the facts, for example, is isomorphic in its structure with that of the facts. This is a matter of empirical discovery. But such a theory is the rational reconstruction of the conditions that obtain when such a correspondence is discovered.

---

if we take the simple relation structures (ABBA) and (BAAB), then the function $f(A) = B$ maps the first onto the second, in one-to-one correspondence. When a theory has two models which are isomorphic in this sense, the theory is said to be *categorical.* Consider the two relation structures (A, B, C, D) and (1, 2, 3, 4, 5, 6, 7), however. We may map the second onto the first by mapping (1, 2, 3) onto (A), (4) onto (B), (5, 6) onto (C) and (7) onto (D). These two structures thus take a many-one mapping (from the second to the first) but not a one-one mapping. The relation here is called a *homomorphism* (as, for example, of wives to husbands in a polygamous society).

Because the most universal means of representation in science is number, or the system of arithmetic, it seems reasonable that a formalization of arithmetic would be a major instance of such a theory, and we will briefly consider how this may be accomplished.

THE FORMALIZATION OF ARITHMETIC

Our ordinary number intuitions and our experience with counting, ordering, and collecting things are the foundation of arithmetic, insofar as arithmetic is a representation of the facts; and arithmetic certainly is a representation of the facts in the sense that we interpret the symbols of arithmetic in terms of real operations in the world. Thus, in scientific measurement we assign numbers to designate magnitudes of length, of time, of quantity, just as we assign them to designate rank order. However, what we seek now is the formal theory of which such arithmetic is an interpretation, or of which measurement, for example, is a model. We rely then on the familiarity of what we all know about counting, collecting, and measuring for our initial source in constructing such a formal system.

Certain relations which we learn in learning to count may be singled out as central here. For example, in counting we go from one thing to the next, and in enumerating what we count, we go from one number to the next, which we may call its *successor*. We also always begin to count somewhere, so in enumerating there is a *first* number which has the distinctive property of not being the successor of any number, and we ordinarily assume that in counting we will not run out of numbers (though children do, of course), so that however large is the collection of things we count, we may continue to count indefinitely. We assume therefore that there is no *last* number.[9] Because, in ordering things by counting, we want to retain the uniqueness of this order, not counting the same thing twice nor enumerating two things by the same number, we may formulate this requirement by saying that no two numbers have the same successor. We may conveniently list these familiar properties of counting as follows:

I. n is a number.
II. The successor of any number is a number.
III. No two numbers have the same successor.
IV. n is not the successor of any number.

[9] The assumption, therefore, is that for any number n, there is a next or its successor $n + 1$, so that there are infinitely many numbers. In order to give a logical proof of this assumption in deriving the foundations of arithmetic from logic, Bertrand Russell introduced into the logical system the *Axiom of Infinity*, which states that there are infinitely many concrete individuals. This is the subject of much discussion in logical foundations of mathematics, i.e., in the work of providing a formal theory for the model of mathematics, but we will not discuss it further here.

It may be seen that in this form n is the *first* number, because by IV, it is not the successor of any number. I and IV simply give us an explicit statement that the "first" is a number, for, as we shall see, the property of being a number then gets passed "down the line" to anything meeting these requirements. We may characterize the relation "successor of" in terms of its formal properties if we think of the properties of counting. Suppose we take two ordinal numbers such that y is the successor of x. Then clearly, "if ySx, then not xSy." We take the relation *successor of* to be asymmetrical then. Further, the relation is intransitive, because "if zSy and ySx then not zSx. (This may be seen to follow from III, because if the relation were transitive, then z would be the successor of both y and x, but III states that no two numbers have the same successor.) Thus, "successor of," as we have already seen, is an asymmetric and intransitive relation.

Despite the attempt here to be casual about our counting intuitions, it may be seen that the statements I–IV begin to have a formal look about them. And it is no secret that these statements which we understand by virtue of our arithmetic interpretation of the terms "number," "successor," and "first number" are in fact the first four axioms of a formalization of arithmetic by the Italian mathematician Giuseppe Peano, who with Dedekind, Frege, and others, began to set out the formal theory of which our interpreted arithmetic is the model. We will shortly say more about this as a formal system. But we need to add one more axiom, not as evident as the rest but strongly grounded in our arithmetic intuition. We may state it in a somewhat awkward way as:

V. All the (natural) numbers have a given property, if it is the case that
  (*a*) the first number has it, and
  (*b*) if any number has it, then its successor also has it.

This axiom concerns so-called mathematical induction, and states the strong arithmetic intuition which leads us to conclude from one or two instances that something holds of all the numbers. For example, we would readily conclude from the examples "$2^2 = 4$" and "$8^2 = 64$" that the square of any even number is an even number, even though we could never possibly test the conclusion for all the even numbers. Or in the slightly more complex theorem in arithmetic that the sum of a series with n terms, where it is the series of natural numbers beginning with zero as the first number, is equal to half the difference between n^2 and n [or arithmetically, $S = \frac{1}{2}(n^2 - n)$]. One can readily show that this holds for the series with only one member (0), and for $n = 2$ (0, 1), or $n = 4$ (0, 1, 2, 3). We might conscientiously try it for $n = 17$, or $n = 372$ (which would make a long sum!) But in general, we would assume it held for all values of n, even though we could never test this. In number theory we might give a proof of this theorem, supporting it by the proof instead of by the axiom. But somewhere along the line, in the system of arithmetic, some such appeal will be made, and it has been a matter of lively discussion whether the axiom is grounded in our arithmetic intuition (Poincaré's view) or whether it can be justified on the grounds of a logical proof in the theory or the logical foundations of arithmetic.

Given these five axioms, we can see how a deductive system may be constructed in which theorems are derived as inferences from these axioms. But a deductive system is something we have not yet examined, and we may set out the requirements for such a system briefly here.

If we reconstruct formally what we have said thus far, we may say that the formal system *P* (for Peano) is an uninterpreted formal system or theory of which any progression is a model or interpretation.[10] The elements of such a formal system or theory would be

(i) Primitive or undefined terms: "0," "number," "successor."
(ii) Axioms I–IV in which the primitive terms occur. These axioms are the primitive statements or formulas of the theory. All others are derived from these, by proof.
(iii) Formation and transformation rules: these are the rules for well-formed formulas or the admissable statements in the theory, and the rules for inference which permit "moves" to be made from one statement to another.
(iv) Definitions: these introduce defined terms in terms of the undefined ones, and may therefore be eliminated by reduction to the undefined terms. But the definitions facilitate the procedures of inference.
(v) Theorems provable from (i)–(iv).

For our purposes, we will adopt the following form of the axioms, using 0, *number*, and *successor*. For abbreviation's sake, we will use the notation x' for *successor of* x, where x is a variable standing for any number.

I. 0 is a number.
II. If x is a number, then x' is a number (the successor of x is a number).

[10] As Bertrand Russell pointed out (*Introduction to Mathematical Philosophy*), Peano's axioms do not uniquely take the natural numbers (0, 1, 2, 3 . . .) as their model or interpretation. The progression of odd numbers or of even numbers or of every fifth number, for example, each fulfills the conditions set by the axioms. For example, for the even numbers 2 would be the "first" number, the even successor of every number would be a number, etc. Since the set of natural numbers, as ordinals, may be mapped one-to-one onto the even numbers $\left(\text{e.g., } \begin{matrix} 0 & 1 & 2 & 3 & 4 & \ldots \\ 2 & 4 & 6 & 8 & 10 & \ldots \end{matrix}\right)$ or onto the odd numbers $\left(\text{e.g., } \begin{matrix} 0 & 1 & 2 & 3 & 4 & \ldots \\ 1 & 3 & 5 & 7 & 9 & \ldots \end{matrix}\right)$ or onto every fifth number $\left(\text{e.g., } \begin{matrix} 0 & 1 & 2 & 3 & 4 & \ldots \\ 0 & 4 & 9 & 14 & 19 & \ldots \end{matrix}\right)$ all such sets are isomorphic or have a one-one mapping. They thus all have the same number of members, or are of the same cardinality.

III. No two numbers have the same successor.
IV. 0 is not the successor of any number.
V. All the numbers have a property P if
(a) $P(0)$
(b) If for any x, $P(x)$, then $P(x')$.

We introduce two definitions; defining the operations "+" and " · "

D1. *Addition* ("+"): (1) $x + 0 = x$
(2) $x + y' = (x + y)'$

D2. *Multiplication* (" · ")
(1) $x \cdot 0 = 0$
(2) $x \cdot y' = (x \cdot y) + x$

These are easily interpreted as (1) the sum of any number and 0 is that number, (2) the sum of any number and the successor of any other number (or of itself) is equal to the successor of the sum of those two numbers. For multiplication, (1) the product of any number and 0 is 0 and (2) the product of any number and the successor of any other number (or of itself) is equal to the sum of the product of the two numbers and the first number. On interpretation, of course, this comes to the trivial examples such as $2 + 4 = 6$ and $3 \cdot 7 = (3 \cdot 6) + 3$. But these are precisely the mappings which we want our formalism to fit. The scheme is, therefore, tailormade to fit arithmetic. But it is constructed as a formal calculus, in which the theorems, when interpreted, will yield mappings of the theorems of arithmetic—*and of anything with which arithmetic is isomorphic.*

As a relatively simple proof, in this system, we may take something easily recognizable in its arithmetic form as the "theorem": "3 + 1 = 4." But whereas we learn this in the practical experience of counting and adding sets of objects, when we interpret "3" and "1" and "4" in terms of the physical magnitude properties of sets of objects and interpret "+" operationally as combining these sets or taking them together, we have recourse only to the elements of the system itself, each step of the proof justified either by the axioms, or as a definition, or by the definitions D1 and D2 which we have introduced, or by a logical rule (e.g., substituting equals for equals), or by something already proved (e.g., a previous step in the proof). The odd-looking thing about such a formal proof is that our ordinary numbers are introduced by definition. So, for example, $(0')$ or the successor of 0 is the definition of the numeral "1," and $(0')'$ or the successor of the successor of 0 defines "2," so that the transformation to the usual arithmetic notation "3 + 1 = 4" is entirely by means of defined terms reducible to the primitives. The proof is shown in the following list, each step justified in the right-hand column.

To be proved: $3 + 1 = 4$

1. $0'$ is a number.	1. Axioms I and II.
2. $0' = 1$.	2. Definition.
3. $(0')'$ is a number.	3. Step 1 and Axiom II.
4. $(0')' = 1' = 2$.	4. Substitution and Definition.
5. $2'$ is a number.	5. Step 3, Substitution and Axiom II.
6. $2' = 3$.	6. Definition.
7. $3'$ is a number.	7. Step 5, substitution and Axiom II.
8. $3' = 4$.	8. Definition.
9. $(3 + 1) = (3 + 0')$.	9. Substitution and Addition.
10. $(3 + 0') = (3 + 0)'$.	10. Definition of Addition, part (2).
11. $(3 + 0) = 3$.	11. Definition of Addition, part (1).
12. $(3 + 0)' = 3' = 4$.	12. Substitution, step 11 and step 8.
13. $(3 + 1) = 4$ Q.E.D.	13. Substitution, step 9 and step 12.

In the formal system, the expressions "3," "4," "1," "+" do not mean anything except what they are defined as, in terms of the primitives. They could just as well have been written "A," "B," "C," "%," for syntactic purposes, just as the primitives "0," "number," "successor" could have been written "*," "snerk," and "addressor." But clearly the theory is intended as a mapping of arithmetic. Still, what do numbers stand for? We have seen that the ordinal numbers mapped by Peano's axioms represent relations of order or sequence, as "first," "second," etc. (Note that 0 rather than 1 is the first number here, which is somewhat unlike ordinary counting.) But naming what position in a series something has, in terms of some linear ordering or sequence, is different from counting how many members there are in the series. Here we come upon a distinction in mapping, between *ordinality,* as position in a sequence, and *cardinality,* or numerousness. The difference may be seen from the following: to preserve the relations of sequence or rank order invariantly through transformations, the ordinals have to be uniquely mapped on the series they represent (as, e.g., heights or weights). However, to establish a one-to-one correspondence between two sets of things that are equally numerous, one need not count at all but simply notice that every member of one set has a corresponding member in the other. This may be established simply by seeing whether there are any "left over" in either set. Thus, for example, if there are any seats left empty in a concert hall in which everyone who is present is seated or if there are any people standing without seats because all the seats are full, then we know without counting that the number of people and the number of seats is not the same; and if there are no standees and no empty seats, then we know that there is an equal number of seats and people.

The interpretation of number in terms of numerousness may also be formulated in a theory; but here a great economy may be wrought. For the formal theory we have just considered, with its apparatus of inference, works equally well for ordinals and for cardinals. One has only to interpret the numbers—the so-called natural numbers or integers—as cardinals, for the theory to map cardinal numbers. But what is such an interpretation?

We may begin by considering an invariant property which we take countable things to have: they are what they are, and remain that way. This may seem an odd requirement to make of things countable. Yet, if what we counted as one decided to become two, or seven, things, and then perhaps one again, then counting would be a haphazard if not a hopeless task. Thus, whether we count fingers or stars, we take our count to be valid if one finger remains one finger and one star remains one star. But counting one finger, one star, or one anything else is based on the fact that whatever it is we are counting, it has the same formal property as anything else which may be counted as one. We may say this by describing "one" as a property which all things countable as units, i.e., as self-identical and relatively permanent units, share in common. We may, if we like, call this property of "unicity," but it is closer to our intuitions of countable things to speak of them as members of sets or classes of things. If we adopt this way of speaking, then what we mean by *one* is this common property which all members of a certain class share. Anything which is *one* may be said to constitute a class with one member, in terms of its unique identity as that one thing. Now all things in the universe may be said to be self-identical, but insofar as they are discriminably unique things, each has its *own* identity, or the unique set of properties which make it *that* thing, and not some other. Such one-membered classes, or unit classes, themselves share a property, though their members are unique, it being that each has only one member. We may define the cardinal number *one*, then, as the class of all those classes with only one member, or the class of unit classes. Similarly, the cardinal two is defined as the class of all two-membered classes, and the cardinal number zero as the class of all classes with no members at all, or the empty class (or "null class") (We may see that there is therefore only one empty class since it has no members.)

We may then (to use Quine's term) "construe" the numbers in such a way that we get an interpretation of the natural numbers in terms of cardinality, i.e., in the sense of the numerousness of members in each class of same-membered classes, generating the cardinals for each successive term in the series of natural numbers, 0, 1, 2, 3 . . . , now in the sense of "how many." There are several ways to do this, by various alternative approaches to set theory or number theory. Intuitively, each successive number is generated by adding *one* to the previous number. If we begin with "0" as the first number, and construe this as the empty class, or the class with no members, then we may "generate" the second number, or "1," as the class which has the empty class as its sole member, thus, if Λ, which stands for the empty class, is 0, then $\{\Lambda\}$ or the class which contains the empty class as its sole member is 1). Then, the class which contains the unit class which contains the empty class as its sole member is 2, or $\{\{\Lambda\}\}$, and so on. This is Zermelo's way. Alternatively, with von Neumann we may begin with Λ as 0, then with $\{\Lambda\}$ as 1, but take the union of 0 and its successor 1 as the "next" class, thus $\{0, 1\}$ or $\{\Lambda,\{\Lambda\}\}$ as 2. Thus, 3 would be the class of all classes smaller than 3, and so on: $\{0, 1, 2\}$ thus becomes 3, $\{0, 1, 2, 3\}$ becomes 4, etc. Similarly, we may take our definitions of addition: ($x + 0 = x$ and $x + y' = (x + y)'$) to show that the successor of any number is generated by adding $0'$ to that number, i.e., by adding 1. For example, if $2' = 3$, then since $2 + 0 = 2$, and $2 + 0' = (2 + 0)'$, then $2 + 1 = 2' = 3$. Our operational notion of addition is formally mapped by this representation. If we take two classes whose members may be uniquely paired off with each other, then the cardinal class of the "next" number, additively, will be one which can be set in one-to-one correspondence of each of its members with either of the first two classes, except for one member left over (this one corresponding with or pairable with any unit class).

Isomorphism, in terms of the property "numerousness" or the relations between number properties of things in the world, is therefore defined by these definitions of number. All two-membered classes may have their members set in one-to-one correspondence, as may all three- or four- or n-membered classes. With respect to "how many," two sets of things are isomorphic if they are members of classes with the same cardinality. Once our "numbers" in the uninterpreted formal system (or the numerals, which are the names of numbers in this system) are interpreted as cardinals, that is, once the numeral "2" is taken to denote the class of all two-membered classes, i.e., the number 2, then the mapping of number properties by means of an interpreted formal system becomes feasible. Relations among magnitudes as properties of sets of things in the world may then be mapped or represented by our mathematical systems. The test of such a representation is never itself simply formal, for whether or not number properties of sets of things in the world are in fact isomorphic with their mathematical representations is a matter of empirical discovery. Addition, subtraction, division, multiplication, just as much as differentiation and integration, have their empirical counterparts in relations among the facts, and our concepts of such mathematical operations derive originally from practical concerns with measuring amounts, ordering sequences, determining rates of change. Our representation of these relations among the facts, of the structure of nature and the form of its processes, depends on our ingenuity in constructing systems of symbols which preserve these relational structures in the mapping, and through the transformations of symbolic calculation.

Our intellectual domination of nature, our control and manipulation of the environment, depends heavily on our representation of nature in a way which preserves the truth of our experience and can be put to the test of new experience. In one sense, all such representation is a matter of taking the measure of nature; and it is to the concern with such measurement, in its empirical and formal aspects, that we turn in the next chapter.

CHAPTER 7
Measurement

THE PROCESS OF MEASUREMENT

MEASURING IS ONE of the basic things we do, day and night, winter and summer, in all seasons and in all conditions. The recognition and preservation of order is a condition of living organisms in general; in a broad sense, an organism is a system of activities preserved by an apparatus of measurement, or by a mechanism regulating itself by measurement. The conditions of organic integrity are those which the Greeks early recognized in their wisdom-literature and in their medical theory: "Nothing in excess." Too much and too little are the conditions of disease, of threat to the homeostasis which marks organisms as organisms, as self-regulating systems able to compensate, to make good, to offset—to balance intake and outgo of the stuff of life processes: air, food, heat, water—in that delicate exchange of measure for measure which preserves life.

Much of the complex activity of human life involves measuring of another order. Whereas the body is an unconscious system of measuring mechanisms, man performs conscious measurement in that whole spectrum of actions which mark him as a thinking and speaking being. Once concept formation and language attain to the ideas of *thing* and *same* and *different,* discourse already exhibits the notion of *class* as an ordering concept, as names and descriptions collect and relate individuals in some collection to each other. Here measurement already has its roots, in the process of identification, comparison, and classification. The empirical practice of counting, apportioning, distributing, and arranging the goods and instrumentalities of family and social life introduce the new techniques of measurement appropriate to a more than brute existence. The development of property, communal and private; the organization of work and duties, in production, in war, in the hunt, and in the arts of poetry and dance which are part of the ordinary rhythms of early societies; the institution of classes in society, and of state organizations, with their assignments of powers, rights, duties, in a pecking order; the formalization of this hierarchy in law and political theory; the growth of the art of building construction, imposing order on materials in view of some form and purpose, by ordered techniques; the observation and recording of recurrent events, to mark the cyclic intervals which order the life of agricultural and herding societies—these and many more provide the unremitting demands out of which measurement techniques and the concepts of measurement arise.

The process of measurement thus grows out of the demands of practical existence. However esoteric it becomes, its fundamental processes remain part of the warp and woof of the fabric of everyday life. As one might then expect, measurement concepts become part of the everyday language, built into its commonest terms and its most ordinary usage, and into its structure itself. The refinement of these basic measurement concepts is one of the greatest of human achievements, often providing the instrumentalities for technological change and social transformation. We will examine some of these basic concepts first, discovering with the help of formal analysis such fundamental features of measurement as are represented in the concepts of *comparison, magnitude, ordering,* in the relations of *quality* to *quantity,* in the construction of *scales* of measurement and their *calibration.* Finally, we will consider the *uses* of measurement in the sciences, to see what power this process and its formal theory make available to scientific thought.

KINDS, COMPARISONS, AND CLASSIFICATION

At the very foundations of any process of measurement is the humblest and most modest of intellectual and linguistic operations: that of identifying something as of a given kind. We shall see later, that this "simple" first step is often also the last step of a process of measurement, and that it requires a subtle and complex interplay of theory and observation. At the outset, however, we require only that "simple" process of identifying by name or description. In observation, we already classify, in that preliminary way which the observation language exhibits, predicating this of that. What we single out, then, are features of things, which in various contexts or by different conventions we call *properties* or *attributes* or *qualities*. To say a thing is of a certain kind is to say that it is a member of the class of things of that kind. Even with proper names,when we single something out as "one of a kind," we have seen that the unit class concept still makes it possible to take it as a member of a class. But *kind* is already a comparative concept. Things of a kind are alike in some property, or share some quality in common. To compare any two things is to undertake to discover what is the same or what is different about them. In the classic language of classification, first developed by Aristotle as an instrument of biological and physical classification, the distinction is made between *genus* and *difference*, the genus being the class to which any two or more things compared belong in common, the difference connoting the proper *subclasses* of this class which mark differences within it. Generic classes would then be, for example, *canine, feline, equine*. Dogs and wolves are like in genus but are distinguished within that genus as dog and wolf. If we take as genus, *dog*, then again we *divide* this class by its differentia, say, hound, terrier, and so forth. The result of this sort of classification is, diagrammatically, a *tree*, or a branch diagram. What is significant about such classification is that it is more than a matter of mere identification; for here, *relations* among things identified are set forth, in the form of class relations. This permits the development of a formal system of classification, with all the properties of formal systems, namely, the explication of observed relations and identifications, in such a way as to permit inferences to be made by rule. The initial development of such a formal system, in the syllogistic logic of Aristotle, was in effect an explication of the classificatory character of ordinary language, and of the extent to which the very subject-predicate form of descriptive statements is already a primary classificatory device. The fuller development of this formal analysis of classification, apart from its refinement in empirical classificatory work, took place as a mathematization of class relations, in the class calculus or in the form of an algebra of class relations, as developed by George Boole and others in the nineteenth century. This Boolean algebra, or Boolean logic, formalized class relations, and the concept of class membership, so that calculation could be carried out in purely formal terms.

The fundamental notions of such a class logic or elementary set theory, are *class membership, class inclusion, class union,* and *class intersection.* We take the domain of such a logic as some fixed set or class of individuals, and the class relations as holding between subclasses of that domain. The notation used in formal representation of this operation of assigning individuals to classes varies. Where it is in terms of individuals as members of classes, or as belonging to them, these individuals are taken as "elements" of the class (or set), and the relation of membership or of belonging to a class is indicated by the symbol "ϵ." Lower case letters are used for the elements: conventionally, $x, y, z,$ for individual variables, and $a, b, c, \ldots,$ for individual constants. Thus the expression "$x \epsilon B$" means "x is a member of the class B" or "x belongs to B." An alternative notation represents the assignment of predicates to individual variables or constants so that "$B(x)$" or simply "Bx" represents the assignment of the predicate B to the individual variable x, where B stands for some property which x has. This latter case is an adoption of the functional notation of mathematics (read "B of x").

The symbol "{ }" is used for a class or set and gives the names of its members inside the braces, so that the representation of the set of individuals Sam and Harry is written {Sam, Harry}. This is the same set as {Harry, Sam} since the order of the members is indifferent. Two sets are said to be identical if they have all and only the same members. Relations among such sets or classes may also be defined and symbolized.

The *inclusion* of one set in another, where all the members of one set are also members of the other, is given in ordinary speech as "All —— are ——," as in "All dogs are canines." This is represented by the inclusion symbol $\supseteq$, so that our example would be abbreviated as "$D \subseteq C$." This means that every member of the set D is also a member of the set C. D is therefore said to be a *subset* of C.

Because it is clear that "All dogs are dogs" and "All canines are canines," we may further say that every set is a subset of itself, or for any set A, $A \supseteq A$. By our condition for identity, if two sets A and B have the same members, then $A = B$, and both $A \supseteq B$ and $B \supseteq A$. But when all the members of A are also members of B and not all the members of B are members of A, or when $A \neq B$, A is called a *proper subset* of B. Thus A is a subset of itself but not a proper subset of itself. The set {hounds, terriers} is both a subset and a proper subset of the set {hounds, terriers, spaniels} but {hounds, terriers, spaniels} is not a proper subset of {hounds, terriers, spaniels}. The notation for *proper subset* is $\supset$.

The *union* of two sets is symbolized by "$\cup$," and is the set of all things which are members of at least one of the sets joined by this relation. Thus, the union of the set of baseball players and violinists is the set of all those who are *either* baseball players or violinists, and would thus include, as a joint class, all baseball players and all violinists. (Sometimes the notation "+" is used for this relation so that the union of two sets is called their "sum".)

The *intersection* of two sets is defined as the set of all things which belong to *both* sets, and is symbolized by "$\cap$" (or alternatively by the algebraic dot, "$\cdot$", of multiplication, so that this relation of intersection is called the "product" of the two sets). Further, when two sets are mutually exclusive, or there is nothing which is a member of both, the intersection of these sets is called the *empty set,* that is, the set with no members. Thus, for example, the intersection of the set of baseball players and the set of violinists is the set of all baseball players who are also violinists (or equivalently, all violinists who are also baseball players). If there were no baseball-playing violinists, then the sets would be mutually exclusive, and their intersection would be the empty set. The empty set is symbolized as Λ, and is taken to be a subset of every set. Further, if A is a set which has no members and B is a set which has no members, then it is true that everything which is a member of A is also a member of B and vice versa, so that $A = B$; thus there is one and just one empty set. The *universal* set, by contrast, is the set of all the individuals in the domain or the universe of discourse of the logic. Depending on choices of universes of discourse, the universal set, symbolized by "V" may variously be taken as, e.g., "the set of all real numbers," or "the set of all physical objects," or "the set of all baseball players," and the logic will range over all the subsets of this domain. (It follows from the definitions that the empty set is a member of the universal set.)

Such a formal system of representing class relations exhibits the ordering relations among classes such as asymmetry and transitivity. We may see, for example, that the relation of a class to a proper subclass of that class is asymmetrical (if $A \supset B$, then not-$B \supset A$) and transitive (if $A \supset B$ and $B \supset C$, then $A \supset C$). We may also see that such formal properties of the class relation of inclusion may be mapped on the formal properties of another formal system, as, for example, that of the natural numbers, with regard to the ordering relation "larger than." Such an ordering of classes may then be seen to be isomorphic with the natural number system, providing the possibility of assigning numbers to classes which stand to each other in a certain relation, because the numbers map this same relation. In this sense, we may take one system as an interpretation of the other. Thus the initial step of identifying things as belonging to a certain class and establishing relations among such classes starts us on the whole enterprise of measurement and scaling, once our formal analysis of these empirical operations is seen to be isomorphic with the number system or some subset of the number system whose formalization we have previously discussed.

In general, then, any two things compared, if they are taken as members of some class in common, are therefore taken to be equivalent in some property which is the condition of membership in that class. To put it differently, things which share some property in common may be said to *generate* the class of that property; however different they are in other respects, they bear a relation of *equivalence* to each other in that property. Let us suppose that many things are being compared with respect to their color properties. Some are red, some green, and so on, yet they all have *some* color property and are equivalent in this respect. We may then say that the class of things comparable in some property is an *equivalence* class with respect to that property, generated by all those things having the property. The relation which any member of that class bears to any other, whatever the property, is one of equivalence in that property. But this relation of equivalence has certain formal properties: It is symmetrical and transitive. But now we may enrich our vocabulary of the properties of relations in the following way. We may say that anything is equivalent to *itself* in some property, and we may also say that any member of an equivalence class bears the relation of equivalence to any other member. The relation is therefore *reflexive* and *strongly connected.* We may therefore introduce these definitions:

1. A relation R is reflexive in a set A, if and only if $(x)(x \epsilon A \rightarrow xRx)$.
2. A relation R is irreflexive in a set A, if and only if $(x)(x \epsilon A \rightarrow \text{not } xRx)$.
3. A relation R is strongly connected in a set A, if and only if $(x)(y)(x \epsilon A \cdot y \epsilon A \rightarrow xRy \vee yRx)$.
4. A relation is connected in a set A, if and only if $(x)(y)(x \epsilon A \cdot y \epsilon A \cdot x \neq y \rightarrow xRy \vee yRx)$.

In comparing things with respect to a property, however, we may go no further than distinguishing between things that have this property and those that do not. Among the things sharing a common property, there are, as we have seen, specific differences that may be said to divide the equivalence class of that property, as lions and tigers divide the class of felines (together with other feline species). But we cannot say of such subclasses that one is "more feline" than the other. We might colloquially express tastes in pets by saying that a coon-hound is "more of a dog" than a toy poodle, but then we would have to have some scale of "dogginess" arranged in degrees of this property.

Some properties lend themselves to this interpretation, and admit of the ordering of degrees or amounts. Thus in a stricter use of "comparative," the members of an equivalence class of comparison may stand to each other in relations of *more* and *less* of that property. Length is the property of all things which have length, as sweetness is the property which all sweet things have in common. But such properties admit of degrees or amounts. *Length* implies comparison between different lengths, as *sweetness* does between degrees of sweetness. All the property terms which take the comparative form, as *longer* or *sweeter,* permit the members of the equivalence class of that property to be ordered, in the same way that classes and proper subclasses are ordered. However, a class is not "more" of some property than is a proper subclass in terms of comparative degree, no more than a greater degree of a property "includes" a lesser degree of it as a subclass. Yet the relations of degrees of a property and of class inclusion both have the same formal properties, namely, *asymmetry, transitivity, irreflexivity,* and *connectedness.* We may exhibit this relation now in a number of ways (Fig. 3) which are formally isomorphic with each other.

We may also define any two members of an equivalence class of some property which have the *same* degree of that property, as those and only those which have *neither more nor less* of it. Thus, for the relation *greater than,* in the system of natural numbers, two numbers *a* and *b* are equal

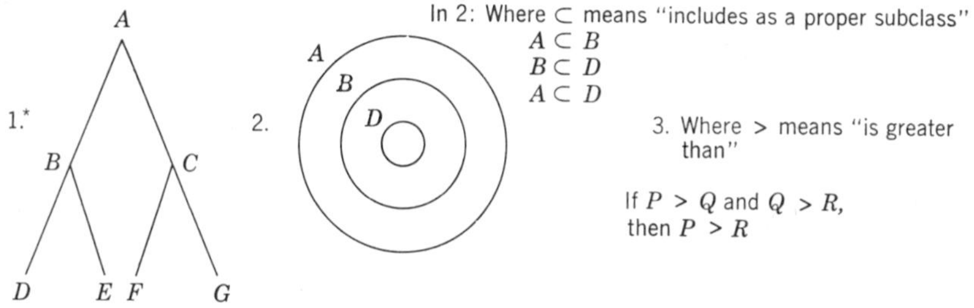

Fig. 3

* Note that in (1), *B* and *C* are connected in *A; D* and *E* in *B;* and *F* and *G* in *C;* but note that *E* and *F* are *not* connected in *C*. Thus *E* and *F* are comparable in A, but not in C or B.

(have the same ordinal position) if not-$(a > b)$ and also not-$(b > a)$ If we introduce the logical connective which stands for "neither-nor," written "↓," then equality may be defined as

$$(5) \qquad (x)(y)\ [(x = y) \leftrightarrow ((x > y) \downarrow (y > x))]$$

for members of all those equivalence classes which admit of differences in degree or amount of some property. Not all equivalence classes may be ordered in this way, but clearly some of them may. Let us then call that subclass of the class of equivalence classes that may be so ordered, the class of all *magnitude* classes, and define a magnitude class as an equivalence class that admits of an ordering of its members. If we interpret this in terms of the classification "tree" or branch diagram (section 1 of Figure 3), we may order along the following branches: *ABD, ABE, ACE, ACG*. But *DE* and *FG* are not comparable along these branches, and thus are not ordered. In the set-theoretical notation introduced previously (where "{ }" brackets a set and "⟨ ⟩" brackets an ordered set), we may describe this order as

$$(6) \qquad \langle A, B, \{D, E\} \rangle \qquad \text{and} \qquad (7)\ \langle A, C, \{F, G\} \rangle$$

Such an order, in which not *all* elements are comparable in degree of some magnitude, as *DE* and *FG* are not comparable here, is not *connected* in all its elements, and is called a partial order. It falls short of a simple *linear* ordering of all its elements. An order that is connected in all its elements, as those along *ABD, ABE,* and so on, is called a simple order. We will therefore define a magnitude class as one whose members permit of at least a partial ordering. As we will see, any stronger type of ordering *includes* this condition, but not all magnitude classes admit of stronger than partial orderings.

MAGNITUDES AND QUANTITIES

Ordinal Scales: More, Less, and the Same

Magnitudes are properties that admit of being ordered in terms of degrees or amounts. Such properties are often spoken of as *variable qualities* and in the development of the concept of motion, the notion of degrees of a quality, or *intensities,* or *latitudes of form* were early attempts to deal formally with magnitudes.[1] Historically, those qualities or properties which could be so ordered were called *intensive qualities,* by contrast to the *extensive* or *dimensive* qualities which could be further ordered in terms of unit differences in degree or amount. This distinction is one which we often speak of as between quality and quantity, a *qualitative* difference involving identity and difference, i.e., difference of more or less of some property distinguishable usually by sense perception alone, whereas a *quantitative* difference involves *how much* more or less, and ordinarily involves what we take as a quantitative measurement.

By our definition, however, not all magnitudes are quantitative. Ordinary use fastens on certain properties as characteristic magnitudes: length, weight, size or bulk, force, and so on. We do not usually conceive of sweetness, edibility, intelligence, anger, or mercy as magnitudes. Yet because all of these may be ordered by degrees, "qualitatively," our definition would include them as magnitudes. Yet it is commonly felt that these are somehow not *precise* nor precisely measurable magnitudes. It is much harder to reach agreement about comparative degrees of mercy or anger than it is to agree about lengths or weights. And we take the precision of the latter to lie in the fact that some unambiguous scale of measurement of quantitative differences is available for such properties as length or weight but not for mercy and anger. But "precision" is not an intrinsic and measureable property of things, or of relations among them—it depends on the purpose of measurement. What we require is a precision appropriate to the task at hand. In order to arrange objects by size, we do not need a micrometer *if* the differences in size are far above the threshold of perceivable difference. Thus in any measurement, we admit *tolerances* within which differences do not matter and thus may be ignored for those particular circumstances.

If the precision required is no greater than that of a qualitatively establishable rank ordering, then we require no more than that some property be unambiguously describable in terms of comparative degrees; in formal terms, that the ordering of this property be isomorphic with the set of ordinal numbers, or in other words, that the relation among degrees of this property be asymmetrical, transitive, and connected. This means that the

[1] See Appendix A, Section 7 on medieval analyses of the "quality" and "quantity" of motion, by the so-called Merton Calculators, who discovered the Mean Speed Theorem in mechanics.

degrees of any magnitude property of this sort, or the members of such a magnitude class are *mappable* in one-to-one correspondence with some set of ordinal numbers. Thus we may talk of degrees of sweetness 0, 1, 2, 3 . . . , *n,* and similarly, of mercy, edibility, and anger. Obviously, for any two things sharing the same degree of some property, they will occupy the same ordinal position on such a scale. Operationally, if we could not decide which of two sweet things was sweeter than the other, we would take them as equally sweet. Such an assignment of ordinal position for a degree of some magnitude in a formal representation of this relation, as by ordinal numbers, or successive letters of the alphabet, or some geometric diagram of serially arranged points on a line, will be referred to as a scale, and following its characterization as isomorphic with the ordinal numbers, as an ordinal scale.

Because any two magnitudes sharing this ordinality are isomorphic in this respect, they may be brought into correspondence with each other, or into joint correspondence with some third such order, taken as a scale (that is, the formal property of the relation of isomorphism is transitive). The importance of this is that for any two such isomorphic magnitudes, one may be used to represent the other, as a transformation of that other.

Intervals, Units, and Additivity.

A difficulty arises here, however. We have seen that Peano's axioms for the countable set need to be supplemented with definitions of the arithmetic operations of addition, subtraction, etc., if we are to use numbers for anything beyond counting. Ordinality in itself does not permit us to say that one number is twice as great, or half as great, as another, but only that it is greater or smaller or equal to another (where we define *greater* as "successor," or "successor of successor," etc.). We might introduce a notion of "how much greater" in terms of the number of successors of some number *n* which stand between it and some number greater than it is. For example, if $(n')'$ is the successor of the successor of *n,* then we may say that it is greater than some other number greater than *n* by 1 degree, or that it is 2 degrees greater than *n*. But in order to give this more than an ordinal interpretation, that is, to interpret it quantitatively, we need first to establish a unit of quantity, and not merely a degree of position in some ordinal scale. Thus, we may arrange the quality of mercy in degrees 0, 1, 2, 3, . . . *n*. But it is not at all clear that we can say that degree of mercy 3 is three times as great as degree of mercy 1, and certainly it has no arithmetic relation to our "first" degree, 0. Or we may take randomly collected lengths of pipe and arrange them by size, but we may not then assert that the one in third position is three times as long as the one in first position. It may accidentally be so, but it may just as well be ten times as long. In order to know that it is three times as long, we have to establish some interval of difference between one length and another, which we will take as a standard interval. But to take it as standard is to take it as an invariant interval, so that if we took this interval to be m, we would need a way to establish that some set of intervals m', m'' would be such that $m = m' = m''$. Suppose (see Fig. 4) we took a set of pipes in the order of increasing lengths A, B, C, D. The interval of length between A and B would be the difference $(B - A)$. If we took this as our standard interval, we presumably could measure any other interval difference against this one to decide whether it was equal, larger, or smaller. But then we would have to transport a representation of the interval $(B - A)$ to measure these other intervals against. Our assumption of invariance would require that $(B - A)$ remain the same in its representation.

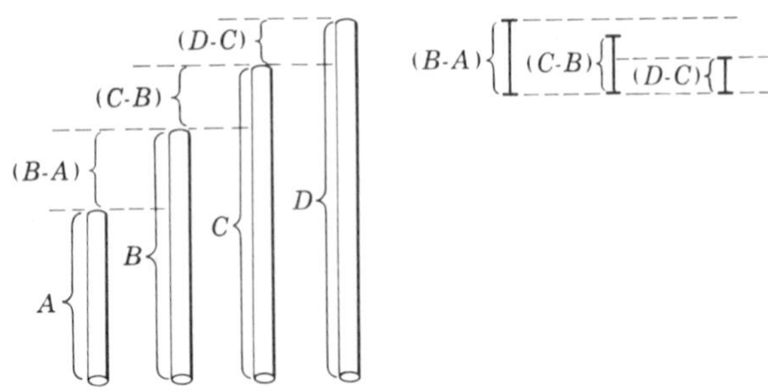

Fig. 4

If we used a rubber band to measure $(B - A)$, our confidence that we could transfer the length of the interval with appropriate precision, as a measure of $(B - A)$ against $(C - B)$ or $(D - C)$, would not be very high. We would need a way of testing whether a difference in length, taken as a standard, remained equal to itself in all instances of its application in measurement, under different conditions, at different places and times. We certainly can not know in advance, or *a priori,* that this is so. If we know the properties of rubber bands, we may conclude that they vary in length under varying tensions. If we knew how to maintain exactly the same tension, perhaps even the rubber band would do. But then we need another measurement of equal tensions, defined appropriately so it could be tested, from one rubber band to the next, or at two different times on the same rubber band. We rely rather on some rigid instrument of measurement, one which we take to retain its length invariant through transformation, such as a steel bar, or calipers. But what is the test that assures us that these remain the same? Presumably, somewhere along the line we have to stop at something which we will take as standard, by convention, such as the standard meter bar at the Bureau of Standards in Washington, D.C.

A common simplification of the concept of measurement scales falls into error at this point. For with the use of a standard meter bar, we have not solved the problem, but postponed it. The physical lengths of such standards are not conventional, though which of these lengths we *choose* as standard is conventional, i.e., is selected by an agreement to use that one, rather than this, for reasons of convenience or practicality. For if we take length as a magnitude, we take it as a property of some set of things, and a quantity of this magnitude is not a convention but (in the case of length) a physical property of certain objects or their parts.

The specification of a standard *quantity* of some magnitude is therefore a physically defined operation. We may formally determine what properties such a quantity should have if we want to use it in a certain way; but we discover quantities which have such properties by empirical investigation. Our practice elicits certain of these properties, one of the most important of which is that certain magnitudes admit of addition of parts, or degrees, which is isomorphic with numerical addition, and may thus be represented mathematically by a system with addition. The prerequisite for such additivity is the one we have been discussing, namely, that we establish some unit of magnitude taken as standard and that we use this unit to generate a set of such standard units all of which are equal in that magnitude. Operationally, we may compare two lengths by superposing them, one in contact with the other at all points (technically, we would say the curvature of the bodies having these lengths is equal at the boundary of contact; if the bodies are "straight," then their curvature is 0). We then test empirically to see if the ends, or certain lines or marks inscribed on these bodies, are coincident. For example, we may feel along the ends to see if one overlaps the other or visually assess the coincidence of finely scribed lines. The conditions of *congruence, superposition,* and *coincidence* therefore define the empirical requirements of equal lengths. Any number of lengths established in this way to the degree of precision required (or possible) will constitute a standard set of unit magnitudes. But this is only a step toward the condition of additivity.

We want to say further that two such lengths joined together end to end will constitute a length twice as great as either of the parts, or in other words, a length of two units. It may seem that all we need do to check this is to take some unit magnitude and lay it off twice along this double length. Then, if the end of the unit coincides with the end of the double length, presumably it is twice as long. But this is plainly circular, because we are only performing the same operation twice, once in establishing the "double length," then again, in "checking" it. We might try "adding" a liquid at 45°F to an equal volume at the same temperature, and say that this "addition" gives us "twice as much temperature." If we checked this by comparing the "combined" double volume of temperature to that of a *new* combination of our two units, of course, the temperatures of the two "double volumes" would be "coincident," or would *correspond.* Yet this kind of "addition" does *not* give us a *combined* temperature of 90°F for the double volume.

What we mean by "additive," then, is *not* defined by the operation of adding things or magnitudes together. (In some instances it would even be hard to know what this would mean. Can we "add" mercy to mercy in equal degrees? Can we measure equal amounts of *justice?* Rather, additivity is defined in relation to the arithmetic operation of addition. It is defined in terms of the number property of *cardinality,* in terms of which we interpret addition for the physical magnitude, number. In effect, this asserts that if certain operations of combination of units of some magnitude are carried out, then the combined sets of these units will stand in one-to-one correspondence with cardinal sets, the members of which have undergone similar or analogous operations of combination. But what, in practice, is a cardinal set? It is a collection of units of some magnitude, which are taken to be invariant in this magnitude and which may be numbered by counting; and further, such that a set of this sort corresponds in cardinality to some standard set, by one-to-one matching of units.

But consider: Is not this in fact what we already were doing with lengths? When we say "cardinal set" are we merely repeating, in another language, what was already said about standard sets for any magnitude? Is not the definition of additivity in terms of cardinality circular, once more? Or is cardinality precisely what we have been talking about in attempting to establish a standard set of unit magnitudes? In establishing that the set of fingers of each hand have the same cardinality, we match them one for one. And each finger is taken as invariant in the property of being one finger. Other properties such as its length or weight or configuration do not count here. What counts is what is countable, one by one, assuming or postulating the invariance of our units.* If we call this in itself a magnitude property, because it can be ordered, and further, if we define *quantity* as that which is measurable in terms of this countability of invariant units and of their correspondence with other sets of such units, then this magnitude is not something *like* number, it *is* number. But it is not ordinal number; it is not merely rank-ordered, but is ordered in terms of standard units which mark off equal differences between degrees of a magnitude. The cardinal set three differs from the cardinal set two by the same interval of difference as that between the cardinal set five and the cardinal set four. But the discovery that this relationship is true of some magnitudes and not of others is an empirical discovery. And we have seen that if we attempt to define it within

* See M. Wartofsky, "From Matter to Mass—Comments on E. McMullin's View" in *Boston Studies in The Philosophy of Science,* Vol. II, ed. R. Cohen and M. Wartofsky, New York: Humanities Press, 1965, for a discussion of this postulation of invariance for units.

the confines of a single magnitude, such as length, we attain at best circularity, or an infinite regress.

How in fact are unit magnitudes established? The most common example is that for weights. Weight is an additive magnitude. To establish this we need a standard unit, and some empirical interpretation of its additivity. Two weights are taken to be equal if, when one is placed in each pan of a pan balance the balance is in equilibrium (a redundancy here which means that the weights are equal). Operationally, we might determine whether both pans are at the same height or one is discriminably "lower" than the other. For precision beyond qualitative perception of the horizontality of an imaginary line joining both pans, we would presumably measure the heights of the two pans from some plane surface taken to be horizontal. But this depends not on a standard of weight, but of length or distance, and horizontality (since we intend the heights to be taken from the same base). Or we might take the pans to be in balance if a pointer remained coincident with the same point after the weights were added to the pans as when they were empty. But this is again not a direct comparison of weights, but an interpretation based on some equivalence of or coincidence of lines, or points, which once more depends on rigid bars or equal tensions of a spring.

The conditions for measuring equal weights are thus intertwined with considerations of magnitudes and qualities other than weight. A standard unit such as the gram may be defined as the weight of a cubic centimeter of distilled water at 4°C. The weight in turn is defined in terms of inertia, which relates it to force. Are we to say that two weights are equal if and only if they require equal forces to move them equal distances? Or that two forces are equal if they move equal weights equal distances? Or that two distances are equal if equal forces move equal weights through them? Since the concept of motion involves time, equal or different times will presumably also require specification. In short, the establishment of a standard unit, insofar as it goes beyond the simple convention of choosing some degree of a magnitude to represent it, requires the establishment of a whole system of correspondences. These correspondences are not conventional choices; they are discovered empirically as relations among magnitudes or, in other terms, as isomorphisms among magnitude classes. The most significant isomorphism, which holds among those magnitude classes which we call quantitative, is that which holds between all such classes and the class of cardinal numbers. The formal properties of this relation are those characterizing additivity, which is not a feature of ordinal classes as such. Peano's axioms therefore require supplementation, in this respect, by definitions of the arithmetic operations, as we have seen. If we then interpret Peano's undefined term *number* as "finite cardinal number," and understand somehow the concept of set as a collection of entities having the invariant property of cardinality, then in generating the set of cardinal sets we also generate the standard set of quantitative magnitudes. Any quantitative magnitude will then be one which can be brought into correspondence with this set. This is a formal conception, which does not guarantee at all that such sets exist in concrete experience. It is the physical interpretation of these properties and relations that gives us the various magnitude classes which are quantitative, as distinct from those which are not. What formal structure must such a magnitude class have, then? Summarizing some of the things we have already said, and adding others, we may describe these conditions as follows:

1. For any degrees of magnitude x and y, there is a degree of magnitude z such that $x + y = z$.
2. The sum $(x + y)$ of any degrees of magnitude is greater than either x or y.
3. If we add any degrees of magnitude x, y in the order $x + y$, the sum will be equal in degree of magnitude to the sum of these same degrees of magnitude added in the order $y + x$.
4. For degrees of magnitude $x = x'$ and $y = y'$, the sum of $x + y$ will be equal to the sum of $x' + y'$.
5. For any three degrees of magnitude x, y, z, the sum of $(x + y)$ and z will be equal to the sum of x and $(y + z)$.
6. For any degree of magnitude x smaller than some other degree y, there is a sum of equal degrees of magnitude $(x + x' + x'' \dots)$ which is greater than y.

When these conditions are formulated for the *formal system of numerals* as names of numbers interpreted as finite cardinal sets, then these are the familiar rules of addition. Condition (4), for example gives the *substitutivity of identity,* our old "equals for equals"; condition (3) gives the *commutative rule,* $x + y = y + x$, which says that addition is a symmetrical operation, or that the relation sign '+' denotes a symmetrical relation. Condition (5) gives us the rule of association: $(x + y) + z = x + (y + z)$.

The development of a formal arithmetic, if it can be interpreted for physical magnitudes, offers a way of representing the relations among those magnitude properties which are isomorphic with this arithmetic, i.e., those which exhibit, in empirical practice, these same formal properties of the relations among degrees of magnitude. In short, such magnitudes have number properties, of the sort we have just discussed, and may thus be mapped by the formal system of arithmetic which exhibits these same number properties. It is in this sense that we may define a quantitative magnitude as one which may be brought into correspondence with numbers, or which a formal system of metric mathematics may represent (where *metric* is defined by the conditions (1)–(6).

Quantitative measurement thus has two aspects: first, it involves the empirical discovery of additive relations among the degrees of some magnitude. This does not involve *formal* mathematics at all but the actual processes of using standard empirical units such as lengths, weights, times, forces, etc., and discovering structural correspondences among systems of such units. Second, it involves assigning numerals to degrees of magnitude, by setting magnitude relations in correspondence with numerical relations. The standard set of all magnitude classes having these properties is the set of cardinal numbers, and we may call it the equivalence class of *number,* and take number to be the physical property shared in common by all such magnitude-classes. They are *all* number classes, therefore, and any number class (i.e., of a given cardinality) may be brought into correspondence with any other number class (of the same cardinality). For physical magnitudes the discovery that they are also number classes is an empirical discovery, realized in the process of actual measurement operations; and this is not a convention, although we may conventionally choose which of such number classes we will take as basic in the practice of measurement. This will depend on convenience in actual operations, on practical utility, availability, taste, and relevance to particular problems of measurement. It is clear that the establishment of standard units, such as the standard meter bar, the standard gram, or the standard second or year, aims to fulfill this condition, by choosing reproducible standard units so that standard sets of such units may be produced, transported, checked against each other, and their reliability tested in a system of correspondences capable of being widely carried out.

Thus it is that the foundations of quantitative measurement involve an ever more complex interrelation of formal and empirical concepts, and an ever wider network of systematically connected correspondences, as the demands of the scientific community for precision and clarity in measurement, and for new and unsuspected applications, grow with the progress of scientific inquiry.

SCALES, RATIOS, AND CALIBRATION

The process of measurement involves the use of standard sets as *scales.* Any ordering, whether by identity and difference, or by degrees of magnitude, or by differences in degrees of magnitude in terms of some standard unit, involves, as we have seen, a correspondence of something to something else. That to which the correspondence is made is taken as our scale, in practical use. In testing for concentrations of some chemical substance in a solution, for example, we may use a specially prepared paper as a scale, marking off degrees of magnitude of this concentration by changes in color. In a standard test for sugar in urine, the scale is an ordinally arranged sequence of color gradations against which are matched samples of impregnated paper or chemically treated samples of urine. In the more precise techniques of paper chromatography, specially prepared papers are used to measure the amounts of various chemical elements in a compound. Rates of diffusion, color properties, heights on a graphed scale, dark and light areas on a photographic plate, are all translatable, for purposes of computation, into numerical relations. The translation itself depends on setting up some standard correspondences or numbers and other magnitude properties which are qualitatively ascertainable. This involves *graduating* a scale. In the familiar standard measuring cup the graduations appear as numbered lines at different heights on the side of the cup, where the numerals represent relations among the heights of the lines, which represent relations among the volumes. More complex systems of correspondences are involved in more sophisticated instruments of measurement, often relying for their justification and understanding on highly systematic and complex interrelationships set forth in physical theory. Thus to read a number on a scale marking off a qualitatively perceivable correspondence (as the coincidence of the height of a column of liquid and some numbered line on a scale) is not yet to make a measurement. Only the *interpretation* of this correspondence constitutes measurement proper.

For example, to read off the number 50 on a centigrade thermometer in anything more than a vacuous way—that is, to make a measurement on such a reading, is already to read off a *quantity,* or a dimensional number, "50°C" and not simply the numeral 50. The graduation of scales, such as the thermometric scales, involves the establishment of a standard set of correspondences among quantities of different (or the same) magnitudes. What, then, does the 50 represent on a centigrade thermometer? What does it represent in the way of graduation or calibration of the scale?

Some interval of the scale, if it is to measure the quality *hotness,* is set in correspondence with certain empirical properties of water which are distinctively correlated with differences in this quality: thus, the limits of water's liquid state, between freezing and boiling. The choice of a means to measure the change in hotness over this interval depends here on the purposes of measurement. Clearly, the qualitative distinctions that we may make by means of thermal receptors at the skin surface are unreliable, both with respect to their lack of fine discrimination and to their variability. (A classroom experiment that shows this clearly is the one in which one hand is held in hot water and the other is held in cold, after which an attempt to judge the temperature of some surface or solution is made with each hand, each hand apparently registering a different temperature.) Therefore, by empirical means, we discover the thermal properties of different substances in order to find which can be set in correspondence with different degrees of hotness to give a good measure of such differences. The history of this development is a remarkable case study in scientific thought, involving as it does the close interplay of theoretical formulation and empirical discovery. At any rate, suppose that, after some experimentation, mercury, among the elements in a liquid state, and gases in general have been fixed upon as exhibiting the property of expansion in proportion to the heat to which they are subjected. These are set in correspondence with water at the ice point and at the vapor point, in some tubular container which permits their volume expansion to be measured as a height of liquid mercury or of gas in the tube. The interval between the heights at freezing and boiling is marked off as a standard interval, on the centigrade scale as 0° and 100°; 50°C then clearly marks half of this interval, or fifty units of the 100 into which this interval has been divided. Fahrenheit marks this interval as that between 32° and 212°, dividing the interval differently into 180 units or degrees. The ratios between proportional intervals on either scale remain invariant, so that half of the interval "ice point to steam point" is a "distance" of fifty units on one, and of ninety units on the other, which permits the conversion or transformation from one scale to another which retains this ratio invariance. (i.e., 50:100 :: 90:180), and the fixed points at freezing and boiling are set in correspondence by the simple equality 0°C = 32°F, which gives the conversion we learn in grade school: $F = \frac{9}{5}C + 32$. But this is simply a conventional invariance, by arbitrary choice of numbers. The ratio invariance we seek in measurement is that between the qualitative change in degrees of hotness and the change in the height of a column of mercury or of gas. The standard interval between the ice point and the steam point of water, in degrees of the hotness of the water, is set into correspondence with some standard interval of a column of some substance whose thermal properties register changes in hotness as changes in volume, and these in turn, by changes in height of a column which may be graduated in terms of lengths. The qualitative change in hotness, which we take to be a variable quality in terms of degrees of more and less, is here transformed into a magnitude (length) which permits this same ordering.

This is a grossly simplified account, clearly, and the bibliography supplies references to the rich and extraordinarily interesting literature on this subject. We have ignored or simplified considerations of thermal expansion, heat transfer, proportionality of volumes to lengths. But the point of this simplified model is that in graduating a scale we are in effect establishing that correspondences among ratios of some magnitude or magnitudes may be set up. We say, in effect, a degree of hotness A is to a degree of hotness B as a volume A' is to a volume B', or $A:A'::B:B'$. To establish such a proportionality or such a ratio invariance, we suppose that quantities of some magnitudes or orderable degrees of some magnitude stand in these relations to each other. But to justify such a supposition we need the work of empirical discovery to find out whether in fact such invariances obtain. In thermometry if we take the heights of a column as distances, then on the assumption that distance or length is additive, two equal lengths added together should give one twice as long as either. But if we "add" two solutions together, each with a temperature of 50°C, we assuredly do not get a combined solution of 100°C, so that temperature in this sense is not additive. Yet we may discover what a unit amount of some substance is, which is related to temperature, and which is additive. Thus, to establish the unit amount of *heat* (not the quality *hotness* now) we measure an amount of this substance in terms of "how much of it" will raise the temperature of a gram of distilled water one degree C, if the water is at sea level or a pressure of 1 atmosphere and is at 4°C to start, (or under other standard and specified conditions). What we do, in effect, is to interlock our measurement scales, appealing here to measurements of atmospheric pressure, scales of mass or volume of some standard substance, and to the thermometric scale to establish a new one of heat, measured in units of an additive sort. The preceding definition of the unit *calorie* clearly may be translated into the Fahrenheit scale for temperature and into the pound scale for weight, and thus be correlated with the British Thermal Unit (B.T.U.), which is the amount of heat required to increase the temperature of 1 lb. of water by 1°F. Moreover, the calorie is effectively defined out of existence by the standard physical measure which measures heat energy electrically, i.e., the *joule,* which in turn is defined by the unit of work or energy, the *erg* (1 joule $= 10^7$ ergs), and one *erg* in turn is defined as the work done when a *force* of 1 *dyne* acts through a displacement of 1 cm in the same direction as the force. The gram-calorie, for example, at 15°C has a value of 4.185×10^7 ergs. Thus, measurement establishes not simply a correspondence or an invariance between this and that, but a whole network of such invariances, within which some degrees of a quality or amounts of a quantity are transformed into measureable magnitudes in terms of some other magnitude properties. Such a network involves the close interplay of physical theories and empirical correspondences which go into the apparently "simple" setting up of scales of measurement. Thus, the graduation of a single scale is already a proposive enterprise: What else will be discovered with which this scale is isomorphic through some group of transformations? What light will such ratio invariances shed on relations among physical properties in the world? This, then, is not simply a matter of reading a numeral off an instrument.

To summarize: the use of a scale then involves the establishment of such proportionalities among *ratios* of quantities of some magnitudes. An instrument of measurement is therefore one in which changes in degree of some magnitude are correlated to changes in degree of some other, which is taken as a scale. The calibration of a scale therefore depends on correspondences between such changes in degree, marked off in standard empirical units which are discovered in empirical inquiry. There is no way to know *a priori* that gases expand with temperature, or that the rate of expansion is uniform. As with the motion of free fall, there is no way to know *a priori* that this corresponds in nature to the ideal concept of uniformly accelerated motion. These are hypotheses and are tested in empirical experiment. The graduation of a scale is in fact itself such an experiment, or the result of one. We may choose our calibrations conventionally, but they are locked into the system of such physical correspondences, in which they may be taken to indicate measurements of some quantity, only when an interpretation of the calibrations is available. These correspondences, although they may be hypothesized, are physically significant in measurement only when they are verified in experimental observation.

The distinction between those magnitudes which allow direct comparison of ratios and those which do not is often made as one between *fundamental* and *derived* measurement. Thus, we cannot directly compare hotnesses, in numerical ratios of their quantities, for the measurement of a quantity or degree of hotness depends on its definition in terms of volumes, lengths, and so on. However, we may rank-order hotnesses, in terms of such phenomena as boiling, freezing, melting, expansion, or color changes of those things upon which it has effects, and which are qualitatively discernible. The distance between such qualitative differentiation of degrees of hotness as lends itself to commonsense observation and the measurement of quantities of hotness in some metric system of standard units extends over centuries of scientific work and thought. In physical science the product of this work has been the determination of a set of so-called fundamental magnitudes and of the correspondences which exist between these and other, derived magnitudes. For example, the concept of average velocity, as an intensive *quality* of motion (i.e., speed), is defined for purposes of measurement of *quantities* of this quality, in terms of the ratio of distance to time. Acceleration, by derivation, is defined as a ratio of differences in velocity to differences in time. Force is defined in terms of a ratio of accelerations taken to be proportional to a ratio between masses. Recursively, this can be tracked back to ratios between distances and times, therefore. Similarly, masses are defined in ratio to some unit mass, and this in turn to ratios among weights, and these, as we have seen, are defined in terms of units of volume of some standard substance at a standard temperature. Units of electrical charge and of electrical resistance are similarly defined in terms of weights, distances, and times. Density is defined in terms of the ratio of weight to volume, and volume in terms of ratios of lengths.

Which, then, among the fundamental magnitudes is *the* fundamental magnitude in terms of which the others are defined? From what we have said thus far, it should be clear that there is no one fundamental magnitude, but only fundamental *relations* and *correspondences* among degrees of different magnitudes, and the process of measurement depends on the discovery of empirical *invariances* in these relations. If any magnitudes may be said to be fundamental in the physical sciences, they are *distance* and *time*. But these are no less systemically involved than are the others. For example, we cannot compare units of time with each other to test their equality; we do this by reference to something else taken as a standard: a number of oscillations of a pendulum, or the frequency of electromagnetic oscillators, the astronomical year, or some other recurrent or periodic interval *taken* to be regular, and in terms of which regularity is defined. Such presumed regularity is useless unless some *other* regularity or periodicity may be brought into some invariant correspondence with it. When man first regulated his working and sleeping with the periodic sequence of night and day, a fundamental correspondence was set up. The invariance here seemed a matter of choice. Yet animal organisms are regulated in a surprisingly autonomous way, by so-called biological clocks, and the plasticity of regulation which man exhibits in *choosing* his correspondences becomes less and less as we proceed through "lower" organisms and into the realm of ultimate physical constituents of nature. To the extent that man lives "by the clock" he establishes a correspondence between the order of his activities and some scale. A working schedule is therefore a calibration of enormous plasticity. But it shares the features of all calibrations: correspondences arrived at in experience and experiment between magnitudes relevant to inquiry.

Numbers are characteristically the order we use for calibration for all the reasons previously discussed. But if the isomorphism is established, then any magnitude having number properties may be used as a scale. Why then use numerals as names of numbers? Why calibrated rulers and clocks? Here convenience is central; numerals are easy to carry around, and they stay the same. You can "carry" them mentally or on paper. So too clocks and rulers are conveniently transportable. Volumes get bulky or heavy and hard to manage, and electrical resistances are hard to take from place to place, though one can tell how to reproduce them. Here economy of operation and of thought takes over, specifying *which* standard sets we shall use as scales, which calibrations are most useful and serve computation best, and which ratios are significant and relevant to the specific tasks of inquiry.

THE USES OF MEASUREMENT

The continuity of theoretical science and common practice is nowhere more evident than in the development of the techniques and theory of measurement. That rationalization of common practice which we call technology is the matrix in which the concepts of measurement are formed, and to which they are referred for the test of their adequacy. But the discontinuity of scientific thought and common sense is also sharply brought forth in this context. In the technical and workaday practice of measurement its use is to facilitate the planning and organization of the production and distribution of goods, to help guarantee control over quality, and to meet the requirements of standardization. In science, the use of measurement is to serve theory, in its two contexts of discovery and justification. The typical experiment eventuates in a measurement, or a set of them. The typical hypothesis becomes testable in terms of predictions in the form of measurement statements. The typical theoretical formulation, in those sciences which have advanced in the use of mathematics, involves calculation in some formal system which is linked with some system of physical magnitudes which serve as its interpretation.

In the following chapters we will examine the procedures of experimentation, generalization and hypothesis, and the concepts of law and theory. Measurement will then be seen in its native scientific habitat, not in the museum in which we have placed it for special consideration in this chapter. Here we will limit ourselves to a brief consideration of how measurement may be said to "empiricize" scientific concept formation, linking theory to practice. We will consider first the role of *precision* in scientific measurement, and its relation to testing and to confirmation and falsification of scientific predictions. Then we will suggest the relation of measurement to the discovery of laws, leaving the fuller discussion of this topic to a later chapter.

PRECISION AND TESTING

To call a measurement precise is to take for granted that one understands the framework within which some measurement is relatively *more* precise than another. It was remarked earlier that precision is hardly an intrinsic property of measurements. We could not know, without making the relevance of a measurement explicit, whether a tolerance of plus or minus 2 inches is precise or imprecise. The accuracy of a foot rule would certainly be destroyed if the limits of its accuracy were this wide. However, if one "aimed" a rocket at some small crater on the moon's surface, the requirement that it land within 2 inches of some hypothetical "point" of impact would be insane, and in practice unfeasible. Within the limits of measurability, attainable precision is not always the same as requisite precision. The question for the practice of measurement in science is to establish the requisite precision for a specific inquiry. But what is the object of measurement in such a case? It may be to collect information whose interpretation is not yet clear or whose use in computation is not yet worked out. Astronomical observation to the limits of attainable accuracy proceeds in this way, often, in that initial procedure of data-collection which postulates that the *more* accurate the information, the more likely it is that certain relations among the physical phenomena will be discovered. Measurement to the limits of attainable accuracy is also often part of the ongoing testing of accepted laws and theories, which has historically led to their refinement, modification, and even overthrow. In such contexts, where the test of measurement is not keyed to the refutation or confirmation of a specific and severely circumscribed prediction statement, and where what measurement will reveal is beyond the "horizon of expectations" (to use Karl Popper's phrase), we may say that the requisite precision is the maximum attainable precision. For such purposes, which reach beyond the horizon of present scientific formulation, the invention or discovery of more highly precise instruments of observation and measurement is always important. Thus the telescope and the microscope revealed a depth of information which shook the older science to its foundations. Similarly, today the mass spectrometer, the laser beam, the ion accelerator, the atomic clock reveal distinctions in magnitude which serve in the ongoing testing of theories and in the discovery of new laws concerning the invariant ratios between magnitudes. The limitations here are practical and theoretical. There are conceivable accuracies not yet attained, degrees of precision conceptually but not yet technically feasible. There is, however, a proposed theoretical limitation on precision of measurement of the very small, which quantum theory introduces. It says, in effect, that in terms of the classical fundamental physical magnitudes which relate mass, length, and time, and in terms of which the classical description of simultaneous momentum and position of elementary physical particles is given, measurability has a lower limit beyond which it cannot physically proceed.

Another use of measurement, however, is the confirmation and falsification of scientific predictions *already* framed within a certain *range* of meaningful and relevant precision. For example, if one were to predict that an eclipse of the moon was to take place on Sunday of this week, the scale of time measurement relevant to such a (hopelessly vague) prediction would be a calendar rather than a stop watch graduated in tenths of a second. More realistically, the classification of blood types requires only relatively crude approximations, given the maximum attainable precision we can achieve today in chemical analysis or in microscopic techniques. But this is to say that the limit of attainable accuracy is reserved to those experiments and to those inquiries for which such accuracy is significant. For a given task at hand the allowable tolerances of measurement are defined in relation to the nature of decision that such measurement observations are to support or refute. A scientific statement capable of being supported or refuted by measurement observations is always framed in some context which defines the range of requisite precision.

We may then say that one use of such measurement observations, or of measurement statements referring to such observations, is the *testing* of scientific predictions. If, as we claimed earlier, every observation statement is made in some framework within which it is significant, and if we consider that measurement includes the continuum of such observation statements, from the simplest identifications to the most sophisticated statements of ratio invariance among magnitudes, then all scientific observation is, to one degree or another, measurement. The simple observation statement, "I observe that the ball is red," already carries with it the framework within which "ball" and "red" are distinguishable from "not ball" and "not red," by some criterial attributes which permit us to classify. The use of these would then permit us to decide, within such a scheme, that something was not a ball or not red. But scientific measurement differs from commonsense observation in the degree to which it does specify the criteria for such divisions (explicitly or implicitly, within the "culture" of scientific practice). Thus, to say that we have separated off the "pure form" of some chemical element is to claim that no trace of impurity, or no presence of any other element is *detectable*. But in every such case the standard conditions of detection are included or understood as measurements within a certain degree of precision. It is always possible that with more refined methods some such impurity may be discovered. The *tolerance* of such measurement is always specified, therefore, as within "so many parts in a thousand," or "plus or minus some amount." The empirical test of a scientific statement is therefore always a test within some range of precision, whether it is explicitly stated or tacitly understood.

If, for example, a prediction states that within the range of precision determined by a smallest unit of measurement, say 0.001 in. the length of some object should turn out to be 7.532 in. ± 0.001 in., we understand the prediction to mean that the length will be *between* 7.531 in. and 7.533 in. Two *different* measurements will not *falsify* this prediction if they are within that range, no more than the observation of both three-legged tigers *and* four-legged tigers would falsify the statement, "Tigers have more than two legs." We *do* assume, however, that a length measurement of 7.5326 in. is *more* precise than one of 7.532 in., because it contains *more* information. Yet it would be meaningless to say that the statement, "Tigers have 4.375 legs," is more accurate than the statement, "Tigers have 4 legs," because fractions of the unit *leg* are undefined and meaningless magnitudes in this context. Precision is therefore always relative to some unit taken as standard, or as the feasible or meaningful limit of precision in measurement. But does this mean that we may always define precision as relative to whatever we happen to choose as a smallest unit-magnitude? Our intuitive notion of precision does not accord with this relativism. In general, we relate the notion of *degree* of precision to some notion of *absolute* precision. Presumably, the most precise statement concerning any matter of fact is the one which most adequately represents the *truth* of the case. The conceptual limit of precision is the limit of empirical content or information concerning some matter of fact. Absolute precision would therefore give us all there is to be known about anything; it would be the "whole truth," and as such would be absolute knowledge, where nothing remains to be learned. But the fact that tigers have four legs is presumably all we can ever find out about tiger-leggedness. If we found two-legged or six-legged tigers, we would account for them as abnormal freaks, or as not, properly speaking, tigers at all. At most, we would subclassify tigers into two-legged, four-legged, six-legged, and *n*-legged subspecies. Yet our unit magnitude would remain a countable "unit-leg."

Yet there are magnitudes which we take to be variable not in *discrete* degrees. Length, time, weight, electrical charge, angle, volume, velocity, acceleration, and energy are among the fundamental magnitudes which we ordinarily take to be *continuously variable*. When we choose a smallest unit magnitude of length, we conceive that there is a length half as great as this, or that this magnitude is infinitely divisible. So too, when we speak of uniformly accelerated motion, the assumption is that between any two degrees of this magnitude, there is a third, however close we take these degrees to be. Part of the reason for this is that in our use of mathematical representations of such magnitudes we use a system which takes the magnitude *number* to be infinitely divisible, so that any quantity is divisible into its parts. There are no number atoms, or length atoms, or time atoms in such a view. Thus, the imposition of any numerical representation on a degree of such a magnitude, which "quantizes" it, is the choice of a standard unit *taken* to be discrete, and distinguishably different from any multiples or fractions of it, however little the difference. The *physical* assumption of such continuity, in a physical magnitude, is not something we know *a priori*, however. Thus, even if we *knew* or theoretically affirmed that there *was* a smallest physical length L in numerical computation, we would still hold that $\frac{1}{2}L + \frac{1}{2}L = L$, or that $\sqrt{L} \cdot \sqrt{L} = L$. Yet such expressions as $\frac{1}{2}L$ or $\sqrt{L}$ may be denied any physical significance and asserted to have only computational significance.

This differs, however, from another proposed limitation in contemporary physics, which asserts that *measurement* has inherent *physical* limitations, at the level of the *quantum of energy*. This is a unit magnitude which theoretically has no "parts" or fractional values, but is discrete, in integral units and multiples of these units. Such a magnitude is not continuously variable, but discretely variable, and thus numerical values which are fractions of such units are physically meaningless, as in the case of tiger legs.

Within such a framework, precision *beyond* the theoretically asserted limitations on measurability is redundant and empirically impossible to achieve. That is to say, there is, within this system, no *language* which may be used meaningfully to name a degree of magnitude smaller than this unit. For continuously variable magnitudes, where this condition would not obtain, we would need a system in which any degree of a magnitude would be meaningfully specifiable. For the Greeks, as we have seen, the length of the diagonal of a square was "incommensurable" with the sides, and was an "irrational" number, in terms of its magnitude. That is, it could not be named in the language of rational numbers, which were taken as ratios between integers. Yet in a physical sense, such a diagonal would have *some* length and would be a magnitude of some degree, although it might be *between* the values of any degree of length namable in the usual way. Such magnitudes as are not namable within the rational number system require some specification. So, although a length of $\sqrt{2}$ inches is only specifiable as lying between two other rational lengths, it is specifiable in this way. The real number system, which includes such irrational numbers (more than there can be names for), that is to say, the irrationals constitute a non-denumerable infinity, is thus the appropriate scale for continuously variable magnitudes. Thus measurement which proceeds on the assumption of unlimited measurability of some magnitude, such as length, makes use of this scale. Barring some fundamental length, beyond which the concept of length breaks down (for example, beyond which it is no longer additive), precision in such measurement is limited in practice by the conditions and instruments of measurement available, but theoretically it is unlimited. The thesis of limited measurability in quantum physics states only that the *joint* measurement of two magnitudes simultaneously is limited. When we realize that physical description often involves ratios of magnitudes, (as velocity involves the ratio of distance and time), then this limitation can be seen to be physically important.

We have seen earlier that precision has a special use in the falsifiability of empirical statements in science. It is, in some intuitive sense, "easier" to refute the claim that all the students in a class are between 6 feet and 6 feet, 7 inches tall than it is to refute the claim that they are all "tall students." The precision in the former case permits one to decide the matter unambiguously (within the limits of precision of, let us say, inch measurement), whereas in the latter, the qualitative concept *tall* remains too vague, without further specification, to admit of an easy decision. Karl Popper has proposed that the degree of testability of a scientific statement is in proportion to its precision. Taking *range* to mean the "tolerance in measurement," he asserts that the wider the range, the less the amount of empirical information, and the less the precision. But the less the precision, the lower the degree of testability, or the harder it would be to refute or falsify a statement. He thus tries to order degrees of precision with relation to degrees of falsifiability and degrees of empirical content. Thus, a science has an empirical content to the degree that its statements are falsifiable—that is, to the degree that there is a test in terms of which the statements could be shown to be false. Precision in measurement is therefore an instrument of this testability, greater precision indicating a greater empirical content in the statements.[2]

Another view (which Popper rejects) would claim that with increasing precision in measurement, measurement statements which accord with scientific predictions *confirm* such statements, and confirm them more highly as increasingly precise measurements more fully approximate the ideal mathematical statement of physical laws. Galileo's claim to have gotten exact agreement between his predictions and his measurements in the

[2] K. Popper, *The Logic of Scientific Discovery* (London: Hutchinson & Co., 1959), Ch. VI.

inclined-plane experiments has often been challenged, or explained as caused by the cancelling out of errors, in the crude approximations to the "real values" of the magnitudes he attained with his relatively crude measuring devices. However, Galileo's explicit testimony in other instances shows that he was willing to overlook discrepancies between theoretical predictions and observed results, in the interest of what he took to be revelations of ratio invariance *within the limits of observational error*. The confirmation of the ideally formulated laws of physical science is then taken as the *approximation* in measurement, to predicted results, where increasing precision shows an ever-closer approximation to some ideal limit.

MEASUREMENT AND DISCOVERY

Related to this view of the role of measurement in confirmation of laws is the view which sees measurement as an instrumentality in the *discovery* of laws. We will discuss the *inductivist* view of the discovery of laws in a later chapter. But here we may briefly characterize this position as it relates to measurement in a specific way. Mendeleev's establishment of the periodic table of the elements was the result of a history of measurements and their theoretical interpretation, from the time of Lavoisier and Dalton on. The *periodicity* of the table, as is known, is arranged according to the periodic *properties* of elements. Thus, elements having similar chemical properties are listed under each other in the table, the whole sequence following the order of atomic weights (Mendeleev's original scheme, which breaks down in a number of places), or more accurately, in the order of atomic numbers. The recurrence of similar properties in elements, in some periodic way, was early noted by the English chemist Newlands, who sought to define this regularity in terms of "octaves" as in a musical scale, a similar property occurring in each eighth element of the series. This works only within certain limits, as the modern periodic table shows. But if we take a periodic property which defines such a "family" of elements as alkali metals as the key to their listing in the table, then in the column of alkali metals we will have Hydrogen (H) which is not *uniquely* related to any family and has special properties but is related to the alkali metals and halogens; lithium (Li); sodium (Na); potassium (K); rubidium (Rb); cesium (Cs); and francium (Fr). The list of this family and of their atomic numbers will look like this:

Hydrogen	(H)	1
Lithium	(Li)	3
Sodium	(Na)	11
Potassium	(K)	19
Rubidium	(Rb)	37
Cesium	(Cs)	55
Francium	(Fr)	87

This listing is the result of quantitative and qualitative analysis of the properties of these elements, and the numbers therefore represent certain measurement-derived relations between these elements. Their grouping depends on their classificatory similarity in certain properties, e.g., that they are soft metals, that they are alkali, that they react violently with water, and so on. If we inspect the sequence of atomic numbers, it certainly gives no immediate clue to any recurrent periodicity. On inspection, however, it may be seen that the differences, in sequence, between each of these numbers gives the series 2, 8, 8, 18, 18, 18, 32. Again, except for repetition in parts of the series, there is no immediately obvious periodicity. Yet the numbers 2, 8, 18, 32 *do* bear a serial relation to each other, proceeding as they increase, in the relation $2(1^2)$, $2(2^2)$, $2(3^2)$, $2(4^2)$, or twice the square of the successive integers beginning with 1.

When this was first noted there was no explanation for this periodicity, which exhibits a numerical law. Only with the development of Bohr's model of the atom, with its electron "shells," do these numbers take on some physical significance, as the "shells" are conceived to have groupings of electrons in such characteristic groups as 2, 8, and 18. Thus, for example, all the elements in this list are monovalent, having one electron in the outermost shell. But this can be seen from the interpretation of the numbers 2, 8, 18 as characteristic of the groupings of "completed" shells. Thus, Li, with an atomic number of 3, would be arranged 2, 1; Na, with an atomic number of 11, would be arranged 2, 8, 1, and so on. (See Fig. 5.) The

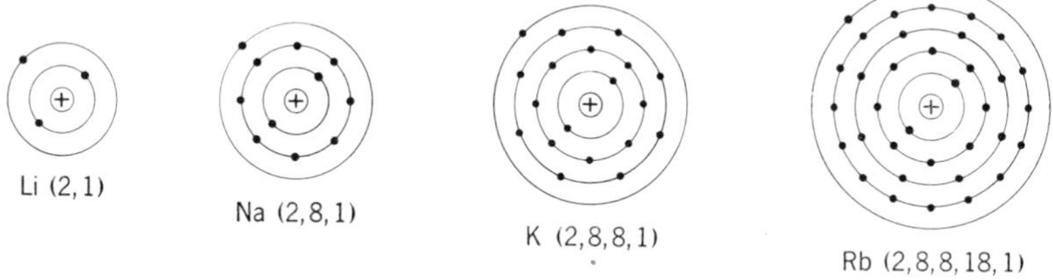

Fig. 5

so-called noble gases (neon, argon, krypton, xenon) have "complete" outer shells of eight electrons and the arrangements are

Ne	atomic number 10	2, 8
A	atomic number 18	2, 8, 8
Kr	atomic number 36	2, 8, 18, 8
Xe	atomic number 54	2, 8, 18, 18, 8

In the case of the periodic table, the discovery of a numerical law in the results of measurement did not lead directly to a physical interpretation of this law. Bohr's atomic model was not derived by him from the numerical properties of the periodic table. But the model of electron shells led to a physical interpretation of these numerical relations, and thus to a theoretical explanation of them. In this instance the abstract mathematical sequence generated by $2(1^2)$, $2(2^2)$, $2(3^2)$ . . . $2(n^2)$ was not derived from some fundamental postulates or theoretical formulations in physics or chemistry; rather, it was discovered in the results of quantitative measurement.

This revelation of mathematical order in nature lends comfort to all those who feel, as did the Pythagoreans, that mathematics exhibits the fundamental features of reality itself. James Clerk Maxwell, in his *Scientific Papers,* saw the significance of this correspondence in the more sober terms of the working mathematical physicist: "All the mathematical sciences are founded on relations between physical laws and laws of numbers."[3]

In the case of Galileo's formulation of the law of freely falling bodies, the numerical law (in modern terms, $s = \frac{1}{2}kt^2$), preceded any quantitative measurements. Instead, it was derived from more fundamental postulates concerning uniformly accelerated motion and was used as an experimental hypothesis to be tested by the approximations to its predictions which measurement revealed. (See the full discussion of this in Appendix A.)

The discovery of numerical laws in the data provided by measurement is far from a straightforward matter of "discovering laws of nature." Mathematical ingenuity may come up with any number of *ad hoc* formulas which order the data of measurement in terms of some mathematical function. At most this sort of mapping suggests that there may be law-like invariances which are scientifically significant, that is, which express some order in nature. In Chapter 9, we will examine the problems which such inductive claims to the discovery of laws of nature raise; and in Chapter 11, the relation of such mathematical invariance to causality will be considered. But it is clear, even prior to a more detailed consideration, that the discovery of some mathematical invariance among the data of measurement is not yet the discovery of a law of nature or of a causal relation. But it does nevertheless serve the important functions of ordering the data in an economical way, and of suggesting that some physical interpretation of such numerical laws may be found which does reveal some aspect of natural order or causal relation. Once such law-like hypotheses are proposed, it is measurement once again which offers the means of testing the hypotheses. Thus measurement operates both in the discovery and justification of empirical laws.

[3] J. C. Maxwell, *Scientific Papers,* Vol. I, p. 156, cited by H. Weyl, *Philosophy of Mathematics and Natural Science* (Princeton, N.J.: Princeton University Press, 1949), p. 144.

CHAPTER 8

Hypothesis and Experiment

IN THE COMMONSENSE PICTURE OF SCIENCE, hypothesis and experiment figure as the two poles of scientific activity. One represents the "thinking" of the scientist, as the other represents his "observation," repeating once more that duality of reason and sense which runs through the development of science and of ordinary knowledge. Here, however, the crucial emphasis is on something *tentatively* proposed, by reason or by imagination, and then tested for its truth or validity by some direct confrontation with "the facts." Like all commonplaces, this one also has its grain of truth. But the concepts of hypothesis and experiment hide as much as they reveal in the common view. At this point in our examination the explication of these concepts will take into account all our previous considerations concerning observation, formal systems, and measurement. If we are to distinguish the hypotheses and experiments of science from the day-to-day posits and tests by which we regulate our ordinary activity, then the scientific sort will be distinctively placed in our more systematic framework. If, on the other hand, we seek for the continuities between commonsense supposing and scientific hypothesizing, they lie in this: that the "plain facts of observation" are never so plain that they do not take on their character as "facts" within some framework of interpretation and supposition. The lowliest purported fact, in the most common observation statement, already *pre*supposes a conceptual framework within which it attains to significance, and goes beyond the brute and ineffable idiocy of sheer sensation.

In this sense, every conscious act of observation is a probe, an encounter of expectation with environment. In some generic sense, admittedly vague but still further specifiable, this probing is the characteristic of all organisms, and of what used to be called the "irritability" of cell tissue. The amoeba's pseudopod extends the cell into a new environment, and on encounter with this or that, it engulfs, or retracts, responding to different stimuli in ways characteristic of its structure and chemistry. One can hardly talk of anticipation or expectation at this level, but the more highly complex organisms have structures which respond in ways which we, by analogy to our own behavior, call anticipatory. Our own anticipations proceed to the point of conscious expectation, the imaginary rehearsal of an anticipated occurrence, or outcome; and the structures within which we shape these anticipations are the relatively new and remarkable ones we call language and thought. Thus, as we have seen, naming and identifying involves the proposive activity of taking something as a member of a class, but to do this is to engage an object in a network of relations within which our class-concept is already held, in virtue of our very use of a language as speakers and comprehenders. *Tree* is thus not a tag, like *X* or * (by which we may also "name" objects); rather, it is a word in a language in which its meaning is already contextually bound with the myriad syntactic and semantic associations which any language user brings to bear.

All this is by way of stating an initial thesis: that any descriptive utterance, any observation statement is already a hypothesis; and further, that every such hypothesis already carries with it a matrix of relevance which guides us to engage in those tests of experience which we take to support or to fail to support this hypothesis. Within the framework of language the name and the description give us this matrix: *The bear is a furry animal* already contains a designation and a set of tests for the validity of this designation. *Furry* may be further described, as may also *animal.* But commonsense hypothesis and experiment stop here, for the instrument of common sense is fashioned for ready use and economy of operation in its context. No use telling the five-year-old that the concept *animal* is extraordinarily complex and that the full range of "confirmations" required to test whether anything falls under this concept involves a sophisticated biology and a laboratory procedure. The five-year-old is right if he refuses to accept your qualification. Language is fashioned, in matters like this, for decisions whose rapidity and practical certainty are their crucial characteristics.

But if anything is true of the hypotheses of science, it is that they are *not* certain, nor are they quickly decidable. Their strength lies not in their decisiveness but in their precision. And this is tied to the framework within which they are formulated. It is not the framework of ordinary language and commonsense concepts, but that framework of scientific language and concepts which takes the measurement statement as the characteristic observation statement. This, as was noted in Chapter 7, gives science its empirical character and makes it more than simply the rational criticism of concepts. We take the truths or the valid statements of science to be such as are supported by experimental evidence—such, therefore, as have withstood the test of attempted refutation in *scientific experience.* And we consider as empirical or empirically relevant hypotheses those which can conceivably be put to such a test. But such an apparently straightforward conception raises problems of philosophical analysis concerning hypothesis and experiment, and calls forth often sharp differences between philosophers of science.

THE MEANINGS OF *HYPOTHESIS*

No term in science suffers a greater ambiguity than does *hypothesis.* One could make up a list of contradictory statements about hypotheses and their status and use in scientific discussion which would make the scientific community look like something on the other side of Alice's looking glass. The most famous statement about hypotheses is probably Newton's, in which he claims not to "feign" them (*"Hypotheses non fingo,"* the sense of which is still disputed, but is ordinarily taken to mean that he plain does not *make* them). In much scientific writing, especially of the descriptive and biographical sort, in which one reports on what one has done, or what someone else is doing, the term is used in a variety of ways. For our discussion then, it will be useful to sort some of these alternative meanings out, and then to specify, if possible, some more restricted sense in which we will use the term here.

In general (and about this there seems to be some agreement in usage) a hypothesis is taken as a proposal to accept something as true. In this sense, it is tinged with tentativeness, with the conscious qualifier, "What if such and such were taken to be the case?" as against the assertion, "Such and such *is* the case," or, "It can be shown that such and such is true." This general sense we will want to retain and elaborate. But there are differences with respect to at least two contexts: the status of such a proposal and its scope.

With regard to the status of hypotheses, the question may be raised as to what sort of statements they are, and also as to what their sources are. In the empirical sciences (disregarding for the moment the special senses of *"hypothesis"* which obtain in mathematics and logic) hypotheses are taken to be proposals concerning *either* matters of fact (e.g., the heliocentric "hypothesis" as a proposal that the sun is in fact at the center of the solar system) *or* concerning how it would be best to conceive of matters of fact. The distinction is subtle, but important. For in the first case, something is being proposed which is purported to be true, or whose truth may conceivably be established, presumably by experiment and observation. In the second, however, there is a reticence concerning any matter-of-fact interpretation; rather, the claim of such a proposal is that it would be useful to picture or arrange things in a certain way. The hypothesis here serves as a *model* whose justification is the convenience or pleasure it affords, or the aid it gives to the understanding. It functions therefore as an aid to thought or an exercise in imagination. This heuristic use is, for example, the one which is a classroom commonplace: "Let's imagine that two masses in space are connected by a spring," or, "Let's suppose that all of space is filled with a perfectly elastic fluid." The qualification here is always more than just the tentativeness of the hypothesis; it is rather the explicit sense that this is *not* to be taken as a conjecture about what the facts are, but only how it might be profitable to conceive or picture them. We might distinguish between these two as *factual* and *ideal* hypotheses, keeping in mind that this makes no claim as to some intrinsic preference either for "facts" or "ideas," in empirical science, but only marks the distinction as to what each takes as its object.

But this raises the following epistemological question: if a hypothesis is conjecturally about matters of fact, then, in the economy of our knowledge where does it *come* from? And if indeed it is only a proposal to think a certain way about something, what is the epistemological or psychological origin of this sort of proposal? Here the question is not "What objects does the hypothesis refer to?" but "What is the subjective source of such proposals." Or more sharply, do hypotheses refer at all, or are they *meanings* or *senses* useful only in the systematic framework of bringing concepts together in our understanding? Here we may distinguish among four views:

(1) *Hypotheses are generalizations from experience.*

A hypothesis is a summary statement, in universal form, which generalizes a whole set of observations, in terms of some feature or relation found to be *invariant* in the set. The proposiveness of the hypothesis goes beyond mere summary, however, in that it tentatively conjectures that what is generally true for a finite set of observations is also true for any additions to the set that one may make. This claims, in effect, that hypotheses are genuine *inductive generalizations* (about which we shall say more in the next chapter) and that they have their sources in the "direct experience" of observation or "fact finding"; or, to qualify this somewhat, that they are discovered in examining the results of observation or of experiment.

(2) *Hypotheses are deductive inferences made from some higher-order premises.*

In science there are certain established and accepted principles and theoretical statements of universal scope and high generality, such as, "Every action has an equal and opposite reaction," or, "No effect without a cause," or, "In a closed system, energy is conserved," or, "The part is less than the whole," which may serve as major premises of a formal deduction. We may disregard the origin or the status of such statements of high generality—for example, whether they are postulates, or axioms, or self-evident truths, or intuitions, or analytic truths, or inductive generalizations, or wild hunches. What is important is that they serve, together with certain other statements taken as minor premises, and with some rule of inference, as the grounds of formal inference in which an empirically significant conclusion is drawn. Such a conclusion may then serve as a prediction, generated with the help of such premises and testable by measurement or observation. The acceptability of the statements of high generality which serve as major premises is based either on some autonomous grounds—e.g., that they are "truths of reason" or synthetic *a priori* truths—or on the grounds of their utility in generating interesting or testable predictions, or on their presumed confirmation by virtue of the success of the predictions they help to generate. (In each of these cases there are serious problems which we shall examine later.)

We may then consider a hypothesis to be the "instantiation" of such a high-order principle or theoretical statement; that is to say, a deductive inference, by way of a minor premise which connects the general principle to some particular instance of it. We may call such a hypothesis an *instantial hypothesis.* For example, if our general statement is some well-established theoretical statement such as, "The atomic weight of mercury (Hg) is 200.61," then the instantial hypothesis may be, "If this particular sample x is a sample of mercury, then x has an atomic weight of 200.61." The truth of the antecedent ("This particular sample x is a sample of mercury") would presumably depend on some tests of the sample. Taking the truth of the antecedent to have been thus established within the limits of empirical test, we may separate the consequent ("x has an atomic weight of 200.61") as the actual prediction which the hypothesis makes.

In some popular usage this conclusion itself is taken as the hypothesis. That is, the prediction itself is called the hypothesis, as in, "It is my hypothesis that the atomic weight of this sample is 200.61, in the light of other facts we know about it, and about the atomic weight of mercury." But this seems merely an elliptical way of stating the instantial hypothesis in the form we have given. However, we may also choose to take as our hypothesis the major premise itself ("The atomic weight of mercury is 200.61"), reserving to "hypothesis" the sense of high generality and regarding all the rest as testable consequences of this hypothesis.

The difference may be schematized thus. In the first case, of instantial hypothesis, the major premise serves as a categorical statement taken to be true. Thus, the form of the argument is (where P stands for the major premise, Q for the minor premise, and the instantial statement R for the conclusion),

$$P \text{ and if } Q \text{ then } R$$

In the second case, the hypothesis is, "If anything is a sample of mercury then it has an atomic weight of 200.61." Schematically, where Mx stands for "x is Mercury" and Ax stands for "x has an atomic weight of 200.61,"

$$\text{For any } x \text{ if } Mx \text{ then } Ax$$

The hypothesis in this form is then said to be "confirmed" or at least subject to test by its instantiation, that is by the instances *Ma* and *Aa, Mb* and *Ab*, . . . *Mk* and *Ak*. The expanded form of this hypothesis and its testable consequences would then be

If *P* then (if *Q* then *R*)

But plainly, such a hypothesis is not generated by its own instantiations, and we may take it in turn as the conclusion of a deductive inference from premises of still higher generality, e.g., from some law which predicts what the atomic weight of an element will be on the basis of other theoretical considerations. Thus, what serves as the conclusion in such a deductive argument of higher generality may serve as the premise in a deductive argument of lower generality. In this sense, higher-level laws or principles may serve as premises for the deduction of lower-level laws. The test of such laws presumably rests on being able to deduce statements of the sort which are instantially testable, that is, which are capable of being tested in particular instances of measurement or observation.

(3) *Hypotheses are postulates or suppositions, created freely by the mind so that other statements may be ordered by or derived from them.* A hypothesis in this case needs no "justification" in terms of its source, or derivation, but only in its use. Like the folk heroes of fable, such postulates appear and do their work of ordering things and saving appearances, and no one inquires into their mysterious and godlike birth. They prove themselves by their deeds. The connection with experiential sources, with "deep structures" of the human mind, or with creative genius thus falls outside the scope of what concerns such postulates. Their function is not to describe what is the case, or to allege that the facts are such and so, but to provide a means of ordering or reconstructing the order of known facts in some way better than some previous ordering. Such postulates must also permit one to deduce consequences as yet not tested and known, so that the function of such hypotheses is both formal-systematic and empirical-fruitful in suggesting new factual consequences.

(4) *Hypotheses are intuitions concerning either what appears self-evident, or necessary to believe or what suggests itself as plausible in some vague but insistent way.* The sources of hypotheses here are taken to be some deeply working "intuitions of the mind" (especially of a mind prepared to make use of such intuitions by wide knowledge of the facts to which they would be relevant). In one or another version of this view, hypotheses are "hunches," or the work of deep recognitions of analogy in the subconscious or preconscious mind, or felicitous recall or archetypal patterns or the explicit form which the *a priori* structures of knowledge take when they are brought to the surface by the suggestions of experience. Such a hypothesis is the "flash" or "click" of recognition, the "Eureka" experi-

ence, in which discovery takes place by some undecipherable and non-inferential activity. Archimedes' bathtub, Newton's apple, and Planck's stepping up on a trolley are the paradigm cases. The explanations for such intuitions vary widely, from the views which see this as in general the feature of creative genius in art as in science, to the speculations concerning sources in some Jungian Archetypes of racial memory, to the notions of patterns or *Gestalt* recognition of form in variety, to Kantian notions of the Transcendental Unity of Apperception, to views concerning underlying structures of language and thought. In short, much of the explanation of such intuition, as direct or immediate recognition of some unifying idea, lies in psychological and epistemological discussion of scientific thought, or of creative human activity in general. But the use of such hypotheses, as in the case of postulational or supposititious hypotheses does not demand a birth certificate. Here, as in paragraph (3), the role of speculative activity, of the exercise of the imagination, freed from considerations of empirical sources or logical deduction within some system, is "justified" by the role which such hypotheses play in ordering and unifying known facts and in producing testable consequences, in the form of predictions concerning facts not yet known.

The scope of hypotheses also varies. Some of this variety has already been suggested; the degree of generality of a hypothesis is thus one measure of differences in scope. Instantial hypotheses, as predictions concerning particular matters of fact, are narrowest in scope, in this context, corresponding in effect to observation statements, where these are taken as hypothetical. Hypotheses of wider scope would then be generalizations concerning whole classes of observation statements, and these in turn would vary from low-level empirical generalizations ("The body type of inhabitants of Boston has a normal distribution which peaks at the ecto-morph-mesomorph line," or, "Iron expands when heated"), to higher-level generalizations ("All metals expand when heated," or, "The periods of the planets are incommensurable"), to statements whose scope is such that it would be hard to call them generalizations at all ("Space is curved," "The inertial path of a particle on a sphere is a geodesic"), but which still presumably have testable consequences in observation. One common division of such statements is to call them hypotheses when they are first proposed and then to call them laws, "when they are proven," which usually means after some experimental test has been performed which supports the initial conjecture. When laws are of high generality they are "theories."

This usage has little to commend it, except that it marks degrees of acceptability and degrees of generality of hypotheses. But it engenders more confusion than clarity, and when we discuss laws and theories we will propose an alternative distinction. One philosopher of science proposes grouping these levels of generality in terms of their functional differences. Thus, Ernst Cassirer (in *Determinism and Indeterminism in Modern Phys-*

ics) proposes that the lowest-level statements are measurement statements; empirical laws come next; and principles are last, representing those *forms* of thought within which alone any science is possible (as, for example, the principle of causality). Duhem, whom we have previously cited, distinguishes between empirical laws and theories, the latter being no more than economical ways of ordering and classifying the former, for purposes of mathematical representation in physics, thus permitting the powerful inferential apparatus of mathematics to operate symbolically with respect to empirical interpretations. In each of these cases, however, it is not clear how the term *hypothesis* is used, because laws and theories are both tentative and subject to refutation, and thus "hypothetical" in that sense. Duhem, however, uses *hypothesis* to mean theoretical postulates of the highest order of generality, such as that of universal gravitation, which lie at the base of physical theories, or which function as postulates used in the derivation of theories. Duhem further holds that, "The physicist does not choose the hypotheses on which he will base a theory; they germinate in him without him."[4]

All these views, however, agree in general that hypotheses (however they define the scope or degree of generality) are within the domain of scientific thought. There is a view which would hold that the scope of hypotheses varies not only in degree but in kind, and here we may suggest three kinds of hypotheses in which scope is so far divergent in each case as to make for a discontinuity in the domain of hypotheses.

(1) *Commonsense or observational hypotheses.* These, plainly, would be hypotheses concerning such matters of fact that could be directly tested in some versions of looking and seeing: "The milk will turn sour if you leave it in the sun," for example, or "Early to bed, early to rise makes a man healthy, wealthy, and wise." Both of these can be shown to be false, and so as proposals about matters of fact, testable and refutable, they would function on a low level, not with respect to their generality, but with respect to the kind of experiment needed to test them.

(2) *Scientific hypotheses.* Scientific hypotheses would go beyond commonsense observation, in the sense that the *observation language* for the testing of such hypotheses would not include such commonsense terms as *sour* or *wealthy,* but terms whose meaning and reference are defined within some theoretical framework in a science. Clearly, all measurement statements in which numbers and such fundamental physical magnitudes as mass, electrical resistance, and acceleration are used would require more than ordinary observation as their basis. Thus, any hypothesis, the observation language for which is a theoretically defined language (as we have seen, the language of magnitudes is in science), would be a scientific one, whose testing would presumably demand the controlled experiment, requir-

[4] Pierre Duhem, *Aim and Structure of Physical Theory,* tr. P. Wiener (Princeton, N.J.: Princeton University Press, 1954), p. 252.

ing the use of instruments of measurement and a framework of interpretation within which such measurements would be significant.

(3) *Metaphysical hypotheses.* The most important distinction in kind among these hypotheses is provided by metaphysical hypotheses, for in one view, such "hypotheses" are not hypotheses at all, but pseudo-hypotheses, because they are not subject to empirical test or to experimental procedure. Thus, these would not be scientific hypotheses; conversely, any presumably scientific hypothesis which could not be subjected to some empirical test, or which was unfalsifiable by such a test, would be not a scientific, but a metaphysical hypothesis. In another view, the "principles" of Cassirer, previously mentioned, and the postulates which serve only as grounds for inference (and are as such neither "true" nor "false," but only useful) might also be considered such metaphysical hypotheses. These are the sort which Newton presumably claimed not to be making. An anti-metaphysical view would take these in the sense of suppositions concerning "occult qualities," with which one could *dispense* without harm to scientific theory and, indeed, with economy. Ockham's Razor, which dictates that one not multiply entities needlessly in any explanation, would then shave all such unnecessary suppositions from the hide of science. But an alternative view would hold that such metaphysical hypotheses are merely the most general of scientific hypotheses, being in themselves conjectures about the nature of the facts, and therefore true or false. In such a view, metaphysical hypotheses are wide-ranging, systematic frameworks for scientific theory, or they are "world hypotheses," as Stephen Pepper calls them. Thus, atomism, or the view that *nothing comes from nothing,* or Galileo's view that nature is "written" in the language of mathematics are all conjectures about the nature of the physical world, which have found some interpretation in terms of scientific hypotheses of the sort described in paragraph (2). Duhem, in *The Aim and Structure of Physical Theory,* after a staunch defense of physics as no more than a mathematical instrumentality for ordering the facts acquired by experiment (as laws in some theoretical way which cannot be an explanation of reality), then goes on to make a case for an interpretation of Aristotle's metaphysics as a viable framework for an interpretation of modern physics. The issue between metaphysics and science is, as we have noted at several earlier points, a crucial one for philosophy of science, but we will not pursue it further here.

This variety of ways in which the concept *hypothesis* may be sliced suggests that one specify to some degree how the term will be used. Still, except for the plainly incompatible views (e.g., those which regard metaphysical hypotheses as part of science, and those which do not) the range of meanings permits one to see relations among them which a restricted use would not permit. For our purposes, we may specify a broad sense, including several of those discussed earlier, which would single out one feature these have in common, yet leave open the issues which arise on interpretation. We will take *hypothesis* to be defined in coordination with the term *experiment,* as a statement of any degree of generality whose validation or justification is in some clearly specifiable way related to an experimental procedure of testing. The narrowness or width of usage now depends on two things: what the scope of "experiment" is and what the criterion for clarity is in specifying a relation to experiment.

TESTING AND PROVING: THE FRAMEWORKS OF EXPERIMENT

It may seem unfair to define hypothesis with respect to experiment and then in turn to characterize experiment as deriving its significance from hypothesis. However, this is how we shall begin talking about experiment. The justification of this procedure is that *hypothesis* and *experiment* will be taken as two aspects of a more complex procedure, and as complementary concepts whose meanings are bound up with each other. Thus, the very concept of experiment entails some deliberate and controlled observation whose relevance and significance is partially determined by the hypothesis which it presumes to test, and is further determined by the wider framework of the whole system of theories which afford bases for interpretation of the experimental results. As *experiment* characterizes what is empirical in science and defines the concrete reference of a hypothesis, so *hypothesis* already delimits what is scientifically relevant in an experiment, or the range of its significant reference. When to perform an experiment, what experiment to perform, and how one may proceed to interpret experimental findings (*i.e.,* how narrowly to conceive these findings, or how open one should remain and how little one should be held within the framework of initial expectations) are all matters of choice and selection. As Sir George Thomson, the British physicist, notes, "the selection of things to do in science becomes an art."[5] Sir George quotes his father's (Lord Kelvin's) advice, "The great thing is to get hold of the right end of the stick." Getting hold of the right end of the stick is a matter of art, and possibly of some luck; but putting oneself in the way of a stick to get hold of is a matter of scientific theory. For it is only within the framework of the larger system of scientific language and concepts and within the narrower framework of a particular hypothesis that observation attains to that focus and selectivity which makes it germane to science.

Experiment, then, is observation controlled by the framework of scientific hypothesis. But what is this framework, and what, in this context, makes a hypothesis scientific? If the criterion for a philosophical "hy-

[5] Sir George Thomson, "Some Thoughts on Scientific Method," in R. S. Cohen and M. W. Wartofsky, eds. *Boston Studies in Philosophy of Science,* vol. II (New York: Humanities Press, 1965), p. 82.

pothesis" is rational criticism and conceptual analysis, then one may add to this the "criticism" which a rational construal of observation brings to bear, in characterizing a scientific hypothesis. But the beginning of scientific rationality, with respect to observation, is deliberate limitation of observation within some system of ordering, i.e., within some system of measurement. Goethe wrote, in a frequently quoted phrase, *"In der Beschränkung zeigt sich erst der Meister."* "Mastery exhibits itself in delimitation." The complaint that scientists are a narrow-minded lot, is a narrow-minded complaint, if one is talking about the scientist at work. It is the narrowly delimited and precise result, whose significance is lost on the layman and whose triviality may be the despair of the scientist, which becomes the necessary link in the chain of inference and interpretation which constitutes the systematicity of science, and its cumulative power. But precision of observation in itself does not entail significance and has no intrinsic virtue, as was noted earlier. Appropriate precision is required, and this is determined by the scope and the intention of an experiment. Experiment is thus controlled by its observation language, by measurement, by the theory which frames it, by the instrumentation available and known to be relevant, and by the all-important aspect of expectation of the observer. The psychological study of observation has shown what importance the "set" or anticipatory framework of the observer plays in what he will choose to observe. The scientist's perceptiveness is therefore a combination of theoretical background, as a restriction on relevance, and open-minded, free construction which is a liberation for the recognition of unsuspected and unanticipated relevance. Discovery by "accident" often plays a crucial role in science. (The fogging of photographic plates by radioactivity led, for example, to Becquerel's discovery of radioactive emission from uranium.) But even "accidents" are prepared for, or they would remain forever unnoticed, nothing more than accidents. What controls are there, then, which operate in experimental observation?

We may list four types of control that are among the most important:

(1) *The system of measurement.* There are, as has been seen, three distinctive and interrelated forms of such ordering by measurement: identification, within some classificatory scheme; ordering of qualities by degrees, in some ordinal scheme; and quantitative measurement, in terms of differences of degree of some unit magnitude, and more systematically, in terms of ratio invariances discovered in such ordering. The quantitative measure assigns some number to a difference in degree of some magnitude, generating a system of concrete or dimensional numbers (constituted by a number joined to a magnitude, in terms of some unit: as *3 cm.*, *10 lb.*, 3×10^9 *Mev*). Measurement, as we have defined it, takes place in all of these forms. Qualitative determination of properties of things, as in determination of the properties of chemical elements or compounds by their color, hardness, smell, reaction to heat, and so on, plays an important role in

the laboratory before any numbers come to be assigned. A chemist remarked (privately of course) that he regarded his nose as an essential part of his laboratory equipment and would like to find some way to get financial support for its maintenance and approval for depreciation costs on it. In mathematical physics, however, a nose is of no instrumental use, beyond its ordinary functions. But counting, as an empirical operation, is an instrumentality of observation, and a basic one. Visual acuity in noting scintillations on a screen or aural acuity listening to clicks; manual dexterity in laboratory procedures; and technical skills in building equipment are all backgrounds of measurement, the "taken-for-granteds" of the practical work of deliberate observation. The confusion of skill and perceptual capacity with measurement itself, however, is a mistake. It is the measurement language which is the control here. The system of units of measurement, and the fabric of deductive relations into which such units enter in mathematical reasoning and in computation, becomes a significant control in experimentation. Thus, what to measure, and within what limits of precision and error, becomes more than a practical question. When the language of the hypothesis is mathematical, as it is in a good part of science, then relevant findings will be translatable into the language of number, functioning to confirm or disprove the mathematical statements which are consequences of the hypothesis. The matter of approximation and experimental error enters here, and we will consider this shortly.

(2) *The theoretical framework.* The theoretical framework is closely linked with a system of measurement. A theory is either already framed in terms of some measurement language or it is experimentally interpretable in such a language. But in a broader, conceptual sense, a theory is an apparatus for delimiting relevance in experimentation. Any experiment is an abstraction of certain and only certain features in the whole field of observables and measurables. Physics chooses its magnitudes for the widest systematic import and coherence among different magnitudes. Thus it chooses distance, time, mass, energy as its characteristic parameters, interpreting relevant qualities in terms of these precisely measurable quantities. Even so, to choose a magnitude is not yet to choose what to measure in this magnitude. The physicist does not measure everything in the laboratory, nor does he measure every measurable occurrence in the experiment, but only certain severely delimited ones. And the scientist's guide here is hypothesis, and the broader framework of that theoretical science whose child he is. Thomson says, "What it really comes to when you say you repeat an experiment, is that you repeat all the features of an experiment which theory tells you are relevant."[6]

Galileo's inclined-plane experiments are often taken as models of early experimental method. These are more fully discussed in the context of

[6] *Ibid.*, p. 84.

Galileo's analysis of motion to be found in Appendix A, especially on pp. 463 ff. When Galileo repeated the inclined-plane experiment "a full 100 times," as he claims, he did not sometimes measure the distance the ball rolled, sometimes the temperature of the ball, sometimes its weight. He noted the experimental apparatus, but not the lighting conditions, the time of day, or the weather. The hypothesis he was testing delimited the experiment's significance to the parameters of distance and time alone, and determined that the measuring instruments relevant to such measurement were a measuring rod and a clock. The various inclinations of the plane were not measured, because Galileo's theoretical assumption was that only the height of the plane mattered, and this was kept constant. The proportional form of the mathematical hypothesis eliminated the comparison of a distance to a time, and admitted only a comparison of ratios of distances to ratios of times, and thus did not direct Galileo to discover the constant of proportionality, $\frac{1}{2}g$. Nor does Galileo report his actual measurements; he only claims that they agreed in their ratios exactly with those predicted by the hypothesis, namely, in the relation of distance ratios proportional to the ratios between the squares of the times. And because exact agreement is highly unlikely, it is reasonable to believe that Galileo took a close approximation in fact as sufficient evidence to support an ideal mathematical hypothesis. Thus, he appealed to an intuitive (though not explicated) theory of experimental error. In all of these ways, broad theoretical assumptions and the specific language of the hypothesis concerning distances and times controlled the experiment, in its plan and apparatus and in its choice of relevant parameters, as well as in its interpretation. Thus, too, the theoretical framework controls the choice of a measurement language, and of the magnitudes which are experimentally significant. Within some older theoretical framework Galileo might have included information about the astrological concurrences of certain heavenly bodies as significant, as scientists in fact did for many years.

The elimination of certain measurable features as irrelevant is thus the complement of the choice of others as relevant. Now this advantage of restrictedness can be a dangerous advantage, as the importance of accidents and anomalies in the history of scientific discovery shows. If a hypothesis or its broader theoretical framework does not allow for certain features of the experimental situation, it will tend to turn the experimenter's attention away from them; more radically, such features may not even be expressible in the language of the theory, or may fall beyond the scope of the measuring apparatus. There is, thus, an analogy between the introduction of more refined instrumentation and the theoretical formulation or discovery of new magnitudes and new concepts. As the telescope enlarged the scope of relevant observational facts, the theoretical formulation of the frequency and amplitude of waves enlarged the scope of significant measurement, introducing a new language for the description not only of mechanical effects, but of energy and the whole range of radiation phenomena. Recently, in the physics which deals with the limits of measurement at the quantum level, the question of "hidden parameters" has come up. The question of hidden parameters is not new, but a general question of experimental interpretation: when certain experimental effects do not find an adequate explanation in the terms of a theory, or within the measurement terms of the experiment, then what suggests itself is that some unknown cause or some unnoticed or unrealized phenomenon, whose description is not among those regarded as relevant, may explain the effects. In the sense that such a possibility is not noticed or does not come to be measured because it is not among the things explicitly expected in the experimental situation, it is a "hidden parameter." In quantum theory, however, the theory has no language for the description of any phenomena *beyond* the quantum level, in terms of which such phenomena could be theoretically conceived. The two views which this situation produces are occasioned by the fact that there is no comfortable model for what happens at the quantum level, in any ordinary conception of physical nature. One view claims that such a model is unnecessary and is demanded only by an unscientific desire to construe this new domain of physics in terms of an older classical conception. Thus, the "strange" behavior of something which seems to have mutually exclusive properties, sometimes those of a particle, sometimes those of a wave, is strange only if we impose the classical picture of particle and wave on this "somewhat." Its behavior, therefore, does not need to be explained by something more basic, in terms of a hidden parameter, and the theory as it now stands eliminates the possibility of such parameters, within the framework of the theory. The alternative view claims that the theory is therefore incomplete and that it will ultimately have to be extended or revised to include a new language and new measurement interpretations in terms of such more basic hidden parameters. But this latter claim can make experimental sense only if there is discovered a way to talk about such parameters and to measure them. At present no such way has yet been proposed, although analogies have been used to make clear what this might be like. Here the control which theory and measurement capacities exercise over experiment becomes crucial. If a theory includes the explicit specification that certain limits of measurement are built into the very physical nature of measurement itself and that measurement cannot in principle go beyond a certain precision (in establishing two simultaneous magnitudes, e.g., the momentum and position of a physical particle), then any experiment which attempts to do this will be futile unless it can be framed in terms of some alternate and physically meaningful theory. It is as if one were to say, first, that the smallest possible difference in magnitude for which any ruler can be constructed is a unit magnitude k, and then to ask for a measurement of the difference between two lengths, both of them smaller than k. The notion of "length smaller than k" breaks down as an operational concept in measurement under these conditions. The criticism of the demand for such measurements (because "after all, there is always a length smaller than some given length,") holds that such a view carries over into the domain of the very small something which we only know empirically concerning the domain of middle-sized things. If a successful theory is based on the notion of a smallest unit magnitude *k*, it will not easily give this up to meet the demands of an intuitive analogy. Thus theory plays a fundamental role, not only in controlling this or that experiment, but also in delimiting the concept of what is experimentally feasible.

(3) *Instrumentation.* We have already suggested some of the ways in which instrumentation enters into delimiting and controlling experimental observation. We may say that instrumentation, the physical tools and apparatus of measurement, is the embodiment of a system of measurement, representing in hardware and technique a conceptual structure in which magnitudes are theoretically ordered and in which concrete numbers are fixed in a deductive theoretical network. Thus a ruler is not merely an instrument for reading off numbers, but in the significance relations into which such concrete numbers enter, it is a way of measuring expansion, or the length of a path, or a rise in temperature. Pan-balances do not simply give readings, but are instruments whose theoretical justification is imbedded in the physical theories of statics and dynamics, so that a measurement of weight is taken to be proportional to a measurement of mass, on theoretical grounds. A meter reading, which any idiot can transmit, is more than a number, in measurement; it measures electrical charge, or a reversal of current, or the energy of a particle. Thus a network of theory converts a bundle of wires, springs, nuts, and bolts into an instrument, converting marks and coincidences of points into significant numbers, as relations between magnitudes.

Beyond this, however, the instrument brings to measurement certain properties which extend the range, accuracy, and stability of observation. Our eyes, ears, fingers, noses, tongues are also instruments of measurement, and highly refined ones for certain uses. But for the magnitudes of quantitative science, invention has extended our perception by physical means, as well as theoretically. The subjective variation of personal perception is radically reduced by instruments whose variability is known to a high degree of precision and whose standardization introduces a uniformity unavailable in ordinary perception. The mathematical division of a magnitude, made possible by periodicities of a standard sort, such as those of pendulums or atomic oscillations, gives us measurable unit magnitudes far beyond the perceptual threshold and also gives us equalities of magnitude beyond the acuity and accuracy of sense perception. But there are no infinite instruments. Every instrument measures within finite limits of accuracy, range, and stability, and thus delimits the significant results obtainable in experiment. In conception, a mathematically expressed magnitude is not an approximation. The two mathematical statements "This is 12 inches long," and, "This is 12.000002 inches long," are not "approximately the same"; they are utterly different. *Approximation* is a term which enters only with the conversion of mathematical magnitudes into measured magnitudes. Measurement imposes approximation. The range of real numbers which mathematics puts at our disposal has no limits of precision. The magnitude *number*, in its mathematical expression, is infinitely divisible, to the extent that there are more real numbers ("real" here in the mathematical sense of the system which includes the irrational numbers) than there are names for them. Where number is continuous, in this sense, measurement is discontinuous. Beyond a certain point a measured magnitude can only give an approximation to some mathematical expression. This is what we mean when we say that all measurement is within tolerances. Yet in classical measurement the limits of approximation are the practical limits of refinement of measurement apparatus. Galileo's water clock was sufficiently accurate to permit him to support his ideal conclusions by relatively crude approximate measurements. Increased refinement has approached the ideal mathematical limit more closely than Galileo could imagine.

Now whereas classical measurement theory contains the formal condition that for any number *n*, measuring a degree or difference in magnitude, there is a number smaller than *n*, this condition has two limitations in actual measurement. We may call the first *practically limited measurability*, signifying by this the limits of the instrument and the techniques of calibration beyond a certain degree of precision. But the second introduces a more fundamental limitation, in terms of *theoretically limited measurability*. In the ordinary commonsense view, and in classical physics, we take length, for example, to be a continuous magnitude. In other words, we conceive that for any length, however small, there is a smaller length, or the physical property *length* is infinitely divisible. But suppose theory interposes and now says: length, apart from our commonsense physical intuitions, is defined as what is conceivably measurable by some conceivable operation using an instrument. And suppose that the ultimate physical structure of matter is such that the instrument itself, being a physical object, is ultimately discontinuous, beyond a certain point, that is, that a certain length is such that it has no parts. It is in effect an "atom" of length, being further indivisible. And suppose, further, that this is not merely a speculation, but a consequence of a well-established and well-tested theory. If the length is *k*, then measurability stops at *k* and, with respect to length, can go no further.

Now suppose we translate this in terms of energy and say that there are units of energy which are atomic, in the sense that they are indivisible quanta. If an instrument is brought to bear on any object of measurement, it must somehow physically interact with what it measures, as a ruler must somehow be brought into contact with what it measures. But now suppose that such a quantum of energy is the minimal interaction between an instrument and what it measures, and suppose further that what the instrument measures is of the order of magnitude of just this quantum of energy. The object measured is going to be disturbed by this quantum, so that the very act of measuring, on this scale, would radically disturb what we measure in such a way that we could not tell what it was like prior to the disturbance. If we ask someone, "What are you like when you're not with anyone else," he cannot very well tell us to watch him when no one else is present. He may tell us what he thinks he is like, but we cannot observe to find out, for in observing, our presence destroys the possibility of an answer. (This is why psychologists use one-way glass to observe children and why ethologists use screens and camouflage to observe animal behavior in the natural state.) But the physical system, at the level of quanta, can not tell us what it is like when it is not being observed, and our observation disturbs it by the interaction. Here measurement involves a situation in which instrument and object of observation are linked in a tight system, of which the instrument itself is an integral part. It would be like asking the instrument to measure itself in this situation and then subtract this from the situation. Aside from the paradoxical notion of self-measurement, the separation can not be effected here, so that measurement is limited by the very situation of measurement at this level. Niels Bohr suggested the analogy that this would be like thinking about what one is thinking about at a given instant. In thinking about one's thought, one changes irremediably what one has been thinking about. In such a situation, where physical theory itself sets a limit beyond which measurement irremediably disturbs what is measured, by affecting its magnitude, we would have a theoretically limited measurability. No improvement in instrumentation could offset this, and only a theoretical alternative in quantum theory could conceivably extend measurability in this case.

In classical measurement, of things of the middle-sized sort, instruments also interact with what is measured, but here we either know how to compensate for this distortion or such distortion is insignificantly small. Thus, when we place a thermometer in a solution, we change the temperature of the solution by introducing the thermometer. Thus any instrument operates within this context of approximation, within tolerances which we take to be within the limits of required precision. In any experimental situation, then, we test the instrument as well as some hypothesis to ascertain the limits of its accuracy against some standard, and our results are always framed within the limits of measurement which the instrument imposes.

(4) *The observer.* One standard view of scientific experiment, and of scientific work in general, is that in the ideal case the observer is eliminated as a variable factor. His presence is obviously required, as is also his interpretation of experimental results. But the idea is to restrict or eliminate the

subjectivity of the observer as a variable in the experiment. The ideal observer is therefore a standard observer, whose presence may be taken as a constant, not affecting the results and constituting at most a transparent presence in the background. The means of attaining this ideal, in experimental work, may be characterized as the epistemological conditions of objectivity in science. The foremost among these conditions is that experimental results be *reproducible* in some standard way, so that agreement among observers may be attained. The ideal of scientific judgment then is that concerning which universal agreement among observers can be achieved. Everyone agrees that $1 + 1 = 2$, universally, and this ideal should be the goal of observational and experimental work as well. The corollaries of this demand for reproducible experiment are important. For one thing, all observers must speak a common language, so that results can be communicated intelligibly and without ambiguity. Mathematics again presents the ideal of such a universal and universally agreeable language. The training and education of scientists should also be standard enough that one will know what it means to reproduce the experiment of another. Further, and this is obvious, the experimental occurrence or event must be one which is recurrent, for a unique event is by definition not reproducible. Some such axiom as "same cause, same effect" operates here. And we have already cited Thomson on what the theoretical function is in assuring us that we take the same things to be relevant twice in a row. Ideally, then, the scientific hypothesis puts forth something of the sort which is reproducible and recurrent for experimental observation, and such a hypothesis is therefore "intersubjectively testable," which is to say that objectivity in scientific observation and experiment is intersubjectivity, agreement being the sole technique of the public enterprise called science which guarantees the validity of scientific findings in practice. On a smaller scale, the single experimenter may repeat his own experiment to further strengthen his conviction of reliability. The more severe the test and the more often it has been carried out, the greater the degree of confirmation of the results. (This then would hold for both a verification or a falsification of some predicted result.)

This picture, although it sets forth an ideal experimental situation which serves as a norm for scientific experiment and objectivity, is not a descriptive account of experiment, but a normative one. It does not describe what is the case, but proposes what ought to be the case. But such an ought implies that this is not always the case, and may never be the case, as a matter of fact. The relation between this norm and the fact is analogous to that between mathematical expressions deduced from a theory, and measurement expressions obtained in experiment. The latter are approximations to the former. Our question is how the observer serves to control the experimental situation. But the experimental situation is artificial; it is a choice, a selection made by the scientist. And in this sense, there is no norm for *which* experiment a scientist should perform (except the innocuous norm of "the *right* experiment"). The reduction of subjective variation, by introducing standard parameters and instruments and by reducing perception to the simplest possible acts of reading numbers on meters, does operate to ensure objectivity, as do all the conditions previously mentioned. But the design of experiments, the choice of parameters and instruments, and the disposition to notice this or that as significant, beyond the mechanism of experimental technique and beyond the frame of expectation which a theory sets, is a subjective variable which not only affects the experiment, but dominates it. We should distinguish, then, between the conditions of objectivity which concern the validation of an experiment, and those conditions which lead to the choice or invention of an experiment to be made. Beyond the experiment itself, as a procedure, there is the interpretation of the experimental results, and indeed the decision as to *what* to take as the relevant results (because this relevance may turn out not to agree with that originally anticipated).

This divides the work of the experimental observer as two-fold: on the one hand, the experimental scientist is the most collective of men, operating within a community of common language, uniform standards, and publicly reproducible results. On the other, he is a lone thinker making decisions and drawing conclusions in that activity which we characterize as creative. The extent to which the moral virtues of the scientist enter into these two functions also affects the control of the experiment. His honesty, integrity, lack of personal prejudice or pride which would distort or misrepresent his findings, his openness to criticism, all enter into the practical contexts of real science. But in modern experimental work a new feature enters which has profound philosophical and epistemological consequences and which is not often noted.

With modern techniques and instrumentation the experiment becomes more nearly a public affair at the outset, results of measurement and computation being processed in large part by the apparatus. More and more, then, the work of theoretical inference becomes the act of the "observer," all preliminaries now becoming automated and computed. What such an observer may be said to observe, then, is a set of "uninterpreted" measurement statements (which have already gone through levels upon levels of "interpretation" within the apparatus which links direct interaction with the experimental event to the removed observer). Watching a radar screen for blips is an act of observation that is removed in this sense, and getting tapes of transmitted numbers which reconstitute a photographic image of the surface of Venus is also removed observation. If there ever was a Golden Age of direct measurement, in which Nobly Savage Scientists Really Saw What Was Going On, in direct observation, it is fast drawing to a close. It would be more accurate to say that all measurement and observation is relatively indirect, if directness requires confrontation with some theoretically "naked" or "pure" data. But the publicity of observation has been enormously increased, in the advanced sciences, and presumably, so too has objectivity. Observation, and the role of the observer, becomes a highly theoretical and inferential activity, in which symbolic and linguistic communication links scientist to scientist, and scientist to apparatus and experimental event. The older philosophy of science took its epistemological problems from the seventeenth century, or sometimes from the Greeks. The new science imposes a new epistemological schema, in which the control of the observer over the experiment needs to be re-examined and reconsidered. The relation of the observer's conceptual framework to the decisions concerning relevance and interpretation remain crucial. But the long concern for the empirical link of observer to experimental event needs to be thought through again. If measurement statements are indeed the empirical language of science, then science's observation statements are no longer clearly distinct from its theoretical statements, in this systematic connection of measurement, theory, instrumentation, and observer which constitutes the framework of experiment.

TYPES OF EXPERIMENT

Thus, in each of these four aspects of experiment, involving the measurement system, the framework of theory and hypothesis, the instrumentation, and the observer, the interpretation of theoretical and hypothetical framework and the experimental procedure itself is seen to be crucial. But all this is background to the function of the experiment. Too often the imposition of a system on the analysis of experimental procedure leads to a narrow characterization of this function and tends to single out some essential function. It would be better to talk about the *functions* of experiment and to distinguish that experimentation which has directly to do with the testing and confirmation of hypotheses and that experimentation which has the function of discovery. These two aspects are not always dissociated and may constitute elements of a single experimental instance. There is, moreover, a generic sense in which both of these aspects of experiment have common roots and background. But first let us examine the distinction. In the case of an experimental test of an articulate hypothesis, something is proposed, and the test is a method of finding empirical agreement or disagreement with the proposition. Thus, the highly ordered test of Galileo's Theorem II in the inclined-plane experiments (see Appendix A, section 10) is designed in view of what the hypothesis offers as an explicit prediction, concerning relations among ratios of magnitudes, in terms of numbers. In this context the sense of "proving" a hypothesis is the sense of the original latin root *probare,* meaning "to submit to test to see if something resists refutation or falsification." Thus, in colloquial (older)

English usage, one speaks of "proving one's mettle," meaning by this not merely convincing someone else of it by means of some logical or rhetorical "proof," but showing that one can endure severe tests of character or courage. Yet quite another sense of *proving* derives from *probare,* in the etymologically closer terms *probe* and *probate.* Here the sense seems to be one of an inquiry to discover something not previously known, or not yet established. If, in the narrower sense of *testing,* one operates with a prediction which is the consequence of some wider theory, or with what we have called an instantial hypothesis, in this wider sense, one attempts to discover what property or numerical value will reveal itself under certain conditions. Thus, if the chemist experiments to discover the properties of some element, as yet not established, or the physicist experiments to discover the magnitude of a given thing, he need not make a prediction concerning this. Rather, the experimental data is such that it will serve in the formulation of hypotheses for further testing, or will fill in needed information in the formulation of a theory. We may compare three different types of experiments here to examine this distinction.

(1) *Experiments of discovery or probing.* Let us take two instances. In Galileo's "Dialogue of the Third Day," in the *Dialogues Concerning Two New Sciences* he speaks of the relation between distance of fall and force of impact as a way of relating acceleration to force. Without a clearly articulated concept of momentum, he still gives the observation that a heavy body dropped on a stake in the ground will drive it further into the ground if it is dropped from a greater height (appealing to commonsense observation and also to the technological experience with pile drivers). The "experiment," if one takes it as a proposal to discover what will happen if one dropped a weight from different heights, does not give any predictions, although it seems to. It is rather an appeal to what has already been discovered in day-to-day "experimentation" which discovers the properties of things. It asks, "What will be the relation between the distance the stake is driven into the ground and the height from which the weight is dropped?" Similarly, a chemical test for the properties of an unknown substance will inquire into such properties without predicting them; yet the same test may take place in the context of a hypothesis which does predict such properties. The latter, although it is a "probe," works within the framework of a theoretically based prediction. [See paragraph (3), which follows.] The former does not.

Again, Millikan's oil-drop experiment was to determine what the mass of an electron was, by means of a measurement of its charge (because its inertial properties can be examined only in terms of its acceleration, and this is produced by the action of an electrical or magnetic field). Previous estimates (by Thomson, Wilson, Ehrenhaft, and de Broglie) deduced this elementary charge from the average behavior of large numbers of charged particles in electrical and gravitational fields. Millikan proposed to compute this value from observations of an oil drop in an electrical and gravitational field. If the gravitational and electrical effects are known, then the motion of the oil drop is known as it falls toward an electrical plate and as an electrical charge repels it back up again. When the drop captures an ionized particle, this causes a change in its known motion. From the measurement of such changes, Millikan computed what the unit charge was, his list showing that all values of charge on the drop were whole multiples of this unit. He thus discovered a value for this unit charge with an accuracy far greater than that of earlier estimates. Of course, the knowledge of this unit charge served to confirm hypotheses concerning the discrete or atomic structure of matter. But the direct intent of the experiment was to *discover* a value, not to *confirm* a predicted value.

(2) *Experiments of testing the consequences of hypotheses.* Testing the consequences of hypotheses is most often taken to be the model of what an experiment is for. In Galileo's inclined-plane experiment, as we have seen, a predicted relation among measurable values is tested against actual measurements of these values. If the measurements are in agreement with the prediction, then the prediction is said to be verified, otherwise, it is falsified. The bearing of such verification of an instantial prediction on the general hypothesis from which it is deduced—whether the general hypothesis is thereby "confirmed" or "corroborated"—is a matter for later discussion. But the point here is that such an experiment is designed not only to discover what the values of measurement are, but to discover them to be in agreement or disagreement with predicted values.

(3) *Mixed experiments.* The close systematic relation between paragraphs (1) and (2), within the theoretical framework of a science, is clear, although the intent and focus in each case is distinct. A mixed experiment is one in which the discovery of certain properties leads to their inclusion in some already established systematic framework of theory; that is, when it is shown how a prediction of such newly discovered properties may be derived deductively within some hypothetico-deductive framework. Thus, a mixed experiment is one in which the discovery of some property not yet known or predicted leads to a classification revealing a systematic relation between it and other properties. In this way, a hypothesis not being directly tested is indirectly confirmed. This new property thus classified now finds a place within the hypothetical scheme.

When Mendeleev noted that certain common properties occurred among "families" of chemical elements, he used this fact to construct the periodic table of the elements. We might say that the historical instances of discovery of these properties (as, for example, of the alkali metals discussed earlier) were the consequences of probing experiments. The classification of these elements in the sequence of atomic weights utilized the results of other probing experiments. But the periodic table was more than a device for *ordering* known results, for its periodicity left blank places in the table. The hypothesis that the columns of the table grouped elements with similar chemical properties led to the prediction that such elements would be found. Mendeleev, for example, predicted that the blank space of atomic number 32, which lies between silicon and tin in the vertical column, would contain an element which was greyish-white, would be unaffected by acids and alkalis, and would give a white oxide when burned in air, and when he predicted also its atomic weight, atomic volume, density and boiling point, he was using the periodic table as a hypothesis from which predictions could be deduced. This was in 1871. In 1886, the German chemist Winkler discovered germanium, an element with all the properties predicted by Mendeleev (approximately). It then found its place in the periodic table, and helped to confirm Mendeleev's hypothesis. But Winkler was conducting probing rather than testing experiments when he discovered germanium, though the significance of the data was clear once the properties of germanium were discovered.

Duhem, in the work we have cited, makes a distinction between experiments of *testing* and experiments of *application*. The latter are performed to determine by measurement certain facts relevant to the production of a known result. He gives the example of lighting an electric bulb. In order to do this a certain electromotive force is needed. Measuring the electromotive force available from a battery of generators to find out whether it will produce the desired effect in accordance with known theories is an experiment of application. It is a test within the framework of an experiment, concerned with utilizing what is known to establish the conditions for solving practical problems, regarding matters such as instrumentation. An experiment of testing, on the other hand, is set up to test a theory. But here, Duhem introduces a distinctive consideration. He considers that the framework of any experiment is so knit up with the theoretical system that no isolated hypothesis but only a whole system of them can be submitted to a decisive test. An experimental result does not tell us that the hypothesis we had in mind is either confirmed or disconfirmed. If the result negates a prediction deduced from such a system of hypotheses or theories, it does not tell us *which* element of the system needs to be revised. He writes,

> Physics is not a machine which lets itself be taken apart; we cannot try each piece in isolation. . . . Physical science is a system which must be taken as a whole; it is an organism in which one part cannot be made to function except when the parts that are most remote from it are called into play, some more so than others, but all to some degree.[7]

The effect of this interpretation of the organic character of physical science is that, in Duhem's view, a crucial experiment is not possible. The claim amounts to a denial that any experimental hypothesis can be defin-

[7] Duhem, *op. cit.*, pp. 187–88.

itively rejected as such; it may always be retained by making adjustments somewhere else within the whole system of theories which constitute a science. This is like saying that a test showing that a patient's arm was diseased does not entail the *crucial* decision to leave the arm intact or cut it off. Because the arm is part of the whole organism, there may be preferable adjustments (for example, the use of antibiotics) elsewhere in the system to remove the disease. Thus Duhem says the physical theorist is more like a doctor than a watchmaker. In short, Duhem is asserting that the import of an experiment is not a simple case of heads or tails, in which a particular hypothesis is put to a particular test, leading to its rejection or acceptance. Rather the interrelation of experimental findings and theoretical framework is so intimate that an unambiguous decision is not available on anything less than the whole system of theory undergirding an experiment.

Science is a coherent and organic unity of which hypothesis and experiment are complementary aspects. Just as a rational consistency of the hypothesis with all other parts of a theory is not enough to lend it confirmation without experimental test, so too an experimental test is not enough to decide, in itself, how it should be interpreted except within the whole system of theory framing it. This leaves a certain free play in the creative work of determining the significance of experimental results, in which alternative hypotheses, if they are rationally compatible with the theoretical system, remain options within science, with an indefinite life; experiment does not decide the issue but only indicates that some theoretical adjustment is needed. It is here that matters of practicality, in the economy of choice of the scientist, determine that one rather than another path should be taken.

CHAPTER 9

Induction and Probability

INDUCTION: HABIT, EXPECTATION, AND WARRANTED BELIEF

THE FUNCTIONS OF SCIENTIFIC INQUIRY are to discover new facts about the properties of things; and to discover among such facts, relations which order our knowledge of the great variety of nature, and serve us both to explain and predict the operations of nature. Rational action is based on the belief that what we have learned in past experience is significant beyond the past, and has some bearing on what we should expect to happen under given conditions in the future. Our control over nature, developing from basic technical rules of operation to sophisticated technology founded on theoretical science, is derived from our capacity to generalize, to go beyond the present instant, and to regulate our action by conscious criticism of the lessons of experience. The commonsense maxim *live and learn* connotes more than a mere accumulation of experiences; it suggests that our earlier empirical beliefs can come under the scrutiny of a wider experience and a critical reflection, to be modified and, if necessary, rejected and replaced by something better. In all of our discussion thus far, the assumption has been made that such learning does take place, in science as in ordinary life, and that the methods of scientific inquiry are superior ways of ordering and testing knowledge, so that what we conceive to be the case and what we discover to be the case in actual practice are in constant critical interplay. Thus in observation, in measurement, in the procedures of experiment, the framework of conceptual expectations, in delimiting the focus of empirical relevance and test, brings these more sharply to bear on our initial beliefs and conjectures. We constantly and methodically risk our earnings against the contingencies of fact, by a technique of selective confrontation in our testing and criticism. The product, unless science is illusory knowledge altogether, is a cumulative increase in what we know, and presumably a growing assurance that what has stood the test of time is more secure knowledge.

Against this sanguine view there stands the history of reversals, refutations, and revolutions in science, concerning not the marginalia of our scientific acquisitions, but the fundamental ideas themselves, whose seniority provided no security.

The double purpose of experiment, as we have seen, is discovery and further testing. But in the experiment, an instance is systematically related to a class of instances, and each observation enters into a conceptual framework of *generalized* expectations—a measured time and a measured distance, under particular conditions of measurement, representing somehow the fulfillment of an expectation concerning an *invariant* relation of distances and times. The conditions of objectivity were those which secured the publicity of observed relations, and these, we saw, involved the repeatability of an experiment. We might say, then, that the sum of the claim to generality is the claim that if *you* do what *I* did, you will observe what I observed. And the theory and technique of experimentation is so devised as to insure that you and I are, in fact, doing the *same* thing on two occasions.

The source of this claim, that what has happened once, or twice, or more times under given conditions, will *continue* to happen if those conditions are reproduced, is so basic that in some accounts it is seen to derive from our animal behavior, and to lie at the basis of the very possibility of learning. For the formation of a habit, as we discussed it earlier, is precisely the creation of a disposition to respond in the same way on different occasions to what is taken as the same situation. Experimental psychology describes not only the patterns of such habit formation in animals and men, but also the ways in which such patterns arise optimally. Thus some initial response, either instinctive or random, already has a certain plasticity; it can be reinforced or inhibited, by appropriate "reward" or "punishment," so that *desired* patterns can be created by the experimenter within the wide range of possible behaviors. The concepts of habit-taking and conditioning thus intersect with that of innate dispositions, for punishment and reward (or reinforcement and inhibition of responses) already presuppose some initial structure of habit-taking under certain conditions and not under others. But to form a habit is to do more than to give a certain response similarly on similar occasions. It concerns, rather, the *likelihood* that such a pattern of responses will be forthcoming. The habit is thus more general than its instances or occurrence, *if* the word habit means more than a summary description of past instances. To say, "I am in the habit of smoking after meals," may be no more than a report on what I have done over several years. But we ordinarily take it to mean that if one were to observe me after a meal, it would be likely that one would observe me smoking. Thus I am said to have the habit even when I am not smoking; and this does not mean that it is *inconceivable* that you might observe me not-smoking after some meal. Presumably, there are conditions one could create in which the habit could not be fulfilled (for example, if there were nothing to smoke; or more significantly, if I *decided,* in an exceptional case, not to smoke, which I could presumably do). Habits, unlike rules of logical inference, do not entail *necessary* instances, but only likely ones.

The point here is that on one account at least learning is habit formation, or includes habit formation as a basic constituent. The difference, presumably, is that in learning one can go beyond mere animal habit, and intrude the activity of conscious, critical intelligence. But this takes learning to be that activity which involves conscious criticism. It is partly a verbal question, as to how one may want to circumscribe the use of the term *learning.* But in one view at least, learning may be taken broadly as the acquisition of any generalized pattern of behavior, in response to patterns of stimulation in the environment. C. S. Peirce uses *habit* synonymously with *pattern,* and to the degree that there are ordered or patterned features in the natural world, Peirce takes all of these as the result of habit formation as well. "The universe is habit-taking," in Peirce's terms, means that the laws of nature are no more than patterns of relation between events derived from nothing more transcendent than a universal propensity throughout nature, animate and inanimate, to generalize from instances. (What would be *less* transcendent than a "universal propensity" is hard to say.)

That such behavior exists and is typical of organisms is a matter of fact (or at the very least, a matter of what we can mean by *habit*). That we acquire habits of response and that such generalized responses operate to influence or determine future instances of response is thus a matter of how we ordinarily describe action which is not random. For random action we can state no rule; any other action presumably exhibits some rule-like character, in that we can represent certain invariant relations in it in some symbolic universal statement. Commonsense knowledge and belief is a compendium of such descriptive rule-like statements: "Bears hibernate in winter," "Bees make honey," "August is warmer than June in New England." The objection that the bear at the zoo does not hibernate, or that there are bees which do not make honey, or that in 1904, June was warmer than August in New England, does not impinge on the generalization in quite the same way as the statement "the diagonal of a square is incommensurable with the sides" impinges on "all geometric lengths are commensurable." The generalization, we say, expresses *only* a likelihood, and admits of exceptions; for what it expresses is incomplete knowledge, of only a certain range of instances, and the belief that, in general, all other instances will accord with the known ones.

It is this sort of knowledge and belief that is sometimes called *inductive* with respect to the way in which it is acquired and *probable* with respect to its status as a claim to truth. In the broadest sense, all knowledge acquired by experience, as distinct from what we come to "know" as a necessary consequence of other things known (i.e., by logical inference) is contingent knowledge. Insofar as what we come to know in experience is based on a finite number of instances, the claim that generalizations will hold true of all possible instances is characterized as having no more than a certain probability. To the extent that science is empirical and concerns matters of fact, it too constitutes such contingent knowledge, and its claims are taken as conjectures or warranted beliefs rather than as necessary or certain truths.

But if all such knowledge, or the belief based on it, is no more than a highly refined sort of habit formation, then the cognitive status of science as an inquiry into truth becomes problematic. Is the habit we can induce in the laboratory-rat continuous in kind with the habits of belief which are induced in a theoretical scientist by the particular "stimuli" he has been subjected to? If so, it would seem strange to talk of "true" habits and "false" habits; at best, we might then speak of "good" and "bad" habits, if we could decide what habits, in general, were "good" and "bad" *for*. And at worst, our account of science would be no more than a description of the (peculiar) habits of a particular subclass of the genus *homo sapiens*. One might imagine what some extraterrestrial observer would make of the activity of science, in his report to some galactic institute of comparative behavior. (The only solace here is to consider what some extragalactic observer would make of the behavior of the extraterrestrial observer, and so on, *ad infinitum*.) If we take this one step further, and regard the laws of science as generalizations from experience, then such laws become no more than habits of belief induced in us by reinforcements and inhibitions, which we dignify as "confirmations" and "disconfirmations." We might say that unless some Cosmic Daemon is playing some great trick on us all, the kinds of beliefs we come to accept are "reasonable" on the grounds that the "evidence" of past experience supports them. Such beliefs would then be conceived of as highly complex instances of conditioning, and as such they would be habits of behavior of the sort we call *expectations*. Because incompatible beliefs would lead us to expect both that something of a certain sort would happen and also that it would not, rationality would then intervene in sorting out such incompatibilities and arranging our beliefs systematically, making choices among incompatibles by such rules as "choose the stronger belief," or "choose the one most compatible with the whole set of beliefs," or "choose neither but search for evidence to support or refute both; then, at some point, choose on the basis of this evidence," or perhaps, "choose the belief which best suits your purposes."

By this account, the salivation of Pavlov's dogs when the bell was rung would be removed from the instance of acceptance of a belief only by the number of intervening conditionings in the latter, more complex case. One's acceptance of a belief would be "secreted" by the brain-mind organ as saliva is secreted by a gland. The delay in response, while some activity of comparison and inference went on, would distinguish the belief response from the salivation response in that it involved the higher centers of the nervous system (including what Pavlov came to call the *secondary signaling system* which involves our responses to symbolic stimuli and thus to language in general). In his formulation of the pragmaticist theory of knowledge and belief, Peirce characterized a belief as a habit of action, a propensity to act in a certain way under given conditions. The statement of a belief would then be no more than a report on such a propensity, and could be true or false only in the sense that a false statement of belief would be a case in which one did not put one's money where one's mouth was, that is, where one stated falsely what one's belief really was. A reasonable belief would then be a warranted belief, in the sense that it was not clearly incompatible with other held beliefs, and was, as a matter of fact, well reinforced by the conditionings of experience.

This might do as one account of the psychological conditions under which scientists, like other men, come to hold certain beliefs. The only questions of the "justification" of such beliefs would be whether in fact a certain habit of belief had or had not been established, or whether it had been properly conditioned. But this would be a vacuous criterion, for *any* belief whatever would be the product of *some* conditioning, and where two scientists disagreed one would not look for error, but only for *differences* in conditioning. Or one might postulate such differences as due to "hidden variables." The ultimate claim for alternate beliefs would then be that they were matters of habit, or of "animal faith," and the most that could recommend them would be that some of them were widely held, whereas others were held only by deviants from the norm. A theory of truth concerning such beliefs might then be formulated as: the true is that concerning which there is a consensus of beliefs—and degrees of truth might then be set up in accordance with an empirical investigation of degrees of (expressed) consensus on various matters. Periodicially a truth census might be taken, in which one would vote for one's beliefs from a proffered list of "truths." Choosing beliefs would then be like choosing what tooth paste to buy.

As ludicrous as this sounds, it would seem to be the case that we take as true precisely what we *believe* to be true, and in general we believe that to be true for which there is, to our minds, the best evidence. Furthermore, our judgment of "best evidence" is very often that which has occurred most often in the past, and which we have thus come to believe will continue to occur under similar conditions in the future. Or else, we take as "best evidence" that which has been established by the greatest number of observers, and concerning which there is the widest agreement. From much of what experimental and physiological psychology tells us, we are inductive mechanisms, operating in the continuum of living organisms which are adaptive to environmental changes in such a way as to preserve their homeostasis or their organic integrity. One might say, then, that induction is nature's own way, and its test or justification lies in a million years of evolution. If we take natural selection seriously, then this method of habit formation, from the lowest types of acquired patterned behavior to the highest habits of theoretical belief, may be considered as the optimal choice of possible methods or strategies of behavior, selected for preservation by the test of evolution.

From such high-blown speculations, it might be a good thing to descend to the more sober consideration of what induction is, how it functions in scientific inquiry, and whether it does or does not require "justification." This much of the foregoing account we may carry with us into the following examination: Does induction give us *more* than what we come to believe, as a matter of fact? Or is it a normative or methodological rule, which provides a criterion for what we *ought* to believe, in terms of what constitutes "sufficient" evidence for "reasonable" or "warranted" belief?

INDUCTIVE GENERALIZATION, INDUCTIVE INFERENCE, AND THE JUSTIFICATION OF INDUCTION

Statements like "Bees give honey" and "Iron is a metal which oxidizes quickly and expands when heated" are descriptive general statements, presumably discovered to be true by observation. In order to identify something as a bee, in the first place, we would have to recognize certain characteristics of size, structure, etc., just as recognizing something as iron involves certain empirical tests, e.g., of its specific density, appearance, reactions to chemical agents. We may thus come to classify something as a bee, or as iron, and then discover something *more* about it, such as that *this something* which is a bee gives honey, and *that something* which is iron expands when heated. Seeing enough bees, and heating enough iron will then lead us to say either: (a) all the bees I have ever observed give honey and (b) all the iron I have ever heated expands, or (a') bees give honey, (b') iron expands when heated. (a) and (b) are summaries of a set of observation statements (a_1), (a_2) . . . (a_n), and (b_1), (b_2) . . . (b_n), where n is the number of observations I have made. But not so (a') and (b'), for these claim that whatever has been observed to be the case for (a_1), (a_2) . . . (a_n) will also be held to be the case for (a_{n+1}). In short, anything I observe to be the case for all given instances of a certain class, I take *without additional observation* to be the case for the *next* instance of this class; or on another view, for *all* instances of this class. The generalization from particular cases to a class of particular cases is thus a genuine generalization only when the class has more members than those I have observed, and all the members are taken to be observable. If it is merely a summary statement concerning a set of individuals which make up all the members of the class, all of which have already been enumerated and observed, then no generalization is involved. The first case is an inductive generalization, induction being defined as the "inference" from particulars to universals, i.e., to statements about all members of a given class. The statements (a) and (a') are related, however, for the assumption in (a') is that if I *do* enumerate all the members of the class of bees, then (a') and (a) will be identical. But what permits me to assume this? What grounds are there for inductive generalization? If, indeed, I do speak of this as an inference, then if I take this to mean a logical "move" from one set of statements to another, there must be some rule in accordance with which I make this move. If I mean by inference something less than a deductive move according to a rule, then there must be assumed to be at least two kinds of inference: deductive and inductive. If, instead, I take the statement (a') as a *postulate*, presumably I am putting something forth in a hopeful way, but am claiming for it no more than a tendency to believe it, or a certain informal reasonableness. (Peirce says, "To 'postulate' a position is no more than to hope it is true.") If, instead, I express my belief in (a') on the grounds that, if I had believed (a') after observing just (a_1), it would have "paid off" when I observed (a_2), and if I had believed (a') after (a_1) *and* (a_2), it would have "paid off" when I observed (a_3); therefore, if I believe (a') at any (a_n), it will "pay off" when I observe (a_{n+1}), and I am appealing to some *pragmatic* justification of the sort "It always pays to believe that particular instances will conform to those instances already observed." I may instead appeal to the psychological "fact" that "in general" the mind is so structured that it forms habits of belief on reinforcement, and stronger habits on greater reinforcement, where *reinforcement* means that past instances repeat in the same pattern under the same conditions.

In each of these alternative approaches, the fact that we do generalize from instances is not in question; the question is, what warrant is there for such generalization? That this lies close to the heart of empirical scientific inquiry is clear, for the relation of instantial observation and measurement to generalizations as statements concerning *invariant* relations, that is, as general hypotheses or laws, is central to experimental inquiry. The conditions of the objectivity of experimentation, and of experimental results, namely, repeatability and the concurring testimony of any number of other experimenters, would not make sense unless additional numbers of tests or of observers could be said to give greater credibility or reliability to the results. In the court of law, the corroborating testimony of independent witnesses is also presumed to lend additional credibility to claims that something did in fact happen in a certain way. However, in the court of law or in the laboratory, no one raises the question "how do you warrant the belief that more witnesses will give a more credible or a more objective account?" though the credibility of the individual witness and the expertness of his observation does make a qualitative difference. The jump or leap from statements about *some* to statements about *all* has remained problematic, and the alternative justifications of this *inductive leap,* which we have informally listed above, may be classified thus:

1. The "leap" is in fact a deductive inference, which is justified by a premise taken to be (*a*) axiomatic, (*b*) metaphysical, or (*c*) postulational. The deductive inference would look like the following:

Major premise	Whatever exhibits some pattern or relation in each of a finite number of instances in nature, will exhibit the same pattern or relation in all instances in nature (or "nature is uniform").
Minor premise	In a finite number of instances, bees are observed to give honey.
Conclusion	In all instances, bees will be observed to give honey.

From the minor premise alone, no deductive inference follows, so the inference depends on the major premise.

(*a*) If we take this major premise as an *axiom,* and if false statements can be deduced from it, then it is not much good. But it is quite plain that the conclusion, "In all instances, bees will be observed to give honey," or, 'If anything is a bee, then it gives honey" has some instances which are true, and some which are false. [For a statement of the form $(x)(Bx \rightarrow Hx)$, the formal contradictory is $(\exists x)(Bx \cdot - Hx)$, so that any non-honey-giving bee would falsify the conclusion; or strictly speaking, because only statements falsify statements, any true observation statement "This is a bee which does not give honey," would falsify the conclusion.] Taking honey-giving as criterial of beehood, one might argue that the conclusion means any "bee" which gave no honey was not a bee at all, but a bee-pretender, fooling us (and the other real bees) by its appearances. But then, saving deducibility, we would be turning our conclusion into an analytic statement, not requiring all the apparatus of the major premise in the first place; for then we would be saying "All and only honey-giving bees give honey," which is certainly true but descriptively empty. Moreover, the world is full of patterns which range over finite sets of things of a certain kind, but fail to be true of all things of that kind.

(*b*) If we took the major premise to be a *metaphysical* truth, it would be something asserted about the very *nature* of nature. If the grounds for its truth were the wideness of its generality in experience, this argument would collapse into *another* inductive generalization of the sort it is supposed to support, and would be circular—inductive generalization justified by inductive generalization. (Presumably the latter would be wider in scope than the former, but the principle would be the same.) If, on the other hand, we took the statement "Nature is uniform" to be a synthetic *a priori* truth (of the sort discussed on p. 106), then we could take it in two senses. First, it is known *a priori* in the sense that it is inconceivable that it should be otherwise. [This is plainly a weak argument, (as well as a confused sense of *a priori*) because it is quite conceivable that nature is not uniform, and not "self-evident" that it is.] Second, if science is to be possible, and science requires for its possibility the postulate of lawfulness expressed by the major premise, then this postulate needs to be held for the sake of science; without it, the possibility of science collapses, for generalization would never be more than an irrational and random choice.

(*c*) Again, if one took the uniformity of nature as a postulate, this would be the weakest form of these arguments for a major premise, and would put it forth as a hypothesis, justified by the confirmations it receives in practice. But justifying the choice of this postulate (rather than another) by its confirmations is once again an appeal to inductive generalization, if the hope is taken to be strengthened by its "payoffs." This raises the wider question, then, concerning confirmation in science generally. What justifies us in claiming that a larger number of instances supporting conclusions derived from a hypothesis increases its confirmation? All these ways of attempting to reinstate the inductive generalization as a formal or deductive inference, based on some major premise, seem to run into problems, as either falsifiable or circular and vacuous, or leading to inconsistencies;[1] at best then the *form* of the deductive inference may be maintained, but its strength is no greater than that of its premises. If the major premise is a postulate, then the conclusion is no more than postulational in its strength. But this gives us some hope, for if we take the conclusion ("If anything is a bee, it will give honey") as a device for making *predictions,* then it serves to generate falsifiable instantial predictions ("This is a bee, therefore it is predicted that it will give honey"), leading to *revisions* or *rejections* of the postulate.

The plausibility of the premise seems to increase, however, when we take a statement like (*b′*) (Iron expands when heated), for the force of *this*

[1] See, for example, Carl Hempel, "Inductive Inconsistencies," in *Logic and Language* (Dordrecht, Holland: D. Reidel, 1962), for an analysis of so-called quasi-syllogisms, statistical syllogisms, and elementary induction rules, which shows how these lead to inconsistencies when the arguments are construed as deductive. See also Nelson Goodman, *Fact, Fiction and Forecast* (Cambridge, Mass.: Harvard University Press, 1955), pp. 73 ff., on Goodman's "new riddle of induction" in which such inconsistencies are also examined, in terms of the predicate "grue." For further discussion, see pp. 232 ff.

generalization proceeds not merely from a finite number of tests of iron, but of tests on metals in general. The *number* of test instances of a statement (b'') "Metals expand when heated" is presumably much greater than that for (b'), and the scope of the property "expands when heated" is wider than that of "gives honey." By *scope,* we mean that there seem to be a greater number of different kinds of things that exhibit this property. We cannot generalize (as far as we know) beyond bees, in (a'), to say, for example, (a'') "Flying insects give honey." The force of (b') is further increased when we consider that expansion is defined as an increase in volume of some substance, and that it holds equally for gases and liquids, and for solids other than metals. Beyond this, if increase in volume is explained as increase in the mean distance between molecules, and this in turn becomes a function of the mean kinetic energy of a system of molecules, then the scope of "expansion" becomes theoretically wider by a huge factor. One might then be tempted to conclude "All physical substances expand when heated," but this is false (e.g., rubber contracts when heated, and everyone knows what happens to a steak left too long on the fire.) Yet the universal statement (b'') seems incomparably surer than (a'), and lends the major premise, concerning the uniformity of nature, a much more credible air. The difference, in a simple view, seems to lie in the greater regularity of physical processes than that exhibited by living things, and this has led some philosophers to speculate that nature is most uniform at the lower levels of organization, and becomes less rigidly so as complexity of structure increases.[2] But this is again an inductive generalization, depending in turn on inductive generalizations.

2. A second justification of the inductive leap does not presume that it has logical status at all, in any deductive sense. If it is an *inference,* it rests on a distinction between deductive or demonstrative inference and natural or practical or nondemonstrative or inductive inference, so that strictly speaking it is not inference at all. What then is it? Here we may distinguish alternatives within this view.

(a) The inductive leap is a "natural disposition of the human mind" or a "habit-forming capacity," and thus a psychological phenomenon characteristic of learning behavior. In the wider view discussed earlier, it is the characteristic form of a natural disposition in human thought or belief, but it derives from the very nature of adaptive organic life. (This explains very little, but renames inductive generalization as adaptive behavior and thus links it, at least by suggestion, with the study of a wide variety of similar or analogous processes in nature, most universally described by

[2] That is, the individuals in the domains of which physics treats are more nearly homogeneous than the individuals in the domains of which biology treats. Electrons, for example, are presumably all alike in relevant respects, whereas members of animal species have recognizably unique characters and thus differ among each other. This is a vague and problematic distinction at best, and we will come on it again in dealing with laws in the biological and human sciences.

Peirce as "habit-taking." Hume, in arguing against such inductive "inference" as *necessary* inference, sought to distinguish it as such a habit; deductive inference, therefore, is the only form of necessary inference, and the grounds of this necessity lie in the very formalism of deduction, as empirically empty and determined by formal rules for the use of a language, explicitly stated. The necessity is like that of the "necessity" of the knight's pattern in moving in chess or the "necessity" of finding the three-letter word which fits the crossword puzzle.

(*b*) It is hypothetical in the sense of "postulational," and is justified pragmatically. Its "truth" is not at issue, but only its utility or heuristic value in generating interesting and testable consequences. Thus, for example, if I discover that some iron expands when heated and some copper expands when heated, I may be tempted to heat a wide variety of metals to see if they also exhibit this property. If they do, then I have gained *heuristically* from the postulate. It has served to guide research along fruitful paths. Thus, too, we may take Mendeleev's generalization of the relations between families of chemical elements, in the periodic table, as a prediction-generating hypothesis, leading to the discovery of predicted elements. If the predictions fail of experimental verification, then the hypothesis is revised or rejected, and a new one is sought. If the hypothesis is revised in the light of new evidence, then the procedure leads to constant and critical self-correction, and strengthens our belief in the utility of proposing such postulates as stimulations to orderly and cumulative research. This is related to the preceding paragraph (*a*), appearing as a refinement of the ordinary trial-and-error learning, an advance in the common techniques of human learning.

(*c*) A corollary of (*b*) is that such a trial-and-error method proceeds not randomly, but in a guided path along the lines of greatest success. That is, the inductive generalization is justified by the cumulative success of its repeated applications. This view is further developed in the notions of limiting frequency, which we shall examine shortly. Past experience appears to show that with increasing size of a sample from which some inductive generalization is made, the probability ratio of the occurrence of an observed feature to the total number of observations made remains relatively stable, approaching a limit. But this too is an inductive generalization, from a finite set of past instances, and seems to put an inductive generalization in support of the method of inductive generalization. However, the "support" that is claimed is not *logical* support in the form of some premise for a deductive conclusion, but *pragmatic* support, i.e., the commonsense "support" or reinforcement which a habit gains from success in its pursuit.

(*d*) This latter view is modified still further, in the claim that induction cannot be "justified" by appeal to something *else,* especially a logical major premise, which would turn it into deduction. Rather, we regard an argument from past instances as reasonable *because* it follows the pattern of inductive generalization which we take as a standard in such matters. Thus, P. F. Strawson writes that the demand for a justification of induction *in general* (rather than a demand for the justification of this or that inductive generalization) is nonsensical, because it demands ultimately that induction be justified as *deduction*. Thus the justification of the claim that iron expands when heated is the quality of the evidence: if there are "good reasons" to believe this, then the belief is justified. But what we mean by "good reasons" is precisely that it has been often observed and tested, that it accords with what we know about metals in general. Thus, Strawson writes:

> "It is an analytic proposition that it is reasonable to have a degree of belief in a statement which is proportional to the strength of the evidence in its favor; and it is an analytic proposition, though not a proposition of mathematics, that, other things being equal, the evidence for a generalization is strong in proportion as the number of favorable instances, and the variety of circumstances in which they have been found, is great. So to ask whether it is reasonable to place reliance on inductive procedures is like asking whether it is reasonable to proportion the degree of one's convictions to the strength of the evidence. Doing this is what "being reasonable" means in such a context."[3]

In this view, reasonable belief in the context of empirical knowledge is precisely what inductive generalization in accordance with standards for such generalization gives us. But this then requires an examination of what such standards are. Presumably, because generalization from evidence is a characteristic procedure of what we would call scientific inference, it is to the paradigms of such inference, or to the critical reflective inquiry into the methods of such inference, that one should look for "good" inductive examples.

In the preceding paragraphs (1) and (2) we have then two large groups of views concerning the justification of induction. The first appeals to some wider premise which justifies the inductive generalization as a deductive inference, or as a type of deductive inference. The second eschews such a logical justification and appeals either to natural habits or dispositions or to pragmatic "justifications" of inductions either as heuristically valuable or practically successful and self-correcting hypotheses. Finally, the appeal is to the self-justification of inductive generalization, in terms of what we mean when we say that a particular generalization is based on good evidence or that a belief in it is reasonable.

We may also divide these views another way, distinguishing between those which claim an *a priori* support for inductive generalization and those

[3] P. F. Strawson, *Introduction to Logical Theory* (London: Methuen & Co., 1952), cited in Madden, ed., *The Structure of Scientific Thought* (Boston: Houghton Mifflin, 1960), p. 308.

which support it *a posteriori,* i.e., by its operation in experience. The axiomatic and metaphysical views (in one version, where the metaphysical "truth" is not a wide generalization, but is synthetic *a priori* or is regarded as a necessary truth "of reason"), and (perhaps unexpectedly) Strawson's type of view on the "analyticity" of "good reasons" (judged by what we mean by the term or by some paradigm case) would be *a priori* views. All the others, appealing to results in experience, utility, success, or habit, would be *a posteriori.* However, the view that we are naturally disposed to generalize inductively or to form habits, may also be taken as an *a priori* view, if it is interpreted to mean that we do not acquire the disposition, but that it is innate. Peirce exemplifies some such view in several of his writings. He says, for example,

> Side by side . . . with the well-established proposition that all knowledge is based on experience, and that science is only advanced by the experimental verifications of theories, we have to place this other equally important truth, that all human knowledge, up to the highest flights of science, is but the development of our inborn animal instincts.
>
> That there is a general uniformity in nature is not merely an unfounded, it is an absolutely absurd idea in any other sense than that man is adapted to his surroundings. . . . If nature seems highly uniform to us, it is only because our powers are adapted to our desires.[4]

Thus, though Peirce denies a "ground for induction" in the uniformity of nature as some axiom or metaphysical truth, he does see its support in a principle which transcends experience and which characterizes the truth of inductive inference as grounded in the relation of human knowledge to some objective reality. He writes, "Though a synthetic inference cannot by any means be reduced to deduction, yet that the rule of induction will hold good in the long run may be deduced from the principle that reality is only the object of the final opinion to which sufficient investigation would lead. That belief tends to fix itself under the influence of inquiry is, indeed, one of the facts with which logic sets out."[5] In this sense, Peirce's "justification of induction" is based on a theory of truth, and of the function of science, which derives from his view that human knowledge is adaptive behavior rooted in animal instincts.

It remains, then, to examine what the critique of induction reveals as its "method," or as the account of what its paradigm cases are, and what its pitfalls are.

[4] C. S. Peirce, "The General Theory of Probable Inference" in *Philosophical Writings of Peirce,* J. Buchler, ed. (New York: Dover, 1955), pp. 215, 213.

[5] C. S. Peirce, "The Probability of Induction," in *ibid.,* p. 189. For Quine's criticism of this view on a "final opinion," see W. V. O. Quine, *Word and Object* (Cambridge, Mass.: Technology Press, 1960), p. 23.

THE CRITIQUE OF INDUCTION: STANDARDS OF SCIENTIFIC INFERENCE

The kind of induction we have discussed thus far is the sort in which positive instances lead to a generalization concerning the class of instances as a whole. The fuller characterization of this method of induction describes it as induction by *simple enumeration.* The standard form of this is an enumeration of instances, and an "inductive leap" to a generalization:

1. On June 17, the sun rose at 6:03 at place *P*
2. On June 18, the sun rose at 6:02 at place *P*
3. On June 19, the sun rose at 6:01 at place *P*
4. . . . .

. . . .

Generalization: The sun rises every morning.

This sort of enumerative induction has been interpreted in two basic ways:

1. The induction is from past instances to future ones; thus inductive generalization is based on past experience and serves as the grounds for prediction of future experiences.
2. Because from the generalization it may also be inferred that the sun rose in January of that year, and in January 1000 years ago, the characterization of "past to future" is too narrow, and it should rather be from known instances to unknown ones.

Together with a prediction one would then also get a retrodiction, concerning past events. Confirmation of a past event would necessarily be indirect, because I could not observe the sunrise in 965 A.D. But presumably, if it had failed to rise, such a notable event would have been recorded, and we might then search for such highly improbable evidence.

But note that there is more information in this example than is contained in the generalization of it. One might also have generalized from the evidence given here that, "The sun rises one minute earlier on every successive day." On June 20th, the instantial prediction derived from this generalization would have been confirmed, strengthening the belief that the generalization was a "good" one. On June 21st, with some shock, I would notice that things had gone wrong. On June 22, I would suspect that my generalization needs revision. By June 23rd, I might generalize, "The sun rises one minute earlier each day until June 21st, and then rises one minute *later* each day," but now, if I did not already know better, I might feel queasy waiting for the next periodic shift. Would it occur on June 24th, 25th? By the end of September, with confirming instances galore, I would be tempted to generalize that after a reversal, on June 21, 1965, a regular sequence ("One minute later each day") seemed to be well established. October, November, and most of December would continue adding confirming instances (although I might grow hysterical, noticing that daylight was on the way to vanishing altogether, if things kept up).[6] With great relief, but with some confusion, I might notice another reversal on December 21, and begin to suspect that my generalization should be periodic, with reversals every six months.

In this naive example, some of the "dangers" of enumerative induction appear. The generalization is easily overthrown by a single counterinstance. Thus, on June 21st, the reversal falsifies the generalization at one blow. The saving grace here is that I take the generalization as a modifiable hypothesis, constantly adjusting it to the facts of observation, so that all of them are included in the broadened version. The hypothetical generalization is thus self-correcting. But if the corrections are such that no apparent pattern of a general sort appears (e.g., if my time reversals for successive sunrises were so erratic that their order was unstateable in any general form), I would get no more than a modest collection of data, in which no limited sets of recurrent invariances could be discovered. But where the pattern is significantly present, we generally tend to leap to conclusions. Presumably, then, we "discover" laws or law-like patterns exhibited in the collections of facts we know, and adduce them of facts not yet known but capable of becoming known, in observation.

One famous instance of the breakdown of such an inductive generalization based on observed (measured) facts is that of the Bode-Titus law. J. E. Bode (1747–1826), on the suggestion of his friend J. D. Titus, discovered an empirical rule which held for the mean distances of the planets from the sun. It is, briefly, this (as it holds with some adjustment for the planets which were then known): If we take R as the mean radius of a planet's orbit and number the planets ordinally, with respect to their proximity to the sun, so that Mercury is 1, Venus 2, Earth 3, and so on, and if we make two adjustments (to be noted), then the rule for R, or the Bode-Titus law, is:

$$R \text{ (in astronomical units)} = 0.4 + (0.3 \times 2^{n-2})$$

For the Earth, which is number 3, $n = 3$, so that $R = 1$, which is the definition of *astronomical unit* (the mean radius of Earth's orbit, or the mean distance of Earth to the sun). This works only if for Mercury, we set

[6] Dr. Daniel Greenberg has called my attention to the fact that Talmudic interpretations of *Genesis* include a similar "inductive inference" made by Adam, who took the shortening day as God's punishment, i.e., as impending "death" for having eaten the apple. See *The Babylonian Talmud,* I. Epstein, ed. (London: Soncino Press, 1935), *Seder Neziḳin, Abodah Zarah* 8a, Vol. IV, p. 37.

$(0.3 \times 2^{n-2}) = 0$, and if we assign to Jupiter the number 6, though it is in fifth position. From this generalization, Bode inferred that for position 5 there should be a planet (between Mars and Jupiter) with a mean orbital radius of 2.8 A.U. In 1801 the Italian astronomer Piazzi, in looking for something else, discovered a new "star" which turned out to be not a star but a planet, though a tiny one, less than 500 miles in diameter (what we now call a planetoid or asteroid, more than 2000 of which have been since discovered and their orbits plotted). This planetoid, Ceres, had a calculated mean orbital radius of 2.77 A.U., or within 1 per cent of Bode's predicted value. Because the "asteroid belt" of over 2000 such bodies lies between Mars and Jupiter, Bode's law may be interpreted in terms of some cataclysmic or interrupted planetary formation or dissolution, in an orbit in accordance with the law. Herschel's discovery of Uranus, shortly after Bode's announcement of his law, in position 8 after Saturn, had also given still earlier "confirmation," its mean orbital radius of 19.6 A.U. coming to within 2 per cent of the predicted value. Here certainly there seemed to be a general law arrived at as a generalization from empirical measurements and their relations, the law stating a mathematical invariance discovered in six known instances, and predictively successful in two additional, previously unknown, ones. Like the sunrise on June 21st, however, the law seemed to break down with the discovery of Neptune and (later and more seriously) Pluto. The calculated R was off, in these cases, by a significant amount. Despite this, there seems to be some chance of discovering why the law breaks down beyond Uranus, if it can be explained why it holds to that point. This has thus far not been done, but recent work suggests that the periodicity up through Uranus may be explained theoretically by the laws of celestial mechanics.

*Table of Distances of First Six Planets from the Sun

		MEAN DISTANCE $\bar{R}$ FROM THE SUN (AU)	
Planet	*Assigned value n*	*Observed value*	*Value from Bode-Titus Law*
Mercury	1	0.39	0.4
Venus	2	0.72	0.7
Earth	3	1.0	1.0
Mars	4	1.5	1.6
Jupiter	6	5.2	5.2
Saturn	7	9.5	10.0

* From G. Holton and D. H. D. Roller, *Foundations of Modern Physical Science*, 1958, Addison-Wesley, Reading, Mass.

In this case a generalization based on limited information is found to hold for some additional cases but not for others. For the limited domain of the nine planets it fails as a generalization. Yet the extent to which it does hold raises the question of why it should, because any discovered regularity or invariance in so fundamental a case as the relation between the distances of the planetary orbits from each other must be significant of something, even if it fails beyond a certain point. Thus, it may turn out to be an accidental regularity, a false lure with strong appeal because of our predisposition to be taken in by order of any sort as significant; or if the regularity can be explained, in its limited application, as derivable from the more fundamental and universal laws of mechanics, then it is conceivable that both the cases which do fall under Bode's law and those which do not may be shown to fall under some more general law which includes them both or which explains the breakdown.

ELIMINATIVE INDUCTIONS: MILL'S CANONS AND THE LOGIC OF CONDITIONS

The danger or limitation of enumerative induction, as Bacon knew, is that it only includes positive instances in its formulation. The inclusion of negative instances within the method of inductive generalization turns the method into a search for tests which would eliminate those hypothetical generalizations which are false, leaving as a residue only those which had sustained such tests, these latter to be tested further in turn. This method is called "eliminative induction." It is sometimes discussed as a method of discovering and proving causal relationships, and it was characterized in this way by J. S. Mill, who formulated the "canons," or rules, for this procedure in his *System of Logic* (1841).

A brief and simplified version of Mill's *Methods of Agreement and Difference* is given here. A detailed account and fuller discussion may be found in most elementary logic texts which treat of inductive method. (See the bibliography at the end of Appendix C for suggestions.)

Mill states the method of agreement thus: "If two or more instances of the phenomenon under investigation have only one circumstance in common, the circumstance in which alone all the instances agree is the cause (or effect) of the given phenomenon."[7] Thus, for example, if the "circumstances" or antecedents *A, B, C, D* occur together with the phenomenon *P* in one instance, and *A, E, F, G* occur with *P* in another, and *A, H, K, L* with *P* in a third, then the one circumstance in which alone all the instances agree is *A* which is then taken to be the "cause" (or "effect") of *P*. The

[7] J. S. Mill, *A System of Logic,* Chapter VIII, in E. Nagel, ed. *John Stuart Mill's Philosophy of Scientific Method* (New York: Hafner, 1950), p. 214.

weakness here is obvious, because it is possible that *A* accidentally accompanies *P,* or that *P* may be caused by *B, C, D, E, F, G,* and so on, in different ways, or by something which is not included in the circumstances under inspection. Thus Mill suggests the method of difference, stating it thus: "If an instance in which the phenomenon under investigation occurs, and an instance in which it does not occur, have every circumstance in common save one, that one occurring only in the former; the circumstance in which alone the two instances differ, is the effect, or the cause, or an indispensable part of the cause of the phenomenon."[8]

Thus, for example, if *A, B, C, D* occur together with *P,* and *B, C, D* occur without *P,* then *A* is the cause or the effect, or an indispensable part of the cause of *P.* Using both methods in the same investigation (joint method of agreement and difference), one then attempts to discover what is invariantly associated with some phenomenon, in the presence of which it always happens and in the absence of which it never happens. In the former case, where some *A* always eventuates in or occurs with *P, A* is said to be a sufficient condition of *P* (although *P* may occur when *A* is absent as well, so that *A* is not a necessary condition of *P*). In the latter case, when *P* never happens except when *A* happens, *A* is said to be a necessary condition of *P* (although *A* may happen without *P,* in which case it is not a sufficient condition of *P*).

Mill's canons thus give us an account of the common methods of experimental testing, in which presumptive correlations among data are subjected to controlled observation. The use of control groups and the practice of changing one variable or parameter at a time are means whereby agreement, difference, and concomitant variation are tested. Such testing is not (as Mill thought) a procedure for discovering causal relations as much as it is a means of eliminating causal hypotheses which do not stand up to the test (which Mill also recognized).

In any case it is clear that a simple method of agreement alone gives us at best what may be meaningless or accidental "regularities" and that it fails to give us a way of knowing whether all or any of the relevant circumstances have been taken into account; it leaves relevance simply a matter of what we *have* taken into account. Whatever invariance the method of agreement gives us is, therefore, not the causal invariance we seek. Nor does the joint method of agreement and difference give us the adequate test for such invariance, because at best it gives us only an eliminative test, not one which lends positive force to the uneliminated hypotheses, except that they persevere despite our ingenuity in forcing them to the wall. But perhaps this is what the refined method of trial and error which is experimental science offers at its best, leaving the residual hypotheses which have been well-tested, as the victors in the contest among conflicting hypotheses, rather than as certified truths.

[8] *Ibid.,* p. 215.

Such eliminative induction is central to any discussion of experimental inference—the methods of rational choice and decision characteristic of experimental inquiry. We may, then, examine the logical structure of a schema such as Mill's in a formal way.

Suppose we take the *relata* of some conjectured invariance (following Mill) as antecedents and consequents, and proceed to reconstruct the possible relations among them in terms of their presence or absence in some given instance. We take *A* or *C* as meaning the presence or absence of antecedent or of consequent, respectively, and not-*A* or not-*C* as meaning their absence. The conjunction sign " • " is taken as denoting the conjunction in an observed instance of the alternative states of presence or absence of the antecedents and consequents. Then the four possible combinations in a given instance are

(1) $A \cdot C$
(2) $A \cdot$ not-C
(3) not-$A \cdot C$
(4) not-$A \cdot$ not-C

Furthermore, we may characterize certain combinations of these observed instances, in which the presence or absence of antecedents and consequents in alternative ways occurs.

(5) The following instances are observed:

(1) $A \cdot C$
and (2) $A \cdot$ not-C
and (4) not-$A \cdot$ not-C
but never (3) not-$A \cdot C$

In such a case, we say that *A is a necessary condition of C*. That is, whenever *C* is present, *A* is present, or *C* is never present unless *A* is also present, although *C* may be absent when *A* is present. For example, clouds are a necessary condition of rain; there may be clouds without rain, but there is never rain without clouds.

(6) The following instances are observed:

(1) $A \cdot C$
and (3) not-$A \cdot C$
and (4) not-$A \cdot$ not-C
but never (2) $A \cdot$ not-C

In such a case, we say that *A is a sufficient condition of C*. That is, whenever *A* is present, *C* is present, or *A* is never present without the presence of *C*, though *C* may be present when *A* is absent. For example, guillotining is a sufficient condition of death, but not a necessary one, because death may occur by other means as well.

(7) The following instances are observed:

(1) $A \cdot C$
and (4) not-A · not-C
but never (2) A · not-C
and never (3) not-$A \cdot C$

In such a case, we say that *A is a necessary and sufficient condition of C.* That is, *C* is never present unless *A* is also present, and *A* is never present unless *C* is also present. *A* and *C* therefore only occur together or are invariantly associated, in this strong sense of invariance. For example, if the volume of a gas is held constant, then whenever the temperature increases, the pressure increases, and whenever the pressure increases, the temperature increases—it is never the case that one changes and the other does not, concomitantly, (all other things being equal).

(8) It may be seen that when *A* is a necessary condition of *C*, then *C* is a sufficient condition of *A;* and when *A* is a sufficient condition of *C*, then *C* is a necessary condition of *A*. [This may be seen on inspection of (5) and (6), where obviously, if never (3) not-$A \cdot C$, then also never C · not-A, and so on.]

(9) Furthermore, it may be seen that if *A* is a necessary and sufficient condition of *C*, then *C* is a necessary and sufficient condition of *A* [from (8)].

If one interprets causal relation strictly as the invariant relation between some antecedent and some consequent such that the consequent is present whenever and only whenever the antecedent is present, or where *A* is a necessary and sufficient condition for *C*, then to establish this strong an agreement or invariance involves more than just the specification of the positive instances of the connection of *A* and *B*, but also the specification of all the conditions of presence and absence. In Mill's account this is tested by the joint method of agreement and difference. The logical elaboration of the formulation of the conditions under which we may assert that experimental consequences exhibit such invariant causal relation is called the logic of conditions.[9] The logical form of the relation, in this strongest case of necessary and sufficient conditions, is that of equivalence or biconditional implication: $A \leftrightarrow C$, or *A if and only if C* (or *C if and only if A*), which is the joint assertion. $A \rightarrow C$ and $C \rightarrow A$. One consequence of such

[9] A full treatment of this logic of conditions is given in G. H. von Wright, *A Treatise on Induction and Probability* (Paterson, N.J.: Littlefield, Adams and Co. 1960), pp. 66 ff. An early systematic treatment is given in C. D. Broad "The Principles of Demonstrative Inference, I," *Mind,* Vol. 49 (1930).

an interpretation of causal relation is that many laws in science, i.e., those stated in the form of universal conditionals, or as $(x)\ [F(x) \rightarrow G(x)]$, would fail to qualify as causal laws. For example, the law-like statement might assert that if iron is heated it will expand, but it does not assert that it will expand if and only if it is heated, for it may be expanded by other means, e.g., stretching it or beating it thin. Thus, the law in this form asserts only a sufficient condition, not a necessary *and* sufficient condition for the expansion of iron. Yet, such a law certainly states an invariance. What the strict version of causal invariance seems to assert, beyond this, is that something is the cause of some effect only if the presence of this cause is necessary for the effect to occur, and its absence is necessary for the failure of the effect to occur. On such an interpretation of causal relation many descriptive empirical laws would fail to meet this criterion of invariance. If we take this analysis of conditions to be an explication of what we mean by causal relation, then these conditions specify what we will take to be the norm in accordance with which we may infer that experimental observation exhibits an invariance, or causal relation. Whether or not the observed invariance is evidence of "real" invariance thus becomes an empty question, because what we mean by evidence of invariance is what this norm specifies. The acceptance of this norm raises questions of justification, not concerning the inference of such an invariance in a given case, but rather concerning why this norm of evidence should be accepted rather than some other (e.g., intuition, clairvoyance, or random choice).

The methods of eliminative induction may then be taken as either (*a*) proffered norms for what we shall take to be a reasonable experimental inference or (*b*) a descriptive account of the procedures of the experimental scientist in the activity of testing the validity of a claim of invariant relation. In either case Mill's canons assert what conditions a discovery claim should meet in order to be accepted as reasonable, or what conditions a procedure of confirmation or falsification should meet in order to be regarded as valid. Thus they are guides to (and descriptions of) the norms of scientific discovery and testing, rather than being themselves methods of discovery and demonstration. The distinction may seem a fine one, but here is its import: If we take something satisfying these norms as "discovered" or "proven" then presumably we take it as true. Any inductive generalization thus supported by some finite set of observations would be judged true by virtue of the support of the available evidence. But inductive generalizations do break down under the weight of new evidence. We are then in the position of having to say either that the inductive generalization is true only for an enumerated domain (or reference class) of observed facts (which then makes it no longer a generalization, but only a summary of the known facts), or, more awkwardly, that it was true at one time and false at another. But if it is a true generalization of universal scope including all possible instances of the properties which it concerns, then it is odd to say that it once held for all the instances and now no longer does. (This would be true only if the whole domain of facts to which it refers in fact were changed in time, so that the truth of the generalization would be a dated truth, e.g., true only from time t_1 to time t_2.) In the general sense of what we mean by a law of nature or an invariant relation, such a constraint would trivialize it (though we will examine this further in the next chapter). It would therefore be more perspicuous to say that the canons give us the conditions of warranted beliefs where beliefs are subject to change with evidence; but where the truth which is the object of these beliefs remains, and does not shape itself to changing beliefs, but instead has some objective status to which true beliefs shape themselves. Thus, at one time it was a warranted belief, in view of the available evidence, that the earth was stationary and that the heavens circled around it. It no longer is a warranted belief, not because the earth was then stationary and is no longer, but because the evidence has changed. (Aristotle puts it thus: "It is not because we think truly that you are pale, that you *are* pale, but because you are pale we who say this have the truth."[10])

In this sense, inductive generalizations are truth claims, which are reasonable or warranted in accordance with certain norms. Such norms do not guarantee the truth of our claims, but only that it is reasonable to believe them to be true. Thus reasonable beliefs may be false, and unreasonable beliefs true. For example, I may believe that on the far side of the galaxy there is a duplicate solar system with nine planets, that on the third of these there is now someone writing exactly what I am writing, and that "he" is my *Doppelgänger* in every respect but location. This is logically and empirically possible, but I believe it to be false, on the limited evidence we have. So do you. But it is conceivably true, though there is presently no way I could ascertain this, and presumably it is unascertainable in my lifetime. Even if it were true, it would still be unreasonable to believe it at present. However, the fact that we may entertain unreasonable beliefs is a fact of major importance in discovery, and evidences the role of imaginative conception in science. The testability of such conceptions, however, would still be constrained by the norms of experimental inference which exhibit what a scientific community has established as criteria for warranted belief.

To take one more example, by way of making the transition to a new question, suppose that at one time it was a warranted belief that all swans were white (an example which Mill introduces and which has become standard). That is, all observed instances of swans reported them white, and critical observation had made certain that nothing which was a swan had been discounted. The generalization *All swans are white* would then be warranted. With the discovery of black swans, however, the generalization fails (as did our previous two concerning sunrises and Bode's law).

[10] Aristotle, *Metaphysics*, Bk. IX (θ), 10, 1051^b 7.

May we now *re*generalize and say, "All swans are either white or black"? It would certainly conform to the observed instances, now including all of them, and would serve as a basis for predictions that all future observations of swans would discover them to be either white or black. Then, let us say, blue swans are discovered and adjustments are made in our generalization; then yellow swans, and then green swans. We might be tempted to generalize thus, "All swans are either white or some other color," having now achieved a generality that seems immune from reversals. But the predicate *white or some other color* is vacuous, translatable into *white or not-white,* and fails to be an inductive generalization at all; because with respect to anything at all, it may be asserted with certainty that it is either white or nonwhite. The predicate of the form "*P* or not-*P*" is an empty one, because "*P* or not-*P*" is what we describe as a logical truth, true for all values of the variable *P*. Nor, presumably, is the kind of truth we would want to establish of the form *All swans have some color* or *All swans are swan-colored.*

We might ask, in such a case, what percentage of swans are white and what percentage black. Here we would introduce a distinction between what we could call a qualitative generalization and a metrical one. In ordinal terms, we might say *more* swans are white than are black. But in terms of *how many more* we would have to introduce a measurement of the relative distribution of white and black swans; we would, in short, have to introduce statistical generalization as a form of inductive generalization. This leads us to introduce the question of probability in one of its forms.

STATISTICAL GENERALIZATION, PROBABILITY, AND DEGREE OF BELIEF

Instead of abandoning the white-swan generalization, as a qualitative generalization about all swans, we might say, instead, that of all the observed instances of swans, a certain number were white. If we take the total number of observed instances as n, and the number of white swans observed in these n instances as some number $m \leq n$, then we may establish a ratio $\frac{m}{n}$ as representing the relative frequency of white swans to the total observed swan population. As in the previous discussion of generalization, this is no more than a summary report of known instances and is not yet a generalization at all, if n represents the number of observations. The generalization comes with the interpretation of this frequency. If, once again, I make the "inductive leap," and claim that what holds for some assigned number n will continue to hold as n increases indefinitely, then this means that the ratio $\frac{m}{n}$ observed to hold in some instances is taken to hold in all instances. For example, if I observe that nine out of ten swans are white, the ratio $\frac{9}{10}$ or 0.9, will hold also for 100 swans, 1000 swans, and

1,000,000 swans. If I hold this, then I will tend to believe that out of 100 swans, I will observe 90 white swans, and so on.

This has obvious faults. First of all, it is perfectly conceivable that all the black swans in the world are concentrated in one place, in which case I would either have to know this beforehand or be sure that in counting swans I have also included all the places where there are swans, so that the distribution of black swans with respect to the total population of swans is known. But if this were known, I wouldn't need to generalize at all; I could just count. In such a case, n would be a finite number known in advance, and $\frac{m}{n}$ would merely be a report. If instead of completing the count, I assumed that a fair sample would give me a ratio which represented the ratio of the whole population, I would have to know that the sample was fair. The test of the fairness of the sample would presumably be that it would give me a ratio which truly represented that for the whole population. But if I knew this, I would not need the sample at all, because I would already know the ratio which the sample represented.

In working with statistical generalizations all the considerations which concerned us about inductive generalization reappear. I may, for example, hold that the uniformity of nature underwrites the stability of the discovered ratio for a small sample, as the sample increases. Or I might pragmatically take the ratio as self-correcting as the sample increases. Or I might discover that if I choose my sample in accordance with certain norms, this does in fact produce a ratio which remains more or less stable as my sample increases. In this latter case there would seem to be some circularity. For if I chose my sample in such a way as to produce a ratio of 0.9 for 10 swans, and then also for 100 swans, the sampling technique would be based on an *a priori* norm: "a fair sample is one which does in fact produce a stable ratio as the sample increases." Just as it might seem to be "loading" the case if I decided to count nothing but white swans, to confirm the qualitative generalization that all swans are white, it might equally seem to be loading the case to count in such a way that some initial ratio is preserved, and to cry "unfair" if this ratio is radically changed as the sample increases.

One appeal against these critical charges might be that we bring to bear some initial commonsense considerations concerning "fairness." (For example, the simple expedient of not counting the same thing twice seems fair, as does the expedient of not choosing what to count by some prejudiced criterion, or in some preassigned order.) In short, the absence of controls which might weight the sample in some direction seems a fair guarantee that at least some vicious prejudgments do not distort it. This condition of an absence of prejudicial control we may call randomness in the sample. Thus, though there is no guarantee that such a random sample is not coincidentally or accidentally loaded, we thus tend to eliminate to the best of our ability any conscious interference with the process of selection which would weight it prejudicially (or, to put it somewhat paradoxically, we consciously interfere to see to it that we do not "interfere" in a prejudicial way).

Suppose, then, we do our best to ensure these commonsense conditions of fairness, and that then our sample does show certain empirical characteristics as it increases. Namely, that as n increases, the ratio $\frac{m}{n}$ does, after some initial fluctuations, begin to stabilize and remain more or less uniform. If this happens in enough independent instances (i.e., those in which the outcome of one is not causally related in any way that we can tell to the outcome of the other)—say, with swans, with bees, with iron, and with sunrises—where some property of each of these is associated with it in some statistical ratio, then we might be tempted to generalize this result concerning relative frequency of some property in some enlarging sample thus *for any sample n: as n increases, the ratio* $\frac{m}{n}$ *tends to remain stable.* We may judge this to be an empirical result, whose conditions are those which commonsense notions of fairness dictate, that is to say, randomness of the sample. (The important point here is that randomness is not taken to be an intrinsic property of the sample, but of the method of sampling; whether or not the sample is really random is precisely what we do not know.) Having hedged ourselves, in this way, against the charge of *a priori* determination of what fairness is (i.e., defining it by a prior commitment to some stable ratio), we may then claim that the ratio is *discovered* to be stable.

Clearly, there are cases of statistical studies where this stability does hold and cases where it does not. For example, if I were counting the relative number of robins with respect to total bird population in a given region, this would vary with seasonal conditions, so that a ratio at one time would vary greatly with that at another. I might then add the condition *all other things being equal.* This introduces into the problem of sampling the consideration of environing conditions of the sample, and the influence these may have on changing the distribution of certain properties in the sample through time. In physical experiment, as in any other observational technique, we then try to establish standard conditions, as a way of guaranteeing the validity of the sample. We have seen that in measurement the interlocking network of ratios of magnitudes is a way of establishing the invariance of these ratios so that measurement itself does not intrude on the object of measurement to change it; but we have also seen that in some instances this intrusion is theoretically unavoidable, in which case the ratio invariance is sought in the linked system of instrument of measurement (or observer) and object of measurement.

The interpretation of the statistical result still remains to be made. If the claim is that the statistical ratio of frequency of some property relative to total number of observed instances may be generalized inductively, then the claim may be seen in two different contexts. (1) The claim may be that in fact this exhibits the relative frequency of a whole domain in some fair sample. I may then say that the ratio $\frac{m}{n}$ is the objective probability that what holds for n, where n is some assigned number, will also hold for $n+1$. Or (2) the claim may be that the *belief* that what holds for n will hold for $n+1$ is a warranted belief in accordance with the norms of fair sampling; that these norms tell us in effect what we mean by *reasonable belief*. The difference here is that in the first case something is being said about the relation between sampled members of some population and the whole population; that is, a synthetic or descriptive statement of fact is being put forth. In the second, on the other hand, something is being said about the relation of what we know observationally to what we may reasonably infer about what remains as yet unknown.

There are at least two senses of *probability* here which are so ambiguous that a statement like Aristotle's, "The probable is that which occurs frequently," may be taken in both senses. First, *probable* may mean no more than *frequent*, and in this sense is no more than a descriptive term, connoting a comparative concept, so that *more probable* means no more than *more frequent* and *less probable* no more than *less frequent*, where frequency is the ratio of recurrences of some observed property to the whole class of observed instances. But when we use the term *probable*, we usually have in mind some such sense as *likely, expected* or *believable*. To say of something that it is improbable then means to express a disbelief or a low degree of belief in its occurrence (either in the past or the future, or sometimes even present, as when one might colloquially say of a giraffe, on observing it, that it is an improbable animal). What confuses the distinction is the generalization of the first sense, when one inductively extends the description *frequent* to mean that an observed frequency will continue to be observed. Thus, if we define probability as the ratio $\frac{m}{n}$ interpreted inductively, then the formula $P = \frac{m}{n}$ will be taken to be an inductive generalization from which predictions can be made. Because m and n are numbers, P is a numerical ratio, expressing an anticipated constancy of the ratio for any values assigned to n. To interpret it thus goes beyond a merely statistical report of the facts of observation. If, as we said earlier, we hedge this so that under conditions of fair sampling we merely record the changes in P as observed instances increase, we may indeed find that P remains fairly constant. But this too is nothing but a report of the facts until it is interpreted inductively or generalized. In some set of observations, the values of P may vary in the following fashion:

m :	9	42	87	431	866	4327
n :	10	50	100	500	1000	5000
P :	.9	.84	.87	.862	.866	.8654

or graphically:

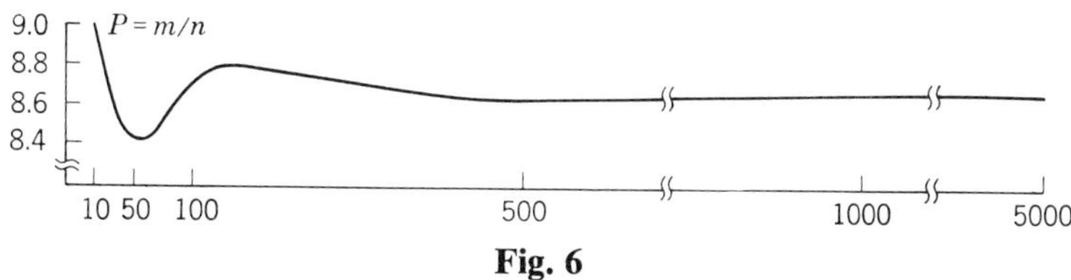

Fig. 6

If we make an inference from this, to the effect that unobserved values of m and n will yield values close to given values of P, then all the considerations of what "justifies" this inference reoccur. Since, from many observations of recurrent events which we take to be highly homogeneous or "standard," it is empirically observed that P converges on a limit as n increases (in terms of the graph, the fluctuations become smaller and smaller), one may make the inductive generalization that probability, in terms of relative frequency is the limit upon which ratio $\frac{m}{n}$ converges as n increases. For the "populations" of those domains which we take to be indefinitely large, or infinite (e.g., those in the physical sciences, where we do not expect ever to make a "last observation" having enumerated all the instances one by one), we may take this as the case where n approaches infinity. The formulation of this inductive interpretation of the ratio may then be given thus: P (of m with respect to n) $= \lim_{n \to \infty} \frac{m}{n}$.

Because what we mean by the "probability of m with respect to n" may be taken to mean the probability that a statement of a universal sort (e.g., "All swans are white") will be true of all the instances of its application, where these instances serve as the evidence for or against the statement, another interpretation of this formula may be given. Where h stands for the universal statement taken as a universal hypothesis, and e for the evidence (a set of statements: "swan one is white," "swan two is not white", and so on), we may read the formula as $P(h, e) = \lim_{n \to \infty} \frac{m}{n}$. But this introduces another sense of "probability"; something like "the probability that a hypothesis framed as a universal statement is *true*, or the probability that it will yield true instantial statements, or predictions." If this is taken as a description of the relative frequency with which a hypothesis is confirmed instantially, then again *more highly confirmed* remains merely descriptive. But *more highly confirmed* carries a normative sense. A hypothesis which yields more true statements predictively seems to have the edge on one which yields fewer, with this difficulty: a hypothesis from which a single false statement can be derived is false, if it is a universal hypothesis. *All swans are white* is not merely more or less highly confirmed, depending on the ratio of white to nonwhite swans. A single black swan is enough to make the hypothesis false.

Here the "inductive inconsistencies" which arise on the construal of inductive or statistical inferences as deductive inferences may be seen to arise. (See footnote 1, p. 213.) If the generalization is cast in the form of a statistical quasi-syllogism from which assignments of probability or likelihood to instances may be deduced, then the following situation may arise:

Suppose our premises are

John is a member of Alcoholics Anonymous.
Less than 1 percent of the members of Alcoholics Anonymous are college professors.

If we use a rule of inference which assigns to individuals the probabilities or likelihoods which hold of the classes to which they belong, the conclusion would be

Almost certainly John is not a college professor (or the probability that John is a college professor is 0.01).

Suppose it is also the case that

John is a regular reader of the *Journal of Philosophy*.
and More than 99 percent of the regular readers of the *Journal of Philosophy* are college professors.
then Almost certainly (or with a probability of 0.99) John is a college professor.

Statistically, we then have the incompatible conclusions that it is almost certain both that John is a college professor and that he is not; or that with probability 0.99, John is a college professor, and that with probability 0.01, John is a college professor). As Hempel describes this situation,

> we have a pair of rival arguments conforming to the same rule and starting with true premisses, and yet leading to incompatible conclusions. Despite its apparent plausibility, then, the construal of certain types of statistical arguments as having the form of broadly statistical syllogisms is untenable; for these syllogisms generate inductive inconsistencies in the following sense: for an argument with true premisses that has the form of a statistical syllogism, there exists, in general, a rival argument of the same form, again with true premisses, whose conclusion is logically incompatible with that of the first argument.[11]

If, however, we restate the hypothesis as a statistical generalization, then presumably it may be taken as a hypothesis which is modified constantly

[11] Carl Hempel, "Inductive Inconsistencies," *op. cit.*, p. 131. See also S. Toulmin *The Uses of Argument* (Cambridge: Cambridge University Press, 1958), pp. 109 ff. and J. Cooley, "On Mr. Toulmin's Revolution in Logic," *The Journal of Philosophy*, **56**:297–319 (1959).

as new facts come in and as the ratio expressed by P changes. The ideal hypothesis is then one which states the limit toward which P converges as n increases, and the empirical version of this hypothesis is one which states the ideal hypothesis within the limits of "error" or "divergence" which show up in actual measurement. As we have seen, a mathematical hypothesis is false for all values other than the ones predicted, unless it is interpreted approximately. Thus Bode's law is false for every measurement of mean orbital radius, strictly taken, even for the planets for which it is said to hold. But it holds within some percentage of error small enough to be taken as an approximation. Mathematically, a miss is as good as a mile, if our mathematical formulation states the ideal limit as a literal empirical expectation. But experimental error, the limits of measurement accuracy, and other such factors may be adduced to explain why the divergence from predicted values occurs, and norms for such error may be set up, as they are in a theory of errors.

We may instead take the domain of investigation itself as one which is intrinsically variable, within some limits, however; and in this case, we would be attributing a certain contingency to nature itself, asserting of her, "Sometimes she does and sometimes she doesn't." Our described probability ratios would then not be the results of error, or of the size of the sample, so much as the more accurate description of nature's own fickleness and waywardness, with respect to an oversimplified and ideal conception which permits us to arrange all these variations in a convenient way for our purposes of computation, or for the economy required for our comprehension. Our ideal generalizations may then be Procrustean beds to which nature is fitted for our convenience. Probability, in this sense, would be the expectation or likelihood that, based on past experience, any sample would fit one such bed.

But *probability,* in a sense which has been suppressed in the foregoing discussion, also means some measure of the subjective estimate concerning the likelihood that something will occur in the future as it has occurred in the past, and this also has to do with the evidential strength of past observations. Suppose that a certain ratio $\frac{m}{n}$ does remain stable, for all the cases $n = 1$, $n = 2 \ldots n = k$, so that I get something like the series $1/2, 2/4, 3/6 \ldots 50/100$. Though P remains the same as n increases, my confidence presumably increases as more and more evidence piles up, so that P does not reflect any increase of confidence, but only the stability of the ratio. *Probable* here cannot be used for both these senses unequivocally, nor can it be so easily represented metrically. How would one judge that one was "twice as confident"? Would twice as many instances of confirmation of a prediction derived from some hypothesis make the hypothesis twice as credible? In fact, would it even make it more credible? In general, we might say that confidence and credibility increase with evidence, as habits acquire strength from repetition and reinforcement. But in the rational economy of science, sometimes once is enough. In a major experimental test the conditions are so rigidly standardized, the community of scientists is so well attuned to what the conditions of repeatability are, and the integrity of scientific reporting is believed to be so immune to falsification of results in public communication that a single result in a single experiment in such a case inspires a degree of belief which a thousand tests in another instance would fail to achieve. At the end of his chapter on the "Ground of Induction," in *A System of Logic,* Mill writes,

> Why is a single instance in some cases, sufficient for a complete induction, while in others, myriads of concurring instances, without a single exception known or presumed, go such a very little way toward establishing a universal proposition? Whoever can answer this question knows more of the philosophy of logic than the wisest of the ancients and has thus solved the problem of induction.[12]

We may sum up the distinctions drawn thus far as follows:

1. A statistical report is one which gives a ratio of relative frequency of some property or some relation among properties (e.g., being a swan and being white) in the total number of observed instances. A statistical generalization makes the inductive inference that this ratio will continue to be observed as the total number of observations continues to grow.
2. This statistical generalization may be taken as a probability, i.e., an estimate or anticipation, in comparative degrees, that some universal hypothesis concerning all cases will be confirmed. The hypothesis may then suffer revisions from instance to instance, as dictated by the ratio change as observations increase. For example, beginning with an induction from a single case of an observed white swan, we might hypothesize that all swans are white, from the ratio $1/1$, where $P = 1$. If all swans observed continue to be white, then P continues to be $= 1$. As nonwhite swans are observed, P changes, becoming less than 1 in proportion to the percentage of white swans to all swans counted, including those nonwhite.
3. This estimate, in (2), confuses senses of "probability," however, because the estimate is a belief that some ratio will continue to be observed, whereas the relative frequency is only an objective report on an observed ratio. The sense of "subjective" probability refers not to the frequency, but to the belief or confidence that a frequency which continues stable as instances increase will increase with the number of instances, or with the degree of success of predictions derived from this frequency ratio taken as a hypothesis.

[12] J. S. Mill, *op. cit.,* p. 186.

4. The sense in which degree of belief or confidence increases with increased instances is either once more the standard case of inductive generalization, whose grounds we discussed earlier; or it is problematic beyond this in the special case where the quality of an experimental test may outweigh the weight of a large number of instances. (A simple case would be the confidence placed in an expert witness as against that placed in casual or untrained observers.)
5. Ideal probability, in the relative frequency case, represents a situation of sampling in which randomness of the sampling is assured, or postulated.

THE MATHEMATICS OF CHANCE AND THE CALCULUS OF PROBABILITIES

Just as arithmetic and geometry may be formalized as a system of operations of inference, so too the inferential procedures involved in judgments concerning probability may be formalized. Thus far, we have considered the concepts of probability as they derive from our ordinary commonsense habits of induction and from the consideration of the kinds of operations of inference which are involved in inductive and statistical generalization. Another commonsense usage concerning probability is that which is exhibited in *What are the chances of your stopping by today?* or *The chances are that you are right.* Here, the senses of *chances* and *probabilities* merge in common use, in the common meaning which concerns an estimate, favorable or unfavorable, of a situation in which the lines are not drawn hard and fast. Thus all the modal terminology ("I *might* make it"; "It's *possible* that I may come), which indicates tentativeness or lack of absolute commitment, flirts with the idea of chance. *Chance,* in this sense, connotes the unforeseeable, that concerning which no sure estimate can be given, the margin for the unexpected, which we learn from experience to take into account both in daily life and in science.

Yet the conditions of sheer chance are such that they lend themselves to analysis of a formal sort readily, if we define what we mean by *chance* in certain ways. One way has already suggested itself: in order to avoid prejudicing some sample, we select our instances *randomly,* or we may say, *by chance.* To common sense it may appear that this means that no rule of selection is used, but in fact the very condition of randomness already states a rule, albeit a negative one, and perhaps a paradoxical one: "Do not select your instances in any way that can be ordered by a rule." Thus, one may not choose every third instance to observe, for this would ensure randomness only if we already knew that the population we were choosing from was not ordered in such a way that some property appeared in every third case. Thus, we "mix things up," so that any sequence of instances we choose to observe is, to the best of our knowledge, an unordered or random sequence. We might state this thus: that for every instance we choose to observe, it would be equally possible to choose some other instance. If I were observing a population of swans, then the selection of a fair sample would be dictated by this equipossibility of selection. A game of chance, like the simple Blind Man's Buff, ensures this by blindfolding whoever is "it," so that he cannot know that he is tagging any one person any more than he can know that he is tagging another. Shuffling cards "sufficiently" is supposed to ensure this same "blindness," a "marked deck" being one in which this "blind choice" is vitiated. Thus too, justice is portrayed as blind, meting out equal judgment to all, with scales initially balanced so that no judgment is a prejudgment. Yet in the economy of justice, evidence will show one man guilty, another innocent, and where there is no reasonable basis for choice, the indifference will be reflected in hung juries and suspended judgments. The ancient philosophical school of skepticism (sometimes called Pyrrhonism after one of its major figures, Pyrrho) recommended precisely such a suspension of judgment, on the grounds that evidence for and evidence against some point of view could always be skeptically assessed as indecisive, and that rational choice, in the sense of necessary choice, was not available concerning matters of fact.

Yet the conditions of ideal equipossibility are such that, on analysis, laws of chance may be rigorously formalized and a mathematical calculus of chances, under given initial conditions, may be set up as a system of deductive or necessary inference. Such a calculus will not be presented here but is available in its elementary forms in any introductory texts on mathematical probability and statistics. Some of its fundamental features, however, bear on the question of induction and probability in a distinctive way. The probabilities we have discussed thus far may be said to be characterized in two ways: first, with respect to relative frequency interpretations, probability is an empirical account of observed ratios. Thus, there is nothing "ideal" or "necessary" about the account which establishes the ratio $\frac{m}{n}$; this is the result of observation. Yet the inductive generalization of this result, in concepts of "limiting frequency" or in inductions which lay claim to uniformity of nature as a postulate, entails, as we have seen, some such notion as "fair sample," the conditions for which are random selection. We have seen the difficulties of such an assumption, and have modified the claim of "randomness" to a norm for the selection of instances, from the stronger one concerning the objective properties of the sample, which we cannot know without already knowing what it is we want to find out.

In a calculus of chance, we may, however, set up an ideal universe of such equipossibilities and calculate the results of combinations of certain choices within this framework. Thus, for example, given the equipossibility of heads and tails in successive tosses of "fair" coins, we may calculate what the probability is that one will toss two heads in a row, or three, or more, if certain conditions are assumed to hold: (1) that the outcome of any toss is causally independent of the outcome of any other toss (namely, that instances are independent) and (2) that the variety of outcomes is limited (in coin tossing there are two outcomes, Heads and Tails; in pulling cards from a deck, the variety of independent instances is known beforehand to be 52; and so on). Classical probability theory thus calculates, on the basis of such conditions of independence, of limited variety, and of finite and known classes of entities fulfilling these conditions, what the values of certain combinations of choices would be, in terms of their probability. The key to such ideal probability is that its computed values hold for the whole class of entities, and not for particular instances. Thus, the chances of throwing a six with one die is one in six, because all six sides in a fair die are, by definition, equipossible. The number of combinations which permit one to throw a twelve with two dice, out of the total number of equipossible combinations is one in thirty-six. But this does not mean that every thirty-sixth throw will be a twelve, and that in each thirty-six throws, each combination will come up once. Rather, the postulate of an ideal probability is that for the whole class of throws, the distribution of probabilities is as calculated, and this defines a fair die as one which will give such predicted values in the long run, where *long run* may be defined as "approaching infinity." Practically speaking, we could never decide that a die was fair, using this criterion. But, practically speaking, in empirical tests, this ideal set of frequencies of sixes to total throws does show up as the limit upon which empirical ratios of sixes to total number of tosses converges. In this sense, ideal probability states a norm of what we will take to be a "fair" die, within the limits of practical testing.

However, in the domain of natural events, we cannot know that two events are causally independent or that the variety of outcomes is limited independently, without knowing the whole class of facts which are the subject of inquiry (knowing which, inquiry would be redundant). But empirical results do give approximations to those which are predicted deductively within a mathematical theory which is based on certain axioms. That is, in certain domains, outcomes which are in accord with the predictions arrived at by use of a probability calculus lead us to believe that such a domain possesses the features of equipossibility which the formal calculus postulates. We may be said, in such a case, to have found an interpretation of the calculus in empirical terms.

The force of this "discovery" is that throughout scientific inquiry and experiment, the grounds for generalization are that instances are indifferent, in a class of instances under investigation. For certain fundamental features, such as time of observation or spatial location, classical physics assumes that these play no role in affecting physical events. The postulates of the homogeneity of space (in that geometric conceptual space which replaces the qualitatively differentiated space of Aristotelian dynamics) and of the "equability" of time's "flow," alike in all its parts, are postulates of such indifference. The time and space conditions of events are thus, in classical physics, randomly choosable, without affecting results. This is the condition for asserting laws as universal and not merely local. Thus, we take electrons to be "indifferent," so that any one is substitutable for any other. This raises the following problem: If we "discover" that a realm of objects of some sort is "standard" in the sense that all electrons are standard, or all samples of a standard tub of butter exhibit the same fat content, or all standard parts produced by a manufacturer fit all the machines for which they are made, indifferently, or all faces of a die show up in the "fair" ratios on protracted tests—then we may insist that having "discovered" this standardness or indifference the domain is then one to which one may apply the probability calculus, because it meets the requirements of, or may be taken as an interpretation of, such a calculus (as all additive magnitudes may be taken as meeting the "requirements" of the formal system which includes addition as one of its operations). But one may reasonably object that standard machine parts and tubs of butter and dice are the sorts of artifacts which are made so as to fit these requirements; the norm for their production is that all instances will be equivalent to each other in the criterial respects. Electrons, however, are not "artifacts" but natural entities or events, whose indifference we cannot ensure, but only discover. Any die which did not conform to the norm of equipossibility and indifference would be judged not "fair" and would be rejected. But we cannot very well choose only those electrons which are "fair"; we have to take them as they come, and if we are lucky, then we find that they are "really" all alike as peas in a pod (except more so), and we can compute statistical combinations within a probability calculus, with indifference.

Is this simply the case, however? If we found an anomalous "electron," would we consider it an "electron," or would we consider that it is something else, because all electrons are alike, and this one is different? What leads us, in the first place, to decide on the identity of this particle as an electron, and not a positron, a neutron, or an Omega-minus particle? Presumably, it shows the criterial characteristics of an electron, and not of any of the others (in terms of its charge, its mass, its angular momentum, and so on). In short, it is an electron, in the first place, because it is like all the other electrons. We postulate indifference as the very condition of identity of this particle, and in this sense we may be said to have created an artifact, such as a "fair die," by defining the conditions of its acceptance in such a way that it conforms to the conditions normatively set forth in a calculus of probabilities. Certainly such a calculus will work for fair dice, because fairness is the ideal condition for which the calculus is set up. It should also certainly work for electrons and for ensembles of electrons, because the empirical definition of the particle is such that to be one, it has to conform to the condition of indifference, of its *kind.* Anomalous or unexpected values, unlike predicted ones, would then force us to make a choice: either of preserving the framework in which electrons are postulated to be indifferent (in which case we would have to account for the anomalies in terms of hidden variables, or in terms of introducing a new elementary particle, and finding some systematic place for it within the theoretical framework); or of abandoning the whole framework of theories in which this postulate is embedded. In short, can we be said to discover that some empirical domain is isomorphic with the formal system of the probability calculus, or do we instead construct the empirical domain in such a way as to ensure that it will have these features? Are we, in effect, introducing self-validating hypotheses of the sort, "All and only honey-giving bees give honey"?

In summary, if inductive generalization asserts or proposes law-like universal statements concerning an indefinitely large or infinite class of events, then a condition of the validity of such hypothetical laws is the presumed randomness of the sample from which such generalizations are made. The norms for such randomness are set forth in the ideal case in the axioms and theorems of the mathematical calculus of probabilities. The problem arises whether in conducting empirical inquiry we can be said to discover that the conditions of causal independence of instances, of limited variety of outcomes, and of indifference or equipossibility hold of a certain domain of objects or events, or whether we instead construct the domain in such a way as to exhibit these properties. These questions bring us to the consideration of the status of laws in science and of the status of the entities whose relations of invariance these laws describe. Is the condition for the assertion of lawfulness and for the postulation of universal laws one which we create in choosing our theoretical frameworks and our entities in such a way that laws may be said to hold in these contexts? Or do we discover laws independently of such considerations and then find it necessary to construct our frameworks in such a way that in order to explain these laws we are led to postulate that our domain of entities is indifferent and that our evidence is accounted reasonable by being taken as a random sample?

In the next chapter we will consider the alternative realist, conventionalist, and pragmatic interpretations of these questions. The considerations raised here concerning inductive generalization, sampling, and formalization of the conditions of randomness will then be seen in the light of their role in explanation in the sciences.

CHAPTER 10

Scientific Explanation: Laws and Theories

TO EXPLAIN SOMETHING is to have come to an understanding of it in such a way that one can bring another to understand it. The request, "Explain this to me," presumes that the one of whom the request is made understands it in a way that the one making the request does not, and that this understanding can be communicated. Thus, one might approach the question of explanation, hoping to resolve it by appeal to the concept of understanding. But unless one understands the term *understand* this is hopelessly circular or evasive. One might underline this circularity by examining such a request as, "Explain what *explain* means." Unless both parties start from some initial understanding in common, the request is senseless or paradoxical. If, instead, we attempt to "show" what *explain* means, by giving instances of it and exhibiting the features which such instances have in common, then we are presumably giving an ostensive definition of explanation, on the assumption that by reducing the uncomprehended "explanation" to comprehensible instances with comprehensible features, we are transforming or translating the uncomprehended concept in such a way that it turns out to be no more than a certain conjunction of familiar features. But this, in turn, depends on the notion of *familiarity* (and, *a fortiori,* of *unfamiliarity*). In short, the concept of explanation and the correlated concept of understanding present fundamental problems at the very basis of human knowledge. Any attempt to deal with scientific explanation which evades this profound and complex question makes some presupposition that the sense of *explanation,* in some primary and undefinable way, is already a common property of a community of speakers or thinkers. At best, then, one can do no more than present paradigms of what it means to explain something, and work from tacit or explicit consent that these paradigms are understood. There is no intrinsic proof that you and I understand the same thing, on having it explained. Instead, we rely on the most fundamental of human gestures of communication, the nod of assent. Yet for all the complexity of the concepts of understanding and explaining, we do understand, and are explained to, and explain successfully, so that what seems a problem in analysis of concepts is no problem at all in practice. (Just as, for example, the analysis of *seeing red,* which may be said to introduce all the classical problems of epistemology, is problematic in a sense in which the act of seeing red is not.) But if scientific inquiry and thought is, in some profound and simple sense, an attempt to understand, and if the system of science is a means of explaining what is understood, then the analysis of the conceptual foundations of scientific thought is at bottom an attempt to understand science itself, or to come to understand what scientific understanding is. This is either a genuine puzzle or a confusion. We might say that what is unproblematic in practice ought not to be problematic on analysis, and that reflective critique of concepts ought to clarify rather than muddle what is elementary. The impatience with philosophical analysis is often an impatience with what appears to be an obscuration of plain and simple truths. The therapy required by such an obscuration is some return to clarity and good sense, in the faith that what is simply performed may be simply understood; and if it is not, something is wrong with the mode of analysis itself. The quick rule of thumb for the solution (or dissolution) of such problems as appear obscure is to write them off as pseudoproblems growing out of some initial error; and the proverb, "When one takes a wrong turn in the road, the faster one goes, the further one goes astray," seems to be fitted for precisely such initial errors. We may then be said to have two alternatives: (1) The problem of explanation is not a problem in any profound sense at all: everyone who has learned English knows what *explains* means. The job of work is both to show how paradigms of commonsense explanation are related to their second cousins, in instances of scientific explanation, and to account for the differences. (2) The concept of scientific explanation cannot be understood in terms of some reduction to a primary sense of explanation and understanding. There is no such primary sense, apart from a theoretical reconstruction of the "facts" of understanding or of the practice of explanation. The assumption in the first case is that there is some basic sense of *understanding* and *explanation,* beyond which there can be no further analysis. *Understanding* is intuitively known and can only be exemplified, not explained. The assumption in the second case is that to explain *explanation* is to formulate a concept, in terms of some theory of explanation; thus, to understand something is to bring it under a concept, to see it as an instance of some universal.

However odd it may seem to begin an account of scientific explanation with a muddle concerning "scientific explanation," the muddle is instructive. For all the alternatives which are previously mentioned are embodied in alternative accounts of scientific explanation, as it is examined in instances of such explanation in the sciences. The philosophy of science has the peculiar additional task of explicating the concept of scientific explanation itself, to examine, in what science understands, the same characteristics which, when turned reflexively back upon the activity of scientific thought itself, constitute the conditions for understanding science. Reflective inquiry thus requires more than an examination of instances of scientific explanation, as if of some "external" objects of inquiry ("What science understands" or "the scientifically known facts"); rather, reflective inquiry becomes an examination of inquiry itself: the apparently paradoxical, self-referential task of understanding *understanding* and explaining *explanation*. The following account may therefore be taken as an account of alternative approaches to the concept of understanding itself, under the guise of views of how scientists come to understand nature.

LEARNING, UNDERSTANDING, AND EXPLAINING

To learn something one may have to learn how to perform a certain task in a certain way, in accordance with certain rules or canons of performance. To learn to play the violin means to learn how to hold the bow, how to position the fingers on the strings, how to reproduce in sound what is transcribed in musical notation (thus, to "read music"); one learns also to "phrase," to "express," to vary the qualities of sound within the less explicit canons of "musical sense." What is learned can presumably be taught, in the sense that an understanding of these rules or canons can be communicated by a teacher, by means of example, criticism, interpretation, and evaluation of the performance. At the lower levels of technique, *explaining* how to hold the bow may mean no more than *showing* how it is done, in a model instance, or correcting how it is done, by adjustments and direct instruction, until the desired performance is attained. At the more complex levels of performance, these same techniques of explaining how a passage is to be phrased, how a tone is to be sustained or varied in quality may be employed. Yet if one were to ask one's teacher, "Why is it to be phrased in this way, rather than another," or, "Why should there be no vibrato in this passage," one does not expect the answer to be a model performance, or a repetition of the original correction or suggestion which gave rise to the question. Presumably the answer will be that the structure of the piece requires a certain phrasing to fulfill it, or that the tradition within which the music falls is violated by vibrato in certain passages. In short, the explanation is in terms of some wider framework, within which the explained feature finds its place; the finding of such a place thus constitutes an explanation. Such an explanation, then, depends in turn on the acceptance of the framework, and an understanding of its requirements. For example, "This is Baroque music and should therefore not be played as if it were nineteenth-century Romantic music," thus explains why a quality of tone of a certain sort is inappropriate, the connecting argument, unstated or stated, being, "Baroque music is characterized by a tone of quality *Q*, and Romantic music by a tone of quality *P*." One might instead be told that to produce a tone or to phrase a passage in a certain way is a matter of how it is usually done: "This is the standard or accepted way," or "All performances do it in this way." A critical student would regard this as an incomplete explanation if it is to be taken as an explanation at all. One could not be said to "understand" the particular instance merely on the grounds that in all other "standard" instances, the tone or phrasing is produced in a certain way. An additional premise of the following sort would be required, "Things ought to be done in the standard way, and that's *why* you ought to do them in this way." If one regarded the standard as a norm, as somehow representing the "right" way, then the principle, "Do it right, if you're going to do it at all," may be appealed to as a reason for doing it in the standard way. Still another pedagogical ploy might be an appeal by the teacher, "Just listen to it yourself; does it sound 'right' to you? Does it 'feel' right? Are you comfortable with it? If you heard someone else playing the passage in this way, would you approve? Would it please you?" Here the appeal is to some primitive or intuitive sense of "rightness" or assent, beyond which there is presumably no appeal. (*De gustibus non disputandum est.*)

Learning something, in these alternative interpretations, thus means attaining to one or another sort of approved performance (at the lower end of the scale) or coming to understand the framework within which the approval is understood in terms of its reasons (at the upper end of the scale). Coming to understand, in this sense, may mean no more than the acquisition of some perceptual-motor skill, or habit, and it may mean as much as is required by a theoretical or conceptual justification for something of a certain kind. We may distinguish, therefore, between the kind of learning which involves habit formation, in the simplest perceptual-motor terms (from learning how to walk to learning skilled performance of a complex sort) and the kind of learning which involves the formation of concepts and the use of inference in some form. This, it will be remembered, is the very distinction which Aristotle drew between that knowledge which is of principles and causes and that kind of understanding which is a matter of applied skill in particular instances. The former he considered scientific knowledge; the distinguishing mark of the man who possessed such knowledge, according to Aristotle, was that he could impart it. Yet we do talk of "teaching by example"; in this sense, watching a model performance by a skilled craftsman, one may learn how a certain task should be performed. Imitating the master is the time-honored method of apprenticeship, but it would be strange to say that an exemplary performance *explained* how something should be done. The term *teacher* in this sense has a distinctive connotation here. The teacher by example may thus lead one to an understanding of how some task is to be performed. He may exhibit the mode of operation to intelligent scrutiny. But the generalization of exemplary instances, so that one attains to some reflective or conscious understanding of the principles of the performance, or of the universal standard of which this is the paradigm instance, requires something more than *understanding how.* Extending the analogy, one may say that the scientist learns how nature operates by observing what he takes to be exemplary instances. The metaphor which makes nature the teacher of man never extends so far as the claim that nature imparts the principles of natural operation to observation. Yet it is in these natural operations that the scientist discovers the principles, or (now we may say it) the *laws* of nature. Nature may be said to exhibit its laws, but within this metaphor, nature does not explain these laws; man does. But if nature may be said to exhibit laws of operation, she does so in particular instances. An instance is not a law, nor is a collection of instances a law. Thus, observation of instances cannot be said to reveal laws governing these instances. The relation among these instances, when it is invariant, may be said to exhibit a law. But we come to know this invariance only by means of the conceptual activity which involves *generalization.* As was seen in Chapter 9, such generalization involves framing hypotheses or universal law-like statements, whose scope is such that they postulate invariance beyond what can be summarized as an account of instances of observation. Hypotheses are therefore conceptual leaps which go beyond the "lessons of nature." They are general formulations linked to instances of observation in the framework of a system, in which the statements referring to observations are deducible from the hypotheses and from information stating the conditions under which the observation takes place. A hypothesis is therefore a conjecture that an order discovered to be exhibited among observations[1] does in fact exhibit a law of nature, and not merely an accidental conjunction of short-run features. The test of this conjecture is therefore continued observation under conditions which link the observations made to the hypothesis, as instantiations of it; i.e., observations guided by the hypothesis in the sense that the statements of proposed observations to be made, or the predictions, are systematically derivable from the hypothesis.

When, in our earlier example, it is explained why a passage in music should be phrased in a certain way, the appeal is to some framework within which it follows "logically" that this phrasing is the "right" one. But here we are appealing to a norm of the "right" way, which is presumably a matter of aesthetic or historical interpretation and involves some value judgment

[1] We will shortly consider in what sense this view of hypothesis as inductive generalization may be challenged.

that, in general, norms of this sort are to be observed. It would be odd to claim that a law of nature, postulated in some hypothesis, is such a norm, prescribing what one ought to observe. There are norms of how we ought to observe and norms of reasonable inference and interpretation, concerning the uses of evidence. But it would be odd to say that a law of nature is a norm which prescribes how nature should perform in given instances. But this way of talking does give us a clue to the analogy between normative laws and rules, in the human experience of coming to learn how to behave, and the conception of natural laws. Here too lies a clue to the relation between ordinary learning, understanding, and explaining, and what we take to be the special case of scientific explanation.

We may summarize this brief introduction thus: One can be said to *learn* in several senses:

1. Learning how to perform in accordance with some norm, by example and practice.
2. Learning to understand why something is a proper performance, in terms of understanding the relation of the norm to some instance of it.

In both cases something may be said to come to be understood: in the first, a way of operating or performing is "understood" when one exhibits a proper performance of it. Thus, we may say, someone "understands" the English language if he knows how to use it properly, can answer questions in it, and shows all the other signs of being a speaker of the language. Performing properly here means making sense, and this involves the use of the rules of sentence formation, the grammar of the language. But the user of a language may perform properly without being able to explain the rules, or what we might call the "laws" of proper use. (We are not concerned with "correct" grammar so much as with the basic idea of making sense.) The explication of these rules requires the formulation of hypotheses about generally invariant structures or orders in the language. Such knowledge would then permit us to explain that something is a proper performance, because it follows from the explicated rules of use.

We may then say that learning *how* involves understanding how one should proceed; learning *why* involves understanding why one should proceed in a certain way. In the second case one gives a reason for proceeding in this or that way. Explaining may then be said to be that kind of understanding which involves giving reasons.

But if you have followed closely you may realize that there is a problem in this formulation. In the example we noted that it would not be much of an explanation, if an explanation at all, to say that one should proceed in a certain way *because* others standardly proceed in this way. "Why do you do *X?*" "*Because* my father before me did *X,*" or, "*Because* everyone does *X,*" might in fact explain why you do *X*. But, we would say, it is a bad reason for doing *X*. You would have to supplement it with some general premise to the effect that, "What everyone does is best to do," or, "Fathers are the best guides," and this in turn would need support and could be questioned severely. Yet it does explain why you do (or why you think you do) *X*. There are obviously good explanations and bad explanations, and one sense in which an explanation may be said to be bad is that the reasons it adduces are bad reasons. If, analogously, I explained why a particular piece of metal expanded when it was heated by giving as the reason, "All metals expand when heated," I would be giving an explanation. But the reason would not be much better than the one which explains that I do *X* because everyone does it. Although it is clear, in this case, that one is appealing to a general principle as a way of coming to understand why something happens in a given instance, and that the instance (or a statement describing it) is deducible from this principle, and that therefore one is giving a reason, it is not at all clear that such a reason exhibits the kind of passage to enlightenment that we would hope a good explanation would provide. The relations among learning, understanding, and explaining will provide the framework for a consideration of types of explanation. In the earlier discussion on prescientific modes of explanation, we examined what might be considered the genetic or historical prototypes of scientific explanation. We might summarize these briefly here, by way of distinguishing among types of explanation and by way of introducing the distinction between laws and theories in terms of which we will discuss scientific explanation.

In prescientific modes of explanation, as in the examples given earlier in this chapter, we may distinguish among the following:

(1) *Rules.* Rules are prescriptive or regulative instructions as to how a "proper" performance should be carried out. These, we suggested, arise out of the practices of technique, of social organization, and so on, and may be given: (*a*) By *example,* "Do it in this way," exhibiting the paradigm or model instance to be followed, or criticizing performance. The scientific and philosophical generalization of this notion was developed in Aristotle's conception of learning as based on a disposition or ability to imitate. Ideal imitation, according to Aristotle, is a case of emulating ideal or universal features in some model. Where nature or natural process is taken as the model, understanding nature means coming to know the universal features of natural processes, and this means learning them by emulating them. Proper technique is therefore action in accordance with the "rule of nature," where the study of nature provides the model of such action. The Stoic philosophers developed this idea further, both in their philosophy of nature and in their ethics: the rule for right behavior or proper functioning here is, "Follow nature." In this context it is not merely a matter of describing natural processes, but of taking them as giving a rule prescriptively, by example. In this first case, then, the rule is given in

the instance; it is a rule by example. (*b*) By *precept*. The rule is given in a general formulation instead of an instance. The technical rule for operation is embodied in a prescriptive, law-like statement. Such a prescriptive generalization may be a rule of technique, or a recipe: "When the metal turns blue-white in the flame, quench it," or as a social or political law: "You may not marry the offspring of a blood-relation," or, "All citizens will perform military service for two years upon reaching their eighteenth year"; or an ethical precept, "Do unto others as you would have them do unto you." The concept of *natural law* obtaining equally in nature, in society, and in individual life borrows the prescriptive or legislative notion of such rules and therefore conceives of nature as the product of legislation, from which we inherit the commonsense notion that nature "follows laws."

(2) *Laws*. Closely associated with paragraph (1) is the notion of law, with this distinction: that such laws are taken to be empirical generalizations of a descriptive sort. We will therefore take a prescriptive "law" to be a *rule* and will reserve the term *law* for assertions of invariance. Thus, proverbs and "rules of thumb" represent such generalizations and have the form, "Whenever *X*, then *Y*." ("When the cat's away . . ." and, "Red sky at night . . ." were our earlier examples.) Taking such laws as guides to behavior obliterates the distinction between Paragraphs (1) and (2), of course. The distinction we may retain is that a law asserts that something is known as a matter of fact, and a rule interpretation of such law involves the use of this knowledge.

(3) *Theories*. Our earlier examples were of explanations of otherwise uncomprehended events in terms of some model, which introduced some entity having a certain "nature" as the explanation of the event. Anthropomorphic theories thus explain natural events as the outcomes of the action of some humanly acting or humanly motivated "being" (a "Thou"), as in the example of the devil theory of disease. Metaphysical theories adduce some general and abstract principle or nature stripped of anthropomorphic allusions. Thus, for example, the principle in terms of which the variety of nature is said to be ordered is the *Logos;* or when such metaphysical principles find their interpretation in physical terms, the variety of phenomena is said to be reducible to combinations of the four "elements," earth, air, fire, and water. In metaphysical and physical theories of this sort, as in anthropomorphic or mythopoeic theories, explanation is in terms of some "entity" or "stuff" or "principle," from whose nature one can derive particular operations or the properties of some natural event. Similarly, the laws in terms of which natural events are ordered (prescriptively or as a matter of fact) are seen to be explained by the nature of these entities. The laws are thus the rules or the pattern of behavior of such entities.

In each one of these cases the explanation offered is a reason of a different sort: the rule says how one should perform in terms of a reason, implicitly stated as an exemplary instance or explicitly stated as a precept. Where science is performance, as it may be said to be in all the aspects of its methods which we have examined in the previous chapters, then the role of such rules in explanation becomes clear. These provide the norms of proper observation, proper evidence, proper experimental technique, proper inductive inference, proper form in deductive or formal representations of relations among facts, proper hypotheses, and so on. In this sense rules do not explain natural processes or matters of fact, but they do explain why one should come to accept or approve the conclusions of scientific inquiry, and they serve also to guide the conduct of such inquiry. One may then say that such rules provide the criteria for what will be taken to be a proper explanation; they are, in short, explanations of *explanation,* or norms of what will constitute the conditions of a scientific explanation. Laws give, as reasons, universal generalizations or postulates in which particular instances are "explained" by virtue of their coming under the law. In one view, which we shall shortly examine, this constitutes the essential form of scientific explanations. An event is explained if it can be subsumed, or can be shown to follow inferentially as the consequence of a universal or law-like statement. This has come to be known as the "nomological model of explanation [from the Greek *nomos* (νομος), or *law*]. Theories explain by virtue of postulating or asserting the existence of "theoretical entities," whose properties are such that from them one can infer what the laws of their operation would be. Knowing what laws describe the invariant relations among some natural properties, or events, one may then construct a hypothetical entity such that its existence would explain the laws.

Here a difference of views appears: on the one hand, theories are sometimes conceived as laws of high generalization, from which laws of lower generality may be derived by a procedure of inference. On the other hand, theories are sharply distinguished from laws in virtue of the existential assertions of the former. In the first view, theories are convenient summaries of empirical laws, which also serve to reveal what *more* follows, if known empirical laws follow. For example, it may follow, from such a high-level generalization, that a set of laws, otherwise empirically distinct, may be alternative descriptions of some common empirical domain, which the theory permits us to conceive as the common reference of the different laws. The theory makes explicit, or reveals the isomorphism obtaining among discrete laws, in terms of which it may be postulated that the *common* invariance bespeaks a common subject matter. Thus, for example, electricity and magnetism are seen to reveal common formal properties in their *laws* (in the inverse square law for electrical and magnetic force—Coulomb's laws—and this may suggest that both are phenomena of some common "force"). In this view, theoretical "entities" are not entities in any other sense than that they are the *terms* (or the concepts which these terms represent) which occur in the higher-level generalization, which may be "reduced" to the terms used in alternative empirical laws which are explained by the theory. The laws are therefore explained by the theory, by virtue of being subsumed under it in a formally similar way to that in which particular events are said to be explained by the laws, by virtue of being subsumed under them. The alternative view distinguishes sharply between laws, of whatever level of generality, and theories, in that theories make the additional and unique existential or ontological claim, or conjecture, that there exist entities of a certain sort, to which theoretical terms refer. The sense in which such theoretical entities "exist" thus concerns an ontological claim absent in the other view of theories as higher-level laws.

LAWS

Much of what has been discussed in previous chapters has had to do with the concept of law. Especially in Chapter 9, the object of scientific inquiry appeared in large part to be the formulation of statements of universal scope which state some invariance between properties or events. Such a statement, of the form $(x)(Fx \rightarrow Gx)$, for example, formulates a law, asserting conditionally that if anything has the property F, then it also has the property G. From our earlier discussion it should be clear that this simple formulation conceals a number of problems. First, the import of the statement is that as a matter of fact, if anything has F it has G, unrestrictedly. Suppose that F is the property of being a day in the month of June, 1961, at some location L, and that G is the property of *not* registering a temperature lower than 45°F at L. The presumed law would then be asserted in the statement, "If anything is a day in the month of June, 1961, at L, then it will not register a temperature of less than 45°F at L. One could state this as a hypothesis to be confirmed by the evidence and then check the suitably defined "readings at L" for each of the thirty days in June of that year at L, and discover whether or not the law is true. The law would then be nothing but a summary statement not only of all the observed instances of x, but of all the possible observed instances of x. The condition of the law statement being a true statement is precisely that for every instance of x, what is asserted of it is true. We cannot know that the statement is a law unless we know whether it is true or not, or we would be in the peculiar position of stating "laws" that were sometimes true and sometimes false (or in the no less peculiar position of stating laws that were not known to be true or false). In the former case we might claim that the statement, "June 22, 1961 at L yields temperature readings of 78°F at L," is a law which is true from 2:30 P.M. to 3:15 P.M. and false at other times. In the latter case we might claim that it is a law that the temperature on Ceres varies within a range of ±247°F, but we do not know whether this law is true or false. But unless we knew whether or not this were true, it would be odd to assert it as a law. We save the situation by talking of it as a hypothesis which, if it is true, states a law; therefore, a "law-like statement." But the only sort of instance in which we could know that a law is true on these grounds is one like the "law" concerning the days of the month of June, in which all the possible observations can be made in a finite time, in a complete enumeration. But a simple enumeration of all known instances is not what we generally regard as a law, though it does state an invariance, and states it to hold universally over all the members of a class of facts. We require a law to state that something is unrestrictedly true for all possible instances where the number is presumably indefinitely larger than that of the observed instances, for we take a law to be a generalization which goes beyond the presently available evidence. Yet if it goes beyond the available evidence, we cannot know that it is true in all instances. We are thus in the unhappy position of saying that if a law is true, we cannot know it, and if we know that a universal statement is true for all of its instances then it is not a law. As "unhappy" as this may sound, it sets forth certain conditions for laws which are important in explicating our concept of law and serves to interpret the sense of a statement like $(x)(Fx \rightarrow Gx)$ when we take it to be a law.

In order to make this clearer, we may distinguish between "laws of nature" and the "laws of science." If we mean to preserve the sense of objectivity in the claim that something is a law of nature, we ought to consider that it is a law of nature whether anyone knows it or not. Thus, we assume that Galileo's law concerning the acceleration of falling bodies did not come into being as a law of nature when Galileo formulated it. Rather, we assume that this law holds true for any time at all, including the time before there were conscious beings on this planet. If laws of nature are capable of being discovered (that is, if it makes any sense at all to say a law is "discovered"), then the relations of invariance which the laws assert hold whether they are known or not. Further, we assume that the law will hold in future, or as yet unobserved instances, whether or not these instances in fact come to be observed or not. We may formulate this in an assertion that underwrites the empirical nature of the law, thus, "if any instance *were* to be observed, then it *would* conform to the law." This is precisely the assertion that the law holds in those instances which have, as a matter of fact, *not* been observed; and stronger yet, whether or not they are ever observed in fact. Because this raises, as a condition, the epistemologically impossible situation of there conceivably being observers before there were any conscious beings on the planet, we may say that such a contrary-to-fact assertion cannot be meant to assert the possibility of observation in such instances, and so even this condition of the empirical nature of the law seems too strong, if we want to maintain that Galileo's law held in fact prior to the appearance of conscious beings.

The claim we tend to make for a law of nature is that it holds independently of whether anyone knows it or not, and even independently of whether it is possible to know it (which is a good deal stronger). But this is the claim for its objectivity. For if we made any lesser claim than this, we would have to say that natural laws hold only for those instances which are known, or only for those instances which may, as a matter of factual possibility, come to be known. Thus, the factually unfulfillable epistemological condition, "if anyone *were* to observe a falling body prior to the appearance of conscious beings . . ." may be reduced to the ontological assertion, "If there *were* a falling body, then it *would have* accelerated in accordance with Galileo's law." Such an "if-then" conditional in the subjunctive mood ("were-would") is called a subjunctive conditional. There may in fact have been such falling bodies (and we assume there were), therefore such a conditional is not contrary to fact. But it is contrary to fact that there was an observer before the appearance of conscious beings, and in the epistemological form of the assertion, this would be called a "contrary-to-fact conditional" or a "counterfactual conditional." We may formulate this in an even stronger sense. We might say, even if there never was a falling body, and never will be, in fact; still, if there were, it would fall in accordance with Galileo's law, thus taking the law to hold in every possible world, regardless of whether it holds in any actual world.

We may also assert counterfactually in the case where we do know that something did not occur as a matter of fact, "If I had dropped the Professor out of the window ten minutes ago, he would have accelerated in accordance with Galileo's law," where as a matter of fact, the antecedent is known to be false, because I did not do it (though this may also be said to be epistemologically dependent: "I *know* I did not do it, because I remember, or because there he is walking in the hall without a scratch, to all appearances"). Our sense of "law of nature" in this case is that the law is "real" or "out there" in the world or in nature, with or without my consent or even the possibility of my observing instances of it. Thus, the assertion of the law is an *inference,* either from certain evidence or from other laws from which it can be deduced. If it is an inference from certain evidence, then it is presumably an inductive inference; namely, one which if it is in accordance with certain norms, is taken as the ground for a rational or warranted belief. If it is deduced from other laws of greater generality, as a deductive consequence, then its force is no greater than that of the weakest of the premises from which it has been deduced. If it follows deductively from some premises taken to be *necessarily* true (e.g., synthetic *a priori* "truths," or metaphysical "truths," or logical "truths"), then I may claim that the law is also necessarily true; but observation would then play no role in confirming it, because it would be true independently of any observation and would thus be an *a priori* law, not an empirical law, i.e., it is not one which may be confirmed or falsified by test. My assertion of the law, if it is empirical at all, is at best a warranted assertion on the basis of evidence, if any of the premises from which it is deduced are in turn empirical generalizations taken to be universal statements warranted on the basis of evidence. Thus, I cannot *know* the law to be true as a law of nature, but I can know that my belief that it is true is a rational or warranted belief, on the basis of the evidence.

We may then say that the "laws of science" are hypotheses or postulates which are the objects of rational belief on the basis of evidence and that if in fact the laws of science are true, then they state laws of nature. This is a version of the "correspondence theory" of truth (or the "semantic theory of truth" which is formulated by Tarski and others with respect to statements in general, but not specifically with respect to laws or law-like statements). Where "*L*" stands for the law of science and *L* for the law of nature, this states that "*L*" *is true if and only if L.* Or, for example, "$s = \frac{1}{2}gt^2$" is true if and only if, as a matter of fact, the distances which a freely falling body traverses stand to each other in the same ratio as the squares of the times of fall.

This may be called the realist view of the nature of laws of nature. You may be sure that not all philosophers are realists in this sense and that there are therefore alternative views. We will examine these next, under the headings *nominalist* and *conceptualist* views. But having introduced some initial ideas, let us summarize them briefly.

(1) A law states an invariant relation among all members of a given class (with respect to some parameters taken to be relevant). This may be in the form of a universal conditional—$(x)(Fx \rightarrow Gx)$—or a biconditional—$(x)(Fx \leftrightarrow Gx)$— or in the stronger form of the subjunctive or counterfactual conditional: *For any x, if Fx were the case then Gx would be the case.* We take a law of nature to hold for an indefinitely large or infinite class of natural events or instances and, in general, to be unbound to any particular time, or to hold indifferently at any time. (As we shall see, this raises special problems concerning laws for historical epochs which are assumed to hold *within* a bounded time, or to be time variant, such as geological, biological, or sociological laws of a certain sort.)

(2) A law-like statement states a law of nature if it is in fact true for all the instances subsumed under the law, when these instances are of the sort set forth in paragraph (1), and thus the domain of the law is such as to support a genuine generalization, and not simply a summary description or list of all the instances. The conditions under which the law could be asserted to be true are expressed by the subjunctive-conditional form, "If, for any *x*, *Fx* were the case, then *Gx* would be the case." The subjunctive conditional leaves open the possibility that in fact something was, will be, or is the case, but implies that this is not known to be true. The epistemological condition of knowing that something was not or is not the case, as a matter of fact, combined with the assertion that if it were, the law

would hold, expresses a belief that the law is true unrestrictedly and takes the form of a contrary-to-fact conditional or counterfactual conditional. The distinction between not knowing whether something was or was not the case and knowing that it was not the case distinguishes the subjunctive from the counterfactual conditional.

(3) A law of science is a statement of a law of nature which is not known to be true in all of its instances, but for which there are grounds for rational or warranted belief. (Thus, a law of nature is predictive: that is, it makes a claim about instances not yet known to be true. "Predictive," more restrictedly, relates to future instances; reference to past instances is "retrodictive," therefore.)

The *realist* view of laws is "realistic" in the technical sense which this term has in epistemology and ontology. In this view, a law is a universal and the relations of invariance which it asserts exist in nature independently of their being known, or of the conditions under which they come to be known. Knowledge of this universal is therefore a discovery of it, and belief that such a universal law exists, as a matter of fact, is warranted by the validity of the knowledge claim in terms of certain norms. In this context, at any stage of science the prevailing laws state warranted beliefs about the laws of nature, or about the truth of the propositions which state such laws. In another interpretation of this view, any scientific law is a perspectival or partial "truth," relative to the evidence and the framework within which the evidence is significant. Thus, the true propositions in which the laws of nature are asserted are objectively true, but our knowledge of them, at any time, is relative. The fallibility of laws of science lies, therefore, in this relativity, so that what was once a warranted belief turns out no longer to be so, when the evidence is increased, or when the framework within which the evidence is significant is abandoned and a new framework adopted. The reasons for such changes are in part the ones discussed in Chapter 9. In such a view, the constant "correction" of a statement of relative frequency, with each additional instance, would assume such a constant approximation toward a limit.[2]

[2] C. S. Peirce, who proposes the theory of "fallibilism" and also the notion of a self-correcting relative frequency, states the realist position in a striking way in an early essay, "How to Make Our Ideas Clear." Talking of the variety of scientific inquiries, he says, "They may at first obtain different results, but as each perfects his method and his processes, the results are found to move steadily together towards a predestined center. So with all scientific research. Different minds may set out with the most antagonistic views, but the progress of investigation carries them by a force outside themselves to one and the same conclusion. This activity of thought by which we are carried, not where we wish, but to a foreordained goal, is like the operation of destiny. No modification of the point of view taken, no selection of other facts for study, no natural bent of mind even, can enable a man to escape the predestinate opinion. This great hope is embodied in the conception of truth and reality. The opinion which is fated to be ultimately agreed to by all who investigate is what we mean by the truth, and the object represented in this opinion is the real."

The realist view of laws thus assumes that there are objectively true propositions asserting such laws, to which scientific laws constantly approximate as alternative hypotheses are eliminated, or as evidence increases and as criticism and refinement of methods proceeds.

Thus, one sense of *realism,* which we may characterize as the epistemological sense, takes laws to be true or false objectively, independently of whether they are known to be true or false. Laws, therefore, are not simply ways in which we shape the world of experience to our knowledge but that to which our knowledge has in some way to conform, if it is veridical. In another sense of *realism,* related to the first in a complex way, laws of nature are taken to be "real universals" (in the Platonic tradition of the "forms") which exist (or subsist) objectively and are discovered by means of rational inquiry. Thus, the instances simply exemplify these universals, or are the means whereby these are revealed to us.

If the realist, in this sense, assumes that universal laws of nature exist in reality, the nominalist challenges the view that universals exist at all. The distinction in names comes from a medieval philosophical controversy on the nature of universals, the realist view asserting that *Universalia sunt realia* ("Universals are reals"), and the nominalist arguing that *Universalia sunt nomina* ("Universals are names"). The force of the nominalist's objection, as it has been interpreted, has a certain empiricist flavor: in our experience, we do not come to know universals, but only particulars (whether sense data, or particular instances or events). We collect such instances in accordance with common features which we recognize among them. Universals "exist" only in the common *names* which we used to mark these common features. They may be conveniently named in common, but the common features do not exist apart from the particular instances which we experience or which occur. Thus, the only status universals have is as names, and these names "exist" also only as particular marks, or inscriptions, or utterances on particular occasions. Thus universals do not exist. With respect to the account of laws, this asserts that laws "exist" in nature only in the instances in which certain features are exhibited. There is no universal connection among these features, except in the sense that they may all be gathered under a single expression, which serves conveniently to group them for purposes of reference. Thus, for

---

[*Philosophical Writing of Peirce,* J. Buchler, ed. (New York: Dover, 1955), p. 38.] Norman Campbell states a similar view, "Science is the study of those judgments concerning which universal agreement can be obtained." [*What Is Science?* (New York: Dover, 1952), p. 27.] Quine, as we noted in an earlier footnote, challenges this view of truth as a limit at infinity, to which we may be said to be closer at any time than at some other. "There is a faulty use," he writes, "of numerical analogy in speaking of a limit of theories, since the notion of limit depends on that of 'nearer than,' which is defined for numbers and not for theories." [*Word and Object* (Cambridge, Mass.: Technology Press, 1960), p. 23.]

example, "The people of United States," does not denote a universal, but only a collection of individuals, who may be named in common. Only the name *The people of the United States* exists, and exists only in particular instances such as the one in this sentence, which is a particular inscription in ink on paper. Such a law as $s = \frac{1}{2}gt^2$ is also such a name, whose reference is not some universal "real," but only the collection of the particular instances in which a particular object at a particular time and at a particular place falls in such a way that its time of fall is in a certain ratio to the distance of fall.

There are major philosophical difficulties with both these views, realist and nominalist, which we cannot pursue here. But it may be recognized that this view lends itself to the interpretation that a law of science is only a convenient "mark," which serves a linguistic community as a way of denoting or sorting out a set of instances. The "convenient" or "economical" shorthand description which such law-like statements give is their only function. In this way, the nominalist tends to support an instrumentalist view of laws and theories, taking them simply as more or less adequate means of dealing with nature, rather than as true or false, as the realist sees them. But this function can be of great importance precisely because it facilitates and extends the range of human memory, inference, computation. It is this sense of "economy of thought" which Mach has in view, in the characterization he gives of mathematics, for example. But a conventional or convenient mark is neither true nor false. The sense in which a statement of relations is true or false, in the nominalist view of laws, is entirely comprehended in its "extension," i.e., in the instances to which it refers. Thus, many of the versions of "instantial confirmation" which mark empiricist approaches to hypotheses carry over this nominalist emphasis.

The conceptualist view of laws is an attempt to overcome difficulties in the nominalist view and in the realist view. If the nominalist says that laws are not real universals, but are "universal" only in the collection of instances marked by a common name or description, and if the realist claims that universals exist or are real, in nature or in the world, the conceptualist raises questions about each view. Does the realist mean that the universals exist *apart* from the instances which embody them? If so, then there is some realm of universals apart from the world of particular facts, and the relation of these universals to the world of facts presents insuperable difficulties. This creates a dualism of universals as "ideal forms," subsisting in some ideal realm (as in Platonic realism; see Chapter 4), and thus grants to the world of our experience or thought only a shadowy, second-hand reflected existence. If, on the other hand, the only real existents are particular facts, then the fact of their relation becomes an incomprehensible one, for a collection is no more than a collection unless there is some law-like relation which "really" holds among the particulars. (In Poincaré's phrase, "Science is built up of facts, as a house is built of stones; but an accumulation of facts is no more a science than a heap of stones is a house."[3] If the nominalist claims that he is arranging the facts under some conventional name or mark, then he disguises the contribution he makes in making the arrangement under the pretense of doing no more than naming. In effect, the statement of relations contributes something which the mere listing of accumulated particulars does not contain: the discovered order or relation among these particulars, or that in virtue of which they permit themselves to be grouped commonly. This is not *explicit* in the particular facts, as some real universal in which they are bound together, like raisins in a lump of dough. Rather, in discovering the relation, the mind makes the connections, explicating what is implicit in the particular facts. The universal is thus constructed in the mind, or is conceptualized as the order which is revealed by inquiry. In the Aristotelian version of this sort of conceptualism, the order or relation among the facts is potential, but is actualized by the process of conceptual discovery and construction. A law of nature is, so to speak, *in* nature, but not apart from the particular and concrete processes of nature. (The notion of process thus lends itself to this view more readily than the notion of discrete and isolated events, which already requires some glue to put together the pieces.) Thus, the universal or the law has no independent subsistence as an ideal form. By virtue of its implicitness in the real relations among events which constitute natural processes, the mind can bring this form or order into explicit consciousness, emulating or creating an ideal imitation of nature. Thus laws represent natural processes in the form in which these become known to a rational intelligence. Laws of science are therefore the form in which laws of nature come to be objects of reason, or of conceptual judgment. The laws of nature are realized (or actualized) in this conceptual activity, but are true or false because they do or do not adequately represent the lawful relations in nature. Thus, they are not conventions, although the form in which they are expressed may be conventional. Thus, the expressions $s = \frac{1}{2}gt^2$ and $AD/AE = (HM)^2/(HL)^2$, which are alternate ways of stating the same law or relation of physical invariance, are conventional, in that the choice of a language in which to express the relation is conventional. But both of them express the same proposition, and the proposition is not conventional, but true or false about relations among facts. The conceptualist might charge the realist with constructing abstract universals as if they were real things, thus hypostatizing a set of factual relations, in terms of their abstract expression. The nominalist avoids hypostatization at the expense of losing the objectivity or concreteness of the relations among facts. (The nominalist might answer that relations are also particulars in his scheme.) In laying claim to the best of both worlds, the conceptualist may then talk of laws as concrete universals, thus more than abstract universals and more than the mere aggregation of concrete particulars. In other versions, the con-

[3] H. Poincaré, *Science and Hypothesis* (New York: Dover, 1952), p. 141.

ceptualist may claim that laws are universal forms imposed on experience as the condition under which experience comes to be known as more than undifferentiated flux. These conceptual forms are, in different versions, either *a priori* conditions of human knowledge (and thus conditions of the possibility of science), as a Kantian view might propose, or they are intuitions of an intellectual sort which immediately perceive the forms in terms of which experience comes to be known. These forms, then, constitute the rational structures themselves as the concretely presented features of nature, where the particular experiences are viewed as abstractions (abstracted from the whole, or the *Gestalt,* which is directly known in intuition and conceived of only abstractly as particulars, for the sake of analysis, or as explication of what is already known).

Within each of these philosophical positions the relation of universals to particulars is conceived differently; and in this context, the relation of laws to their instantiations is conceived differently. It is clear that this will have a bearing on the sense in which laws will be taken as explanations of particular events or occurrences.

In the realist view, a particular event is explained by a law, in the sense that the fact is an instance of the law, and can be shown to "follow" from the law: that is, the particular fact finds its place in the systematic relation which the law asserts.

For the nominalist, because there is no underlying "reality" beyond the facts themselves, the "law" is only a convenient shorthand description or summary of the particular facts, and thus laws cannot be said to explain at all. In this sense *Bees give honey,* does not explain why a particular bee gives honey, or why any particular bees whatever give honey; it is only another way of saying the same thing, and at most gives a description which is true of all the instances. But *true* here means no more than the adequacy of the description, in its use as a mark *understood* by some linguistic convention as standing for the whole list of statements: *Bee*$_1$ *gives honey, Bee*$_2$ *gives honey, Bee*$_3$ *gives honey. . .* just as *The People of the United States* stands for the list containing the proper names of each individual in the United States (or each citizen, or each voting adult). The proper listing is thus a matter of a convention as to what *The people of the United States* will mean. In legal documents, for example, the description *The party of the first part* is explicitly defined, and thenceforward, the descriptive phrase stands for all and only those individuals for which it is explicitly defined.

For the conceptualist a law explains in the sense that what is implicit in experience is brought into conscious and explicit form as an object of the understanding. Thus, the scientific law explains by virtue of realizing or exhibiting to conscious thought what was previously implicit in experience, or "in nature." Explaining and bringing to conscious understanding or to explicit conceptual formulation are thus one and the same, so that explanation becomes a matter of explication, of making explicit to the understanding. One variant of this view is that explanation consists of interpreting or translating what is unfamiliar into terms which are already familiar, as in the instances of anthropomorphic explanation we have discussed. This is also characteristic of the use of models and analogies, as aids to understanding, because the model or the analogy converts an unfamiliar set of relations into the form of some familiar configuration, as the ping-pong ball model of chain reaction, or the analogy of "lines of force" as strings under tension "makes clear" in more familiar terms what sorts of relations obtain in chain reactions and with respect to "lines" of force (where *line* is already an analogy, to geometric concepts).

This account of alternative positions is not to be taken as a literal distinction establishing cubbyholes into which alternative views of laws fit neatly, because any such position in the "pure" form is probably not to be found. Rather, these distinctions indicate emphases, and help to explain how these emphases give rise to or reflect alternative views of the nature of laws.

HOW ARE LAWS STATED?

Although we have given the general form of a law stating an invariant relation, we may ask whether all laws are stated in this form; and further, even if this is the formal structure of all law-like statements, we may ask whether there are distinctive interpretations of this form in science, or within the different sciences. We will briefly consider the forms in which (*a*) numerical laws, (*b*) physical laws, (*c*) laws in biology and in the human sciences are stated. And we will consider whether there are laws of history, and if so, what their form might be.

Numerical laws

We may distinguish between laws which state invariant relations among numbers as physical properties of collections of things and the formal relations within the mathematical language whose syntax concerns relations among numerals as names of numbers. In the formalist interpretation of this mathematical language, we may construct this numerical syntax freely, using any well-defined connectives we like, as long as certain logical conditions are met: among these are (1) the rules which delimit ambiguity, so that we do not confuse numerals with each other; (2) rules (or norms) for consistency, so that our constructions do not yield contradictory theorems; (3) rules of formation and transformation, i.e., rules for forming meaningful expressions (or "well-formed formulas"); and rules of inference, for moving from statement to statement. Assuming the syntax of the formal system of arithmetic, as we discussed it earlier, we may say that a numerical law is a universal statement of invariant relation among numerals, consisting of individual variables, constants, and some arithmetic connectives. Suppose we construct a law which will generate a series of numerals in such a way that the law expresses an invariant relation among the successive numerals of the series. Thus, I might say that the *n*th term in the series (where *n* represents the ordinal position of some numeral in the series) is always derivable from the following invariant relations: $(n^2 - n)/2$. Thus, the first term will be equal to $[(1)^2 - 1]/2 = 0$. The second term will be $[(2)^2 - 2]/2 = 1$. Similarly, the third term will be 3, the fourth will be 6, and so on. The series will be 0, 1, 3, 6, 10, 15. . . . Examining this series, I may then note that the difference between each successive term and the one before it is also a recognizable series, namely, 1, 2, 3, 4, 5 . . . and that the differences between these successive differences is a constant, namely 1. For each of these series, in turn, I may state the law which generates it. We may then say that, for such series, the successive terms in the series are functions of the numerals representing ordinal position in the series, in some invariant relation. Where ordinal position represents some numerical value and the term in that position represents some numerical value, one of these values is associated with the other in some invariant relation, which I may express functionally as $y = f(x)$. Such laws, if they are formally constructed in such a formal system of numerals, are factually empty. (If, however, we regard ordinality and addition as fundamental features of relations among matters of fact, then one might argue that these "formal" relations are generalizations of the widest experience we have of relations among number properties.) For any given value of *y*, there is a value of *x* associated with it, so that given one value, I may *deduce* the other by the transformation rules of arithmetic (or of any extension of this mathematical syntax beyond arithmetic and natural numbers). I may interpret this invariant relation or give it some "content" in another framework, defining, for example, *ordinal position* as *point* and defining the associated term in the series as *number of lines connecting the points given in ordinal sequence* (where there is one and only one line between any two points). The series 0, 1, 3, 6, 10, 15 . . . may then be said to be given an interpretation. If I adopt the convention that for one point, there are zero lines connecting it to itself, then for two points, there is one line; for three points, there are three lines; for four points, six lines; and so forth. (See Fig. 7.) In this interpretation the numerical law is seen to "predict" how many lines there are among a given number of

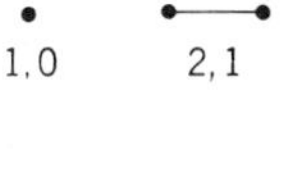

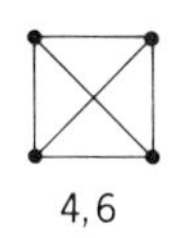

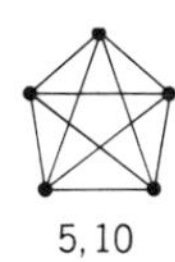

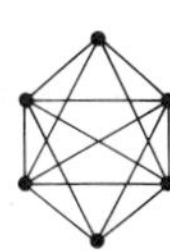

Fig. 7

points; or given a number of lines, I may "explain" the number in terms of the generator function given earlier. But on inspection, I may discover that I have defined *point, line,* and *connection* in such a way that the two versions, one for numerals the other for numbers of points and lines, are completely isomorphic, or such that one is a transform of the other. The numerical law then serves as a representation of any number of relations among any number of postulated entities, as long as these relations exhibit the same invariance. However, if I interpreted this as a model of some geographic situation in which, for example, there is one and only one road between any two towns, then the properties of the numerical law will hold for the interpretation only if I discover what these conditions entail. (More strictly, we would have to say that our "roads" do not cross, or that *road* means *shortest possible distance,* and then we are into the domain of the empirical interpretation of these geometric concepts.) (A well-known model of this function, in communications engineering, is that of communication lines between terminals.) I may also generate the Fibonacci series, 0, 1, 1, 2, 3, 5, 8, 13 . . . in which each successive term is the sum of the previous two (with some convention for generating the first two, 0, 1) and discover that this involves a number of other numerical laws (which are associated with the geometric figure of the spiral, and the so-called golden section, and in biology, with patterns of growth and of structure). The form of the numerical law in each case is such that for every value of some independent variable there is associated some value (or values) of some dependent variable, according to a relation of invariance set forth in the law. The use of numerical laws in science is, as we have seen, related to the interpretation of the numerals as concrete numbers, i.e., with the number properties of some physical magnitude. When such an interpretation is found, then one may expect that the deduction of numerical consequences (values of dependent variables, given values of independent variables) according to the numerical law, will provide physically interpretable hypotheses or predictions, which may then be tested to see if deductive consequences agree with empirical measurements. Thus, in Galileo's formal deduction of a relation between some variable interpreted as distance and another interpreted as time, he arrived at a numerical law, the deductions from which, for given values of one variable, were anticipations of values of measurement in the inclined-plane experiment. (See Appendix A, pp. 463 ff.) Thus, the relations among measured distances were discovered empirically to stand to each other in the ratio approximately equal to that of the squares of the measured times, serving to confirm the interpretation of the numerical law in terms of physical magnitudes. Whereas it would be odd to talk of "explaining" or "predicting" in a purely formal or uninterpreted calculus, these terms do take on their ordinary significance when applied to a physical interpretation of such a calculus. The deductive model of explanation, which we will examine in the next section, defines *explana-*

tion precisely in terms of such a relation between a law and what can be deduced from it (and from values for individual "independent" variables taken as initial conditions), in the way of values for "dependent" variables. This leads us directly to the form of physical laws.

Physical laws

If we regard physical science as quantitative or as a mathematical science whose observation statements are measurement statements, then the form of numerical laws gives us the form of physical laws, with the difference that in physical laws the numerals are taken to represent number properties of physical magnitudes, such as length, charge, mass, weight, and so on. In fact, the quantification of physical science achieves precisely this. The gain here is that with the corroboration of physical interpretations of numerical laws, or with the possibility of the formalization of physical relations in mathematical terms, the immense power of formal inference and of mathematical computation becomes available to physical thought. But the isomorphism between numerical laws and the number relations discovered among physical magnitudes is not ascertained *a priori;* it is a matter of physical discovery and constant test. Thus, it is *discovered* that length and weight are arithmetically additive and that density and velocity are not. The postulate of vector addition, with its unique rules for the addition of velocities, introduces a formal representation of the hypothetical or discovered properties of velocities. In Galileo's case, by means of geometrical reasoning, a hypothetico-deductive scheme generates numerical laws which are interpreted for the physical magnitudes, distance and time, and are then tested in this interpretation. The formal mathematical theory is thus mapped onto a physical model, and this model or interpretation is then tested by experiment.

We may want to include, as physical "laws," such qualitative principles as *Every event has a cause,* or, *The cause is equal to the effect,* or *Matter is neither created nor destroyed.* We may then regard these as higher-level or highly general physical laws or principles, stating invariant relations which "explain" lower-level laws, as these laws, in turn, explain particular events. But this raises serious questions about the status of such principles in empirical science. We will postpone to a later section discussing the question of whether these are "laws," "theories," or some sort of metaphysical or regulative "principles."

Laws in Biology and the Human Sciences

With the advances in quantification in genetics, in molecular biology and biochemistry, and even in the analysis of evolution (e.g., by serological tests for the ordering of species), it may be assumed that a "complete" biology will approach the condition of physical science, and its laws will then be statable in numerical form as well. Similarly, with the quantification of psychology, sociology, anthropology, and economics more and more "laws" in these human sciences come to be formulated as numerical laws. But a distinctive kind of law appears in these sciences which does not take the form of numerical laws. In fact, it is not clear that explanation in many cases is in the form of "laws" which cover instances. In taxonomic and typological studies, in which classificatory technique is uppermost, the law-like character is preserved, in qualitative terms, in the invariant relations among qualitative predicates. Thus, the whiteness of swans, the geotropism of roots of plants, the chromosome number of a given species are all statable in the form $(x)(Fx \rightarrow Gx)$, or in some statistical form related to this. But this invariant or statistically ordered association of properties is characteristic of physics and chemistry no less than of biology and the human sciences. Classification is a common relation of law-likeness in all the sciences and is involved in the fundamental processes of gathering and ordering data. What is distinctive in biological explanations is that they are often functional in the sense that something is explained in terms of its functions within a whole organism. Thus, we explain breathing, in one way, as a process which carries oxygen to the lungs and also carries carbon dioxide out of them; we explain the lungs as organs for the oxygenation of the red blood corpuscles. We explain the oxygenation of the red blood corpuscles as required for the oxidation processes which constitute metabolic activity; we explain metabolic activity as necessary to the maintenance of the whole organism in maintaining its homeostasis as an energy-processing and energy-converting system. In short, our explanations are in terms of functions which are "for the sake of" some end, which is in turn related to some larger end, stopping only at the intact organism, for the sake of disciplinary limitation, and going beyond this in studying living systems or societies of organisms. Such explanations seem to answer the question, "What is *X* for," or in terms of some process, "Why does it function as it does?" In the latter case we may explain the activity of breathing in terms of mechanical and chemical laws, "deriving" the rhythm of contraction and expansion from physical laws. But the *why* in biological explanations is often a *what for*. Thus, such explanations have been called teleological (or teleonomic, where the law-likeness of some natural process is taken in the sense of its function in the life of the organism[4]). The discovery of the function of some hitherto unexplained organ thus comes to constitute an explanation. Thus, for example, the discovery that the pancreas secretes insulin and that insulin is involved in the breakdown of sugars and carbohydrates and their utilization in oxidation (as "fuel," stored and used for the operations of the human engine, to introduce a common model) explains the function of the organ, but not in itself; rather, as it operates "for the sake of" the whole organism, in the processes whose "end" is the

[4] See Ernst Mayr "Cause and Effect in Biology," *Science,* **134:**1501–1506 (1961).

maintenance of the proper life functions of the whole. The form of law-like universal statements is easily maintained here, by interpreting this in the following way: "If anything is a pancreas, then its function is. . . ." One could deduce from this that if there were a dysfunction of this organ, the processes which it supports would not take place normally; and if the further law could be stated, that in the absence of this function, the organism cannot maintain itself, then one could arrive at a systematic conclusion in this system of inference, which could then be experimentally tested. It may be discovered that other organs or functions compensate for certain dysfunctions, in some cases but not in others. Chemical and biochemical study may reveal the microprocesses of this function and how it may be synthetically performed by substitute organs, drugs, and so on. Despite the "functional" or "teleological" form of the biological explanation, the model of "laws of nature" and "laws of science" and the form of the law-like statements is maintained here by incorporating the term *function* in the laws. The sense in which *cause* and *function* are interrelated will be considered in Chapter 11. The same thing may be seen to hold for the so-called teleological features of conscious behavior and of social and economic behavior. The problem of the "reduction" of these "strange" features to the form of laws of measurement, or of numerical laws will also concern us later. However, even the "unreduced" form of such relations as are characteristic of functional and teleological accounts in biology and the human sciences may be stated in the usual form of universal conditional statements. Thus, it is not the forms of such laws that are problematic or unique, but the interpretation of this form for the special features of "function" and "teleology."

Historical Laws

We may conceive of historical laws in two ways: (1) A law may be said to be historical if it describes some process or sequence of events which is time-dependent. That is, if the events or states which the law describes stand to each other in the relation *earlier-than* or *later-than,* then we may say that the law is "temporally asymmetric" or "directional." Thus, all chronological laws which characterize a change in some ordered and irreversible form may be taken as historical. Evolutionary laws, whether in biology, or geology, or linguistics, are historical in this sense. Similarly, thermodynamic laws, which describe irreversible processes in which states are uniquely ordered as "earlier-than" or "later-than," are also historical in this sense. (2) We may, on the other hand, mean only those laws which concern history in the narrower sense, as the record of human actions and institutions. In this case, history proper is distinguished from mere chronology in that it concerns distinctively human actions, i.e., those which are characteristically purposive and are the actions of unique individuals. Even if the processes or events which such historical laws describe are social or institutional, rather than personal and biographical, they are, on this view of the matter, not reducible to, nor even similar to, those "historical" laws which describe natural chronology.

The issue concerning historical laws becomes clear when the claim is made that human history represents just such a process of ordered change as does, for example, evolution or thermodynamics. The strongest form of this claim is that laws of human history are, in effect, natural laws; that the facts of history reveal the same sorts of invariance as those discovered in physics, and that therefore the scientific study of history is no different, in principle, from the scientific study of any natural domain. The counter-arguments adduce the uniqueness of historical events as against the non-uniqueness of natural events, in the sense that laws of nature range over recurrent events, but that historical events are unique occurrences and are thus not subject to law-like description. *History never repeats itself* expresses this view aphoristically. The alternative view is that there are recurrent patterns in history. Though the events and the individual agents may be unique, the relations among them exhibit invariances of the sort which may be described in a law-like way. The notion of "stages" of historical development alleges that similar forms and sequences of change are exhibited at different places and times. For example, comparative historical studies may be said to reveal similar developments in different human societies, which are described as going through the stages of *savagery, barbarism,* and *civilization.* Or, to give another example, on the Marxian view of historical materialism, the socioeconomic stages of Western European development are said to exhibit the characteristic passage from slave societies, to feudalism, to capitalism; and then, by the workings of this same historical process, it is predicted that this development will eventuate in socialism. In the *a prioristic* historical schemes of the nineteenth century (e.g., those of Hegel or Spencer), some innate and necessary law of the unfolding or development of stages of history in accordance with some principle (in Hegel, the unfolding of the idea of liberty; or in Spencer, increasing differentiation and specialization as a universal law of evolution) is said to characterize and order the known facts, and thus to explain them by bringing them under a law. In more limited instances, a historian may characterize a postrevolutionary period as one of "Thermidorean reaction," taking the French Revolution and its aftermath as the pattern characteristic of all other revolutions which he has studied. He may thus hypothesize that Thermidorean reaction characterizes a "law of revolutionary development."

The criticism of such laws is that they are at the level of commonsense generalization and are so vague that they are unfalsifiable. They are therefore untestable, in future instances, and may at best exhibit no more than accidental regularities for some limited instances—precisely what one would not want to call a law. The counterclaim is that all laws are liable to this charge, and one might speculate that the universal law of gravitation is a "local" or "accidental" law, holding only for a limited domain within a cosmically small period of time. (Thus, Peirce speculates that physical laws may themselves be undergoing change or evolution, our limited perspective taking them as unchanging.) Another criticism is that historical facts are always interpretations from some point of view, so that one may always "make" the facts in such a way as to fit the framework of the law one is asserting. Still another criticism is that human history concerns the action of free-willed human agents, and that such actions, if free, are unpredictable in law-like terms. Moreover, the variables involved in such actions are so great that even statistical methods cannot serve to order such actions as comprise human history under law-like form. What one achieves at best, then, is some crude analogy, with no predictive power for particular instances; and if history is made up of unique events, this lack of predictive power vitiates any claim to law-likeness.

The answer to this charge once again is to compare this situation to that of the physical sciences, in which the unique events at the quantum level are also taken to be unpredictable but nevertheless yield to statistical characterization for large ensembles, and probability functions for a "run" of unique events. The further question that has been raised in this context is whether historical laws, because they concern the actions of conscious individuals, are not really psychological laws (sociological laws too may be so reduced, so that *sociology* is another name for *statistical psychology,* which involves the behavior of large groups). We will discuss some of these issues concerning history and the social sciences in Chapter 14.

In this account of the ways in which laws are stated, the general case of a universal conditional statement seems to fit all the cases of what may be regarded as laws, within the confines of the form of such laws. The differences come in interpreting how the terms of the conditional are to be taken. In numerical laws, these terms are numerical values. In physical laws, the numerical values are interpreted as physically measurable values of number properties of physical magnitudes, or of ratios among such magnitudes. In biological laws, the term *function* enters into the formulation in characteristic instances, so that relations among entities (organs, processes, and so on) and their functions, or among various functions, replace the relations among number properties. In historical laws the problem arises not simply as to the form in which such laws may be stated, but as to the conditions under which one may assert, in an empirically significant way, that historical events give grounds for the warranted assertion of such laws at all.

The point, in this chapter, is to see in what sense such a formal structure as the law-like statement, in universal conditional form, may be said to function in explanation. One of the most widely discussed models of such explanation is that in which statements describing particular events or occurrences (or measurement statements) may be deduced from law-like statements. We turn, then, to a consideration of this deductive model of explanation.

THE DEDUCTIVE MODEL OF EXPLANATION

The deductive model of explanation is a formal model which attempts to study the relations between statements in what is taken to be the characteristic structure of explanation in science. The formal theory of such a model is a logical system of deductive inference, in which a particular statement is derived, by a rule of inference, from a major and a minor premise, the first containing a universal statement and the second a particular statement. The rule of inference used in this model is the *Modus Ponens* rule (affirming the antecedent) which we have examined earlier. It is of the form:

$$\begin{array}{l} (1)\ P \rightarrow Q \\ (2)\ P \\ \hline (3)\ Q \end{array}$$

The interpretation of this rule, in the deductive model, is as follows: (1) is taken as a universal conditional statement (or any conjunction of such statements); thus, the major premise is a law-like statement; (2) is taken as the assertion that the conditions set forth in the antecedent (P) in fact exist; that is, that instantiations of P are true; (3) is the deductive consequence that if instantiations of P are true, then instantiations of Q are true. We may rewrite this, with quantification, in the following form.

$$\begin{array}{l} (1')\,(x)(Fx \rightarrow Gx) \\ (2')\,Fa \\ \hline (3')\,Ga \end{array}$$

The justification of this rule of inference is not simply that it happens to be a rule of inference in logic, but that it exemplifies the kind of rule which in scientific inference is a standard one: as a matter of fact, a factual hypothesis is regarded as confirmed instantially, when, if its ancedent conditions are fulfilled, the anticipated consequence is observed. Translating this in terms of the relations between law-like statements and statements regarding initial or antecedent conditions, and particular consequences, the pattern looks like this:

$$\begin{array}{lll} \textit{Explanans} \left\{ \begin{array}{l} (1'')\quad L_1 \cdot L_2 \cdot L_3 \cdot \ldots \cdot L_n \\ (2'')\quad c_1 \cdot c_2 \cdot c_3 \ldots \cdot c_n \end{array} \right. & \begin{array}{l} \text{(universal law-like statements)} \\ \text{(singular statements of initial} \\ \text{or antecedent conditions)} \end{array} \\ \hline \textit{Explanandum}\quad (3'')\quad e & \begin{array}{l} \text{(singular statement describing} \\ \text{an individual event)} \end{array} \end{array}$$

In the interpretation of this as a model of explanation, the premises (1″) and (2″) are called the *explanans* and the deductive consequence (3″) the *explanandum*. That is, e is said to be explained if it can be deduced as a consequence of the universal statements of laws in (1″) and singular statements of initial conditions in (2″). Similarly, we may interpret this formulation to mean that (3″) can be predicted from (1″) and (2″). Thus, explanation is a matter of showing that a statement about a particular event can be shown to be the deductive consequence of some law and some initial conditions. This model is therefore called the "nomological," or the "covering-law," model of explanation.

The model depends on having some universal statement as a premise and on having some true or affirmed singular statements based, presumably, on observation or evidence. It can be seen also that in this model *explanation* and *prediction* are *symmetrical*: When the statement (3″) is known to be true then (1″) and (2″) are adduced to explain it; when (1″) and (2″) are affirmed, then the statement (3″) may serve as a prediction. However, the difficulty comes in affirming (1″). If this is a universal statement, then if it is taken to be a statement of a law, it cannot be known to be true, but only to be the object of a warranted or rational belief. Or it may be regarded as a postulate, constructed in order that, together with (2″), (3″) may be derived from it. If it is a scientific law, then it is hypothetical; that is, it is fallible or may be false. But if (1″) is false, it may yet yield a true conclusion by valid inference. The criterion for valid inference is that true premises may not yield a false conclusion, but falsehoods may yield truths by such inference. The confirming instance *e* (or strictly speaking, the singular statement *e*) may not be said to confirm the major premise (1″) on logical grounds. To hold that it did would be to commit the logical fallacy of "affirming the consequent." (Briefly, the conditional *If it rains, the streets get wet* has *the streets get wet* as the consequent. If it is observed that the streets get wet, it does not follow that it has rained, because they may get wet in other ways as well.) If we take something to be an explanation only if the *explanans* is true, which Hempel states as a condition for explanation, then it follows that not everything from which *e* may be deduced is an explanation of *e*.

The deductive model does serve, however, to generate predictions which can falsify the hypothesis, on the preceding grounds. For if (3″), which is a prediction derived from the *explanans,* turns out to be false, on observation, then the explanans cannot be true. The rule of inference is that truths cannot yield falsehoods by valid inference. Thus, the negation of *e,* or not-*e,* would falsify the *explanans.* Arguing along these lines, Karl Popper concludes that laws of science are not confirmable by positive instances, but only falsifiable by negative ones. The usefulness of hypotheses in the form of law-like generalizations is that they do generate falsifiable instantial statements, which alone make such generalizations testable by the fact of their falsifiability. Popper holds further that a hypothesis is "corrobated" (rather than "confirmed") to the degree of the severity of such tests. At best, such a corroborated hypothesis may be said to have stood up to the test thus far, without being eliminated. But the test does not confirm its truth. A good hypothesis in science, therefore, is one which lends itself to the severest test—that is, one which generates the widest range of falsifiable consequences. (The statements which are the "falsifiers" or "potential falsifiers") of such falsifiable consequences, Popper calls "basic statements.") But because one nonswallow does not make a nonsummer, Popper does not suggest that one falsifying instance (say, not-*e*) can falsify a hypothesis; rather, we need a falsifying hypothesis which can in turn be tested and is therefore itself falsifiable. But then the singular statement derived from the *explanans* in itself is not sufficient to falsify the *explanans,* but only to suggest a testable hypothesis, i.e., one which will generate a whole class of such statements. Thus, according to Popper, singular statements derived from an *explanans* are in themselves inadequate either to confirm or to falsify hypotheses in the form of universal statements. But this goes far beyond the confines of the logical model of explanation, in its simple form. For example, if Galileo's Theorem II (that the distance of fall of a freely falling body is proportional to the square of the time of fall) is taken as a universal conditional, then if we know the ratio of times of fall of some body, we can predict what the ratio of its distances of fall will be through these times. (See Appendix *A,* pp. 454 ff.) Suppose then we observe, in a given instance, that this predicted ratio does not conform to the measurements. We would not reject the theorem as falsified from this instance; rather, we would continue testing, on the falsifying hypothesis that if Theorem II is false, then recurrent measurements would consistently disagree with the predictions made from the theorem and the initial conditions (of particular times of fall).

Thus, if a universal conditional statement is true, it cannot have false instances. That is, if it is a law of nature, stated as a strict universal (i.e., not as a statistical law, with a range of admissible values within some probability distribution), there cannot be a counterinstance. But for scientific hypotheses of unlimited scope, we cannot ever come to know this. At best, we can know that *so far,* no falsifying hypothesis has stood up to tests and that some initial hypothesis has. It would seem reasonable therefore to take such a well-tested hypothesis or law-like statement as a warranted explanation, given the evidence of testing and experimentation. Thus, if scientific laws are fallible and if in fact there is such a thing as a scientific explanation, at any point in history, then it must be the case that conceivably false laws do explain; and it must also be the case that no such explanation is ever immune from being overthrown. The stronger condition, which we have mentioned earlier (set forth by Hempel and Oppenheim in their version of the nomological model[5]) is that the laws in the *explanans* have to

[5] The original version seems to be Popper's, in *Logik der Forschung* (*The Logic of Scientific Discovery*), first published in 1934, and in translation in 1959, (London: Hutchinson, see esp. pp. 59 ff.). Hempel and Oppenheim published the by-now classical version of the deductive model in "The Logic of Explanation," in *Philosophy*

be true, that is, laws of nature, on our account; and scientific laws only if, in fact, these are true. On this condition, however, we never have more than a "potential" or "hypothetical" explanation, and we are in the awkward position of talking of "hypothetical hypotheses." On such a view, the term *explanation* is always a postulational term, relevant to given evidence or to the relative advancement of a science or a system of laws and theories. The alternative is to take any scientific explanation as a proffered explanation which is really an explanation if the scientific laws it adduces are true, but otherwise is not an explanation at all. On this condition we would come to know that something was an explanation only at the limit, i.e., at the completion of scientific inquiry, when all truths will be known. This seems to be a rather exorbitant demand.

This raises another difficulty in the deductive model. If in fact the laws or law-like statements in the premises are generalizations, arrived at by some norms of inductive inference, then what is deductively inferred from such premises can have no more claim to truth than the inductive claim made for the premises. The question arises whether, from the information given in an account of particular observations of the properties of things, one may be said to make a deductive (or "demonstrative") inference at all, or whether this is not classically what is meant by inductive (or "non-demonstrative") inference. If one does no more than to list these observations—or the conjunction of them—as a premise, is not the whole question of logical deducibility compromised? Yet when one takes the generalization from such evidence to be a universal statement, more or less highly confirmed, in this form it certainly would seem to meet the formal requirements for a deductive inference, though we could not claim for the conclusion any greater degree of evidential confirmation than was conferred on it by such premises.

These considerations arise with respect to one of the conditions which Hempel and Oppenheim put on an adequate explanation in empirical science, namely, that the *explanans* have empirical content; i.e., it cannot be construed as an *a priori* or as an analytic truth. There may indeed be such *a priori* elements in the *explanans*, e.g., some of the laws in the conjunction in (1″) may be logical truths, or statements in an "auxiliary calculus" used for purposes of inference, but some elements in (1″) have to have empirical or descriptive content. They must therefore be empirical laws, the grounds for which are evidential, or rely on tests made in a finite number of instances. At best, such a law can be highly confirmed (or corroborated, in Popper's view that it has withstood tests, but may still be

of Science, **15,** 1948 [reprinted in Feigl and Brodbeck, *Readings in the Philosophy of Science* (New York: Appleton-Century-Crofts, 1953), pp. 319–352]. Earlier versions are in Hempel "The Function of General Laws in History," *Journal of Philosophy,* **39,** (1942), pp. 35–48. See the bibliographical note for this Chapter for a fuller range of references on this topic.

false). One proposal to save the model, under these circumstances, is to weaken the relation of *deducibility* and make it, instead of a logical relation, a relation of inductive inference. But then, this is no longer a deductive model of explanation. To save it as a deductive model, some alternative fixing up is needed. One proposal here is to distinguish between the grounds for the acceptance of some generalization as a law, and thus as a premise for a deductive inference, and the grounds for the explanation of some event by such a premise. That is, if we are reasonably convinced that some law-like statement is sufficiently confirmed to warrant our rational belief, then we may assume it as a law of nature, postulationally, and thus use it as the premise of a deductive inference. In Scheffler's account of this sort of "fixing up," we are thus "separating the 'ground,' 'reason,' or 'cause' of events from the 'ground,' 'reason,' or 'cause,' for acceptance of beliefs.[6] This amounts to the hypothetical statement *If the indictive generalization is (warrantedly) taken to be a true universal statement, then if it serves in the premise of a deductive argument, together with some singular statements of antecedent conditions, one may derive some singular statement as a consequence from these premises deductively.*

In the deductive model, when the consequence is some such singular descriptive statement concerning a particular event or occurrence, the explanation is called a causal explanation. However, one may deduce universal statements from universal premises. For example (see Appendix A, p. 462), Galileo's Corollary states a law and is deduced from a law-like statement, i.e., from the Theorem. Similarly, the algebraic form of the Theorem ($s = \frac{1}{2}gt^2$) can be deduced from other universal statements (e.g., $s = \bar{v}t$, $\bar{a} = (v_t - v_o)/t$, and so on). We might add, to causal explanation of particular events, the function of explaining laws. In the deductive model, a law would be explained when it could be shown that it is the deductive consequence of some other universal statements. These would then constitute the *explanans* of the law, and the law would be the *explanandum*. In such an interpretation, the explanatory power of the system of science would lie in the deductive or formal relations which one could establish among the various laws. What we would then have would be a network of laws, of higher and lower generality, all of them connected with each other by patterns of deductive inference. In this way, from laws of high generality, one could arrive at laws of lower generality, as their consequences, and these in turn might ultimately be connected with such laws as permit deduction of instantial statements concerning particular, or testable, events or occurrences. In this model, the most general laws of science would not in themselves have to be stated in such a way that they have directly testable consequences; they would remain empirical laws if it could be shown that from them one could derive, by some process of

[6] I. Scheffler, *The Anatomy of Inquiry* (New York: Knopf, 1963), p. 39. For a full and critical discussion of the deductive model, see pp. 25–57.

inference, directly testable consequences. Such higher-level laws would then be indirectly testable and would thus be empirical laws. The system of science would then consist of chains of inference, so that the most theoretical statements (those with no direct empirical reference) would be connected at some points with statements which make direct empirical reference. If, in some quantitative science, we take measurement statements as our observation statements, then the derivation of dimensional numbers as values of variables in some law would serve as a means of prediction concerning instances of measurement. The deductive model, in this case, serves as an explication of the commonsense notion of science as an "organized body of knowledge," where *organized* is taken to mean *interrelated by processes of deductive inference.* This ideal formal model is exemplified in mathematical physics, for mathematics serves as just such a deductive system based on axioms, definitions, and rules of inference.

This raises another problem of interpretation, however. Suppose we take the definition of acceleration, i.e., $\bar{a} = (v_t - v_o)/t$, or the definition of velocity, i.e., $\bar{v} = s/t$, as one of the universal statements from which we derive the law, $s = \frac{1}{2}gt^2$. These may be interpreted as universal conditional statements, i.e., in the form, *for anything x, if it is an (average) velocity, then it is equal to the ratio of distance to time.* It has the form of a law-like statement, and it functions in a system of inference as a premise from which one may derive a law-like statement which has empirical instantiations. Would we want to consider such definitional statements as, prospectively, laws of nature? Or are they merely conventions, or stipulative definitions which serve as a sort of auxiliary calculus for the derivation of laws? Further, would we want to say that such definitions are true or false? Would an "indirect test" of such a definition be possible, in terms of consequences derived with its help? But if these are stipulative definitions, then we presumably stipulate them as we choose. Can such stipulation be subject to empirical test? Suppose I stipulatively define the term *triangle* to mean *three-sided figure,* do I then check to see if my definition is correct by examining triangles to find out if they have three sides? Obviously, anything I would take to be a triangle in the first place would have to have three sides, and so I could never discover a four-sided triangle, if what I meant by *triangle* were *three-sided figure.* If what I mean by a is $(v_t - v_o)/t$, then it would not make sense to say that I could then discover, by measurement that a was not equal to $(v_t - v_o)/t$. Yet I can discover, in principle, that s is not equal to $\frac{1}{2}at^2$, because it is only by measurement that I discover that the hypothesis that "distances are to each other as the squares of the times of fall in instances of freely falling bodies" is true. But how can I get an empirical law from mere definitions? For all the six steps in the derivation of this law (in the example given in Appendix A, pp. 468–69) are either definitions, or are derived from definitions. Can I then stipulate what the laws of nature will be? Is science as a whole then an arbitrary convention?

Poincaré answers this question thus: "convention—yes; arbitrary—no. They would be if we lost sight of the experiments which led the founders of science to adopt them, and which, imperfect as they were, were sufficient to justify their adoption. It is well, from time to time, to let our attention dwell on the experimental origin of these conventions."[7] His point is that there are any number of "conventions" we might have adopted, but only certain of them yield consequences which are in accordance with the facts of observation; and further, that the adoption of these, in the first place, had an experimental origin. Such definitions as that for velocity go back originally to commonsense observation. It is by means of the explication of the commonsense concepts of *quicker* and *slower* that Aristotle arrived at the definition (which he took to be not a convention, but a true description) of *velocity*. Thus, the definitions of *faster* and *slower* and *speed* go back, for their original sense, to direct or ostensive definitions. What we mean by *faster* is, for example, that in a race, the runner who covers a certain distance in a shorter time is said to be faster. One could argue (and Poincaré did) that it is by means of such empirical determinations of our meanings that we arrive at our earliest "conventions"; and that once established in usage, such conventions of use serve as rules thereafter. Similarly, we might conceive that the rule or convention forbidding incest is grounded in some long historical experience in the organization of social life, or that the rule of *kashruth* among orthodox Jews has its origins in long trial-and-error experience, or that the rule or convention exhibited in Pueblo pottery was originally an achievement of technical experimentation. But once a rule is adopted it is no longer tested to see if it works. In such a view, one might conceive that something like the rule of noncontradiction in logic is the product of the widest practical and linguistic experience and operates in effect as a criterion of rationality in human behavior.

The "conventionalism" of laws is a much discussed and much confused issue in philosophy of science, and it would be worthwhile to consider some main alternative interpretations of this view here.

(1) *Laws are rules in accordance with which we make inferences.* As rules, laws are neither true nor false, and do not assert anything about matters of fact. They are useful conventions which we adopt to order our inferences, and we adopt them because they justify the kinds of inferences we want to make. In scientific explanation and prediction we want to make the sort of inferences that will get us testable consequences from some set of observation statements, so that we may assert that when conditions c_1, c_2, . . . c_n hold, then we may expect or predict that e will be associated with them. That is, we want a rule that will permit us to make an inductive inference. For if rules are neither true nor false, they certainly cannot be premises in a deductive inference. Rather, they state the norms of inductive inference for a given domain of facts. In such an interpretation of laws,

[7] H. Poincaré, "The Classical Mechanics," *Science and Hypothesis, op. cit.*, p. 110.

however, the deductive model would have to be abandoned. For it would be reduced to, "If you follow the rule of *modus ponens,* then if certain antecedent conditions are observed to hold, you may infer that certain consequences will follow." The law is then nothing but an interpreted form of the *modus ponens* rule, and thus is not a statement about invariant relations among facts, but only an "inference ticket" which gives us the right to infer inductively that some observed consequence should hold, if some set of antecedent conditions is known to hold. Thus the form of the universal conditional as the form of a law-like statement still obtains, but is interpreted as a rule.

(2) *Laws are postulates.* Laws are postulates that are stipulated by convention but chosen so that they will serve as the premises of a deductive inference. As conventional postulates they are true or false only within the syntactic or logical context of the deductive model; i.e., they turn out to be logically true or false, in accordance with the rules of logic, in terms of the relations among statements in the model. Thus, if some instantial statement of the consequent is false, the postulate is formally falsified, because the logical rule does not permit the deduction of a false statement from a true premise. Thus, such postulates serve a logical function. They are not taken to be empirically true or false, but only useful in the ordering of our empirical statements in some deductive scheme. When such postulates are taken as the axioms of some formal system—say, as the axioms of Euclidian geometry—then they are only "true" by convention, and usefully "true" in this sense because of the inferences they permit and the systematic economy they effect in ordering a body of scientific thought. They are invalidated only when a more convenient convention can be found to replace them. Such choices of axioms are not simply conventional; rather, they are choices in terms of what Poincaré colorfully calls an "unconscious opportunism," i.e., choices based on pragmatic or even on aesthetic grounds, from among the innumerable conventions we may stipulate.

Another way of stating this view is to talk of laws as "disguised definitions," in the sense discussed earlier; and definitions cannot be invalidated by observation precisely because they determine what we will take to be a proper object of observation, in terms of its relation to some law or system of laws. Thus, having defined *straight line* in a certain way, we cannot then discover that for some straight line between two points, there is another line which is shorter in distance between the same two points. By definition, our first "straight" line would not be straight. We do not call the definition of *straight line* a law, however; it is a straightforward definition, without disguise. But a law such as Newton's second law, which states that force is equal to the product of mass and acceleration, is, in this view, a disguised definition, for what we mean by *force* is entirely contained in the product *ma*. It is not as if we were stating an invariance between some independently measurable force and some other independently measurable mass and acceleration. Rather, a conventionalist of this sort would hold that *force* is just a name of some property which is defined in terms of the product of mass and acceleration.[8]

(3) *Laws are conventions only with respect to the form in which they are expressed.* The view that laws are conventions only in relation to their forms is based on the distinction between statements or sentences and propositions. The choice of what form of expression we shall choose to express a proposition is entirely a matter of stipulation, or of convention. But once the meaning of some statement is determined as this or that proposition, then the statement is significant in some language, and what it then asserts is some proposition that is either true or false. For example, I may choose to use the word *cool* to mean *detached, sophisticated,* or, in current jargon, as a synonym for *good* or *I approve,* as well as for the usual meaning signifying some temperature or some sensation. But having chosen one or another meaning, the statement *This is cool* is then true or false (or expresses approval). It is true or false as a significant statement, i.e., as expressing a proposition. Although the form of expression is conventional, its truth or falsity is not conventional. Thus, Poincaré writes that "all a scientist creates in a fact is the language in which he enunciates it." And arguing against a view which states that scientific laws are conventions (concerning which Poincaré has been much misunderstood), he writes,

> [M. LeRoy would say] "When I say heavy bodies falling freely pass over spaces proportional to the square of the times, I only give the *definition* of free fall. Whenever the conditions shall not be fulfilled, I shall say that the fall is not free, so the law will never be wrong." [But] it is clear that if laws were reduced to that, they could not serve in predictions; then they would be good for nothing. . . . That then is a law which may be true or false, but which does not reduce to a convention.[9]

[8] This is a well-known and instructive example of the conventionalist view which has many versions and has generated many arguments. The classical account is in E. Mach, "On the Definition of Mass," included as a note in his *History and Root of the Principle of the Conservation of Energy* (Chicago: Open Court, 1911), pp. 80–85. Poincaré also gives a clear account in several places, but see esp. "The Classical Mechanics," pp. 97 ff., and "On Geometry," pp. 35–50, in *Science and Hypothesis* (New York: Dover, 1952).

[9] "Is Science Artificial," *The Value of Science, op. cit.,* pp. 121–124. In a similar vein, Moritz Schlick gives a clear account of this view, in his "Are Natural Laws Conventions?" (H. Feigl and M. Brodbeck, *op. cit.,* p. 187): "What is arbitrary are . . . the rules which . . . in their totality form the grammar of the scientific language. . . . All these "grammatical" rules and these alone, together determine the meanings of the propositions of science. For the meaning of a sentence is indicated if and only if it is precisely stated how the sentence is to be used; and that is precisely what these rules do. They are the only conventions, not the natural laws. It is those rules which turn mere sentences into genuine propositions, for they determine their significance.

Thus, in these three alternatives, *convention* means a different thing in each case. In the first, laws are conventional as rules; in the second, as postulates serving as premises in a deductive inference; in the third, what is conventional is not the law but only its form of expression. There are other variations on this theme, and it intrigues philosophers of science. For at bottom, this issue contains the central epistemological question of what the nature of explanation and of understanding is in science. Do we explain or understand by virtue of *ourselves* determining what the shape of our world picture will be? Do we thus shape our picture of nature, our science, to our language, and do we thus "create" the facts in our own image, in coming to understand or explain them? Does *understanding* entail bringing experience into the mold of an already established primary sense of understanding? Do we construe experience to fit our *a priori* concepts, in the language of science? Or do we rather confront objective orders in experience, which impose themselves on us, or which we seek out and discover in inquiry, and which our scientific laws reflect?

A last word on the deductive model of explanation: If it can be said that we explain some fact or some law by showing that it is derivable from some covering law, then is explanation a matter merely of arranging our knowledge in a certain way? We do, common-sensically, say that something becomes clear to us when it is put in order. But if explanation is no more than an orderly arrangement of what we already know, it would seem to be a strictly formal exercise, and informationally empty with respect to what more could be got out of it. Two features of the deductive model argue against this: first, the formulation of hypotheses which will "explain" in this sense would seem to be a genuinely creative act, an act of understanding, if the hypotheses are more than summaries of facts already known and are truly general laws of unlimited scope; and second, predictions based on such a model seem also to be new and not merely restatements of what is already known. In short, both the explanatory and predictive aspects of this model seem to demand an act of synthesis, of intellectual discovery which goes beyond mere rearrangement. The alternative is that rearrangements of a certain sort elicit some significant hypothesis because it is already "contained" in the facts, or in what we already know, so that explanation is really explication, i.e., making explicit what is implicit in the "plain facts." But in such a view, the "truths" thus elicited would be analytic and obtainable by inspection of meanings. If we require, however,

---

Once the rules are fixed, i.e., once agreement is reached concerning the grammar of the scientific language, then there is no longer any choice about how to formulate any facts of nature. . . . A natural law can then be represented in only one quite definite form and not in any other. . . . Thus we see that all genuine propositions, as for instance natural laws, are something objective, something invariant with respect to the manner of representation, and not dependent in any way upon convention. What is conventional and hence arbitrary, is only the form of expression. . . ."

that of the possible or proffered explanations or predictions, only those are true which are confirmed by test, then the patterns of arrangement which grant us such hypotheses or predictions must be, in some profound sense, isomorphic with patterns in nature, and this suggests some such notion as synthetic *a priori* truth. Thus, coming to understand would be a matter of apprehension of form in nature, or in our experience of nature. The creation of such a form in our representation of the facts would then itself be an act of rational discovery; *giving reasons* would be a matter of *discovering reasons.* If "coming to understand" or "explaining" is a matter of finding or giving reasons, then this goes to the heart of what we mean by rational knowledge.

THEORIES

Theories and Laws

Thus far we have spoken of laws in two senses: first, as the "empirical laws" which state invariant relations among "observable" or "measurable" properties. (The reasons for the quotes will become clear.) These are "directly" testable, in that one can deduce instantial hypotheses or predictions in the observation or measurement language from them. Second, we spoke of higher-level laws, from which one could deduce other laws. Such higher-level laws stand in the same relation of *explanans* to the lower-level empirical laws taken as *explananda,* as the empirical laws stand to statements of particular facts. One may then call the higher-level laws *theories,* which are only indirectly testable by means of the consequences of the lower-level laws derived from them, indicating their greater detachment from the direct connection to observation and experiment. In fact, common use often arranges, in ascending degrees of dignity, such terms as *hypothesis, law,* and *theory. A hypothesis* is a hunch, a guess, a speculative and as yet unconfirmed posit; it is the child playing with alternatives but not yet seriously engaged in work. The *law* is a hypothesis which has attained to citizenship in the republic of science: no longer playful or operating on hunches, it is more serious, and having outgrown childish experimentation and imagination, it is busy working and making a living. The *theory* is the legislator, judge, and executive of the republic; having earned his position through successful performance as a law, the theory now assumes a certain objectivity and detachment, in the reflective wisdom of old age. It is, in short, *theoretical,* with all the weighty commonsense connotations which that term bears. It is abstract, if not abstruse, and it is reflective, and others look to it for guidance.

In either of these views, laws and theories are regarded as alike in kind and in form but different in generality, abstractness, or degree of confirmation. A theory is a much surer thing, presumably, by virtue of its seniority.

But there is a fundamental feature which such accounts of scientific explanation leave out. For the discovery of laws, the generation of hypotheses, and the use of hypotheses to generate predictions is not the whole work of scientific inquiry, nor the sum of scientific understanding. All this presumes that somehow we know what we are looking for, and what we are looking *at*. That is, the deductive or covering-law model merely states the formal relations among statements; but statements to be significant have to have a use, that is, they are not simply statement-forms, but have to be semantically meaningful; and as synthetic statements which are true or false, have to have reference outside the language framework itself. Thus, we may say that observation statements refer to what it is we observe, as measurement statements refer to measurements. In general, then, statements which assert that something has a certain property, or that properties of some things stand in a certain relation, may be said to refer to properties and to relations among properties.

The form of the laws of science which we have just considered $[(x)(Fx \rightarrow Gx)]$ represents a law-like statement as a universal conditional which asserts that for any individual x, if it has a certain property then it also has some other property. The law may be confirmed or falsified only if it can, in addition, be asserted or denied that there is some x or that at least one x exists such that it has these properties. This in turn can be asserted if in fact we can say that in an individual case, i.e., for some individual constant a, it has the properties in question. What is confusing in many interpretations of this model is that the abstract notation, using x and a, makes these terms transparent. We are led to consider the properties as the essential reference of such descriptions (given by our predicate terms), and to dispose of what it is that bears these properties as no more than a vehicle, a kind of abstract entity or substance whose sole function is to carry properties. The individual variables or constants x or a which take the predicates F or G (as names of properties) may thus come to be referentially dispensable, as properties or collections of properties are taken to be all there is to refer to. The notion that science is the search for invariant relations among properties, especially those that we can represent in terms of measurement statements, reinforces the sense of the abstractness of the vehicle. We rely on common sense to fill in for us, with the assurance, that we tacitly mean that if something is a property it is a property *of* some *thing*. But the point is that we are not interested in the *thing* as some empty or unqualitied entity, but only as it is given its qualifications, as we come to know it by its properties. Finally, we may come to define the thing away as nothing but a collection of properties, with no "underlying" individual or entity which has these properties.

At every important stage in science, however, a theory is proposed and developed, in terms of what we come to know about the properties of *things*, and concerning just what these *things* are which have such and such properties. Thus, in the discussion of the concept of motion (see Appendix

A) the "things" that move, "drop out of the equations," so to speak, for they remain in the background, not affecting the laws of motion as phenomenal laws. Or so it appears. What is the "thing" in question, however? Very simply, it is a *body in motion,* and the "picture" we have of such a body is that it moves from one *place* to another *place* in *space,* through some *time*. The transparency of these concepts is due in large part to their familiarity. Just as we do not notice our own heartbeat except under certain conditions when it is unusual, or when we choose to take a pulse, because it provides the steady background of our lived experience, so too we do not intrude the consciousness of space and time, or even of body, in our considerations of motion; we merely take these background concepts for granted. But Galileo's conception of space is very different from that of Aristotle; and on a little reflection, it is also clear that the relevant concept of time is a distinctive one: it is like the geometer's isotropic space, the same in all its parts. *Time* is conceived as qualitatively homogeneous, or in Newton's phrase, "flows equably." *Body* too enters into our background of conception unobtrusively. A body is bounded, is at a place at any given time, remains self-identical as it moves from one place in space to another, can be divided, may be elementary or compound, and so forth. This appears nowhere in the laws of motion, but provides the conceptual framework in terms of which the laws are framed. We may see that a difference in such a framework leads to a different conception of the laws. Aristotle's space was qualitatively *in*homogeneous, with respect to any given body; for each natural body had a natural location, or a place at which it was naturally at rest. Aristotle's scheme produced explanations of accelerated motion quite different from Galileo's, and it followed, from the Aristotelian model, that things of different weight would fall at different speeds.

Sometimes it is easy to forget that all of our laws are understood in terms of some conceptual framework, or some model of the things whose properties we are investigating. All of this falls outside the framework of the formal model of explanation we have considered. But if these conceptual elements do enter into the understanding of the scientist, and into the understanding of the laws, however transparently, then the deductive model of explanation is incomplete as an account of scientific explanation, for it leaves all this out.

In this sense, the use of "theory" to mean simply a more general law hides a sense of theoretical explanation which involves a grasp of a conceptual framework or a model of what it is the laws describe. One might answer this objection by pointing out that the law *is* a model, in that it represents relations among properties. And this is true if we take the properties themselves as the entities which are the objects of law-like descriptions, or hypotheses. But then we have to adopt as our model of the world which science describes, a world constituted simply of properties, without any "things" of which these are the properties. One may argue that by *proper-*

ties one means *observables* or *measurables.* If so, then one has to construe nature as a structure whose entities are observables or measurables (e.g., in an empiricist interpretation in terms of sense data, or, in different philosophic accounts, *sensa* or *sensibilia*). But then, one's view of what exists in the universe or of what we ordinarily conceive of as physical nature, would be replaced by that of a universe made up of sense data or sensibles. (Bertrand Russell, among others in this phenomenalist tradition, proposed at one time reinterpreting physics exactly in this way, replacing the notion *physical object* with the notion *sensible,* including here the *sensed sensibilia,* which at any time entered into someone's sensory field, and the *unsensed sensibilia,* which would enter the sensory field if anyone were in the right position and sensing. Before him, J. S. Mill has defined *matter* as *the permanent possibility of sensation,* and Ernst Mach had spoken of physical objects as "bundles of sensations," in a tradition which went back to Berkeley and Hume.)

In our discussion in Chapter 5 we distinguished between those views which took the objects of sense perception to be phenomena, or appearances, from which we then, by inference, construct physical objects, and those views which took the objects of sense perception to be physical things themselves, existing independently of our perceiving them. These phenomenalist and realist views, which are the concern of epistemology, enter into our present consideration in the following way: If one claims that the laws themselves are models, then the entities which appear in the laws are taken to be the entities out of which the construct or picture of that nature which the laws describe is fashioned. But it is also plain that an alternative view would insist that properties are always properties of something (as appearances are appearances of something) and that what is transparent in the law becomes the subject of explicit concern in the model whose patterns the law describes. In short, in this view, the model is the concern of theories, which are thus distinct from laws, in that a theory explicitly asserts that something exists of such and such a sort, whose operations and whose relations are described in the laws. In this sense a theory explains the laws, by picturing them as descriptions of the behavior or relations among entities characterized by the theory. Thus, to claim that the laws already contain the theory by virtue of the terms which occur in the laws, is already to propose a theory or a theoretical model. The phenomenalist may propose, then, that the observation terms in an empirical law name the entities of his model, as the realist may then claim that these self-same observation terms in effect name theoretical entities of the sort called physical objects, for what we "observe" are not pointer readings and sense qualities, but things or relations of which these are the marks.

The distinction may be drawn in another way: In the deductive model, the "theories" are higher-level laws, and the terms in such laws are theoretical terms. But these are reducible to empirical terms, by the reduction of theories to their empirical consequences—say, empirical laws—and these are the ones which contain the "direct observation terms" or the "basic terms" by means of which, however indirectly, the theory may be said to refer to experience or experiment. The question of the asymmetry of explanation arises here, however; i.e., if T explains L, and L explains O, we cannot in turn also say that O explains L and L explains T. Yet if we say that the explanation of a statement containing a theoretical term like *the charge on an electron* is by means of its reduction in terms either of the observation-statements concerning pointer readings in a laboratory or of the operations of measurement, then we cannot in turn claim that the theory explains (by means of laws deducible from it) the pointer-reading statements. That is, we cannot have it both ways, on pain of circularity.

But what is the difference between a theoretical model and a law? If it is not a distinction between the terms used in either one, or if in fact the same terms may come to figure in each, in what sense does a theoretical model explain a law? Let us take, as a case in point, Faraday's model of an electrical field with lines of force, and Coulomb's law of electrostatic force. Coulomb had devised a law for the characterization of electrostatic force, in the form of an inverse square law, like Newton's law of gravitational force. Newton's law is $F = G(m_1m_2/r^2)$ (that is, the gravitational force between two bodies is proportional to the product of their masses divided by the square of the distance between them, where G is the gravitational constant of proportionality). From the suggestions of some relation between gravitational attraction and repulsion and electrical attraction and repulsion, Bernoulli, Priestley, Cavendish found experimental results which upheld this suggestion indirectly, and Coulomb devised a direct experimental demonstration. He formulated the law as $F = C(q_1q_2/r^2)$, where F is the force of attraction or repulsion between two charged bodies, q_1 and q_2 are the charges, r the distance between the bodies, and C the constant of proportionality. Now the law in itself merely states observed and observable relations among measurable properties of something called electrical charge. But what makes it an electrical and not a gravitational law is that it is a description of a different phenomenon, involving charged bodies and not masses, and thus inherits the whole history of the concepts of electricity. The peculiar thing is that this history introduced models of electricity, from the early Greek atomist conceptions of an *effluvium,* which is a physical "stream" which pours off from rubbed amber, by "chafing" (and thus the adoption of the term *electric* by Gilbert, from the Greek for amber, *elektron*), to the anthropomorphic models of a "sympathy" or "innate desire" or "virtue" acting from the charged body, to the notions of "subtile fluids" (either two different ones, for attraction and repulsion, or finally a single one which was "lost" or "gained," and thus "negative" or "positive"). Thus, in these models, electricity was conceived of as acting by some mechanical or material means (or in the "sympathy" model, by some functional "nature" or "virtue"). But the force of the analogy of electrical and gravitational force equations was such that the Newtonian model of gravitational force as action at a distance through empty space supplanted the electrical models, in the understanding of Coulomb's law. Faraday, working from the similarity between the arrangement of iron filings around a magnet and the arrangements of particles around an electrically charged body, suggested that electricity acts through a *medium,* and not through "empty space," and that this medium transmits the electrical force in a characteristic way, along "lines of force," and that the medium whose structure is such that it transmits force along such characteristic lines is an electrical field. The same law, then, may be said to be interpretable in terms of *alternative* models. But from this fact, two conclusions emerge: (1) that the law *in itself* does not determine a unique model, but the interpretation of the terms and relations in the law in one or another conceptual framework is such a model of the domain or the entities whose properties and relations the law describes; (2) that laws in themselves do not constitute a complete account of explanation, for the function of the model is to reach some understanding of what the law is about, and *why* it operates as it does; thus, the model serves to explain the law, in the sense of helping us to understand it, but not simply in the form of a higher-level law from which the law is deducible.

The charge has often been made that models are no more than aids to the imagination, but that the scientific understanding is content with the formal statement of invariant relations, intellectually grasped without the need of pictures. Models are therefore only pictures in our minds. But if pictures do help us understand, and indeed, if understanding is tied up as intimately as it is in scientific thought with imagination, then certainly the "picture" or the conceptual model, mechanical or otherwise, serves to aid the understanding, and thus serves to fill out any explanation. One might object that this sort of explanation is outside science. But the human tendency to take science as being about the world in the ways in which we can imagine it is so strong a component of understanding that it is hard to know where imaginative reconstruction leaves off and purely intellectual understanding begins. This is more clearly the case when we consider that the origins of hypotheses in science are very much a matter of the imagination and involve, in many historical instances, the suggestiveness of models, or pictures, or material analogies. This may be said to work as much for abstract as for concrete or mechanical models. It is the "picture" aspects of some mathematical law which often suggests the analogy which leads to the formulation of new laws, or new applications of the *form* of some mathematical law. The example here is the variety of interpretations which the inverse-square law has as a mathematical "model"—that is, as a configuration, or an abstract pattern of mathematical "entities." Thus, given the field model, Faraday was able to formulate mathematical descriptions in terms of such a field, and later, Maxwell was to formulate the characteristic "field equations" in terms of differential equations which lie at the basis of much modern physics. For an undifferentiated and qualitatively homogeneous space, one cannot formulate equations which characterize *spatial* inhomogenities. Instead, one formulates equations for *curves* in such a space, and the curves are taken to represent the paths of bodies, in a space which is itself indifferent. But if space is taken as a medium (or as containing a medium), then action through this medium is describable by a mathematics of such a field, taken as an *entity* of a certain sort. The sort it is then helps to explain the laws in terms of this field.

We might turn this back upon the model of explanation itself: it serves to help us understand what explanation in the sciences is like, by providing precisely such a model of explanation. But this should suggest that models are not simply literal pictures or mechanical toys that help us to "feel" the sense of a law-like description. The model may be highly abstract and may involve nonpicturable relations, in the ordinary and literal sense of "picture." A model may, in this sense, represent a theoretical "picture," and not simply a mechanical one. But what marks it distinctively as different from a law in this regard is that the law *in itself* serves only as a framework for interpretation, and does not carry its interpretation with it. It may be hard to separate the statement of a law from its interpretation, because we tend automatically to associate a law with the current or common interpretations which it is given. It is in this sense that the "entities" which a law includes, in its interpretation, are transparent. But these are transparent *because* we assume we understand them; we allege, in effect, that "it goes without saying." Just so for example, in our understanding of the notions of *distance* and *time,* we are heirs to the framework within which modern physical science has developed, and to the Cartesian and Newtonian space and time *model.* Thus we take it as part of our unspoken and tacit heritage. But this model too breaks down. The Euclidian space in which it is framed gives way to alternative geometric conceptions of space which are non-Euclidian, in order to explain laws which are nonclassical. Similarly the simple conception of a body in space breaks down not only in the sense that the hard, solid, classical atoms turn out to have an internal structure of great complexity, but in the sense that the concept *particle,* which represents our general concept of an elementary *body,* having a position in space at any given time, is no longer adequate as a complete model of physical nature in its ultimate structure. The field concept now enlarges the concept of *particle,* where the latter model breaks down as a means of explaining certain law-like relations. Even the concept of a "wave" in some medium proves inadequate as a model, when the medium which alone can support a wave seems to be dispensible (as in the rejection of *ether* theories) because it has no determinable effects.

The feature of models then seems to be that they are expendable and that we adopt them as we need them and drop them when they fail to explain. We may distinguish, however, between *ad hoc* models, which serve the purpose of representing to us this or that particular law or domain of laws of a limited scope, and the *systematic* or *theoretical* models, which attempt to order completely the whole domain of a science. Such systematic conceptions as are represented by such "models" at the foundations of science (e.g., *causality, matter, space, time*), do not permit *ad hoc* adoption, but seem to demand a fuller and more cautious and complex commitment. The question then arises, "What is the status of such models?" That is, what is the nature of the claim that they make, and what is the function of such models in scientific explanation? These are two related questions, and we will consider them together.

THE EPISTEMOLOGICAL AND ONTOLOGICAL STATUS OF THEORETICAL MODELS

By *epistemological status of theoretical models* we mean how they function in scientific explanation. We have already suggested that they have been characterized (critically and otherwise) as aids to the imagination. And we have in general characterized them as functioning to help us understand the laws of science, and as being the interpretations of these laws. But we may examine further what this means. Let us take a typical theoretical term such as *atom*—theoretical, because presumably we cannot "observe" atoms directly, but only inferentially, within the framework of a theory which interprets the relatively uninterpreted "data." This does not mean that given some set of laws, we may infer from it what its theoretical entities are; rather, it is the theory which permits us to infer from some given data that what we "observe" is an atom. But the epistemological question arises whether we can be said to "observe" atoms, or whether atoms are imaginary constructs which we invent to aid our understanding, or to name characteristic configurations of observed properties economically. In our discussion of observation and of measurement we suggested that all observation and all measurement that goes beyond blind sensory "contact" or "raw feel" is observation *that* something is the case, and that this step beyond pure neural response or "immediate sensation" (if there is such a thing) is made in virtue of some *framework* of observation or measurement, in which it attains to significance. It is such a framework, at whatever level of sophistication, that we take here to be a model. The terms *model, conceptual framework,* and *theory* are here taken in the same sense, so that in this sense all observation and measurement is theoretical or within the framework of some theoretical model. The distinction between observation terms and theoretical terms confuses this issue, if it is taken to mean that there is a distinction between uninterpreted and interpreted data, because observation and interpretation as we have argued, are inseparable. But we may introduce the important distinction between relatively uninterpreted data and some interpretation of it, and in this sense, between what is relatively low-level theoretical interpretation and higher-level theoretical interpretation. In this sense the difference between observation and theoretical terms is a difference between an older, common, and more familiar theoretical framework (especially that which is represented in common sense and in the ordinary use of language) and a newer one achieved by criticism of the shortcomings of the older one. The criticism reveals an inadequacy in the older framework: it no longer functions to make intelligible what has come to be known, or contradictions can be shown to arise in it, or it is found to be too limited in scope to describe phenomena adequately. If we take the new theoretical framework as a "language," then the new language is a reconstruction of the older one, fitted to new uses for which the older one is inadequate. In this way, for certain purposes, the "language" of numbers replaces that of qualitative description, and in this way, common sense is constantly replaced by what, relative to it, is a "scientific" framework. This new framework, once absorbed into common use, is itself subject to reconstruction, as seventeenth-century scientific concepts come to be taken for granted as twentieth-century commonsense concepts. The new language affords an interpretation of the old, in a distinctive way; it permits a more systematic account than did the old. It permits, therefore, the synthesis of a disparate accumulation of facts which, in the older interpretation became eclectically ordered, in *ad hoc* ways. In this sense, then, the reconstructed language is a unification of what had developed in separate ways in older languages. A higher-level theory thus establishes a systematic framework for the ordering of old facts, which themselves already represent some theoretical interpretation which has "broken down," not simply in the sense of having failed but of having literally broken apart, so that what once was unified under it has proliferated under newer *ad hoc* interpretations. Thus, Newton's celestial mechanics is the systematic culmination of the attempts to replace an older theoretical framework which had broken down under the impact of new observations which could not be well-ordered under it. The model is supplied by Copernicus, as a basis for interpretation, and the achievement of a systematic framework comes with the enunciation of a formal system, Newton's *Principia Mathematica,* in which this interpretation is fully systematized.

The historical sequence (of simplification under a new theory, proliferation within the new theoretical framework, the discovery of anomalous and unsystematizable facts within this framework, the accretion of *ad hoc* hypotheses and theories and the subsequent proposal of a new simplification) suggests a schema of scientific development which it is easy to vulgarize and oversimplify. Yet theories are successively replaced, and "observation" under the new theory becomes a quite different thing. The "observation" of the composition of distant stars in terms of line spectra is a highly theoretical observation; still, it is no less and no more "observation" than that of missing buttons or eclipses or mutations. But if this is the case, then the line between observables and theoretical entities is a line determined by the relative status of *two* frameworks, and not between a nonframework and a framework.

These epistemological considerations lead us directly to ontological ones. Are atoms real, or only imaginary objects? Here a difficult question arises. Not all models are taken to be claims that things are really the way they are represented in the model. If one represents lines of force by strings, or the mutual acceleration of two bodies by a spring between them with hypothetical forces acting upon it, then it seems plain that we do not intend that things really are the way they are represented in the model, but we do intend that there is a certain isomorphism between abstracted properties of the model and what it represents. In quite the same way, then, mechanical and mathematical "models" are abstractive in this sense. It would be the same mistake to take the mathematical model for the "reality" of what it is taken to represent, as it would be to take the mechanical model in this way. Such hypothetical entities are consciously taken as diagrammatic, as a map is taken as diagrammatic. But what is the difference between the map and the atom, then? Is not the atom also a diagram? Here we may make a distinction. The map is always less rich in content than that of which it is a map; but the atom is conceived so that it is richer in content than the observed phenomena for which it is the model. The model of the atom is such that not only is it conceived so that it explains the laws for which it is constructed, but that it serves to generate hitherto unformulated laws and to unify laws which were previously considered separate. Such disparate properties as heat, solidity, color, weight, and the laws of their relation are now deducible from the atomic model (and its mathematical formulation). But laws of these properties hitherto unformulable in the ordinary language of quality terms are suggested by the model. The conceptual development of the atomic model, from Democritus' hard, uncuttable particles to the complex models of contemporary atomic physics, replaces less rich with more rich conceptions. But does this guarantee, any the more, that the atom is real because it is richer in content? Or to put it paradoxically, is our atom more real than Democritus' was? The confusion here is to mistake the model *as a model* for what it is a model *of*. In this sense, the string in place of lines of force and the atom have a common feature: they are approximations of what we take the reality to be. But then why take one as imaginary and one as real? In using the string, however, we are engaging in a conscious self-illusion, much as we do at the theatre or when we play Cowboys and Indians as children. The question is whether we are doing the same thing when we use the atom as a model. One way of answering this question is to relate the question of reality to the question of truth. We may be said to test the truth of a model by testing the truth of the consequences derivable from it, namely, the truth of the laws which it explains. One might hypothetically conceive that from strings, taken as lines of force, and from what we know about the properties of strings—i.e., real strings, of silk, or wire, or anything whatever which would be adequately string-like—we could deduce certain laws about lines of force. But clearly the model would quickly break down on such an interpretation. The partial analogy between strings and lines of force would be very quickly revealed as partial. The atomic model also breaks down regularly and is reconstructed and tested. But this testing is the only "proof" we have that our approximations are in any sense close to what it is we require of the model by way of explaining laws. We may say then that the truth of the model is a function of the severity of the tests to which it has been subjected. If a model is refined so that it can, with such modifications, retain its essential character under such testing, then we seem to have rational grounds for believing it is a true account of the way things are; we have here the same sort of grounds as those which were adduced in talking of warranted belief in inductive generalizations or hypotheses. We cannot know that reality is as we picture it. All we can know is that our picture of it has proved adequate to the most rigorous demands we can make on it. One of these is the direct test of its consequences. But another is the systematicity of the model: how well it "fits" in the framework which defines reality for us at a given time. In science the philosophical realist is one who depends not only on the evidence of his senses, but on the criterion of intelligibility as well. One unspoken ideal in much scientific thought is that reality is not self-contradictory, that it is intelligible, and that the expression of this is the ability to build an ever more systematic and encompassing scientific picture. In this sense the atom's "reality" depends a good deal both on how it fits into the established systematic framework of science and how it serves to systematize that framework itself. It is in this way that we judge illusions in general; they are, after all, given to perception, and in this sense we have the "test" of observation to convince us that the illusion is real. But the systematic test requires more than a single instance of observation, and even more than a successive series of observations as "tests" for reality. Our observation is framed within some systematic *theory* of the way things are. Thus, we take the magician's illusion always as an illusion because "we cannot believe our eyes." We know, rationally, that a hat without a rabbit in it cannot spontaneously produce a rabbit, even if we never find out perceptually what the source of the illusion is.

We may summarize thus: Theories are models which are taken *either* as imaginary constructs or as conjectures about the real nature of things. We may characterize the alternative views on the epistemological and ontological uses of theories as (1) *Realist:* Theories constitute knowledge of the way things are, and thus are warranted approximations to reality, tested both by the empirical test of their consequences and by the systematicity of the theory. (2) *Constructivist:* Theories (and theoretical entities) are imaginary or ideal constructs, or models of a mechanical sort which are known *not* to be true but which function to aid the imagination, or as economical representations of a system of laws.

An awkward consequence of the constructivist view is that if theoretical models are known to be *false,* then we have a false explanation for laws which we presumably take to be true. The falsity here may then be conceived in the sense that *Hamlet* is false: a fictional construct is not meant to be true or false in the ordinary sense; it either serves its purpose or it does not; it is either adequate or inadequate. On these grounds, one may say the construct is neither true nor false, in any empirical sense, but serves only as an instrument of the understanding, more or less adequately. The measure of this adequacy is a problem with which we cannot deal here, but involves all the considerations which arise in pragmatist and instrumentalist views in philosophy, and these may be usefully studied in this context. The realist view, insofar as it relates to theories of truth, also raises serious questions of empiricist and rationalist criteria of truth, to which the study of the rich philosophical analysis of these questions is directly relevant.

In general, one may say that the questions we have dealt with in this section on the methods of science all lead to fundamental questions of philosophy which require separate intensive study of metaphysics, epistemology, logic and of the history of philosophic thought, with the prospect of bringing this to bear on the philosophical issues which science has posed for reflective and critical inquiry. To the extent that science is a rational system of thought, it is fundamentally *theory.* But significant theory as we have seen is rooted in the rational practice of science, its methodology. Thus, science is never empty speculation, but hard speculation under the stern taskmasters of empirical practice and rational critique. But having come thus far, in the passage from observation of the "plain facts" to the realization of how theory is involved in the very conception of these facts, we have one further step to take: the examination of some fundamental theoretical concepts in the sciences, of such generality that one has to separate them from the sense of theory we have thus considered, and think of them as the frameworks within which theories themselves come to be formed. If, in the realist view which has been emphasized here, theories are conjectures about reality, in one or another domain of science, then these fundamental concepts serve to frame the conditions under which we come to know. They also serve to state, in their most systematic form, the alternative world views within which scientific inquiry operates. This is nothing so general as a philosophical metaphysics would deal with, for it is tied to the concrete domains of science. But what will concern us next will be the live intersection of metaphysics with science, with respect to the fundamental concepts of *causality, space, time, matter, life,* and *consciousness.*

PART III

Some Fundamental Concepts in the Sciences

CHAPTER 11

Causality

IN ONE TRADITIONAL SENSE science has been characterized as a search for causes. Aristotle says, in the *Physics* (194^b 19), "Knowledge is the object of our inquiry, and men do not think they know a thing till they have grasped the 'why' of it (which is to grasp its primary cause)." This suits our ordinary conception quite well. However vague and variable our use of *cause* is, we tend often to think of understanding some situation as a matter of "knowing the causes," and ordinary use makes the term carry an extraordinary weight of alternative interpretations without apparent confusion. Yet in a much-cited passage Bertrand Russell writes, "the reason why physics has ceased to look for causes is that in fact there are no such things. The Law of Causality, I believe, like much that passes muster among philosophers, is a relic of a bygone age, surviving, like the monarchy, only because it is erroneously supposed to do no harm."[1] What the conjunction of ordinary use and this criticism suggests is that, like many other concepts, causality suffices for the rough-and-ready uses of everyday life, but is too inexact, too ambiguous, or worse, explicitly pernicious when carried over into science. Just as qualitative characterization fails where quantification takes over, it may be that causality fails and is replaced by more precise concepts which suit the needs of scientific inquiry.

We cannot decide this out of hand, however, without an analysis of the concept of causality. For only in this way can any judgment about it attain to significance, and become more than a preference of use, or an emotive

[1] Bertrand Russell, "On the Notion of Cause," *Mysticism and Logic* (New York: Doubleday, Anchor Books, n.d., p. 174).

expression of impatience or dismay with *certain* uses. Suppose, then, we examine some alternative instances which may be described as causal.

1. Whenever Pavlov rang the bell, the dog who had been conditioned to associate this sound with the presence of food began to salivate.
2. Whenever the sun sets, it gets dark.
3. He missed class because he was sick.
4. A certain species of mosquito was discovered to be the cause of malaria.
5. Smoking causes lung cancer.
6. Whenever the pressure is increased on a given volume of gas, the temperature rises in direct proportion to the increase.
7. The death was caused by a shotgun wound.
8. The origins of the Russian revolution may be traced back to the reign of Alexander I.
9. All consciousness has its ground in complex states of organized matter.
10. The whole chain reaction is set off by a single neutron.
11. If at first you don't succeed, try, try again.
12. The conjunction of inflation, unemployment, revanchist feelings, and the split among the left-wing parties, together with Hindenburg's fear of a revolutionary *coup* led to the rise of Hitler.
13. The glass was broken by the impact of the rock thrown at it.
14. Wishing will make it so.
15. The force of gravitation between the earth and the sun and the inertial force of the earth's motion interact to determine the orbit of the earth around the sun.
16. The more nervous he became, the more he stammered; and the more he stammered, the more nervous he became.
17. When the pressure rises to a certain point, the valve releases the gas, thus diminishing the pressure, and then closes shut when the pressure falls to a certain point.
18. He married her for her money.
19. Salmon swim upstream in order to breed.
20. He intended to say *frightened,* but said *Freudened* instead.
21. He does the right things for all the wrong reasons.

It is not immediately apparent that all of the instances listed here have anything in common. But in a formal sense, we may say that in each instance, something is related to something else in some way. This is vacuous, however, because anything is related to anything else in *some* way (in fact, in an infinite number of ways), and we would not want to call all relations causal. We might say that the causal relation is a subclass of the generic class of relations, but then we have to characterize its distinctive features. In each case, we may substitute the word *cause* (where it does not appear) in a way which will make some sense (though it may make bad sense, or be false). Thus, in (1) we may say that the sound of the bell caused the dog to salivate, and in (2) we may say that the absence of the sun is the "cause" of darkness. In (6) we may say the increase in temperature was caused by a rise in pressure; in (11) we may say that wishing causes what is wished to happen; in (18) we may say that the "cause" of his action in marrying her was his desire for her money; and so on.

This is not to argue that we would use *cause* in all these instances, but only that in one or another framework, each of these instances has found a causal interpretation, in some sense of *cause*. If we attempt to classify these alternative uses or interpretations, we may discover some of the classical and problematic concepts of cause that so upset Russell. But more important, we may then trace the senses of *cause* as they have entered into scientific frameworks and as they have been analyzed in philosophy.

For a first approximation, we may group these alternative concepts of cause in the following way:

(*a*) *Invariant association of one thing with another.* In the "whenever" instances, this is clearly the case. [(1) and (2).] Other instances imply this sort of association. [Try (4), (5), (6), (9), (11), (14), (16), (19) as an exercise in this interpretation.] But this is not unambiguous. For instance, in (1) the invariance is claimed to hold between something which happens first and is followed by some consequence, so that there is a temporal separation, or sequence between what we take to be cause and what we take to be effect. Yet in (6) we cannot say "first the pressure is increased, and then the temperature rises," *nor* can we say that if we *first* increase the temperature, *then* the pressure rises. Theoretically, we take pressure measurements and temperature measurements, in the Ideal Gas laws, as two ways of measuring the *same* thing, namely, the mean kinetic energy of the molecules of the gas, so that we take the increase of pressure with temperature to be simultaneous or coincident. The description *whenever* X *then* Y is sequential only in terms of what some experimenter may undertake to do: he may "first" turn up the temperature, and then observe the pressure, or vice versa. But even this is not clearly sequential: He may do both simultaneously. But there is a sense that he is doing or causing one thing to happen (when either he turns up the temperature or increases the pressure) and that he is observing the effect. For we do not take our observing to be causally efficacious, in the same way we do our acting. We may then distinguish between (*a*) *invariant sequence* (in which the invariance is a relation between something which takes place earlier, and some later consequence) and (*b*) *invariant coincidence* (in which two things are simultaneously coincident). In all cases, however, the kind of events about which such invariance may be asserted are recurrent; that is, they comprise a class of events, and not a single or unique instance. But the claim of invariance is *twofold:* the related events are said to be recurrent in the sense that they happen time after time. But further, they are said to recur in the same relation in each instance, i.e., as sequential or coincident. If there were no association in the recurrence—if bell-ringings were only randomly associated with salivations, or only irregularly so—then we would not have the example of causal relation which we take this to be.[2] As we have seen, invariant relation of this sort is what we take to be the subject of laws. Thus, in this interpretation, a causal relation is a relation expressible in some law-like statement in which such invariant association is asserted to hold. The law is taken to be true when the association it states holds in every factual instance without exception. Yet we have seen that if such an invariant association were to hold over only some small finite set of instances, or for only one unique instance, we would not want to call this a law. If we say that a law is true if every prediction generated by it is a true statement, then in the invariant-association view, we would want to require an indefinitely large domain of instances if we would avoid rendering this view trivial. If we said, for example, "For all instances of my waking up on the morning of June 12, 1966, the time is 7:17 A.M.," then we might formally claim that this represents an invariant association, and that the statement is true for every instance (namely, the one unique instance). Furthermore, the prediction that I will wake up at that time on that day will be true, if in fact I do (or did). If I were to say (whether or not I wake up on that morning, or whether or not it is known that I woke up on that morning), "If I *were* to wake on that morning, it *would* be that time," that is, if anything in the universe were an instance of my waking up, it would occur in accordance with this "law," then we might claim a certain universality for it, as an invariance which pertains to all the possible things which may be instances of it, even if there are no factual instances at all, or even if there is only one. We have seen in our discussion of laws the difficulties that "accidental universals" bring into play, and we have seen the distinctions which may be drawn between such cases which support a universal conditional and those which may be said to support a counterfactual conditional. The invariant-association view seems to raise these same difficulties with respect to those laws we want to call causal laws. The position which such a formulation takes seems midway between the accidental universal, made trivial by its miniscule domain as not properly a law at all and thus not causal either, and the strongest claims of the subjunctive- or counterfactual-supporting case.

[2] One sense in which organisms may be said to be "habit taking" is relevant here, however. In experimental psychology, when so-called variable-interval (VI) reinforcement schedules are used in animal-conditioning experiments, the animals come to make the "law-like" associations even under great variations in the relation between conditioned stimulus and reinforcement, though the rate of learning may be slower under such circumstances. So-called operant conditioning thus relies on such habit-taking propensities which range over widely variable conditions of association. See, for example, B. F. Skinner, *Science and Human Behavior* (New York: Macmillan, 1953), Chapters V through VIII, esp. pp. 99 ff., for an introductory account.

For in general, the commonsense interpretation of this view takes causality to be exhibited sufficiently by the fact of predictability over a wide or indefinitely large number of cases, all of them presumptively actual or actualizable. Thus there is no causality to be asserted concerning single instances, nor is the causal claim to range over possible but counterfactual cases. It eschews "possibility" in general as a troublesome domain, with respect to empirical laws. In summary, the invariant-association view takes causality to be a matter of lawfulness (over an unrestricted domain of facts) and lawfulness to be a matter of predictability, thus tying itself down to those instances in which predictions can come to be known to be true or false.

The job of science, in such a view, is to render subject to law what has been unpredictable in the past, thereby making it predictable. The growth of science is thus the increase in the scope of the predictable, or that which has been brought under law. Science, in this interpretation, smacks of that missionary urge to bring the heathen under the law, to civilize them. Thus, by this analogy, science is the attempt to civilize a recalcitrant nature which resists being made civil, by rendering it tractable to human prediction and control, under ever-widening laws.

(*b*) *Causal Ground: necessary condition, sufficient condition, and necessary and sufficient condition.* In a related but different framework, cause is conceived of as the source, or ground, or condition which gives rise to some consequence. Thus, (1) and (2) may be interpreted in this way too. But so may (3), where no invariant association is alleged. In (8) and (9), the emphasis is on something as an "underlying" cause, but in two different senses. In (8) the emphasis is on a *genetic* cause: something whose operations ultimately eventuate in some consequence, though a series of intervening events of causes. The sense of *origin* here stresses the beginning from which some later effect may be said to derive. With this is associated the notion of *generation, of bringing into existence*. In this sense, one interpretation of causality conceives of every causal instance in this way, so that, for example (14), (11), (10), (5), and many others may be conceived as instances in which something acting as an originative cause brings something else into existence, through some activity through time. In (9) complex states of matter are alleged to be the underlying cause in the sense of *simultaneously* or *continually* underlying some effect. Thus, such a "ground" is not originative in the sense of being the beginning of some chain of causes which eventuate in some effect, but as continuously upholding the existence of something taken as an effect; (9) may be interpreted originatively also, however, as when one says, "Consciousness first arose as the product of some complex organization of matter."

In our previous discussion of necessary and sufficient conditions (pp. 223 ff.) we distinguished between those antecedents which were present only when the consequents were also present; those consequents which were present only when the antecedents were present; and those antecedents and consequences which were never present one without the other. We characterized the first as "sufficient conditions," the second as "necessary conditions," and the last as both necessary and sufficient conditions. This "logic of conditions," as we saw, was an attempt to formulate the framework for inductive inferences which claimed causal relation, in the sense of universal and invariant association. We may then characterize different causal relations in these terms, distinguishing necessary from sufficient causes. Thus (2) alleges the setting of the sun as a sufficient condition of darkness, (suitably defined to exclude artificial lighting and so on); but if eclipses of the sun count, then sunsets are not a necessary condition of darkness. Similarly, in (1) the bell ringing is a sufficient condition of salivation, if conditioning is an all-or-none process (there are no "accidental" or random inhibitions of response) and if all other things are equal (e.g., the dog hasn't had the salivary gland removed). But it is not a necessary condition because the dog may salivate for other reasons as well. These distinctions, as we saw, provide the norms for certain inferences and guide experimental procedures (e.g., setting up of control groups). Because the conjunction of necessary and sufficient conditions supports an assertion of biconditional implication (X if and only if Y), then strictly universal laws would seem to make this sort of causal claim.[3] But this also gives rise to the notion of a relation between two events (which are necessary and sufficient conditions of each other, since as we saw, this relation is symmetrical) which is a "necessary" relation. One way of saying this is that the presence or occurrence of one event strictly determines the presence or the occurrence of the other.[4] If the Ideal Gas laws are true, then (6) would be an example of such a strict determinism. As we noted, the association here is one of invariant coincidence, so it is not clear how the relation of antecedent to consequent could be said to hold in such a case. But because the relation of necessary and sufficient condition is symmetrical, the antecedent and the consequent are logically interchangeable; or, for causal purposes, they are *equivalent*. In this view, strict determinism or this equivalence of cause and effect is the essential claim of the truly causal relation, distinguishing it from all others. Such a relation is precisely the one which we cannot uphold simply on empirical grounds alone. The alternative interpretations are (*a*) Such laws are ideal laws, and the necessity of the relation is a necessity only in the ideal formulation. It thus holds only in the logical relation among statements and is only hypothetically proposed. Since the form of definition is such that the relation between the *definiens* (that which defines) and the *definiendum* (that which is defined) is one of

[3] See pp. 224–25.

[4] This is a matter of natural or physical "necessity," not to be confused with logical necessity, i.e., a relation of entailment between *statements*. Still, as we shall see, such strict determinism has been taken to be isomorphic with formal notions of logical necessity, and thus to be expressible by such formulations.

equivalence, such laws are therefore "necessary," or statements of "necessary connection" by virtue of being definitional, and in this sense, analytic.

We shall examine these alternatives shortly. But let us note first the form in which the issues raised here have been classically stated. The first consideration of a ground or a causal ground raises the ontological question of bringing things into existence, or of supporting things in existence. Lucretius states it in this way: *Nil posse creari de nihilo* (Nothing can be created from nothing). In this form, it can hardly be called a law, because the postulate is that if we were to discover something whose originative cause we could not discover, we would conclude merely that we had not yet adequately explained or understood the phenomenon, and not that it arose spontaneously. The instructive instance is that of alleged miracles: the miracle is asserted not to have had any natural cause, and thus cannot be subsumed under a law of nature. But it is never assumed to have taken place spontaneously. Rather, it has a divine origin attributed to it, so that "God" causes it. And in the compulsion of rationality in even this extreme case, the miracle always has a reason, so that here too, the notion of "creation from nothing" is denied. In science this postulate finds its expression in two forms: in the principles of conservation (in which some quality or substance is neither created nor destroyed, but only undergoes transformations); and in the formal relation of equivalence, which the scholastic philosophers of the Middle Ages formulated as *causa aequat effectum* (The cause is equivalent to the effect.) This, we have seen earlier, is the case where the antecedent condition is both necessary and sufficient with respect to the consequent; and because this relation is symmetrical (see p. 140), the consequent is also a necessary and sufficient condition of the antecedent. If this logical relation, which attempts to explicate causal relation, is given an ontological interpretation, then it may be seen to express the anticreationist view that nothing can come from nothing. On the premise that everything has a cause, and the additional premise that there is nothing in the effect that is not in the cause, then existence cannot be "caused" or brought into being out of nonexistence. In terms of valid inference, this may be stated in the traditional form which asserts that there can be nothing in the conclusion of a valid inference that is not already "contained" in the premises. Quine has pointed out that *containment* in this sense is metaphorical and suffers from lack of clarity as to what precisely it means; yet on it is based the traditional distinction between analytic and synthetic statements. Thus, on this account, the predicate of the analytic statement is already "contained" in the subject, as part of its meaning, so that analysis yielding such statements which are true by inspection of meanings is an explication of the meaning already contained in the subject). The interpretation of this logical norm of analyticity as an ontological claim is by way of taking *existence* as what is "contained" in the premise from which an existential conclusion is derived; thus, one cannot have existence in the conclusion unless it is already in the premises.

If we demote the logical and ontological arguments here to the status of arguments about the "existing state of a system," so that *existence* is taken in a plain way as denoting what happens to be the case or, for a physical system, what happen to be the values of the variables in a description of the physical state of a system, then we may give this argument the following restricted interpretation: Given the laws of the system, the values of the state variables at any time t determine uniquely the values of the state-variables at any other time t' (predictively or retrodictively, because *time* simply comes to nothing but a change in the values of the variables in accordance with the laws of the system). Thus, nothing comes into existence which is not already "contained" in the state description of the system at any time, given the laws of the system. Inference within such a system would then appear to be a matter of effecting the transformations of these values such that every state of the system preserves the invariance which is given once any state of the system is given. A physical law would then be a universal statement giving the rule for generating the values of the state variables for any value of the time (or given our preceding account of time, generating the values of all of the state variables, given the change of values in any one of them). Such a system would be formally *strictly deterministic* and would embody the ontological assertion that nothing can be created out of nothing. LaPlace, formulating an imaginary model of such a system, writes, in his *Introduction to the Analytical Theory of Probability,*

> Let us imagine an Intelligence who would know at a given instant of time all forces acting in nature and the position of all things of which the world consists; let us assume further that this Intelligence would be capable of subjecting all these data to mathematical analysis. Then it could derive a result which would embrace in one and the same formula the motions of the largest bodies in the universe and of the slightest atoms. Nothing would be uncertain for this Intelligence. The past and the future would be present to its eyes.[5]

In such a strict determinism, there would be no unique event which was not included under some law; i.e., every so-called unique event would be one of a class of lawful events, determined by the whole state of the system, and not isolable. On such a postulate, even if some well-established deterministic scientific law broke down, failing to predict or explain some phenomena, there would in principle be a law, remaining to be formulated, under which the anomalous phenomena would find a strictly deterministic interpretation. This claims, in effect, that there are no chance or spontaneous events in nature. (In David Hume's phrase, " 'chance' is nothing but

[5] Pierre Simon, Marquis de LaPlace, *Introduction à la théorie analytique des probabilités, Oeuvres Complètes* (Paris, 1886), p. VI.

the expression of our ignorance of cause.") A quick perusal of some of the preceding instances, in this light, will show what sorts of problems this formulation raises. It says in effect that there are no contingent facts, given the state of the universe at any given instant. But this means that all relations among phenomena in the universe are such that everything is a necessary and sufficient condition of everything else. For example (20) as a "mistake" or an "unfulfilled intention" is as inevitable as fate, and the slip of the tongue is already *predetermined* by the state of the universe at any given instant. The confusion of *predetermination* with a *determinism* in which "all times are present," or which is time-independent, is one of the confusions which such a view presents on analysis. For nothing could be *pre*determined in the timeless or eternal "present" in which time is simply the local prejudice of one or another state of the system. Rather, such a determinism would be timeless (or tenseless, in its expressions), as, in Spinoza's striking phrase, *sub speciae aeternitatis* ("under the aspect of eternity"), and the notion of *pre-* or *post*determination would in effect be meaningless. The very distinction *cause* and *effect* then is abolished as being no more than relative to a particular standpoint which slices eternity from some one or another angle, and *causa aequat effectum* becomes more than a statement of equivalence; it becomes one of identity, and the causal principle is transformed into an identity principle. (The significance of this for science has been profoundly considered in Émile Meyerson's epochal study in philosophy of science, *Identity and Reality*.)

(*c*) *Contingent and Necessary Causal Connection.* A causal relation is said to be contingent when it could have been otherwise than it is. For example, in instance (3), ("He missed class because he was sick") where sickness is taken as the cause of missing class, it is conceivable (*a*) that one could have attended class even if one were sick or (*b*) that one might not have been sick at all. In (*a*) the causal relation is seen as contingent, and in (*b*) the cause itself is seen as contingent (or in traditional terms, the existence of the sickness is not necessary existence). Now suppose one missed class because one was 12,000 miles away at the time. In short, the excuse would be that it would have been impossible to get there on time. But such an "impossibility" is empirical, rather than logical, for it depends on the contingent facts that transportation through such a distance presently takes a finite time so large that it makes it a practical impossibility to attend class under these conditions. However, if one had died of the sickness, then clearly one could not have "attended class" in any conceivable sense (except the metaphorical one in which, for all the attention one paid or for all one learned while attending, one might as well have been dead). In this gruesome case, being dead would necessarily entail not attending class. This would seem to be a perfectly straightforward empirical impossibility; but then if we talk of *cause* in this way, we seem to have a case of necessary causation in an empirical instance. But this is not empirical in any straightforward sense, for if what we mean by *attending class* is taken as *being a living person in the classroom,* then being unable to attend class under these circumstances would follow analytically.

In instance (12) (p. 292) a causal relation is alleged between a number of historical factors, as causes, and some outcome. Yet we may conceive that Hitler's rise to power was not inevitable, even under the circumstances described in the example. We may conceive, however, that the very circumstances which allegedly led inevitably to Hitler's rise to power were not themselves inevitable, i.e., not necessary but contingent. That is, had other things been different, then these events would themselves have occurred differently, or not at all. Such a contingent determinism or conditional determinism then says that if antecedent circumstances are of a certain sort, then consequents follow on them in a deterministic way. Leaving aside the question of whether antecedents could have been different, such a view says that under certain conditions, something follows inevitably. The weaker claim is that if the antecedents do in fact occur, then in fact what follows is determined by them. The stronger claim, as we have seen in the discussion of laws of nature, is the subjunctive or counterfactual one: Although the antecedent circumstances never happen in fact, or have not happened in fact, if they were to happen, then the consequences would occur. Even in this form, however, the statement is conditional. It does not claim that the consequences would happen no matter what, but conditionally, if the antecedents were to be the case.

In a strict determinism, like that outlined here, one could claim that every particular event was itself strictly determined, and so the chain of causal determinations is such that the confluence of these events was also strictly determined. Thus, all causality would be necessary connection and there would be no "accidents." A modification of this view of necessary causal chains holds that the accident is the confluence of independent causal chains, each one strictly determined, but in the economy of a pluralistic nature, not *inter*determined. Thus, for example, an automobile accident involving two causal chains—i.e., involving the mechanical causality of the machines involved and the human causality of intentions, goals, characteristics of the drivers, and so on—is such that the arrival at the same spot at the same time by the two autos is, from the standpoint of any one of the causal chains, an accidental event. Thus A is causally determined to be at place P at time t, and B is causally determined to be at place P at time t, so that by conjunction, A and B are each causally determined to be at place P at time t. But there is no causal chain in which A and B are both determined to be at P at time t, so that chain A and chain B are mutually independent.

Here a distinction should be made between what might be called "fatalistic determinism" and "contingent determinism." If we say that something is "fatally inevitable," then in one interpretation, this may mean that no matter what anyone does, the outcome will be the same. Thus, whether or not one acts in a certain way, some destined outcome will inevitably come to pass. But it may be seen that this brand of fatalism is not deterministic at all, for if it does not matter at all what the antecedent circumstances are, then the necessary connection between events is broken off completely. Paradoxically (if one calls such fatalism "determinism") this view holds that determinism is assured if all causal antecedents are no more than random or chance events, which happen without causal efficacy, and even without causal determination; that is, such events or actions are neither determined nor determining, but the outcome is independently fully determinate. This sort of fatalism is therefore better called a brand of indeterminism, and holds that we are helpless to direct action in a world without rhyme or reason; we may either act or not act, for in either case what will happen will happen. The rigorous pursuit of this view to its final consequences goes one step further: outcomes are themselves wholly random, so that the "fatalism" is turned inside out, so to speak. No matter what one does, or whatever happens, anything at all may eventuate. (*Alice in Wonderland* and *Through the Looking Glass* constitute studies of such a world, and some of the moods of despair of early postwar existentialism envisioned the world in this way.)

The classical Greek view of Fate as some irreparable destiny is different from this, however, for here it is the ignorance of the determination of our actions or of the necessity of nature that leads us to conceive human action as helpless in the face of destiny. Given some initial state, or some action, every subsequent state or action is taken to be fully determined or inevitable. That is, we are helpless to act otherwise than as we do. Such a fatalism does not claim that it does not matter what we do, but that whatever we do is fully determined in a way which we do not, in our ignorance, know or understand, and are thus helpless to control. Thus, in *Oedipus Rex,* Oedipus acts in ignorance of the determination of his action, or without knowledge of the circumstances which lead him to fulfill the prophecy step by step. He acts unconsciously, therefore. His passage to revelation comes when he comes to understand all of his past actions in their deterministic form. His fatal pride, his *hubris,* is his ignorance of this determinism. Here then is a case of strict determinism, in which contingency is only the appearance of things to our finite view, but underlying this contingency is the necessity of the "real" nature of things, which a fuller or complete knowledge would reveal.

This enters into scientific concepts of laws, when these are taken as the limits with respect to which our scientific formulations are approximations. But again, the conditions of our knowledge of necessary and sufficient conditions are such that we can never exhaust the possibilities of contingency; thus, we are never warranted empirically in asserting more than a belief that something is both a necessary and sufficient condition of something else. But the claim for scientific laws is precisely this claim, when they are stated in strictly universal form. And this has led a number of philosophers and scientists to separate the grounds for this claim from the grounds of our empirical knowledge; thus, to separate the conditional statement of laws, from the unconditional postulate of causality in the two forms we gave above in (*b*) ("Nothing comes from nothing," and "the cause is equivalent to the effect"), and thus to distinguish between *law* and *cause,* as we shall see.

(*d*) *Causality as a relation of functional dependency.* The view that causality is a relation of functional dependency reduces the force of the claims in paragraphs (*b*) and (*c*), and claims instead to formalize only the weaker claim in (*a*). In (*b*) and (*c*), talk of "originative causes," or "grounds," or "necessity" is taken to derive from an earlier metaphorical or qualitative interpretation of the causal relation. But all such allegations introduce "occult qualities," which are redundant in the explication of exactly what it is we do claim in such instances. A functional-dependency relation is one in which the values of two variables are said to be related in some law-like formulation. If it is a mathematical or formal statement of the sort $y = f(x)$, then its force is purely formal or empirically empty, and derives from the system within which it is framed—on its axioms, definitions, formation and transformation rules, and so on. If one finds an empirical interpretation for this function, well and good; then it can be used as the adequate description or the economical summary of a domain of facts and finds its "justification" in successful prediction, and in all the other ways in which hypotheses are warranted or supported. But the claim is no more than that for a certain range of values for a variable, there is discovered an invariant relation, in recurrent instances, between these values and the values of other variables. Mathematical laws formulated in this way make no ontological claims about "real" or "necessary" causal relation, but reduce this relation either to the "necessity" of a formal deductive system, empty of content, or to the contingent interpretations of that system for a domain of observed or measured values. An instance of such a relation that can be rendered in mathematical terms would be (6). However, most of the other instances cannot be so rendered, not because we know something more about them, which makes them "really causal," but because we do not know enough about them to be able to formulate the functional dependencies in cogent terms. We might hypothesize, in this way, however: for example, we might say, of (12), that (where *H* stands for *rise of Hitler,* and the other factors are suitably abbreviated): $H = f(I, U, R, S, F)$. But in order to generalize this in some law-like way, we would have to say, "Whenever there is a conjunction of unemployment, revanchist feelings, and so on, then there will be the rise to power of a Hitlerian type." Here the problem of the restriction on the operant variables is very great, and the number of recurrent instances in history of such a confluence is very small, unless we abstract these conditions very severely. In physics it is precisely such abstraction, and such (idealized) isolation of the parameters of a system, that permits formulations of functional dependency. In cases of unique occurrence, as one might take (8) to be, or in cases where we know the relation has as many falsifying as confirming instances (as we might in 3, 5, 7, 11, 13, 14, 16, 18, 20, 21), such a formulation would be of no avail. But if causality is eliminated in any other terms but functional dependency, this would mean one of two things: these other relations are not causal because they cannot be formulated in this way, or these relations may or may not be causal, but we have no clear way of determining this as yet; which is to say, these are not yet fit subjects for scientific formulation in terms of laws, and so remain in the domain of common sense. The paradigm of statements of functional dependency is the mathematical form of differential equations. Thus, in such formulas as that for force, $F = m(d^2x/dt^2)$, or for distance of free fall through some time, $s = \frac{1}{2}(d^2x/dt^2)t^2$, the term for acceleration is given as such a functional dependency of change of rate (of velocity) with respect to time. Causality is scientifically formulable, then, when it can be formulated in this way. Otherwise, if we take this view in its strongest form, we make a claim to causal relation for which there is no worthy validation procedure. Russell's point, semantically, is that physicists do not use the term *cause* in physics, but make do with differential equations. By this he means that the conceptions of cause that go along with ordinary uses are thus eschewed by the working physicist. He thus avoids the animistic and anthropomorphic conceptions that the ordinary uses carry along with them. But this is to claim that the physicist never conceives of what he is doing other than in terms of the mathematical descriptions and laws he uses, and thus separates the formalism of physics from its interpretation. It is not at all clear at what point of interpretation the physicist ceases being a physicist and becomes an anthropomorphic, animistic user of the language like the rest of us. Or more distressing yet, it is not clear when he stops being a scientist and becomes a metaphysician. Russell seems to suggest that the only safety here is in numbers. But it is only the interpretation of differential equations that makes physics what it is, rather than mathematics. Here we must let the problem lie.

(*e*) *One-many, many-one, and one-one causal relation.* In some of the instances what seems distinctive is that some one event is associated with some other in the relation. Thus, in (4) and (5) (the malaria and lung-cancer examples), it is the singling out of the *one* event or thing which is distinctively associated with the other, among all the possibilities, that makes the discovery of a connection important. This is also true in (7), (13), and (18), for example. Yet in (12) we spoke of a *confluence* of causes converging on a single event. And in (10) we take the intrusion of a single event as the cause of a complex of subsequent events. Part of this is semantic, in the sense that we may if we wish, classify *chain reaction* as a single (though complex) event, and we may take a neutron (or the whole situation of a neutron bombardment of a nucleus) as a complex (though single) event. We may thus transform one-many and many-one relations into one-one relations by tampering with what we mean by *one* and *many*. But the distinction between one event and many alternative but exclusive consequences is not the same situation. (I may force the issue by claiming that the class of mutually exclusive alternative consequences is an "event" class, in causal analysis, but this causes problems in our usual sense of *event,* as we shall see.) Suppose that for a given antecedent event, the calculated statistical probabilities of alternative outcomes are given in some law. Would the law then be causal? If I say, for example, that a throw of a fair die has six equipossible outcomes, am I then denying causal relation? In one, sense, the event-class (1, 2, 3, 4, 5, 6) is fully determined in as strict a way as Laplace could have demanded. (Remember, his imaginary model comes from the introduction to a treatise on probability.) One could then say, "It is impossible that any values other than these will be associated with the toss of a die." The determination of the unique event of one of these values showing up (and clearly, the necessary exclusion of the others in this instance) is, however, beyond the statement of the law. If we take this as a case of one-many "causality," then causality may be understood to contain chance within itself in such a context. What is "causal," on such an interpretation, is that a class of events, with infinitely many members, is strictly determined by the law, or is its unique domain. In other words, such statistical probabilites (of the *a priori* sort or of the relative-frequency sort) apply not to individual events, but only to a run of recurrent events of the same kind (and hence the need for the definition *fair die* or *fair sample,* and for the experimental controls on the conditions of the trials). What is not causal, in such an interpretation, is that the causal law does not hold for individual occurrences, or is meaningless on such an application. But then, *a single throw of the die* is undefined, as a unique occurrence, and is replaced by *any single throw of a die,* so that this is in effect a causal relation between one *class* of events and another, rather than between events and events, or events and classes of events. The randomness or indeterminacy of the unique or single event in itself is merely an assertion that the law does not have anything to say about this single event, rather than that the law is not a causal law. This would be like claiming that the color of Galileo's bronze ball, in the inclined-plane experiments, is a random or noncausal "event" or "property" because the law of falling bodies does not predict what the color will be.[6] We shall return to this when we discuss indeterminacy, in the next chapter.

6 One may infer, as in the case of the limited values of the die, that the ball will be *some* color. But this is an inference that falls outside the law, as it does also in the die example. It derives from the assumption that the ball is a solid body, reflects light of certain wavelengths, absorbs others, and so on, just as, in the die example, the assumption is that it is a six-sided and not a twelve-sided die. We may infer from the mathematical proof that there are only five regular convex solids, that the number

Statistical laws of an empirical sort, based on inductive inferences from the stability of a relative frequency (see p. 228) represent a related problem. If these laws are based on invariant frequencies (within certain limits of invariance, for example, convergence toward a limit), then these laws also do not predict for unique events, but only over the range of all observable instances. The question arises whether they are causal laws. If we define *causal* in terms of strict determinism, then the question arises as to what we take the events to be, which the law relates. If these are the individual instances of observation, then the law is not strictly determinist; however, at the level of its semantic reference, which is to *classes* of particular events, it makes the same claim of determinism and has the same empirical conditions of contingency as any ideal law interpreted for an empirical domain, in terms of measurement. Here the considerations of approximative measurement, tolerance, and measurement error enter. But this enters into every consideration of the empirical testing or interpretation of a law. Auguste Comte's opinion was that measurement beyond a certain precision would tend to break down the validity of those laws which had been discovered and were useful in their ideal and approximate versions (where approximation was within limits close enough to warrant the ideal formulation without distress). He therefore held that further precision would be pernicious to science. Modern science has clearly rejected this advice. But it has therefore reformulated much of its causal concept to accord statistical generalizations a fully law-like character. But note that if statistical laws apply only to classes of events, deterministically, then unique events seem to fall outside the law, in their particular occurrences. If there is no stated invariance for the unique events, then they seem to be indeterminate or random, within the limits of some finite possibilities. Thus, it is statistically determinate that rain will fall on a city within a given time (say, half a year), but as the time interval decreases, it is less determinate that it will fall within some small interval (say, between 2:30 and 2:31 p.m. on a given day). Similarly, we may say that rain will fall in a certain area, but the probability that it will fall evenly everywhere is low. We know that the "center" of the rainstorm will receive the densest distribution of raindrops, and that the periphery will receive a scattering that is less dense. Does this mean that the individual raindrops follow some pattern or law of distribution? For one thing, we define *center* and *periphery* in terms of the distribution, so that this would hardly seem to legislate for the raindrops and seems circular or definitional. The probability distribution is then an empirical function of how raindrops fall, which describes not the single raindrops, but the pattern.

---

of possible outcomes of die tosses (where dice have to be regular convex solids to meet some empirical condition of fairness) is limited to the sets 4, 6, 8, 12, and 20; similarly, from other physical and theoretical considerations, we may infer that the color of the bronze ball will be one among a (large) number of discrete wavelengths within the confines of the visible spectrum.

Does this mean, however, that the path of a single drop is a "random" path? Or that the raindrop's motion is not a case of causal relation among individual conditions which determine this path? Here two alternative interpretations suggest themselves. In such a probability distribution, in accordance with a statistical law, we may say that the statistical formulation merely sums up the individual causal relations, which are unmanageable and unformulable because of the number of variables; but here the assumption remains that each particular event has its own unique causal description, and upon isolation, we could determine this. But we may also say that the behavior of the whole *system* of raindrops has causal effect upon the path of each individual raindrop. In effect, the statistical law acts as a causal law, describing a pattern which as a whole affects the individual events, as if the pattern itself were a causal "event" (complex but singular) interacting with its own elements.

Here the relation of "wholes" and "parts" enters into the problem of analyzing causal relation. We may say, for example, that if, in (16), *nervousness* is the state of the whole system, then *stammering* is a product or a consequence of this state; but then we may also say that the individual event of stammering increases the nervousness of the whole system which feeds back into increased stammering. Here the condition of a whole complex system interacts with its elements, in a causal "loop," or in some retroactive relation. This introduces another distinction then.

(*f*) *Retroactive causality*. In (16) and (17) (p. 292) a whole system is seen to be involved in a closed retroactive causal relation. In (16) as we noted, what we might take as a symptom of nervousness becomes itself a cause of increased nervousness. We do not ordinarily think of symptoms as causally efficacious, but as the adjuncts or appearances of some state. But in this example, as in others, we may say that stammering causes increased nervousness as well as that nervousness causes increased stammering. Such a positive feedback loop represents a distinctive causal relation, if we regard it as a general or law-like feature. In (17) we have a negative feedback loop, in which the relation of valve to pressure maintains a more or less steady state of some system, instead of a direction, as in (16). If (16) proceeds, presumably some limit of intelligibility or of nervousness will be reached, at which point the system will break down. Stammering and nervousness have limits; however, we may conceive "open" systems, where such a "positive feedback" may go on indefinitely, as long as there is available energy for such a build-up. Thus, population increase, evolutionary development, and other such systems as may be represented as progressive series, may be characterized as such "positive feedback systems," constrained when there is a limit on available energy needed for such increase, or when other negative features enter into the picture. Traffic jams and nervous breakdowns represent positive feedback systems in which such retroactive causality leads to a breakdown in a system which has certain critical limits.

In negative feedback systems the retroactive causal relation is such that the system is held within certain limits. Stable populations, in which population increase is controlled by limited food supply, as in the ecological balance which is achieved in some natural situations (in ponds, in forests, and so on), may be represented as systems with built-in "regulators" or controls. A thermostat is such a negative-feedback system, as is the homeostatic balance of living organisms. In such systems, because the state of the system as a whole seems to establish a norm to which the parts conform, it seems as if the system as a whole has some regulative or normative effect on the individual elements within it. If this is interpreted as a law-like relation among elements which merely exhibits some overall pattern with a certain invariance, then this is another case of lawfulness, with the one difference that the relation is one of invariant or statistically ordered succession, in which antecedents and consequents are temporally separate but in which a consequence becomes an antecedent for that same class of events which was *its* antecedent. Therefore, this law-like relation is described as retroactive or as a loop. But the description of some normal state of the system which is maintained by this interaction seems to suggest that the system has some "preferred state" or some end which all of the parts subserve. As we have seen, in discussing biological functions, this sort of functional description in terms of "sakes" for which things operate raises questions about the nature of the lawfulness here. It appears as if parts of a whole operate under the causal influence of some such "ideal state" or for the sake of some end, such as homeostasis. The confusion arises here from alleging that this entails, on the part of the component elements of the system, some *awareness* of the end which is being subserved. The causal agency seems to be some "end in view" which operates on the parts of the whole. But such an end state, is presumably in the future, or is otherwise not temporally present in the causal situation. Thus, such systems are described as "goal-directed" or "end-directed" where it would seem that the goal or end would somehow have to be envisioned in order to operate "from the future into the present." Such allegedly teleological causation therefore bespeaks some conscious relation, which it seems hard to attribute to parts of organisms, for example. Because of its association with characteristics of organisms, or with the allegedly causal efficacy of an organization or structure as a whole, such causal relation has also been characterized as "organic" or "structural"; and by association with the study of the effect of "wholes" on parts, in perception and in psychological studies of behavior, this has also been characterized as holist, and as Gestaltist (where *Gestalt* is the technical term for the aspect of whole-structure or configuration).

The account of such retroactive causality in straightforward mechanical terms in accordance with mathematizable laws of regulative "feedback" to some mechanism so constructed as to maintain a "steady state" or *homeostasis* (as in thermostats, or homing devices, or guided missiles) has been developed in the science of cybernetics. Here, the mystery of ends-in-view dissolves under the analysis of such self-regulating mechanisms as law-ordered physical systems, in which retroactive causality means just that the system is so structured that there are loops which close it upon itself in the transmission of cause and effect. But all such systems require an input of energy to operate, and of information on which to "act," and in this sense they are "open" systems.

(*g*) *Causal relation as action by contact, action at a distance, and sympathetic action.* Perhaps the most basic and elementary notion we have of causal relation is that of action. Many of the problems raised in the previous characterizations have their sources in the interpretation of this mode of relation. If we take the immediate experience of causal efficacy to be that of human action, then we have several features of such action which are immediately apparent: (*a*) The action which we undertake involves a feeling of effort. (*b*) It involves some self-awareness therefore, of something like a decision, or an act of will, and on reflection, is understood to be undertaken with respect to some end, or with some motive, or intention, or something for which we could give a reason. (*c*) In acting upon something, our effect seems to be achieved by physical contact, and in particular, by touch-contact (in terms of which we may then interpret "contact" by sight or hearing or by the other senses). The general tendency to explain in terms of human analogies gives many early accounts of causal relation in nature similar features, so that the action of anything upon anything else is conceived on the model of human action, and all relations taken to be causal are conceived in terms of actions. The feature of this action is that it is continuous in the intervening interval between cause and effect, i.e., there is no "gap" between the causal action and the caused effect.

To say that an explanation is anthropomorphic is not to say that it is wrong, however. One might argue that we are familiar with ourselves and our actions in a way which predates our familiarity with natural causal relation and that anthropomorphism is therefore a fundamental and ineradicable condition of our understanding of nature. An alternative view claims that we become aware of ourselves as natural human beings (i.e., as part of nature) by assimilating what we learn of natural causal relations in the conception we have of human action. That is, so-called anthropomorphism already embodies a prior and more fundamental concept of nature, so that instead of reading ourselves into nature, we read nature into ourselves; instead of being a simple case of foisting the human image upon nature it may well be the foisting of a natural image upon our humanity in this regard.

With due regard to such cautions, it yet seems clear that much of what we foist upon natural causal relation is characteristically like human action, particularly that aspect of action which has to do with will, effort, motive, intention, and reason. The metaphors of a "living" and "feeling" nature, especially where they characterize causal models, are therefore called *animistic*. (The term comes from *anima*—"living principle" or "principle of self-activity"—as we saw in our discussion of the Greeks.)

All this is by way of characterizing three major alternative accounts of causal relation in terms of action: action by contact, action at a distance, and sympathetic action. Among the examples on p. 292, (13) is an instance of the ordinary notion of action by contact. The rock strikes the glass and breaks it. The effect is the direct result of an *impact;* but the concept of *impact* contains two elements, contact and force. It thus is akin to both our experience of acting by touch-contact, and our experience of effort. On the other hand the example concerning gravitational force (15) is an instance of action at a distance. In classical celestial mechanics, Newton's space is not a medium through which there is physical transmission of action by successive contact. If space were a field, or contained a field, in the sense we discussed in talking of Faraday's introduction of the field concept for electricity, then action by contact would be maintained. The history of field theories goes back to the ancient Greeks, and the argument over the existence of a void, (see Chapter 4, pp. 76 ff.) is involved in much of this. But in the Newtonian account, gravitational force acts through empty space, at a distance, without a medium. Another aspect of this is that it acts instantaneously, not by causal transmission through time. Yet in our mechanical models and demonstration experiments of this gravitational force, and of inertial force, we often put strings and rods and springs into the empty space in order to picture this action at a distance as if it were action by contact. This is very interesting, for it betrays the uneasiness we have with action at a distance, for it doesn't accord with the common experience of action. Yet even in primitive accounts, action at a distance is countenanced, especially in connection with dreams and magic. Here the disembodied spirit acts without the medium of the body (which is the foundation of ordinary conceptions of contact, as extended substance in space). The "spirit," however, also takes on some quasibodily character (for example, as "ectoplasm," or as "spiritual body") in order to act, repeating the feature of the string and rod models, which are also "as if it were the case" instances. In magic the "contact" is often by something akin to feeling. Feeling responds to feeling in human action and therefore, also in physical action. Thus, much magic "causal" influence is based on some such notion as sympathetic or "homeopathic" action. An instance of this is (14), ("Wishing will make it so"). The paradigm of magical action is given here: the wish become reality by its own force, without mediation. All this might be interesting enough in itself. But it concerns us here as providing the background of the development of scientific conceptions of causality. In Russell's view, which we cited at the beginning of this chapter, it is this kind of causal conception which he wants to replace with differential equations. The charge is that action models of causal relation fail, then, because they are either opaque or redundant. They are opaque in that we cannot come to know that such a relation exists between natural events and thus we interpose it in the interests of imagination and to the detriment of pure reason. (This is the fault charged against the use of models in science. Duhem is especially severe on this point; see *op. cit.*, pp. 69 ff.) They are redundant in that all the information we can have of causal relation may be represented or summarized without the model, so that Ockham's razor operates here to get rid of unnecessary entities.

Still, the natural habit is to picture causal relation in terms of the primary features of one or another action model. For one thing, we think of causal relation as a "real" connection between things, in terms of some production of effects by causes: contact and effort, again. For another, we maintain the requirement of continuity, in denying causal "gaps"; for otherwise, some events would take place "out of nothing" or spontaneously. These elude both our decision and our control, and thus they cannot be ordered by law. We also conceive of a lawful nature as the only proper object of a rational science: what cannot be ordered by law is beyond the scope of scientific understanding or human control. The postulate here, though not one directly concerning *action,* is related to the kind of action we take to be rational: nothing happens without a reason sufficient to account for it. Here especially the confusion of an *account* with what the account is *of* is at the surface: a requirement of sufficient reason is the demand of rationality for a nature in which nothing happens without sufficient *cause.*

The failure of intentions, and mistaken reasons, are represented in examples (20) and (21). But these are precisely what an ideally rational nature is incapable of. Diderot, speaking in terms of the perfect model which nature holds up to art (in terms characteristic of some eighteenth-century aesthetics), writes, *La Nature ne fait rien d'incorrect.* ("Nature never makes a mistake.") Mistakes are human; and nature on this account, is divine. Leibniz phrased this in terms of a principle of sufficient reason: nature could not act except with sufficient reason. This is the claim of rationalistic science that nothing in nature is ultimately hidden from rational knowledge; everything can be ordered according to law, therefore. Thus, a principle of rational action becomes the requisite condition for rational knowledge of this action. Otherwise, there would be pockets of what would be forever unknowable to science.

Thus, this account of the various interpretations of causal relation (which does not intend to be complete or exhaustive) leads us finally to the philosophical questions concerning the status of the principle of causality in science.

LEIBNIZIAN, HUMEAN, AND KANTIAN APPROACHES TO THE PRINCIPLE OF CAUSALITY

We may briefly summarize the alternative positions which arise in the foregoing analysis in this way:

1. *Causality is a principle of Being.* Causal description concerns the revelation of the objective nature of things. The physicist David Bohm writes in this regard, "The causal laws that a thing satisfies constitute a fundamental and inseparable aspect of its *mode of being.*[6]
2. *Causality is lawfulness.* A causal relation is one in which a warranted law of science is affirmed, on the basis of generalization from experience. Lawfulness, in turn, is predictability, and this is supported by warranted assertions of matter-of-fact invariances in experience, in the form of laws.
3. *Causality is a postulate.* Causality is a necessary *synthetic a priori* supposition which cannot be justified simply by inductive empirical generalization, but is required as the condition for the possibility of rational knowledge. It is therefore the postulate of postulates of science, for it underlies the very possibility of there being any science. Ontologically, it is the assertion of the continuity and the uniformity of nature; epistemologically, it is the assertion that something can come to be known only under the form of law; but this is not derived from our knowledge of laws. Rather, it is the presupposition that this knowledge is possible and is not illusory.

The first claim that causality is a principle of Being is the most clearly ontological, or metaphysical. It is an outright assertion about the nature of things, and in this sense represents the most classical realist position: what we come to know in the way of causal relation is the way things are, the way they are objectively related in nature, or in reality. This is the most common attitude among scientists, and in this they share some such belief with nonscientists. Its elaboration involves aspects that get taken up in the subsequent views (2) and (3), however. The test of whether we know the way things are is either fundamentally *empirical* (the product of our experience, and justified by nothing more than this experience; therefore finite and contingent even in this most general claim) or it is fundamentally *rational.* (We know that nature is causally ordered because it is rationally inconceivable that it should be otherwise.) The force of this claim is not that one cannot imagine it otherwise, but that to imagine it otherwise is to admit that nature cannot be rationally known.

The most striking attack upon the classical rationalist notion of causality as the necessary connection of things (on the model of mathematical neces-

[6] *Causality and Chance in Modern Physics* (New York: Harper, 1961), p. 14

sity which dominated Newtonian science and its popular interpretations) is that of David Hume. All we can know in experience, says Hume, is the constant conjunction of experienced properties. If, whenever we see lightning, we then hear thunder, all we can know empirically is that thunder has constantly been conjoined with lightning in past experience. Of a "real" or "necessary" causal relation we can know nothing, for we do not experience something called *the causal relation,* but only the lightning and the thunder; and necessity is a relation which no degree of inductive generalization can attain to, because the empirical possibility of a failure of conjunction in an as yet unexperienced instance is always there. All matter-of-fact relations (i.e., those which come to be known in experience) are therefore contingent and not necessary. They may, in some instance, conceivably occur other than as they have in the past. Yet, says Hume, we always tend to attribute causal or necessary connection to such events; and he asks why, when there are no "visible grounds of support." Because, he answers, we are naturally disposed to do so. The mind is a habit-forming mechanism; associations of ideas become reinforced with repetition, so that we naturally expect those conjunctions of phenomena we have experienced in the past to occur in the same way in the future. Thus, laws are nothing but expressions of habits of expectation, which are congenital to the kind of structure or organ the mind is. Causality, then, cannot be asserted to exist in nature on any other than psychological grounds—that we tend to form habits of expectation. (Hume calls such habits "fictions of the imagination," which has confused many interpreters. *Fiction* does not mean *lie;* it means, in Hume's context, something constructed by the imagination, as a matter of the natural action or disposition of the mind.) Thus, in effect, causality is nothing but the connection which the mind imposes between things which have recurrently been experienced in conjunction. Causality and the empirical affirmation of laws on inductive grounds are therefore one and the same operation of the mind, going beyond experience in accordance with its natural mode of operation. Thus, Hume does not say we are wrong to believe causal relations exist; he says we are wrong to conceive of them as something more than beliefs. That is, he disclaims any ontological status for causality which goes beyond empirically warranted belief. But as belief is always contingent, causal relation cannot be regarded as somehow necessary.

The butt of Hume's criticism is the classic rationalism which claimed causality as a necessity of reason, and thus *also* a necessity of being. In the rationalist view, especially in that elaboration of it which developed side by side with the great successes of mathematical physics in the seventeenth century, the natural world was a mathematically perfect construction, as the new laws of science revealed it to be. On theological grounds, orthodox or deist, it was the creation of a geometer-God, exhibiting His perfection to our intellects. Therefore, the relations in this perfect cosmos are those which a perfect mathematical reconstruction would display. The "necessity" of mathematics is thus the necessity of world relations as well. Galileo held such a view, as did Descartes, Spinoza, and Leibniz. Newton was profoundly influenced by the Platonic tradition in which mathematics was the expression of the formal perfection of things. For the empiricist Hume, this claim was entirely too *a priori.* That the mind may be so inclined that it would tend to think this way he was perfectly willing to agree. But this needed to be explained in terms of the psychological sources of such an inclination to believe. And here the psychological account finds the sources of this belief in the natural habits of the mind. In this sense, Hume was the first modern pragmatist.

Kant, who was deeply disturbed by Hume's critique, rallied to the defense of Newtonian science, but with Hume's critique in view. True, Kant admitted, belief was in fact contingent, and thus a belief in necessity was a contingent belief, in the sense that no more could be claimed for it on the side of the empirical sources of belief. But the natural habits of the mind reveal, in the very fact of their being *natural* habits, an innate structure of conception. The forms under which the mind could come to know things was, as a natural disposition, also a necessary disposition. That is, having minds such as these, there is no other possible way in which we could conceive of things. There is then a formal necessity to believe as we do in fact believe, for these forms of possible belief are universal among men as rational beings; they are the universal forms of reason, so that it is inconceivable that any rational being whatever could conceive things differently. Thus, Hume's critique is turned back upon itself and its fullest consequences are derived by Kant. For Kant, then, there are *a priori* forms, under which our empirical knowledge comes to be known by us: with respect to our sense perception, these forms are the *a priori* forms of space and time. They are *a priori* in the sense that the very possibility of perceptual experience presupposes them. With respect to the understanding, the mind requires an act of synthesis: to understand is to draw things together under some unity. This synthesis or unification consists in conceiving the disparate elements of perceptual experience under the form of relation grasped by the understanding. Thus the presupposition of such a synthesizing relation is the necessary condition for the very possibility of understanding. One aspect of this is the identity of the understanding; it is one and the same (self-identical) understanding which is the ground for pulling things together in this synthesis. The other aspect is the act of synthesis effected by this identical (or self-identical) consciousness. Thus, a manifold is ordered under this form of the understanding; a *this* is conditionally related to a *that* in one and the same act of consciousness. In short, experience can come to be had only under the condition of its being ordered under the forms of space and time; it can come to be *known* or *understood* only under the form of causality, where causality is the synthesis or unification of a manifold under the identity of an act of consciousness. Thus, causality is the presupposition which underlies the very possibility of our scientific knowledge of the empirical world (or of *phenomena,* in Kant's term). In this sense, Kant also can claim that this is the basis of the objectivity of our knowledge, for it is only under these conditions that knowledge is possible.

Because these are universal (or "transcendental") conditions, they underwrite the objective nature of this knowledge, which is such that any knower whatever could have knowledge only under these terms. Thus, *objective* means "universally intersubjective." What things are like, apart from the conditions under which we can come to know them, is something we obviously cannot come to know. Thus, some real or ultimate causality in the relation between *things-in-themselves* is unknowable. Only *things-as-they-are-for-us* constitute the domain of our empirical or phenomenal knowledge. But here causality is the condition of our coming to understand them. Empirically, all we are given is a manifold, an unordered collection of spatio-temporal appearances. From these alone we could never arrive at a law, which asserts invariant relations among some of these phenomena. The lawfulness of phenomena is not something we discover empirically, then. The ground for our assertions of lawful relation is the *a priori* condition for understanding, the unification of a manifold under a concept. The concept under which the mind then orders the manifold as an instance of necessary association is causality. Because this concept is not derived from experience, it is *a priori;* it gives the rule to experience, insofar as experience enters into the understanding. Thus, we may be said to discover laws, but only on the presupposition of lawfulness, without which we would be left only with a manifold of appearances without any necessary connection.[7] Starting as Hume does from a critique of the epistemological conditions of our knowledge of cause, Kant thus makes Hume's "natural disposition of the mind" into a "necessary precondition for knowledge."

For both Hume and Kant, then, causality is not an inductive generalization, but explains or underlies our inductive generalizations: for Hume, as a habit of the imagination and for Kant, as an *a priori* rule of the understanding. John Stuart Mill, on the other hand, explains it as the most general of our inductive generalizations, which is recurrently confirmed in every instance of inductive generalization that we assert, and thus has the widest evidence to support it. We saw, in Chapter 9, that Mill proposed to make this generalization into a premise for any inductive inference, as supporting or justifying induction. We saw that this formulation has notorious difficulties, landing in circularity and justifying induction by appeal to induction.

[7] See especially *Critique of Pure Reason,* tr. N. Kemp-Smith (New York: St. Martin's Press, 1961), pp. 124–25, 138–40, and 218–32 (Second Analogy).

The long history of the causal principle thus fashions it and refashions it, adapts it, disguises it, reinterprets it under various names, and even eliminates it. The alternatives are closely related to those we discussed in Chapter 10. On the one hand, causality is not simply another empirical law. Nor does it simply seem to be a higher-level law from which empirical laws may be deduced. Nor can it be said to be a law of laws in Mill's sense, without confusion or circularity. Is it a habit? Is it a postulate? Does it function not as a statement about reality, but as a regulative idea for thought? Is it merely the most useful of a number of pragmatically entertained methodological principles? Is it an animistic leftover from a bygone age, carrying the pernicious influences of anthropomorphism with it? Is it instead an article of faith in the rationality of nature, or in the unlimited scope of scientific knowledge? Is it merely lawfulness or predictability under another name? Or by contrast to laws, which always distinguish between antecedents and consequences, is it a principle of identity in consciousness, synthesizing a manifold in the "transcendental unity of apperception" that Kant speaks of? (In this sense, Meyerson, in one of the most sustained analyses of the causal concept, distinguishes *law* from *cause*.[8]) Does it then go beyond lawfulness to assert the identity at the limit where cause and effect are equivalent and interchangeable? If it is a theoretical principle, does it have any reference to reality, or does it function only in the domain of formal truths by means of which we help to order our knowledge? Or is it merely another model useful as an aid to the imagination, in comprehending what laws state in terms of what is familiar to us, i.e., action? It is this richness of conceptual alternatives that leads us here to call it a fundamental concept; but it is also its ongoing relevance to the alternative world pictures of science, and to the interpretations of contemporary scientific formulations that makes causality a fundamental concept. The intricate interrelation of the concept of causality with such fundamental concepts as space, time, and matter, and with the questions of determinism and indeterminism which arise in modern physics will therefore concern us in the next chapter.

[8] Emile Meyerson, *Identity and Reality*, tr. K. Loewenberg (New York: Dover, 1962).

CHAPTER 12

The Newer Concepts of Space, Time, and Matter

HERE, NOW, THERE, AND THEN

IN GIVING AN ACCOUNT of the newer concepts of space, time, and matter, it may be best not to begin with them, or even with the older concepts; but rather, to begin at the beginning: with what we may be able to reconstruct as our primary experience out of which these concepts develop. In part such a reconstruction is a philosophical fiction (like those in political and social theory concerning some original "state of nature" prior to human society). In part it is supported by psychological studies of the perception of space, time, and objects, and especially by recent studies with newborn and very young animals and human children. The significance of such a "return to nature," or to some purportedly primitive or phenomenological reconstruction, is that the newer concepts of space, time, and matter, in going beyond the limits of classical and commonsense concepts, force us to consider the fundamental origins of our space-time-object concepts and the limitations of our experience under these modes.

If we may imagine what our experience of the world and of ourselves is like before we acquire a language in which to describe it, we may tend to suppose that this primitive experience is a structureless, kaleidoscopic field filled with changing qualities of color, sound, feeling, of sheer awarenesses without form or definition. Yet everything we have learned about the perceptual structures of animals and men suggests that, on the contrary, the perceptual field is highly structured and organized from the very start, so that the picture of a diffuse and largely undifferentiated continuum of awareness would hardly be the kind of thing such a highly differentiated perceptual apparatus would afford us. We find the eye highly structured for color discrimination, for perception of edges and contours. Similarly, the ear is highly articulated for discriminating relations of pitch and loudness. The regular rhythms of breathing, of heartbeat, of sleeping and waking, of hunger and satiety, connote structure in the very conditions of life. The perceptual constancies—the recognition of the real shape and size of objects as invariant through transformations of apparent shape and size—the operation of so-called biological clocks and the ability of neonate infants to locate sounds suggest that the organism comes equipped with a structure which orders allegedly raw experience in typical ways. Thus, from such evidence we may conclude that experience comes to us already shaped by the very structures which make it available. In this sense of genetically inherited structures, Kant's notion of *a priori* forms of perception is fulfilled.

Still, we want to distinguish between this primary experience, in whatever degree it is perceptually structured, and the reflective awareness in which we conceive of it and make it an object of deliberate consciousness. As we have noted earlier (in Chapter 5), language changes the context of perception, introducing the conceptual frameworks of the race into the ordering of experience and action. The use of language "takes us out of ourselves" and frames our experience in a public world of objects and actions and other persons. In acquiring this frame of reference we go beyond some undelineated autism, some sheer consciousness which is not yet even a consciousness of a self.

In attempting to explore this world of primary awareness, stripped of all such acquired and public reference, some philosophers (notably, the phenomenologists, such as Husserl and Merleau-Ponty, and the sense-datum theorists, such as Price and Broad) have ventured an account of such preperceptual or prejudgmental awareness. But even here the attempt to characterize some primordial state of pure here-and-now, of sheer ongoing presence in which whatever is, is *now,* is caught in the paradox of describing prelinguistic or preconceptual awareness in a language contaminated with conceptual reference. Even the most primitive notions of *self,* or that quality in awareness which we may call self-consciousness, already implicates the complementary notion of not-self, or *other*. The distinctiveness of an awareness of presentness or of *nowness* depends on its differentiation from what is *not-now,* or *then;* similarly, *here* implicates *not-here,* or *there*. Just as figure and ground "take in each other's washing" (to use a metaphor borrowed from John Austin), so that we cannot have one without the other, any reference to presence in space and time already enjoins an awareness of distance and separation. The distinction of our outer and inner awareness marks another discrimination between world and self which is complementary, in which *external* and *internal* are mutually dependent. On the one hand, there is our awareness of what impinges on the surface of our skin, or eyes, or ears, as external, and as that upon which we can act, and which resists our action. On the other hand, there is our awareness of inner sensations or body-states, which we characterize as kinesthesia and proprioception. John Locke, the founder of modern empiricism, characterized this sense of externality in our awareness as *outness,* in his *Essay Concerning Human Understanding.* And Hegel, in the most sustained examination of the logic of this primary awareness of *here* and *now,* and of *self,* already pointed to the necessary intrusion of conceptual frameworks upon this so-called immediate experience, in his *Phenomenology of Mind.* So too, Whitehead, in examining the complex logical concept of instantaneity, saw in this notion of "all nature at an instant" the workings of a conceptual abstraction far removed from sheer sense awareness. He writes, "There is no such thing as nature at an instant posited by sense-awareness. What nature delivers over for knowledge is nature through a period. . . . What is directly yielded to our knowledge by sense-awareness is a duration."[1] Yet even such a duration, involving in Whitehead's terms, "a concrete slab of nature limited by simultaneity," involves the notion of passage, of before and after, of temporal spread, from which is generated our notion of temporal sequence, of extension, or of a series of moments in this duration. Thus too language introduces us to a world of public objects. We speak to others who are not where we are, but *there,* at some distance from us, and yet are present in our *now.* We point and name and refer beyond ourselves, and distinguish *this* from *that,* as we locate objects in the elaborate space-time framework of *here-now* and *there-then.* In some such way, we may try to account for the genesis of that space-time-matter framework in which primary experience is ordered under concepts and takes the impress of our common language.

The abstract concepts of space, time, and matter which arise as language shapes experience to thought, originally contain the qualitative and emotive content of our concrete experience. Abstract terms arise from originally concrete qualitative reference. Thus, a term originally used concretely to connote the spatial boundary of the horizon becomes a general term meaning any limit or boundary. Its negation, connoting boundlessness or limitlessness, becomes substantive rather than adjectival in Greek natural philosophy and for Anaximander it becomes the primal stuff of the universe, *the unbounded* (*To Apeiron*), with its suggestions also of qualitative indeterminateness. (See above, on Anaximander, p. 72). Thus, too, the concrete quality of a duration as it is felt—with impatience or calmness, as vividly close in memory or distant and fading to vagueness—is abandoned for the more abstract notion of an unqualitied duration, alike in all its parts, which, in Newton's phrase, "flows equably." Objects are emptied of their qualities, retaining only their essential or primary characteristics: their being at a

[1] A. N. Whitehead, *The Concept of Nature* (Cambridge: Cambridge University Press, 1920), p. 57.

place and persisting through some time. Space, with its visual and emotive qualities—*vast, near, boundless, contained*—is set up as a relation among qualities with whose character it is fused; the space of our self-referent bodily motion with its qualities of *to, from, up, down, in front of, behind,* each of these characterizing some concrete quality linked to the action and motion of some agent in that space—this too becomes emptied of, or indifferent to, qualities, all of which merely come to "occupy" it in their turn and at their "place." What we are left with is that abstract space which is an object of thought and cannot be pictured because all its perceptual qualities have been removed. We are left with a time bare of imaginative and emotive color which had made it personal, or qualitatively differentiated. Matter too becomes the indifferent occupation of an indifferent space, as the qualities of body become reduced to the one criterial quality, *extension* in space. A certain visual representation of this conceptual abstraction remains, as line and shape and direction are geometrically represented in the diagram. The instruments used for the measurement of distance—the strings and rods—become ideally represented in the geometric line. The operation of measuring by counting off in sequence leaves, as its schematic residue, the notions *first, number,* and *successor* in the diagrammatic or formal representation of the mathematical operation. With the development of language and writing, and with progress toward abstraction of the pictograph, the mark replaces the thing, the event, the action, registering it only as a reminder, but retaining certain of its relational properties, such as *next to, between, before, after*. The enormous gain of this abstraction is the manipulation of marks in place of things, the registration of past events in a mechanical memory replacing the human record in its oral transmission with a more permanent representation.

Such a commonly ordered conceptual space, conceptual time, or conceptual object as extended matter in space, permits a transcendence of particularity and subjectivity and the establishment of a public record, dissociated from the idiosyncrasies of particular location and serving the intellect in its reconstruction of a unitary and unified universe. In the practical activity of the hunt, or of war, or of production, unambiguous location in a language fitted for this special use fixes on the intersection of two roads, the coincidence of two ends of an object, the numbered risings of sun or moon to mark a place and a time. With the use of conventions and formalisms, at first rules and rituals, the scope of spatio-temporal reference is extended until it becomes infinite. Along with the intellectually rigorous abstraction of this infinity, the imagination embodies the gods with these same properties, so that the concepts of space and time are exhibited as qualities of deity: one, immutable, eternal, infinite, omnipresent. The triumph of this intellectual domination of a universe thus conceived and abstracted so that all of it may be held indifferently in mind finds its expression in the concept of an omniscient god, who sees all and for whom all times are present. Thus, in the history of thought, theological representation follows along with the growth of scientific concepts, adding the assertion of existence to the conceptual framework. Matter becomes substance, uncreated and indestructible, underlying the being of all things, and like God, *causa sui,* self-caused. Time vanishes at a point of eternal presence, as space, like God, becomes a unity without center and without bound. All the perceptual characteristics of a particular this or that, of a sequence of then and now, of a here and a there vanish into the universality of an all-being God. Berkeley remarks: "Matter once admitted, I defy anyone to prove that God is not matter." Jonathan Edwards sees, in the consequences of Newtonian mechanics, the conclusion that "God is space." And Spinoza, fulfilling to the uttermost the implications of this conception, shows that matter is divine. Newton himself stops short with the metaphor characterizing space as "God's boundless sensorium," in which all things occur before God's "eye," so to speak.

The whole history of concepts of matter and space and time is a history, for several hundreds of years, of metaphysical speculation. Only with modern science do these concepts become operational in the full sense and tied to measurement. Yet this only fulfills the original impetus to conceptualization: the abstraction of perceptual space-time and of quality for purposes of practical and public action. One might say that the invention of the spatio-temporal object ranks with other technological achievements such as the invention of the wheel. Concepts become instruments of action and guides to action much as rulers and sextants do. Thus, one might say the clock is a consequence of a certain conception of time—as an instrument it embodies an abstract concept and it is made to the measure of the conception. So too is the measuring rod, for the equality of its intervals and its constancy as a unit of measurement make sense only in a space which is undifferentiated and isotropic, and which has no differential effect on objects transported through it. The foundations of the geometry describing such a space are in the assumptions which permit measuring rods to make this kind of sense. God is made in the image of this space, and this time, and this matter; he becomes a mathematician, a geometer, who thinks the way things are. God's reason and the world's structure are of a kind—mathematical. Thus the truths of reason and of mathematics are necessary truths, and the rational-geometrical conception of space and time finally arrived at in the seventeenth century is a "necessary" conception. From this, it is a short step to the Kantian conception that space and time—and, in particular, the space and time of Newtonian physics, operating within the concepts of Euclidean geometry—are necessary *a priori* forms of our perceptual apprehension of things. The blooming, buzzing confusion of our hypothetical primary experience ends up as the primitive structure of a mind conceived on the model of abstract geometry. The illusory image of the senses ends up as the necessary construct of a reason adequate to comprehend the world as Newton frames it.

The lesson of this short excursion is that our conceptions of space and time and matter are historical conceptions, like all others. They serve human ends but are not partial; for in their historical development they have evolved to serve *all* human ends, as particularity and expedience give way to continual refinement and universalization of these concepts. With this introduction, we may now examine the newer concepts of space, time, and matter as the highest refinement and most universal representation of what human thought has achieved in its representation of nature. The interesting feature of the newer conceptions is that at a level of abstraction far exceeding that of the seventeenth-century Newtonian view, they become reminiscent of the relational quality of space and time in our hypothetical primary experience.

ALTERNATIVE CONCEPTIONS OF SPACE AND TIME

Sometimes it is claimed that there is a distinctive commonsense space-time framework which is valid for the ordinary operations of human beings in a world of medium-sized objects; but that science supplants this commonsense framework with an extraordinary one, which holds for the domain of the very small (at the subatomic or quantum level) and the very large (at the level of astronomical distances and speeds approaching that of light). This view assumes that there is some intrinsic commonsense picture of space and time derived from common experience. But the fact is that our present commonsense picture of space and time is the product of science, and especially of seventeenth-century physics, and that *common sense* is a relative term describing the common sense of a period or a certain stage of conceptual development. This is not to say that human beings do not have a common basis of experience in the universe of acting and doing and in their common biological structure. But conceptions of space and time are not always in conformity with the simple "truths" about space and time which we seem to take as inevitable and necessary. The space-time of a primitive society in which magic is taken to be operative is conceived so that magical occurrences will be able to take place in it. The space-time of a society in which measurement becomes fundamental to agriculture and production will provide a frame for this common activity. Yet once philosophical speculation and critical thought arise, alternative conceptions show both the complexity of life, which operates in various spatio-temporal constructs, and the power of creative thought and criticism, which can imagine hypothetical spaces and times apparently unrelated to any typical experience or activity.

Yet we have in common very strong space-time intuitions which seem to us inevitable and ultimate—so ultimate and unshakable, in fact, that they suggest that this is a framework outside of which we could not experience anything at all. Plato expressed this conviction in talking about space as the condition for the existence of anything whatever. And it is difficult to imagine that anything can be, and not be somewhere in particular; just as difficult as it is to imagine that anything can be, and not be at *some time*. Thus if this intuition prevails, it may be concluded that we define existence in terms of space and time, and we typically take spatio-temporal existence as material or physical existence.

If we take as axioms such notions as the ones mentioned above, namely, that space is everywhere the same, and the same in all directions, and that time is likewise undifferentiated; and if we add the definitions concerning the location of regions in this space and time with respect to each other. then we may construct what is called *classical,* or Newtonian, space-time. If we add the additional notion of occupation of these regions, we have the classical Cartesian concept of matter. We also have the classical contradictions to which such a space-time-matter conception gives rise. And we have a good approximation to what has become the commonsense view of space, time, and matter. Let us examine what such a construction is like.

First, the distinction between an undifferentiated and qualitatively empty space and time and one which has regions in it raises the problem of how such regions could be distinguished if, in fact, space and time were really qualitatively indifferent. If space and time were everywhere the same, then the notion of boundaries separating regions of space and time would be difficult to arrive at. Rather, we would have a seamless block-space, a unity with no internal differences. We would have *Parmenidean* space and time (see p. 77), in which places and times could not be distinguished. Instead, what is proposed is that space does have places in it as time has moments, and that these constitute a spatio-temporal order. The indifference is maintained by denoting all such places and times as qualitatively indifferent, so that there are no privileged regions—a random choice of any such region being the same as any other choice. But once a choice is made, then with respect to it some frame of reference is set up *from the chosen region*. Indifference is maintained by making the choice arbitrary. The convention of representation of such space is to analyze it into three dimensions, two of them horizontal and one vertical. But horizontal and vertical are again arbitrary, for otherwise there would be a qualitative difference between some real "up" and "down" in space. Thus, such a frame of reference may be rotated through any degree and retain its invariance through this transformation. This introduces an alternative representation of ordering in space, in terms of angular measure.

But in an undifferentiated space, without some fixed reference frame, there can be no measure of rotation through an angular distance. Similarly, for the standard Cartesian coordinate system, there is as yet no metric, i.e., no distance measure. It is the metric that permits us to use the notions of distance and degree of angular rotation. But how is this introduction to be accomplished? Intuitively, we may suggest that a metric may be introduced by axioms which define certain relations of equality in space. To constitute such relations we need suitable elements, and such elements will need also to be taken as indifferently alike or identical. Suppose, then, we take such elements as space regions or places. We may then proceed to order such regions with respect to each other. Again, operating from our intuitions of space, we may suggest that no two regions can be the same region. This seems harmless enough, because what we mean by *two* is not *one*. But in choosing a single region on these grounds, we have set up a differentiation in space if we then claim that such a region excludes all others. Thus regions in space are self-identical, but with respect to something which we may now call position or location, such a region is no longer identical with or indifferently like any other region, strictly speaking. If it were, then every "other" region would be alike in location, as well as in all other respects. We thus introduce a limitation on the qualitative indifference of space. A region is identical with any other region in every respect but location. Thus every region in space has a unique location, and thus a unique self-identity. This is the postulate of an absolute space, one in which regions or places are "really" where they are with respect to every other region. And this is the fundamental postulate of Newtonian space.

The ordering of such a space may then proceed in terms of this absolute location of space regions. If space is made up of such regions, then there is no space which is not a region, that is, regions are contiguous and space is a continuum of such contiguous regions. If we take regions as small as we like (an entirely intuitive notion, because we have as yet no concept of size), we may express this by saying that between any two regions in space, there is another region. The notion of betweenness becomes a fundamental relation in the ordering of regions, thus permitting us to conceive of space as infinitely divisible into regions. We may alternatively think of any region in space as containing subregions, or converging on a limit (picturing this as circles within circles within circles, as long as we remember that the circle requires a metric which we do not yet have, since by definition, "circle" requires the notion of equal distance). At the limit, we may then introduce the notion of *point* as that upon which the region converges. Points as limits then constitute the ultimate nonmetrical elements of space. Their properties follow from this definition: they are infinitely close or dense, so that between any two points there is a point. If we take dimensions as extended regions in space, then points are at the limit of extension—their extension is zero. Conversely, any extended region is one which includes more than one point. But then any extension contains an infinite number of points, because between any two there is another. Thus, because an infinite set of points has the same cardinal number as any other infinite set of points, we cannot distinguish between extensions in this way. That is, we have as yet no concept of distance. This would require that we set up some notion of equal and unequal sets of points. But in our purely conceptual construction of space, thus far there is no such set which we may take as a standard unit, or as a privileged set, in terms of which we may set up a metric.

It is therefore the choice of such a standard unit that introduces a metric if we include, with the choice, the characterization of the operations by which this standard unit would be used in measurement. Clearly, such a standard would have to be invariant or self-identical through all transformations. Practically speaking, we adopt such units with ease: rulers, distances between a rock and a tree which we may then measure by some instrument, etc. But the conceptual basis for such choices is the assumption that there is a way of measuring which gives unique and invariant values for this distance.

The intrusion of the operational or practical technique of measurement into this purely conceptual scheme comes with the definition of a metric. Thus Euclid introduces such a notion by referring to "the shortest distance between two points." This is defined as a straight line, and it is on the basis of such a straight line that a metric is established. But unless we have a way of determining a shortest distance or a straight line, this is a circular or empty definition. Commonsensically, we would say *straight* means "not-curved," and everyone knows what that looks like. Also, we could say *straight* means that, by sighting along a line connecting points, all the points on the line are coincident—they cover each other successively, so that none are out of line. But such intuitive notions depend on a prior assumption that the light reaching our eyes travels in a straight line. If it traveled in a curve, then, presumably, points on a line arranged in that curve would also cover each other, and we could not tell from this whether we were looking at a straight or a curved line (Fig. 8). But if we retain this definition of *straight* in terms of sighting, then what we really mean is that we take the path of a ray of light as our definition of *straight,* so that to ask if this is "really" straight would be nonsensical unless we had some other independent measure of straightness.

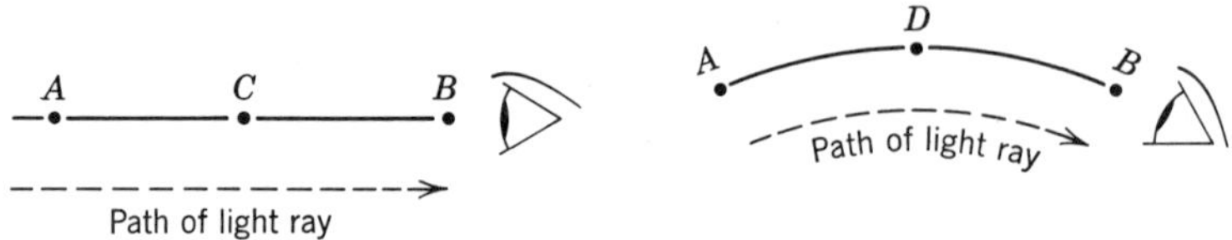

Fig. 8

Once we introduce paths into our space, we introduce more than space relations. We introduce the notion of something moving through space, or of an arrangement of spatial regions that constitutes a preferred, or singular, arrangement which we call a *path.* Now there may be an infinite number of such paths, distinguished from each other by the formal requirement that no two paths have all their constituent regions in common. To put it differently, any path which contained all and only the same regions as some other would be identical with that other; there would not be two paths, but only one. Here our construction becomes more complex. If we talk about the motion of a ray of light along some path, then suppose alternative rays of light traveled along different paths, between two points *A* and *B,* but that we decided to take path *ACB* to be shorter than *ADB,* on some assumption of its "straightness." If rays *ACB* and *ADB* started from *A* at the same time and reached *B* at the same time, then we would have to assume the ray along *ADB* went "faster," because the distance was greater. Here we introduce the notion of time into our framework of distance. We may choose to conceive of equal distances in some purely spatial way, measuring with a "straight" ruler. But we may choose to define this equality such that light rays travel equal distances in equal times. We could then introduce the concept of motion into our spatial framework in terms of a passage through successive space regions. But we would not yet have introduced any notion of equal or unequal motions, because between any two regions of space, as the starting and finishing points of some motion, there would be an equal number of regions traversed, namely, an infinite number. On these grounds alone, any path along which a light ray would travel would be equivalent to any other path, and the distinction *straight* or *curved* could not arise. If, however, we introduce the notion of *shortest path* as defining *straight,* then presumably there is a difference among paths in this respect. All shortest paths between two space regions would be equal. We could say there is one and only one shortest path. However, we could say there are an infinite number of shortest paths (for example, if the only possible paths between *A* and *B* were the lines along the outer surface of some football-shaped spheroid, all of which were equal in length (see Fig. 9). But this would seem to rule out certain contiguous space-time regions as possible paths, without any reason (for example, the lines through the middle of the football). We introduce, then, the notion of velocity, concerning not only a path of motion but the time it takes for a light ray to traverse this path. This is already assumed when we say that if we intuitively assume *ACB* to be shorter than *ADB,* and if the light starting from *A* reaches *B* at the same instant after traversing either path, then it is traveling faster along *ADB*. "Faster" is defined in terms of "greater distance in the same time."

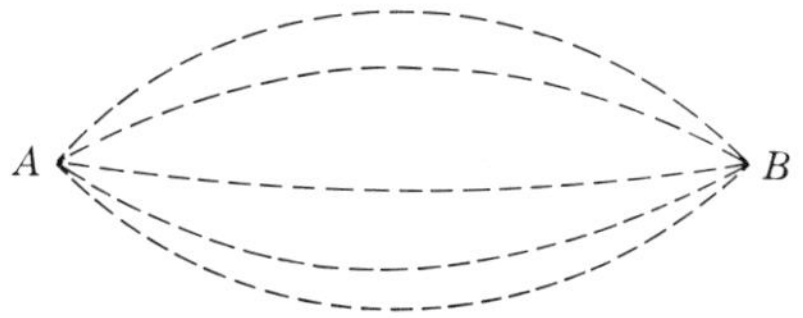

Fig. 9

Now consider the problem we have gotten into. The ruler which tells us that *ACB* is straight is itself defined as a straight ruler by sighting along it. This presupposes that the light ray reaching our eyes is straight. We then use this ruler to determine that *ACB* is shorter than *ADB*. On this basis, we decide that light traveled faster along *ADB* to reach *B* at the same time as the light along *ACB*. This assumes that the shortest distance is the one which it takes the least time to traverse. But by our assumption, "least time" is meaningless unless we assume a constant velocity along alternative paths, for otherwise, we could arrange our velocities so that for paths of any length, the time of traverse could be the same. The light ray would estimate the length of the path, decide how fast it had to go to reach a terminus within a given time, and then adjust its speed so that all paths would be traversed in the same time. By the definition given, then, paths *ACB* and *ADB* would be equal distances if they were traversed in the same time but also unequal distances as measured by a straight ruler, defined by sighting. The problem is obviously in permitting the light ray to vary its speed in proportion to the distance it has to go. Suppose instead, we proposed that the velocity of light is constant, i.e., it traverses equal distances in equal times. Then it would be logically impossible to define *ACB* as shorter than *ADB,* if in fact a light ray starting from *A* arrived at *B* at the same time along either path. The paths would be equal in distance. But a ruler could not measure them as different if it were properly straight, "straight" meaning "shortest distance," and "shortest distance" in turn meaning "traversed by a light ray in the shortest time." We would have to assume that a ruler measuring *ADB* would be bent along the path *ADB,* so that in frame of reference *ADB* it would, on sighting, appear straight just as it does in *ACB*.

This introduces into our purely spatial conception of distance the notion of time as essential to the definition of distance. This is not terribly peculiar, and ordinary usage often describes distances in this way. "How far is it to Buffalo?" you ask. "About two hours by plane," is the reply. Our systematic conception relating distance and time makes this perfectly good sense. It means of course that a plane traveling at a certain speed will cover the distance in two hours. But this is not quite the same thing as what we have discussed. For in the ordinary view, we do separate space and time, measuring each independently, one by rods and the other by clocks. What we have raised is the problem of establishing a standard rod, one invariant through transformations. It cannot bend like rubber or vary in length from one use to the next. Thus, it has to be rigid. But to establish its straightness we are involved in some test (like sighting) which involves light rays. These introduce the question of whether time of traverse along some path is invariant. The invariance we finally have to assume is that of the velocity of light along any path which it takes in space. Any such path, then, by definition, is straight, defining shortest distance in terms of the time that it takes a light ray to traverse it.

Let us see what this does to our spatial construction. Conceptually, we retain the homogeneity and isotropy of space. But "the same" now means that no matter what we set up as a metric, if we transport this metric to another region in space, it will retain invariant all the relations which we have built into it. This seems to say that there is in fact a universal and invariant space. But there is a subtle and important shift here. What we are really saying is that for any local metric (e.g., of distance) there is a transformation which retains the invariance of the relations of this local metric in any other region of space. Thus all local metrics have invariant transformations into other local metrics. This is like saying that although currencies vary from one country to another, there is a universal exchange rate so that any currency may be exchanged according to this rate for an equivalent value in any other currency. But this does not say that all currencies are the same. In fact, one could tell where one was by establishing what the local currency was—that is, by ascertaining the local measurement scheme. The exchange rate would give us the transformation equations for currencies; but these would not be arbitrary. They would be set according to some empirically significant criterion of equal value. The search for the most viable such criterion is a problem for international finance. The gold standard was one such attempt to give currencies international equivalence in a single unit, say, a gram of gold. This does not mean that this equivalence is universal for every other commodity, for some commodities are cheaper in one place than in another.

But the physical space-time system is set up so that the "commodities" which enter into the equations are all intertransformable. Nor are they arbitrary. They are the values of such measurable properties as mass, time, length—our fundamental magnitudes in terms of which we systematically define others. Metaphorically, we may picture this universal invariance as a "world knot," in which the fundamental magnitudes are related to each other in such a way that one relation among them remains constant and invariant, and all other relations are interpreted in terms of this one. In classical physics this is already introduced as an absolute space and an absolute time, on the assumption or postulate that there are equal regions of space and equal durations of time in some conceptually absolute sense; and that the measurement of spaces and times merely show such equalities, by discovering *invariant ratios,* e.g., between the oscillations of a pendulum and the oscillations of a quartz crystal. Without such ratio invariance any standard measure by itself remains purely conventional; but with the discovery of such invariance something seems to be revealed which does not depend on our choice. Thus the seasons vary in a certain ratio to appearances of a full moon, so that the calendar marks not merely an arbitrary sequence, but one which recurs in certain ways within a system of ratios. The period of the lunar month is invariant with a certain number of sunrises and sunsets. The knot is tied tighter when the great variety of such invariances can be reduced or transformed into a more universal one. In this sense the introduction of a single constant as the exchange rate for all invariances relates them to each other, however different they are.

In contemporary physics, after a history of great discoveries in many experimental fields which strained classical space-time conceptions to the limit, Einstein introduced the notion of the constant velocity of light in a vacuum as the universally invariant property in the universe, in terms of which other invariances could be coherently expressed. This derived from an interpretation of certain equations which had been formulated by the physicist Lorentz, in 1895, as a way to "save the appearances." These so-called Lorentz transformation equations were an attempt to account for the null results of the Michelson-Morley experiment, which attempted to establish the effect of the medium, through which light was presumed to travel, in retarding the velocity of light in certain directions, as a kind of frictional drag upon light. Lorentz's equations "saved the appearances" in much the same way as Eudoxus' concentric spheres did for astronomical observations. (See Appendix B.) But Einstein interpreted these equations in a radical way, concluding that light traveled at a constant velocity regardless of the motion of its source or its direction. Therefore, the establishment of a frame of reference for time or space in any region was as "objective" as any other frame in any other region, if this invariant velocity was maintained; for then, the transformation equations merely gave the rule for establishing the relation of one space-time framework to another. In effect, this said that no space-time framework was more than local and that no absolute framework existed against which all frameworks could be checked. The absolute framework, if we want to retain this sense, is the universal relation which can be established among all local frameworks. And this gives us the fundamental alternatives in conceptions of space and time, which we may now summarize.

Absolute or Newtonian Space and Time

Space is constituted of contiguous regions or places, uniquely ordered and immovable. A conceptual space has, as the limits of such regions, points in space, which have no extension. Thus, if matter is defined in terms of extension, space is not matter if it may be said to be constituted of an everywhere dense set of such extensionless points. The distribution of matter in space may be represented as the values of the variable, *mass,* at these points; and one of the consequences of Newtonian mechanics is that the mass of a body in space may be represented at a point. Such mass points are therefore ideal entities preserving certain features of the distribution of matter in motion in some real space. Motion in such a space would be change of point position. Because there are no gaps between points, motion would be continuous and infinitely divisible. At the limit, motion would be nothing but the successive occupation of point positions by some value of mass. Thus the material atom in such an ideal space would also have no extension, but would be an extensionless point. The only differences in space would be among positions which were occupied and those which were empty. But point positions would retain their invariant structure whether or not they were occupied, and in this sense space is absolute. The relation among all such point positions could then be represented by a Cartesian coordinate system, with two horizontal dimensions, and one vertical one. But because the origin of such a system could be placed anywhere in space, each such Cartesian coordinate system could be transformed into any other by rotation or by translation of the origin.

Time is also constituted of an invariant and unique arrangement of parts, which at the limit we may call instants. These are arranged, however, in a one-dimensional order, and any instant is between two others with which it is contiguous, in a linear sequence. The whole time series and the whole space series are isomorphic in that we can give every point a mapping on all the instants or every instant a mapping on all the points.[2] In this sense, space is omnitemporal and time omnispatial. Because both are receptacles, an instant may be occupied by an event, or empty. If matter occupied all of space eternally, there would be no "empty" spaces and no "empty" times. But mass points vary. That is, the same points do not always have the same mass values so that when the mass value of a point is zero, we may say the point is empty. But here the additional classical conception enters: mass values cannot spontaneously appear and disappear. Thus, throughout the whole space-time framework, mass remains constant. If a mass value varies at one point, the difference will show up at another, as if one were squeezing a closed toothpaste tube. The sequence of some hypothetical constant mass value at a point at one time and at another at some other time would be the history or the motion of that mass. If we take this mass as a body filling some space, then of course its characteristic is that it is extended in space. But if we conceive it ideally as a value at a point, then we have a material atom with no extension, with all the difficulties of reconciling body with extensionless point or atom. For, no matter how many of such atoms we packed together, we could not arrive at an extended body by adding extensionless points. We can get around this if we remember that a point is a conceptual abstraction, as ideal space is; that it is a model of some purported real space, in which space regions may be taken as small as one likes, but are never actually at the limit which we conceive of as a point. Thus, a region R is such that there is always a region $R' < R$. Motion then is the passage from a region R_1 to some region R_2 taken as close together as one likes. But the time conditions of motion for

[2] John Locke, writing about the relation between space and time in *An Essay Concerning the Human Understanding* (Book II, Chapter xv) concludes, "Expansion and duration do mutually embrace and comprehend each other; every part of space being in every part of duration, and every part of duration in every part of expansion." [Cited in G. J. Whitrow, *The Natural Philosophy of Time* (Edinburgh: Thomas Nelson & Sons, Ltd., 1961), p. 233] Compare with Minkowski's version, p. 331.

a body occupying a region are that it may determine a region R_{b1} of a size such that the body occupies all of it, and it may be said to *move* if there is a time t at which it occupies R_{b1} and another time t' at which it does *not* occupy R_{b1}. But because classical space-time is constituted of discrete places and durations a body cannot be in two places at the same time nor can two bodies occupy the same place at the same time. Ultimately, a body is conceived of as "impenetrable," i.e., as some infinitely dense matter through which nothing can pass and which thus excludes all other body from its place at any given time. Thus we have a model of hard atomic particles either at rest in their point or region positions during successive intervals or instants of time or in motion in traversing successive point positions in successive times. Space-time is therefore a continuum in which bodies occupy spatio-temporal positions uniquely and absolutely defined in the absolute framework. The main feature here is that there are places and times independent of any contingent occupation of them by bodies.

Relational Space and Time

If, on the contrary, we say that a space-time point is determined by an event (e.g., a mass value) occurring at it, and that as such and in themselves, space regions and time intervals have no independent structure, then we make space and time functions of events. This would seem to be a return to the primary experience of space and time as tied to characters and qualities of experience. Thus, a space would be generated as a relation between objects and a time as a relation between events. The question this raises is, if nothing were happening, would that mean that time was not passing? If there were no things in the world, would there be no space? Strictly speaking, this is exactly what it means. Now one may imagine nothing happening, perhaps. But what exactly would this mean? Psychologically, when we are conscious of nothing happening, as we may be in very deep sleep, then indeed we are not conscious of time passing either. But we assume that while we were sleeping, things of which we were not then aware were happening, whose traces we can check. If everything stopped while we slept, then there would in fact be no way to know that time had passed. Similarly, we never conceive of a space in which nothing exists, except as a relation between regions in which things exist. So we speak of the empty space between the stars, or between the earth and the moon, or between ourselves and the desk. With the introduction of any metric in space, we in effect introduce a defining relation which determines space as a function of some magnitude, e.g., distance or velocity. But as we have seen, to establish a metrical distance involves appeal to some occurrence (actual or hypothetical), as, for example, the passage of a ray of light. This therefore rejects the *a priori* notion of a mapping of all spaces on all times, independently of events or occurrences at some place and time. Minkowski, in arguing against the classical view on the basis of Einstein's proposal of the objectivity of local (i.e., eventful) space-time frameworks, said in his famous lecture, "Space and Time" (1908), "Nobody has ever noticed a place except at a time, or a time except at a place." The force of this is that the operation of *noticing* requires a frame of events, for the classical "empty" space regions and time intervals are not noticeable at all but are entirely transparent. A particular point in space at a particular time was dubbed a "world-point" by Minkowski, and the world is thus the collection of all world-points. A sequence of such space-time world-points, in which space and time are wedded to each other at all points, Minkowski called a "world-line." Thus, a world-line is the continuous history of an individual existent in space-time, or more precisely, the space-time track generated by an individual existence. Each of us would have a world-line, beginning at the moment of our conception and ending with our death; and our moment of conception would not be spontaneous but would involve the confluence of world-lines of the constituent elements (say, ovum and sperm) constituting the zygote from which we develop.

Thus, every particle in the universe would have its world-line, which could be mapped in a diagram (see Fig. 10) which we may abstract and simplify by reducing the three dimensions of space at an instant to a quasi-two-dimensional representation (the plane represented by the elliptical shape *XY*) and representing time by a line passing through such planes. Then if we represent the world as a cylinder made up of all the horizontal planes *XY, X′Y′, X″Y″*, . . ., a world-line such as *AB* would represent an object stationary in space through time and *CD* would represent the world-line of a moving object, occupying successive portions of the space slices in successive times. *CD* would thus represent a uniform motion in one direction, and *DE* would represent something more like the erratic space-time path of one of us, as we rest, hustle about, and return again and again to the same place at different times. What Fig. 10

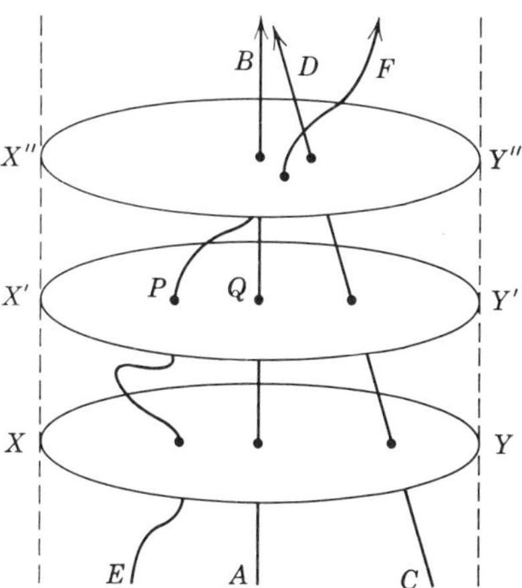

Fig. 10

falsifies radically is the representation of a space through which no lines are passing. In effect, there would be no such space, and the cylinder would consist of nothing but the cluster of world-lines of individuals. Where there are no world-lines, there is also no space-time in the relational view.

THINGS, EVENTS, AND PROCESSES

Minkowski's "world," based on Einsteinean relativistic notions of space and time, has been called a "four-dimensional manifold." Science fiction has made much use of this conception of a mysterious *fourth dimension.* But the fourth dimension means no more than what is ordinarily characterized by the four coordinates of a Cartesian coordinate system, in which x, y, z are the usual three dimensions of space and t is added to constitute the world-point for any values x, y, z. Thus some occurrence at any given values (x, y, z, t) is a world-point, and the continuous values of x, y, z for all the values of t constitute a world-line. We may call an occurrence at some particular time t an *event,* and the occurrence through some continuous series of values $(t_1, t_2, t_3, \ldots t_n)$ a *process.* Viewed in this way, a *thing,* insofar as it is more than an instantaneous occurrence and has duration through time, is a process. This introduces odd results in our ways of talking. For example, talking would be a process but we would hardly talk of it as a "thing"; similarly, it is not usual to talk of a rock or a human body as a process. We rather talk of its processes, e.g., the erosion of the rock or the aging process of the body. Furthermore, our knowledge of a process would involve some information about a world-line and not merely of a world-point. We would have to somehow interact with some world-line in order to know this. Thus, my observing some object, say a rock, would require an interaction of my world-line with its world-line, along a line of sight or by touch, etc. If we characterize such an interaction as causal, then what characterizes it is that unless there is instantaneous contact between myself and the object, I receive the information about the object later than the event which the information contains as its content. If I were at some distance from an object, say, in the space-time slice $X'Y'$, so that my world-point was P and its world-point Q, then the causal interaction of Q with P would be instantaneous if information from Q to P could be transmitted instantaneously across $X'Y'$ (the dotted horizontal line QP). If, however, it is postulated that there is a highest speed of causal transmission, then information from Q can reach P only within some finite time, determined by the distance QP. But such topspeed causal transmission does exist, namely, the constant velocity of light through a vacuum, which has been established as 2.9979×10^8 meters/sec., or about 186,000 miles per second. Thus, if the distance between Q and P were about three yards, the fastest signal from Q to P would take about one ten-millionth of a second to traverse the distance (if it were a light signal, for example) so that information about the world-line AB at its world-point Q would reach my world-line EF not at P but at P plus one ten-millionth of a second, and thus not in the space-time slice $X'Y'$, but in a later one. I could never know what was happening along AB *simultaneously* with my reception of its signal, if *simultaneous* meant *in the space-time slice* $X'Y'$. But in this model of space-time, the term *simultaneous* has no operational meaning except that which can be defined in terms of such causal interactions. I cannot now determine what is presently happening at some distant point, but I can, presumably, determine later what had happened earlier. Thus, for example, if I view a television picture "simultaneously" with its production in some studio which emits a signal to my receiver, I am viewing what has already happened in the past. The situation would be no better if I were present at the live performance, for then the light reflected from the performers would take some finite time to reach my eyes, and the neural discharge along the nerves leading from my retina to my brain would take some additional finite time. In effect, I am always seeing the past; yet I see it as if it were happening now. One may even conceive of the present, or "now" as a collection of messages from points at various distances from it. This is indeed a strange way to talk. For by *now,* I ordinarily mean *right now,* as if my now were an instantaneous present. The question arises whether or not I have any basis for claiming that my present awareness *is* in fact such a knife-edge instant. If my *now* is rather an interval of some finite duration, then the notion of a world-point would be an ideal limit at some infinitesimal instant, not a *now* (which would then take in something on each side of the instant). This is a complex question, which introduces the special problems of awareness or consciousness into the causal picture, in terms of the so-called specious present, which has a spread or duration in time. But suppose that the interaction were between two world-lines in which such considerations of awareness played no part. All we would be concerned with would be the emission of some signal at Q and its reception not at P, but at P' (later than P), on the assumption of a top speed of signal transmission C (the velocity of light in a vacuum). What sort of model of causal interaction would this present?

First, the world-line of the transmission itself would always have some positive slope (upwards, if we adopt the convention of Fig. 10 of representing later as higher on the page and earlier as lower). In this sense, emission and reception may simply (and with some dangers) be denoted as cause and effect. The relations of cause and effect would then define time relations in the following way:

1. The minimum "distance" between cause and effect would be the world-line of a ray of light passing from Q to P'. If, as we assume, C is constant, then the slope of such a world-line is constant and the same in any instance.

2. Causal sequence is asymmetrical. That is, an effect is always in the future, with respect to its cause, and a cause is always in the past with respect to its effect. But then it follows that cause and effect can never be simultaneous, if Q and P are not at the same place. If they were at the same place, then the notion of emission and reception would be anomalous, for the signal would vanish at the limit of coincidence of Q and P. But if we define causal interaction in terms of signal transmission, there is no causal relation at an instant. Absolute simultaneity at an instant then remains causally undefined.
3. It follows from these considerations that a causal event can never interact with the past, if we take it as present; nor can a future event act on the present. The sequence past-present-future is causally asymmetrical; that is, the time series of events is defined in terms of the asymmetry of causal relation.
4. The limits of causal interaction therefore lie within some past-present-future bounded by the top speed of causal transmission C. If this is taken as some constant slope M (defined by the value $C = 2.9979 \times 10^8$ meters/sec.), we may represent all the events within this boundary as world-points on world-lines whose slope is $\leq M$. Then the space-time diagram in Fig. 11 may be modified to represent the domain of possible causal relation of some world-point P. Anything with which P can causally interact would fall within the two time cones generated by a line of slope M about the point present P if the speed of causal trans-

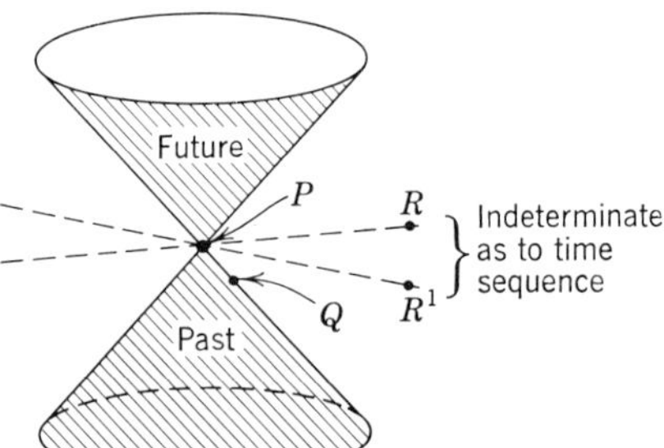

Fig. 11

mission is smaller than C; or it would fall on the surface of the time cones if the speed of causal transmission is equal to C. (The slope would be reckoned from a base line running vertically through P, so that $M' < M$ would fall within the cones and $M' > M$ would fall outside them.) It may be seen from Fig. 11 that the time sequence of events outside the time cones cannot be determined if we take the time series as a function of causal sequence. Events outside the cones (neither within them or on their surface) are thus not determinable either as past or future. Thus the present not coincident at P is the set of world-points with which P cannot interact causally. Because these cones are generated by a line of slope determined by the top speed of causal transmission *C*, which is the velocity of light and of electromagnetic radiation generally, these are sometimes called *light cones*.

5. A causal *process* would be a chain of causally related events constituting a world-line whose slope could vary, within the boundaries of the time cones, but could never exceed *M* and could therefore never turn back on itself. Again, if we define time in terms of such causal sequences, then time is *directional* and, in this sense, irreversible for all events within the time cones. This raises a hypothetical question as to whether events outside the time cones can occur in reversible order. For example, could *R* be said to occur after *R′* and then reoccur before *R′*? In this model the beforeness or afterness of *R* and *R′* remain undefined, however. Presumably, there are events taking place instantaneously at different places. Thus, for example, if some signal were sent from *Q* and *Q′*, and if the distance from *Q* to *P* were the same as the distance from *Q′* to *P*, then if both signals were light signals traveling at velocity *C*, they would reach *P* at the same instant. We may then infer that in the past *Q* and *Q′* were simultaneous world-points. But let us imagine that *Q* and *Q′* are exactly the same distance apart as they each are from *P* (forming an equilateral triangle). Someone (or some registering device) at *Q* could not know at *Q* that *Q′* was simultaneous. Only a coincidence at *P* would show this. If we placed observers halfway between *Q* and *Q′*, then the coincidence of the two signals would take place before *P*, but nevertheless at some world-point of coincidence later than the emissions.
6. Thus, we must abandon the absolute simultaneity of two events at some distance from each other in some container of space in which there is an instantaneous *now* specifiable for all places in the container. Two events are simultaneous with respect to some local framework, e.g., the world-line of some observer passing through *P*, if they are neither in the past nor the future of *P*. Any events *R*, *R′*, *R″* . . . would then be *relatively* simultaneous in the reference frame of *P*.

Now if we return to the question of an awareness at *P*, of some conscious observer, the meaning of an instantaneous present at *P* becomes unclear. In Fig. 11 what impinges at *P* is the set of world-lines which are coincident at P—taken to be signals from some past events. What *P* impinges on is the divergent cone of future events with which *P* can causally interact, as an event in their past. But our awareness of a present is never clearly one of some *point* but rather of some *passage* from past to future. If awareness has a minimum duration, or is a specious present, then the sharp separation of past from future at some point is replaced with a more diffuse passage through some interval. Thus, Whitehead writes,

> Thus (on this theory) the immediacy of perception is of an instantaneous present, and this unique present is the outcome of the past and the promise of the future. But we deny this immediately given instantaneous present. There is no such thing to be found in nature. As an ultimate fact it is a non-entity. What is immediate for sense-awareness is a duration. Now a duration has within itself a past and a future; and the temporal breadths of the immediate durations of sense awareness are very indeterminate and dependent on the awareness of the individual percipient. Accordingly there is no unique factor in nature which for every percipient is preeminently and necessarily the present. The passage of nature leaves nothing between the past and the future. What we perceive as present is the vivid fringe of memory tinged with anticipation. This vividness lights up the discriminated field within a duration.[3]

If we take the notion of the physical coincidence of two world-lines as some physical contact between bodies or particles, however small, then it is possible to conceive this too as a process rather than as an instantaneous event. One may ask, "At what precise instant does the rock break the glass?" or, "At what precise instant does a photon impinge on a surface?" This assumes some infinitesimal limit at which the event takes place—a time instant of no duration. Suppose then we think of the shattering of the glass; the event takes some finite time. If the rock acts causally on the glass, then the instant of impact is not the instant of shattering, but precedes it. Is it conceivable that the impact itself is an event with stages? And that these stages themselves may be further subdivided? That is, may any causal process be conceived as having not some ultimate point constituents but instead overlapping components, between any two of which there may be said to be a third? The alternatives are that either there are physical limits beyond which elements of time and of space cannot be further divided—a smallest time and a smallest length, which yet have duration and extension, and are time-atoms and space-atoms; or time and space do converge on a dimensionless point. This is the same question we raised earlier with respect to the classical problem of a material point. Here, however, if space and time are not taken as independently existent receptacles, but, in Whitehead's phrase, "There is time because there are happenings, and apart from happenings there is nothing,"[4] then whether or not there are space-time "points" depends on whether we can reasonably define something as an instantaneous event.

If we link this to the physical problem of determining the location of a physical object at a particular time, we introduce the distinction between the ideally conceivable construction of a space-time point and its physical

[3] A. N. Whitehead, *The Concept of Nature* (Cambridge: Cambridge University Press, 1920), pp. 72–73.

[4] *Ibid.*, p. 66.

meaning in terms of the conditions and limits of measurement. This introduces the question, raised in an earlier chapter, of limited measurability, and the problems of so-called indeterminacy and uncertainty which arise in quantum physics.

UNCERTAINTY, INDETERMINACY, AND COMPLEMENTARITY

In the Einstein-Minkowski picture of an integral space-time manifold, the objectivity of all local frames of reference is affirmed, and at the same time all relativism in the physical world is eliminated because all the physical laws which hold in one frame of reference will hold on transformation to another frame of reference. Thus, the universal invariance which Newtonian physics postulated on the basis of absolute space and time is retained in a unique way, abandoning this "privileged" absolute framework. The explication of universal invariance goes beyond the scope of this discussion and involves the transformation of local space-time measurements in different frameworks. Measurement, as we have seen, involves congruence, coincidence of points, and the conditions of the transport of measuring rods and clocks through space-time.

If we recall the questions of limited measurability raised earlier (pp. 176 ff.), these were seen to derive from the limits imposed by some smallest unit of measurement below the scale of which differences in magnitude were indeterminate. Simply speaking, if the smallest unit we may set up for measurement is k, then differences between $n < \mathrm{k}$ and $n' < k$ will be below the threshold of measurability, and we will not be able to determine whether $n > n'$ or $n' > n$. For purposes of measurement within such a system, $n \approx n'$, and practically we may decide to take $n = n'$. Leibniz defined *identity* as that relation holding between things which are "indiscernibly different"; i.e., there would not be sufficient reason to distinguish one as different from the other in any way (including therefore differences in magnitude as well).

With the introduction of the quantum theory by Planck, Bohr, Heisenberg, and others, this formulation became more than a practical limitation on measurement, and was seen to have a theoretical interpretation in terms of a smallest unit of energy. The background of this was Planck's hypothesis that electromagnetic waves emitted by oscillating charges can have only certain discrete values; thus the oscillators have levels of energy, between which there is no continuous variation but between which there are quantum jumps. These energy levels are integral multiples of a quantity $h\nu$ where ν is the frequency of the oscillator and h is a constant which may be determined as $h = 6.625 \times 10^{-34}$ joules-sec, and is called Planck's constant. Thus the energies of electromagnetic radiation of some oscillator may be 0, $1h\nu$, $2h\nu$, $3h\nu$, but never $\frac{1}{2}h\nu$ or $1\frac{3}{4}h\nu$. Einstein developed this concept further, in investigating and explaining the so-called photoelectric effect, and proposed that after the emission of an energy quantum, $h\nu$, lost by an emitter on radiation, this quantum remains intact and does not spread out over an expanding wave front. Rather, as the wave front expands, the distance among these packets of energy increases, so that the energy per unit area of the wave front decreases. (A crude analogy would be a shotgun blast, though this does not curve the way a wave front would. The energy at the muzzle, of all the shotgun pellets within the muzzle area, would be greater than the energy within the same unit area ten feet away, for the shot would have scattered.) If we take the electromagnetic radiation as a wave, then it becomes problematic how intact packets of energy can make up a wave. After the long history of conceptual models of light as either wavelike or corpuscular (made up of particles), here was a proposal that light was made up of corpuscles (later called *photons*), reviving the then-settled dispute between the followers of Newton and Huygens, in which Huygens' wave model had finally won out. But a corpuscle is a "body" presumably, and thus a material particle in space; and photons cannot be thought of as material particles with kinetic energy, for if they are stopped, they are destroyed or absorbed. Also, the phenomenon of interference patterns produced by light entering through two slits can be explained if light is wave-like but not if light is corpuscular (as exhibited in Thomas Young's experiments at the beginning of the nineteenth century).

So far, the problem remained one concerning light not as a form of matter but of radiation. It was extended to include X-rays and, more radically, in 1923 De Broglie suggested that the duality of wave and corpuscle might extend to the behavior of electrons. The whole concept of matter was now implicated as well, for the classical atomic particle as a body moving in space with a point position at any given time also sometimes behaves in such a way that the only explanation seems to be that it is a wave. If waves of light are corpuscular, and particles of matter wavelike, then the whole picture of the structure of nature becomes at the same time more coherent and less simple. Instead of a variety of kinds of things—light, electricity, matter, and so on—there is discovered a way of interpreting these various phenomena in terms of a common model But the model is such that the common elements have incompatible properties. If both matter and radiation can be wavelike and particlelike, a fundamental duality in nature seems to be introduced.

The problem becomes sharper when it is seen that the conditions of measurement of particles the size of electrons are radically affected by these considerations. In order to determine the classically conceived position and momentum of a particle (momentum or $p = mv$ so that the measure for velocity involves a distance-time relation), one has to somehow measure or observe. This means to interact. At some point, the observer's apparatus has to coincide with the particle, by means of some physical interaction. But if the smallest energy of interaction is, with respect to the particle, large enough to disturb it, or change its momentum, by accelerating it, then its simultaneous value for position at a given instant of time becomes indeterminate. Let us examine this a bit further.

Einstein's equation which relates the energy of a wave to its frequency is $E = h\nu$. De Broglie related this to the wavelike properties of atomic particles, arguing from the theory of relativity that $E = h\nu$ led to a relation of the momentum of an atomic particle to the wavelength of such waves λ, namely, $p = h/\lambda$. We also know that the relation between wavelength and frequency is one of inverse proportion: the shorter the wavelength, the higher the frequency. Thus, for very high frequency waves, the energy will be high. If we interpret these facts for the situation of measurement, it can be seen that:

1. In order to determine with great precision what the *position* of an atomic particle is, we need a unit of measurement of high resolution with respect to space. Thus, for example, a ruler with millimeter graduations will determine more precisely how long something is than one with centimeter graduations. If our measuring instrument, by means of which we interact with the atomic particle (say, an electron) is to be maximally precise, then we will need an extremely short wavelength, hence a high-frequency wave. But the energy of a single quantum with a high frequency ν will be correspondingly high, because $E = h\nu$. This will significantly disturb the momentum of an electron, the more so the higher the frequency. The change in momentum of the particle may be denoted as Δp.
2. In order to determine with great precision what the *momentum* of an atomic particle is, we need to disturb it as little as possible. But then we need as an interacting instrument of measurement a wave of the lowest possible frequency, and therefore of long wavelength. With such a wave, however, we cannot determine with any precision what the position of the particle is. This uncertainty as to exact position may be denoted by the positional spread Δx.
3. The indeterminacy relation which Heisenberg was led to formulate for these conditions is $\Delta p \cdot \Delta x \cong h$. This says, in effect, that there is a reciprocal relation, or an inverse proportion, between the possible precision of measurement of the simultaneous values of momentum and position of a particle. The more accurately the observer chooses to determine the position, the less precise will be his measurement of momentum, and vice versa.

In relatively short order, the quantum theory thus introduced major changes in the physical world picture, first in the particle-wave duality, which was seen to hold not just for radiation but for matter. The clear and univocal model of a structure of the physical world seemed to be upset by this duality. Second, the determination of the precise boundary conditions of position and momentum for physical particles, which constituted the foundation of the classical physical picture of mass points uniquely and determinately associated with instantaneous time values, also seemed to be possible no longer, in view of the indeterminacy relation. This caused and continues to cause a critical re-evaluation of the conceptual foundations of physical science, especially with regard to alternative interpretations of the quantum theory.

For one thing, is the indeterminacy a condition of measurement, betraying no more than our incapacity to get beyond a certain precision? May we assume that, whether or not we can find out, particles still continue to be at a place at a time? Is it only the uncertainty of our knowledge, or the physical indeterminateness of something like "real" position or "real" momentum, which is at stake here? There are a number of difficulties here. First, the question may turn out to be meaningless, because it introduces as a model of the physical world the classical particle at a classical world-point into a formal system (quantum physics) in which there is no description for such a particle. Rather, quantum theory is an essentially statistical theory in its very form, mathematically, and thus its entities are not particles but statistical distributions of swarms of such particles. Every theory has a certain ontology associated with it, in terms of what entities fall within its scope and its language. But if quantum theory does not speak the classical language of particles with point positions and determinate momenta, one cannot, within quantum theory, talk of the indeterminacy of the classical particle. That is, in the new theory the meaning of *particle* has changed and no longer countenances a simultaneous determination of the precise values of the classical particle.

For another thing, the incompatibility of the wave and particle pictures of the structure of the physical world may mean that what we are dealing with in the concepts *wave* and *particle* are models which are partially isomorphic with the physical reality of which they are models. Our experimental facts may now be such that the limits of this sort of picturing have been exceeded. Niels Bohr proposed that we retain the pictures in the sense of characterizing the elements of the physical world as sometimes (and under specifiable conditions) acting like waves and sometimes like particles. Thus, these two models are complementary, and between the two of them they exhaust the requirements for picturing, so that we may use them both, without attempting to decide which of the two is "really true." This proposal of complementarity of the particle-wave models (which involves not simply pictures, but the alternative formalisms of wave description and particle description) thus gives a bifurcated physics in which nevertheless the relations between the two models may be specified. The alternative interpretations of this proposal vary in epistemological and ontological emphasis. One may say that wave and particle are conceptual constructs which have been shown to be limited. Or one may say that both are aspects of a dual reality, which "really" is both particle-like and wave-like. Or one may say that the "underlying reality" is neither wave-like nor particle-like, and that these are only the appearances of this unitary reality under different conditions or from different points of view. Or one may say that particles are really nothing but certain densities of a field of wave propagation, and that they may be defined in terms of a wave function (like Schrodinger's Ψ-function, giving the density of charge in terms of the amplitude of a wave, such that the density is equal to the square of the absolute value of the amplitude, or $\rho = |\Psi|^2$).

In this view, density has been interpreted as a probability that a particle will be found within a given area. But if this probability is applied to a single particle, then it seems to imply one of two things. First, the particle really is at a particular place at a particular time and the statistical chances of our finding it at a given point P are proportional to the probability density at that point. This, in effect, has consequences like the indeterminacy relation. The longer it takes me to look, the more diffuse the position of the particle will turn out to be. For example, if I put a drop of red ink into a glass of water, its position at the outset will be more or less definable within limits; but the longer I wait, the less I will be able to determine the boundaries of the drop. Here, however, I do not know where to start looking (someone drops the ink into a large tank without telling me where, for example) and so my chances of finding the drop increase if I do not focus on a small area. Second, the particle may not be in a place at all, but may just be the relative concentration of my red ink throughout the medium or field. Thus it would not be a matter of saying it is here rather than there, but that it is *more* here than it is there, so that our ordinary concepts of *being at a place* break down.

The most traumatic effect of quantum indeterminacy is that it appears, on most standard interpretations, to abandon the postulate of *causality* which we discussed in an earlier chapter. This is a deceptive and problematic issue which we cannot deal with sufficiently here, to achieve a clear exposition of alternative interpretations. Classical strict determinism would seem to require that the states of the universe at any given instant be uniquely determinate. But *state* is always tied to some model of *state;* obviously, in the classical particle model, if at the quantum level there are no fully determinate states in terms of simultaneous (really instantaneous) values of space-time location, then strict determinism breaks down. But it would seem to break down because the conception of the classical particle has no equivalent in the quantum-theoretical framework; thus, it is not as if quantum theory itself postulates something which cannot be discovered. It is misleading to talk about the indeterminacy of position and momentum within quantum theory, because to be indeterminate is to be so with respect to something determinate. But this very determinateness remains unformulable within the theory, if by determinateness we mean classical point position and velocity. The claim, made in some popular interpretations, that quantum indeterminacy "proves" that "nature is inherently indeterminate" (if it can be said to make any sense at all) makes sense only if quantum physics is taken as an ultimate description of reality; and then it makes sense only as a rejection of the classical world picture, for only by reference to this does "indeterminacy" make any sense.

If we take quantum physics as operating over a domain in which its existents are the values of the variables in its equations, and if we take invariant association, predictability, or explanation as criteria of causality, quantum physics is as causal in this sense as is classical physics. That is, in a trivial sense its predictions come out right and its equations or matrices order the data of experiment. In this thin sense of "causal," reduced to "predictable" or "law-like," any successful physical theory is causal. But presumably, this is not what is at issue. For the values of the variables in quantum physics may themselves not be uniquely determined if we take these values to represent, e.g., energy states of particles; rather, they will be given as probability distributions operating over a whole ensemble of such particles. What is at issue is the interpretation of quantum theory as a conjecture about or a model of reality. Thus only on the interpretation that, "the position and momentum of particles is indeterminate," or, "the energy state of some particle cannot be uniquely determined, but only the probability distribution of energy states," that is, only on a view that determinism is ultimately a matter of what classical physics took to be determinate, can the theory be called indeterministic.

In general, it is only with respect to some favored view of what determinism must really be like or what causal relation must really be like that quantum theory may be interpreted as determinist or indeterminist. Here there are real conceptual problems, for the views we have formed of causal relation are bound very closely to some notion of a continuous space-time, in which motion is the successive occupation of space-time points, or is generated by events in some such continuum. Bohr's atomic model introduced radical discontinuities here, with the electrons changing state from higher to lower or lower to higher energy orbits or shells instantaneously, and thus passing from one place to another without being anywhere in between. Yet causality is maintained even in this radical spatio-temporal discontinuity. Such a jump is invariantly associated with the emission and absorption of quanta of energy of discrete values. The principle *nothing comes from nothing* is maintained with all its rigor, and the conservation laws are not abandoned. But even here there has been confusion. Because description in quantum theory is essentially statistical, the randomness of particular quantum events has been confused with their spontaneity or acausality. If this were really so, there would be no laws in quantum physics and, in effect, there would be no science. What is seriously in doubt is whether the classical situation of an event taking place at a space-time point can be retained in any meaningful physical sense. That kind of determinateness may in fact break down, together with the concept of the classical particle. The question as to what model will replace it, or whether one needs models at all, then becomes cogent. Some views disdain any interpretation at all, claiming for the theory a purely instrumental use and thus neither truth nor falsity with regard to any ontological interpretation. The theory, lacking systematic completeness, is on such a view admittedly and unabashedly *ad hoc;* but this is taken as a virtue, in disdain of any need to "philosophize."

Another modified version of this view is that the theory as it now stands is not ready for a conceptual model, and any attempts to impose one are premature, speculative, and misleading. This is at present an open and much discussed question. On the one hand, the whole past history of science seems to suggest that intellectual understanding of a physical theory requires a conceptual model, and it is in this sense that Einstein held quantum theory to be essentially incomplete in its present form. On the other, there is the view we have discussed earlier, that models are at best aids to the imagination; in this context, it may be argued that science has progressed beyond the need or possibility of such picture models, and that these belong to an earlier age. To search for them is to search for a will-o'-the-wisp. Yet the history of science and of philosophy strongly suggest that the attempt to understand the implication of the new physics in terms of the conceptual model we have of nature will not easily be put off by such theoretical austerity.

CHAPTER 13

Organisms and Mechanisms: Reduction and Explanation in the Biological Sciences

LIFE AND NONLIFE: MECHANISM, DUALISM, AND REDUCTIONISM

ONE OF THE OLDEST distinctions in human thought is that between the living and the nonliving. In Greek philosophy and physics, the distinction was drawn between those things which had a principle of self-motion, and those which required some mover to move them. Motion[1] was conceived not only as change of place, but also as change of quantity or quality and as becoming, or coming-to-be, in the sense of passing from potentiality to actuality. In the Aristotelian scheme, all such species of motion were the subject matter of physics. Later physics fastened on the species of motion as change of place, or local motion of physical bodies, in the development of kinetics. Here the relevant parameters are space, or distance in some space, and time, and also direction. Such a physics would ideally be geometrical in its expression, or would be entirely formulable in a physical geometry. The problems of a dynamic account of motion, in terms of its causes, invoked the notions of a motive force, passing from the Aristotelian teleological account in terms of natural place and innate tendencies (entelechies) to the impetus theories of the Middle Ages, and finally to the clarification of the concept of inertia in Newtonian physics. The idea of an "inner tendency," a "vital force," or "living force" as the source or cause of motion thus gave way in physics to the descriptive and nonteleological account in terms of masses and accelerations. The ex-

[1] (See Appendix A, pp. 428 ff. for a fuller discussion of the issues raised here.)

planation of motion thenceforth was reduced in Newton's formulation to an account of the laws of motion; and as we saw in the last chapter, the theoretical framework requisite for these laws, and for the Newtonian concept of inertia, was constituted in terms of that absolute space and time which is characterized as Newtonian, or classical.

In this great design of the universe on the model of mechanical physics, there is no place for the entelechies or innate drives of an earlier physics. Matter was desouled. The psyche (*anima,* in Latin), which was the principle of the self-motion of living things, was eliminated from physics. The only end-seeking or vital agency which classical physics admitted lay in the providential design of a universe which exhibited such mathematical perfection; the geometer-God who designed this cosmic clockwork was said to be the final or primary source of the motion of the great world-machine. And being perfect, such a God would produce a machine which could not run down, its original motion being conserved through all eternity, albeit in the transformations and translations of this motion according to laws. Thus the physical thesis of mechanics found its philosophical generalization in what has come to be called *mechanism,* and its theological framework in *deism.* In the former, the universe and all in it is conceived on the model of mechanical physics, all things, events, and processes being reducible to changes in the location of space-time elements (whether points, bodies, or field values). In the latter, the world-machine is seen to be a creation by some intelligent artificer who gives the system its first "push," or motion input, after which, the machine runs on by itself as a perpetual motion device without any further divine intervention. This deist God-of-the-first-push then retires from active commerce with the world, which thereafter merely exhibits the divine necessity of its design, discoverable and expressible in mathematical terms.

With the mechanistic interpretation of the world-picture, such living force or soul as had previously been adduced to explain life was eliminated from the physical world of space, time, and matter, and transferred to the realm of divine activity—self-caused, self-moving, and by extension of this conception, purposive, intelligent, and immutable, that is, immortal.

This dualism of matter and life and of matter and consciousness, with its roots in Greek and Judeo-Christian thought, found its sharpest expression in the world-picture of the new physics of seventeenth-century mechanism. The mathematician-philosopher Descartes expressed this dualism most clearly, postulating two substances, matter and consciousness, as ultimate and irreducible. Matter was *res extensa,* extended substance, occupying space and ultimately describable by the physical magnitudes of space and time. (Indeed, Descartes attempted a purely kinematic physics, reducing the dynamic concepts of mass and force to kinematic ones). For the rest, there was conscious substance, *res cogitans,* which was nonspatial and, unlike extended substance, indivisible, constituting a unity, or unifying activity (fashioned after the conception of thinking itself as such a unifying, or synthesizing activity, on which the self-identity of conscious beings was based).

Because consciousness or thought was a unity, and therefore incorruptible (i.e., it could not be destroyed or dissolved into elements), it was as such immortal. Here Descartes accommodated the theological doctrine of the immortality of the soul. The outcome here, relevant to our considerations, is this: Descartes considered that since human beings have immortal souls, and animals and plants do not, living things in nature, insofar as they were not humanly conscious, were highly complex machines, or *automata*. Their description, like that of all physical complexes, could therefore be given in terms of the arrangement and operation of physical parts in space and time. The laws of motion of such automata would be nothing but more complex forms of the laws of motion of physics. In short, biology was reducible to physics. Moreover, psychology, insofar as it dealt with animal behavior, could dispense with the concern about the soul. It was a mechanical science dealing with bodily motions of physical parts and what Descartes called "animal spirits" or "vital fluid," which could also be described in terms of physical operation. All considerations of purposive or intelligent behavior were thus eliminated from biology, and became instead the subject matter of a science of man as a thinking being, whose humanity or distinctiveness as a species lay entirely in his thinking activity.

The full account of dualism is an important part of the history of modern philosophy, which is often said to start with Descartes. Its importance here is that it introduces several major concepts which have become central and problematic in the philosophy of the biological and behavioral sciences. First, and most important, is the question of reductionism, and specifically of reductionist mechanism, in both its methodological and ontological aspects. Second, and related to this, is the question of the relation of the biological concepts of life to the physical concepts of bodies in motion in space and time. We may rephrase this question as one concerning the relation of organisms to mechanisms. Here the special concepts of teleology, function, and the relation of parts to wholes arise. In general, the problem arises of the relation of living to nonliving systems (or in an older terminology, of the organic to the inorganic). Third, questions concerning consciousness as a specific feature of some living systems arise. Included here are the special concepts of conscious purpose, will, and personality. Related to these are the host of questions concerning the concepts of the social sciences, insofar as these treat of communities or organizations of living systems and of conscious organisms. The main methodological and ontological questions, in all these cases, are the ones most sharply raised by Descartes concerning the reducibility of the sciences of biology and psychology to some form of mechanical physics. Although these questions are first raised in the framework of classical physics, and especially of its atomistic interpretation, they persist and become more complex as physics itself develops and raises new problems concerning its interpretation. In this brief chapter some of these main questions will be introduced; a more sustained analysis may be found in the rich literature on these questions in philosophy and the sciences.

REDUCTION AND EXPLANATION

Meanings of Reduction

In our earlier discussion of reduction (pp. 117 ff.), the concept was introduced in several contexts. First, in considering empirical significance, the question arose of the reduction of so-called theoretical terms to observation terms. The recalcitrance of the concept of observation to be reduced to some simple, unproblematic notion such as immediate perception or sense data as well as the notion of measurement statement, concerned us there. Second, we considered the methodological argument for reducing the different sciences to some ideal unity, interpreted as a unity of the language of science. On this thesis, all the various sciences could find some unique translation (the strongest version of this thesis) or partial interpretation in a canonical reduction language—presumably either that of sense data or of physical things in space and time.

Still another emphasis in this notion of reduction, and one which has strong intuitive appeal, is the interpretation of reduction as from the abstract to the concrete, and from the complex to the simple. These are different, for we may take the concrete as complex (e.g., the concrete organism may be the complex structure which appears to perception with its parts and relations unanalyzed and taken whole) and the abstract as simple (the ultimate parts of this organism may be taken to be such "abstract" entities as electrons, protons, and so on). Thus, although there is a strong intuitive appeal to these concepts of reduction, they beg the question unless they are further specified and we have more than some intuitive conception of what we mean by *concrete, abstract,* and so on. *Complex* and *simple* have a strong methodological appeal too, for we can easily specify what we mean by a whole and its parts (as we may easily specify, for example, that an atom is a whole whose parts are nucleons and electrons, or that an animal is a whole whose parts are its organs or its constituent cells). We also attribute heuristic value to this distinction between whole and part (or complex and element) in terms of the typical technique of problem-solving by analysis—the dissolution of a complex into its elements and their relations. The point is that in each of these senses of reduction, it is seen to be closely related to understanding. We come to understand something, whether theoretical, or abstract, or complex, in terms of its reduction to something more elementary or basic which is already taken to be understood (or is relatively uninterpreted in the explanatory framework). For example, the concept of uniformly accelerated motion comes to be understood when, on analysis, we can state the mathematical law which describes such motion. In this case, some intuitive notion of uniform acceleration is reduced to the mathematical description of a ratio between distances and times, these magnitudes in turn expressible in numerical terms, so that the law $s = \frac{1}{2}at^2$ gives us a mathematical reduction of the concept of uniformly accelerated motion, when s and t are suitably interpreted and a can be discovered by experiment. (See Appendix A.) Similarly, the function of breathing comes to be understood when it is discovered that the lungs serve to oxygenate the red blood corpuscles which supply the oxygen necessary to the metabolic processes of the cells. That asphyxiation causes death was known before body chemistry was understood; but with the comprehension of this chemical process, the meaning of the term *asphyxiation* becomes systematically more complex in terms of microprocesses of the organism. Reduction, in such cases, may be said to serve an explanatory function. In effect, such an explanatory reduction is an interpretation of one thing in terms of another, where what is interpreted is the *explanandum* and the interpretation the *explanans.*

Physicalism, Phenomenalism, Operationism, and Models

We now introduce the question of reduction of concepts in the biological and behavioral sciences to those of the physical sciences. We may consider this the reduction of organisms to mechanisms. On the mechanist thesis, the structure, behavior, and functions of all organisms may be explained in mechanist terms. The pictorial form of the mechanist thesis is that all of nature, including organisms, is machine-like in its operations and its ultimate construction. This may be taken as the thesis that organisms are in fact machines of a certain complex sort. But as an explanatory thesis, mechanism needs to hold only that the formal theory of mechanical physics can give a complete or adequate description of organisms and of the laws of their behavior. The concept of a machine is narrower than the general concept of mechanism, simply embodying the theory of mechanical physics in some physical structure. That such a structure is therefore a "machine" says no more than that it embodies the laws of mechanical physics, and need not be bound to pictorial representations of machines like those we are familiar with, or which we may imagine. This is not a simple claim, and has several different aspects:

1. On methodological grounds alone, if mechanism is interpreted as that mode of scientific inquiry which chooses mechanical physics as its base language, then all the descriptive predicates of this language will ostensibly

be reducible to description in terms of space-time coordinates (x, y, z, t), and the dynamic parameters of mass and force. (As we have seen, on one view, since force itself is defined in terms of mass and acceleration, force too is reduced or eliminated as a distinctive parameter.) This means that only such data as is itself formulable in space-time-mass terms can enter into experimental inquiry.

2. Further, if we admit the role of models in explanation, then the explanatory models will also be formulated or envisioned as mechanical. This does not mean that the models themselves need be embodied as "little machines," for they may be formal or mathematical models in which the values at space-time points (or at world-points) will be values for mass (or electrical charge or energy); on a strict mechanist interpretation, all such magnitudes would be intertranslatable and ultimately reducible to some one unified expression. C. D. Broad characterizes such a "pure mechanism" as one in which "all variables would be geometrical magnitudes or their first derivatives with respect to time, and all the macroscopic differences between one kind of matter or one state of matter, and another, would be those based on differences in respect of these variables among qualitatively homogeneous electrons."[2] Thus, just as the physical interpretation of Dalton's atomic theory in chemistry may be said to have introduced a mechanical model of chemical processes, interpreted and explained by the physical model of the atom, the mechanist reduction of biological processes would also introduce such a physical model as the explanation of such processes.

3. A further interpretation of such a reductionist view proceeds very far from any direct relation to either mechanical physics or mechanical models and emphasizes, instead, the reduction of all theoretical, or abstract, or complex terms in biology to observation terms. This view may take two forms.

a. Phenomenalist reduction. All theoretical terms in any science whatever are reducible to sensation or perception terms, in an empiricist language whose descriptive primitives are, for example, terms for color, brightness, sound, and so on, or descriptive terms for visual or tactile coincidence of two lines or lengths, and so on.

b. Operational reduction. All theoretical terms of any science whatever are reducible to descriptions of the operations or procedures of measurement, so that measurement statements themselves are reduced to descriptions of the experimental procedures in terms of which such measurements take place. To say that something is 10 cm. long would then reduce to a description of the procedure of making this measurement, "A rod graduated in centimeters is placed so that the end is coincident with an end point of

[2] C. D. Broad, "The Mechanical Explanation and its Alternatives," *Proceedings of the Aristotelian Society,* **19:**102 (1919); cited in J. H. Woodger, *Biological Principles* (New York: Harcourt, Brace, 1929), pp. 261–62.

the object to be measured, and the number on the graduation which coincides with the other end point of the object reads '10'; the rod is such that it is congruent with the object, i.e., is superposed on it so that it is in contact at all points along the object, etc."

Both of these related approaches found their most radical expression in the positivist verifiability theory of meaning (see Chapter 5) in which all the statements of a theory which were not, or could not be reduced to, observation statements on a phenomenal or operational basis were regarded as empirically meaningless and outside the domain of "positive science."

We now have three features of reduction: (1) reduction in terms of space-time description, which we may call physicalist reduction, (2) reduction in terms of models, (3) reduction in terms of some empirical base predicates taken to be phenomenal or operational. Strictly speaking, a mechanist reduction may be taken in senses (1) and (2) in the simple sense that mechanism is reduction to physics—notably to mechanical physics—and therefore such reduction is made when scientific inquiry eventuates in a mathematical description in terms of measurable physical magnitudes. This relates (1) to (3), therefore, if measurement statements are taken as basic. Further, mechanism is reduction to a mechanical or physical model in terms of a visualizable construct in space-time. The difficulty here is that not all physical models are clearly mechanical in either the sense of being little machines analogous in structure to what is modeled, or in the sense of mechanical physics. In the latter case, the physics of heat, of electromagnetism, energy, etc., is not simply mechanics. Within physics the mechanist reduction program has proceeded in the direction of reducing theories of nonmechanical phenomena like heat or electricity to mechanical phenomena, both in terms of a mathematical space-time model and in terms of physical models of such phenomena interpreted as particle motion in space. Thus, the kinetic theory of gases reduces the phenomenological concept of heat as some distinct quality to the mean kinetic energy of an ensemble of molecules; energy in turn is reduced to the motion of such molecules. The classic case of such a reduction is that of so-called phenomenological thermodynamics to statistical mechanics. Similarly, electromagnetic phenomena are reducible to the motions of charged particles. In the most striking case of the reduction of one science to another, chemistry, originally concerned with the properties of chemical elements and their combinations and reactions, is reducible in large part to atomic physics, in which the structure of the elements, taken as atomic and molecular entities, is reducible to the subelementary structure of atoms. Here, the typical chemical phenomena are reducible and explainable in terms of the properties of atoms, and the original qualitative distinctions of gases, liquids, and solids may be described in terms of atomic structures. The formal aspect of such reduction is that the laws of the reduced science (e.g., chemistry, thermodynamics) are shown to be derivable from the formulation in the reducing science (e.g., atomic physics, statistical mechanics), giving a deeper explanation in terms of substructures which account for the original laws.

The success of such reduction programs in physics and chemistry, and the enormous practical and theoretical progress to which such reduction leads, inevitably suggests the extension of such a program to the nonphysical sciences, e.g., to biology, psychology, and the social sciences. One simple example of such reduction is given by the physical theory of atomism, now so well-corroborated as to appear unshakable in the physical sciences, that all of nature is ultimately constituted of elementary particles in certain relations describable in either strictly causal or statistical laws. On such a thesis, all living things would differ from nonliving things only in degree of complexity of structure, and not in kind, in any irreducible sense. In such a view, living organisms are nothing but machines, i.e., organizations of physical elements of a certain structure. Therefore the complete scientific description of life would be a physicochemical one, expressible fully in physicochemical laws. The persistence of distinctive biochemical, biophysical, or biological formulations would only be a practical expedient, marking the difficulty of accomplishing the full reduction to physics, because of the great complexity of structure of living things. The issue arises, then, as to whether there are in fact distinctive biological laws and descriptions which are not reducible in principle to some (broadly) mechanist interpretation, and whether the reduction program of mechanism has a built-in limit of relevance to the nonphysical sciences. What then may be taken as the recalcitrant concepts of biology, psychology, and the social sciences, which raise such questions concerning the reductionist thesis? And what is their relation to the three senses of reduction we have considered above?

ORGANISMS AND MECHANISMS: STRUCTURE AND FUNCTION

What distinguishes biology from physics is ostensibly that biology deals with living things. These, then, must be uniquely distinguishable from inert, nonliving matter in some specifiable sense, to constitute a distinctive domain of scientific inquiry. We may characterize this distinction in several ways.

Features of Life

Living things have a certain common property absent in nonliving things. This is ultimately the tautological statement that living things are not nonliving. But what gives this statement its sense? It certainly does not explain or clarify to say that living things have the property *life*. But explication of the concept *life* may clarify this distinction. In general, living things are said to exhibit the general features of self-regulation and metabolism, and such characteristics as growth, adaptation, self-reproduction, irritability, and a variety of similar features *not* exhibited by all things in nature.[3] The claim of nonreductionism, in biological science, is the claim that these features are not reducible to physical description, or that the explanation of the phenomena is not reducible to physicochemical laws. This is a complex and, in these terms, a vague claim, and its explication involves making clear what such concepts as adaptation, or growth, entail.

Organization

In general, we may label the distinction between living and nonliving things as one between organisms and mechanisms. The reductionist claim is that organisms are ultimately mechanisms of a complex sort, or that a full account of organism may be given in mechanist terms; the nonreductionist claim is that organisms are uniquely nonmechanisms. But again, what distinguishes an organism from a mechanism here needs explication. The cue is in the concept of organization. The nonreductionist would claim that the organization of living systems or structures is such that the very fact of organization confers a unique set of properties upon organisms: their organization is self-maintaining so that all parts of an organism have the character of contributing in their functions to this self-maintenance. The description of a part of a whole organism is never complete if the relation of part to whole, and the function of parts in maintaining the integrity or wholeness of the organism, is left out. A mechanism, the argument goes, is not like this, for though parts of a mechanism may function together—as parts of a machine do—they remain what they are, either in or out of the whole structure. They have no essential functional characteristics, only accidental ones. A gear, a lever, or a relay are just what they are as parts, though they may have been designed by an engineer to fit together with other parts in a machine. The parts of an organism have no independent existence apart from the organization within which they function. A cell, which is part of an organism, "dies" outside the functioning totality of the living body of which it is a part. Even one-celled organisms, which may be considered as wholes, can function and live only within a higher-level organization, a medium or environment, in which their processes can be maintained in interaction with this environment. Thus, the organic part is what it is only in virtue of the whole whose self-maintenance it subserves.

[3] These features, while generally characteristic of living things, are not clearly universal; that is, there are counterinstances. Spores may suspend metabolic activities, remaining dormant or inert for long periods. Drones are not self-reproducing, and so on. Thus, not *all* forms of life have *all* these characteristics.

This introduces the additional distinction, the relation between *structure* and *function*.

Structure and Function

In describing a physical system in nature, we do not ordinarily talk of the *functions* of its parts, in terms of what ends they serve. We speak, instead, of its structure and its laws.[4] An earlier physics, oriented towards an organic view of nature, did talk of such functions, thus introducing teleological concepts into physics. (Indeed, we might say they were originally in physics, and did not have to be introduced but eliminated.) Thus, heavy objects were said to fall *in order* to reach their natural place; or, more spectacularly, the heavens were said to exhibit circular motion *in order to* give evidence of the perfection of God's universe, and testimony to the perfect intelligence of its designer. With the elimination of such teleological formulations in physics, functions are also ostensibly eliminated from mechanist description.[5] But in organisms, it still remains an essential feature of description to talk of such functions. In the attenuated sense of teleology here, an organism as a whole exhibits functional behavior and its parts are adequately understood only in terms of their functions.

The division of labor in biological inquiry separates anatomical from physiological studies, one examining structures as such, the other their functions in the intact organism, or in parts of it that may, for purposes of study, be separated from the whole. Thus the comparative zoologist may be interested in certain structural features of various organisms such as skeletal structure, dentition, the digestive system, musculature, or on the microscopic level, tissue or cell structure, serological characteristics, and so on. The physiologist may be interested in these same features as functions within a living system. For example, he may be interested in the metabolic processes of the cell, or the operation of muscle tissue in the life processes and activities of the organism. But plainly, the differences here

[4] One could point out, however, that it is precisely mechanisms, in the sense of mechanical artifacts produced to serve some purpose, that may be said to be functional or even teleological in this sense. That is, their parts are fashioned to work with respect to some function of the whole machine. On the other hand, it is the natural organism which has no humanly referential use or function in its organization, except on the older and cruder accounts of an anthropomorphic nature-philosophy. The distinction has also been drawn between internal and external teleology, in this sense, so that machines are characterized as exhibiting "external teleology," and organisms as exhibiting "internal teleology." Cf. Woodger, *op. cit.*, p. 430.

[5] This is a moot point. Engineers design machines and structures whose description (and the description of whose parts) is functional in the fullest sense. In some attenuated sense, certain holist or organicist views in physics may be said to be essentially functional in their theoretical accounts.

are the result of alternative emphases in the study of the organism. One cannot very well study the shape of an internal organ microscopically or visually examine the locomotion of an organism in terms of its internal musculature. That this is a practical question, and not one of biological principle is evident, for the limitations here may be purely technical, i.e., no more than limits of instrumentation. Many internal processes may now be examined in the living organism by new techniques. Certainly ways have been developed of studying the internal structure and functions of living organisms, by vivisection, by biopsy, by X-ray photography, sound wave photography, radioactive tracers, and so on. But the limits of such study, and the techniques of anatomical analysis often demand that parts of an organism be examined separately and outside the body. Together, then, anatomical and physiological study comprise an approach to acquiring the fullest information about the organism and its parts, in terms of a compound structure and function which together constitute the living organism.

Holism

Many arguments for the uniqueness of living organisms derive from this characterization of the organism as an organic whole, essentially irreducible to a mere collection of parts. Thus, the biologist J. S. Haldane writes, "If we are to get a grip of biological fact—the grip which enables us to predict—we must always keep the whole organism in view."[6] But such arguments differ widely in emphasis. The general view that, unlike mechanisms, organisms are essentially intact systems, and need to be studied as such, may be characterized as *holism*. Wholes are seen to exhibit features which are retained only if the organism is conceived of as an integral whole, and which disappear upon the destruction of this integrity. In the popular version of such a view, the whole is seen as more than the sum of its parts. The mere aggregation of parts would not constitute a whole, for there is lacking that integration which living organisms exhibit, and without which they are merely inert physical aggregates, as a dead organism is. Thus life is a property only of wholes that exhibits this unity. But this unity is seen not as a system of external relations among parts, but as an overriding and efficacious set of internal relations.

The concept of external and internal relations has a long history in philosophy and in science, and is not a self-evident distinction, to say the least. But it means that certain relations among parts can not be characterized by enumeration or by simple analysis of part by part. Rather, such internal relations are characteristic of the system as a whole, and are exhibited only in the systemic unity of a whole. For example, the relation of

[6] Woodger, *op cit.*, p. 243.

endocrine function to the condition of fear is not, in this view, something which may be studied by isolating the glandular structure and studying it as a part but only by studying the whole organism and its situation in a given environment. The mechanist may answer that by studying the chemistry of endocrine function, and by relating this to behavior, one may well discover that the mechanism of fear behavior may be analyzed in a fully physicochemical way. So, for example, knowing that adrenal function is stimulated in typical fear behavior, the mechanist may make his point by inducing fear behavior chemically or by electrophysiological stimulation of appropriate locations in the brain. The holist might then answer that it is only within an intact and functioning organism that chemically-induced fear behavior can take place, and that a concept like fear is therefore irreducible, and has no meaning at the endocrine level, and apart from organic behavior (though the physiological mechanisms which induce this behavior may be localizable, as parts of the organism). The argument that fear is "nothing but" a certain physicochemical state of an organism-mechanism is then a category mistake in the use of the term *fear,* because a cell, a gland, or a muscular system cannot be said to exhibit fear but only a highly complex and integrated organism may. The same mode of argument may be used by the holist to conclude that life as such (as a complex of such properties) is exhibited only by whole organisms as a function of their internal relations in interaction with an environment, and cannot be exhibited separately by any of their parts.

Vitalism and Emergence

On some such grounds, some holists would argue that the phenomenon of life is uniquely irreducible, and cannot be explained by reduction to physicochemical description, because this is always a description of parts only, and of their aggregation, and leaves out the qualitative uniqueness of wholes. But this argument too has different emphases.

a. Vitalism. One philosophical emphasis in biology, essentially dualist in its orientation, sees this unique property or quality as a separate "vital force," not present in any but living organisms and not in any way derived from physicochemical organization. This view, called vitalism, is most radically opposed to mechanism, not only in denying that physical systems as such can attain to such a quality, but in adducing this vital force as a unique *nonphysical* quality. Classical vitalism is closely related in form to Cartesian dualism. Physical matter and life are seen to be ultimately distinct "substances" or "principles," as, in Descartes, mind and body are. Although vitalists make no claim, generally, that this vital force is mental or conscious in any way, it still exhibits some of the characteristic features of the mental: it is seen to be goal-directed, i.e., teleological. It is alleged to be nonphysical in not being a spatial entity of any sort. Instead, it is conceived of, in the older vitalisms, as some innate or internal "push," or "drive," which has directive force and some direction. Therefore, in the late nineteenth and early twentieth century, vitalists characterized this inner drive as an *entelechy* (Hans Driesch's revival of Aristotle's notion of a "virtue" or "principle" which characterized the essence of a thing, and thus explained its characteristic motion or activity, in terms of "final causes"), or as an *élan vital* (Bergson), a vital force or impulse which exceeded any physical description and in fact violated the laws of thermodynamics, acting as a structuring or creative energy, in an instance of negative entropy. That is, the effect of this force was to convert energy into structure, multiplying or enhancing the energy input. Such a view raised serious questions at the time concerning the conservation laws, because apparently the claim was that in living things the total energy of the system was greater than the input. Living things, in effect, were creative systems, adding to the sum of energy and structure in the universe.

These older vitalist views have been largely abandoned, chiefly on two grounds. First, merely naming some mysterious force which was directive of organic activity did not constitute an explanation, but rather hindered inquiry by postulating something which was immune to empirical study. *Entelechy* was, then, a name for our ignorance, hiding the fact that we were ignorant, and committing the fallacy of explaining by naming. Second, the creative activity of living organisms did not in fact violate the law of conservation of energy, but was merely a case in which energy from outside the system of the organism was appropriated by it, and utilized in the process of structuring or growth that characterizes living things. Thus, living systems are instances of negative entropy, but only as "islands of negative entropy in a sea of entropy" (to use Norbert Wiener's metaphor).

The argument of creative activity, in the sense of growth, and of the evolution and proliferation of life forms, is answered by the nonvitalist with the thesis that life appropriates from the constant and conserved store of energy in the universe (in this case, the energy of the sun) and merely transforms this energy into structures, and into such structures as are themselves energy-appropriating. Living organisms are therefore "plugged in" to the sources of universal energy, but do not add any energy to this store, and are not creative in this sense.

Moreover, the mechanist alternatives have proven to be heuristically more fruitful, leading to inquiry and discovery, which vitalist views would have ruled out, or at least de-emphasized.

b. Emergentism. Alternatively, however, some holistically oriented biologists would dispense with the innate *vis* or *élan* of vitalism, and argue instead that organisms are not mechanisms simply because at a certain level of organization, certain properties appear which plainly do not exist at lower levels. The burden of this argument falls on the concepts of *level* and *organization*. It is asserted by these theorists that a quality such as that we call *living* is not merely the additive outcome, the sum of a combination of parts or elements, but rather the product of a certain configuration of different properties. The notion of level of organization thus entails the associated notion of kind of organization. To use a crude linguistic analogy, the words *dearth* and *thread* contain the same elements as letters, but obviously are not the same words. The "quality" of such combinations arises from their typical arrangements. But more than this, even a word like *thread* has different meanings, so that a mere description of the "anatomical structure" would give us little clue to how the word functions. In the context of a sentence the word acquires meanings from its interrelations with other words and from its syntactic function. Such a sentence is a whole, whose parts are significant only in the context of this whole. But further, the sentence itself and the initial alternative possible senses of the word *thread* are embedded in a larger framework of a language, which may for purposes of analogy be conceived as an organism whose parts derive their significance from the integrative complex of their historical development, local use and context, structure, and function, which confer linguistic sense upon particular elements of the language, i.e., upon its "molecules" and "atoms." Thus it would be senseless to ask what the last two letters of *thread* mean, for meaning is already a function of the "organism" and not of its "parts." Analogously, theorists who lay claim to the explanatory power of the notion of levels of organization conceive of the science of organisms as a science concerned with the *emergence* of certain properties of physical systems when these systems display characteristic types of organization. But organization means more than arrangement for the emergentist, and this is where the concept of levels "pays off."

A level of organization may be taken to mean simply a measure of complexity. For example, if the elements α, β, γ are parts of some whole a, and the relative wholes a, b, c are in turn parts of some whole A, then A is more complex than a and a is more complex than α by the asymmetry of the complex-part, or whole-part, relation. Thus, if organisms have cells as parts and cells have molecules as parts, then organisms are more complex than cells and cells are more complex than molecules. But the emergentist means something more than this by *level.* A level has a certain property of organization such that it tends to remain stable in this organization. Stability here means no more than self-maintenance in the face of changes which would otherwise tend to disintegrate the level. It is this feature of integrative persistence, which distinguishes an organization from a mere aggregate. The organization is self-sustaining. Thus the emergent holist speaks of *integrative levels,* meaning by this that the typical laws which describe such a level would have to include a law concerning the self-maintenance of that level. Clearly, such a law cannot be formulated for parts of a whole, because it is not the parts, but their integration which is sustained. This argument then proceeds on the logical grounds that a law describing such a whole is not reducible to the laws governing the parts of the whole, merely as parts. Thus too, from laws of the parts as parts, one cannot predict that certain combinations of parts will exhibit organic integrity, because this very property makes sense only at the integrative level in which the parts constitute an organization.

The emergentist argument, although it is fundamentally an argument within the philosophy of biology, has its extension in physics and chemistry as well. Thus, for example, certain properties appear only at the level of molecular combination, but are not properties either of the contituent molecules or of their constitutent atoms. Color and heat would be such properties. Molecules are neither colored nor do they have the property of heat. The reductionist may argue that color is nothing but the wavelength of emitted electromagnetic radiation, and that elements therefore have typical emission wavelengths which we may call their color when these are perceived by the human eye. Moreover, heat is in fact nothing but the phenomenological effect of the motion of molecules, so that a temperature reading of the degree of hotness of a body is in effect explainable as a measure of the mean kinetic energy of the molecules of that body, and their emission of energy of motion, and not an irreducible quality, as in earlier and mistaken caloric theories. When the emergentist claims that the laws of a system are not reducible to, formulable as, or derivable from the laws of its parts, the mechanist might answer that when we discover such properties of a system, it is precisely the task of the theoretician to formulate laws concerning the elements of that system in such a way that system-preserving properties will be derivable from the elementary laws. For example, the disposition of certain elements to combine with others chemically and the stability of certain elements and combinations and the instability of others is explained physically not by adducing some upper-level law of systems, but by producing a model of the atom which will account for this. Thus, the notion of complete and incomplete outer electron shells of the atom is an account, in terms of the elements, of certain features of systems of such elements, e.g., stable and unstable compounds.

This division between reductionist and nonreductionist views has methodological and ontological aspects. Methodologically, the claim of the reductionist leads to a theoretical attempt to account for systematic characteristics by an enrichment or reformulation of the models and theories of the reducing domain. Thus, for example, one would have to inquire and discover, at the physicochemical level—say at the molecular level—those properties which would account for the emergent properties of the system. Heuristically, this leads to intensified research in the reducing domain, guided by these requirements. The great cytologist E. B. Wilson characterized such a mechanist program as having "kept us moving in the right direction."

But the holist also has a methodological contribution to offer, and that is to warn against the dogmatism which the mechanist may fall into in regarding the reducing domain of physics or chemistry as complete or adequate at any given time, thus relegating what cannot be reduced in these terms to the meaningless or occult. The holist insists on the specificity of certain biological phenomena in a way which puts the burden on the mechanist to account for them in reductive terms. Here the radical vitalist and the emergentist part company methodologically. For the vitalist insists that the specific features of life cannot be reduced to physicochemical terms, and these features are unamenable to such reductive inquiry altogether. This is, in this respect, a dogmatic *a priori* attitude, an article of faith rather than a scientific methodological criticism. If the emergentist were to postulate an unexaminable agency by means of which the emergence of new properties took place, he too would be guilty of such *a prioristic* dogmatism. But the emphasis in biological emergence theories is on a perfectly examinable feature of biological systems—namely, organization—and thus poses the scientific problem of a theoretical account of systems and their self-maintenance to biological inquiry.

But there is another aspect to the division between reductionists and holists which does not fall strictly within the domain of methodological questions, but raises the ontological question of whether organisms are or are not mechanisms. Here, the distinction we drew earlier (Chapter 10) between alternative interpretations of theories and models is relevant. It is one thing to hold that organisms may or may not be explained by the model of mechanism or by a mechanistic theory. This is surely methodological. But it is another thing to hold that organisms are in fact mechanisms of a certain kind, or that they are irreducibly organismic and nonmechanistic. It is hard to say exactly what this can mean, for it means several things at least.

1. Mechanism may mean "mechanical" or "like a machine," and the limits of the concept are not clear, especially if we consider that the simple mechanical devices of an earlier age have been replaced with electronic mechanisms which in turn will surely be succeeded by more sophisticated hardware. It is also unclear in terms of recent developments, how one may clearly separate hardware from software (i.e., the directive and intelligent component of consciousness) when the two are linked in a unified system, in contemporary conceptions of man-machine systems. This model may also be used to conceive of the body of an organism in a machinelike way, for certainly mechanical descriptions of body functions are at present the most adequate ones we have and are highly sophisticated. And it is conceivable, and heuristically fruitful, to envision such a complex of obviously living and conscious organisms and obviously mechanical devices as itself a system which may have organic features as a whole. In short, the practi-

cal distinction between organism and mechanism may become less rather than more clear with the development of systems which intimately link now-distinct organisms and mechanisms. (The classical distinction regarding the power of self-regeneration of parts which are destroyed or used up, which only organisms are said to have, will be discussed shortly.)

2. While mechanism may also mean, as we have pointed out, physicochemical description—classically, in terms of mechanical physics—by extension, it may also be taken to mean description in terms of the state of physical science at any point (thus, in terms of a ramified physics which goes beyond classical mechanics). Such a "pure" mechanism as C. D. Broad describes as a completely Cartesian geometrical reduction would depend on the state of physical geometry at a given time. But the requirement for such a reduction would also put an exceptional burden on biological inquiry at present, for not even the most advanced biochemistry and biophysics is ready to give such a reduction for even the simpler microbiological phenomena. The biologist would have to assume that he has not really achieved very much in the way of an explanation until such a reduction is forthcoming. Still, the program of such a reduction, as a working hypothesis, may prove exceptionally fruitful, as it has in the recent spectacular advances in molecular biology.

3. Mechanism may mean, in the context of our earlier discussion of causality and determinism, no more than the thesis of either a strict or a statistical determinism in the laws of biological phenomena, and may be called mechanism only with respect to the historical accident that such causal and statistical determinism has had its most striking exemplifications in physics. This sense of mechanism is so broad, and so contingently related to the mechanism which is opposed to organism, that it goes beyond our present considerations.

Thus, the decision as to whether organisms are or are not mechanisms requires as much clarification of the term mechanism as of organism. In a critical discussion of this ontological question, J. H. Woodger writes (with respect to what he characterizes as the "ontological dogmatic mechanism" of Sir E. Schafer),

> [Schafer's view] is worthy of mention here as an illustration of the extraordinary simplicity with which biological problems present themselves to the physiologist [mechanist]. He simply picks out all those characteristics of organisms which can be imitated in the inorganic world and omits all the difficulties which arise, when we try to push the analogies a little further, until we wonder how anyone could have come to suppose that organisms presented any problems at all. Moreover, the concepts of physics are taken on their face value as quite concrete and exhaustive in their own sphere. Such a point of view can either be accepted or rejected as a whole: there is no scope for discussion. Ontological mechanism of

> such a simple cocksure kind really belongs to the realm of religious enthusiasm like some ontological vitalisms and is therefore beyond the reach of criticism. It is difficult to avoid the conclusion that such extremes are reached more by way of a "will to believe" than by the simple desire to find out what is the case.[7]

The suggestion here is that the ontological question is really decided on methodological grounds, from the point of view of a particular kind of study—here, for example, physiology—in which the abstractive framework singles out certain features of the domain of inquiry; but then dogmatism hypostatizes this framework and asserts that organisms are mechanisms because that is the way they lend themselves to be studied. By application of the same principle, any abstractive methodological framework generates its own ontology, so that the question of organism or mechanism becomes either trivialized or completely relativized, or reduces to the pragmatic methodological question of what is a suitable, or the most suitable, framework for a given line of scientific inquiry. R. Carnap characterizes such ontological questions as "external questions" regarding the choice of frameworks, and considers these questions of practical rather than of philosophical decision[8] (as opposed to "internal questions" concerning what entities are said to exist within a given framework). This introduces a broader issue in the philosophy of science concerning reduction, which has special relevance to the issue of organisms versus mechanisms.

Explanatory and Ontological Reduction

The question of whether life is to be explained in terms of mechanist or organicist frameworks is a different question, as we have seen, from the one concerning the ontological status of organism. To explain organismic features by reduction to physicochemical laws or mechanistic models is not yet to make the claim that organisms are nothing but mechanisms. For on this claim, there really are no such things as organisms, and *organism* is only a convenient name for a certain subclass of mechanisms. An ontological reduction in this sense eliminates an entity in our ontological conception, and denies its existence. In scientific explanation this often happens, as when the devils in the devil theory of disease were eliminated. We then hold that there simply are no such things as devils that cause disease, or at least that *devil* is the earlier imaginative and mistaken conception of some entity which in fact does cause disease. Similarly, our whole preoccupation with living things and nonliving things may be just such an elementary confusion carried over from animistic explanation, in the con-

[7] Woodger, *op. cit.*, pp. 249–50.

[8] Cf. R. Carnap "Empiricism, Semantics and Ontology," Supplement, *Meaning and Necessity,* 2nd ed. (Chicago: University of Chicago Press, 1956), p. 206 ff.

text of which we are simply postulating a ghost or a devil in the machine, where in fact there isn't any. In place of this naive dualism of ghost and machine, perhaps we need an entirely different monistic concept eliminating both the ghosts and the sort of machines that require ghosts to explain their activity. Such a reduction would indeed be ontological.

The different more modest claim of methodological or explanatory reduction does not deny that there are such things as organisms. Rather, granting that the term *organism* denotes a distinctive kind of entity which exists, it simply says, "What is designated as *organism* in a theory *O* and described in terms such as *self-regulating, self-reproducing,* and so on, is explained by a reducing theory *M* in which self-regulation and self-reproduction, and so on, are explained in physicochemical terms, for example, in terms of negative feedback or molecular accounts of genetic replication and variation." The organism as an entity remains intact in this conception, but its features find their explanation in laws of its "ultimate" constituents and their systematic processes, or the laws of their activity. The question arises as to when an explanatory reduction is entitled to be taken as indeed an ontological reduction, and also as to what the practical sense of this proposal is. Should we in fact stop talking in terms of organisms in current biology, if the mechanist reduction turns out to be successful, or should we retain the organism language as a convenient framework though not a true one. We have dealt with related questions in our discussion of explanation and the role of theories and laws, but it is raised here with respect to reduction in an especially sharp way. For what is at issue is not the reduction of one aspect of some science to another aspect of the same science, as for example, of phenomenological thermodynamics to statistical mechanics, within physics, but of one science to another, for example, of biology to physics. This raises still another question concerning what marks one science off as distinctive from another, and whether alleged "aspects" of the "same" science are not, in effect, different sciences.

The relevance of the interpretations of reduction we have considered becomes clear if we examine briefly some of the developments in biological concepts relating to the distinctive features of organisms.

THE BIOLOGICAL CONCEPTION OF LIFE

Among the central concepts in biology which mark the boundaries of the issue between reductionists and holists are those which deal with (1) self-regulation, (2) growth, and (3) self-reproduction.[9] The fields of physi-

[9] Strictly speaking, these three features of life are not at the same level. Self-regulation is by far a more general concept. And it may be seen that growth and self-reproduction are themselves modes of self-regulation, in the individual organism and in the species.

ology, genetics, immunology, embryology, endocrinology, cytology and virology, among others, contribute to the conceptual issue and its possible resolutions. All the techniques of inquiry—classificatory, comparative, biochemical, and biophysical—are relevant to the issues, suggesting one or another interpretation of the basic concepts. We may briefly consider how some of these basic concepts may be analyzed from the point of view of the broader question of reduction versus holism.

Self-regulation

The hallmark of much of the argument concerning teleology in organisms is the discussion concerning the self-regulation of living systems. *Regulation* carries all sorts of normative connotations associated with the concepts *rule, purpose, goal, end-state. Self*-regulation adds to this the connotations of some autonomous or self-legislative function, suggesting a reflective or conscious agency with its "eye" on some goal or preferred state. Ostensibly, such a goal would not be present but envisioned in the future; or some such preferred state although not present, might be remembered from the past. It is easy to see why the self-regulative features of organisms suggest their distinctiveness in this regard. A mechanism is plainly not conscious and is non-normative, though we may speak of it as "obeying laws." But in a non-normative and descriptive account of mechanism (whether in terms of physicochemical laws or their embodiment in some machine), we may reconstrue all these terms without reference to normative or conscious behavior. The typical case of such self-regulation is the orientation or direction of the activities of some system toward some not-present state, and the maintenance of that state once achieved, without any direction or intervention from outside the system. This case of self-regulation by reference to an end state which is also a steady or stable state of the system further includes the factor of possible disturbances of the system which, were it not self-regulative, would deflect the system from its orientation or destroy it entirely. The earliest accounts of living systems talk of self-preservation as the primary law of life, adducing some such self-regulative function. Thus, animal activities—primarily feeding and reproducing but also the involuntary metabolic functions, breathing, digesting, and so on—all serve this end, either for the individual organism or for the species. The survival of an individual organism of a species is thus the successful operation of self-regulating processes, and among the higher life forms, biological death of individuals of a species is the relative failure of these processes. ("Relative" because the death of the individual may be a condition for the survival of the species.)

The question of whether this is or is not a reducible feature of living systems depends much on definition, for in one sense it has become abundantly clear that the concept of self-regulation and self-preservation has a mechanistic analogue, and the maintenance of a steady state, or *homeostasis,* is as much a feature of nonliving as of living systems. The typical examples of such homeostatic mechanisms are called servomechanisms, so constructed as to "adapt" to changes and still maintain a certain orientation. Among the earliest of such completely mechanical devices was Watt's *governor,* which regulated the steam pressure in a boiler by means of a valve which opened when the steam reached a certain pressure and closed when it fell below a certain pressure. Another simple homeostatic device (or mechanism for homeostatic control) is the bimetallic thermostat, which closes an electrical circuit when temperature falls below a certain point and breaks the circuit when temperature goes above a certain point. Both of these and many other such devices use simple mechanical principles. The governor converts steam pressure into rotational motion, the centrifugal force of which opens a valve; the thermostat utilizes differences in coefficients of expansion of two metals to cause a mechanical stress which effects closing or breaking a circuit. And both require an input of some sort, which varies if they are to operate differentially: The governor requires the heat input in the boiler, and the thermostat requires the temperature variations in the surrounding medium. The development of a highly sophisticated arsenal of self-regulating devices in the last decades—guided missiles, celestial navigation controls for spaceships, automated production controls, and so on—and the development of a scientific theory of such regulation (cybernetics) seems once and for all to settle the question of whether self-regulation is or is not reducible in mechanistic terms. The questions concerning the "teleology" of such homeostatic, goal-seeking, or guided systems are given the simple answer, "If this is what you mean by teleology, well then, here you have it in a machine." This seems to end the debate concerning the reducibility of organisms to mechanisms in this regard at least.

But all is not well. The organicist (or any interested observer, for that matter) may raise the additional question, "What you show in these so-called teleological mechanisms is that certain simple states, in terms of pressure, temperature, direction of motion, and so on (in short, physical magnitudes) may be maintained homeostatically by physical means. But this is distinct from that homeostasis which preserves a living system. For what is preserved here is not temperature, pressure, or direction, nor even the more complex functions of metabolism, but rather something which, in the living system, all these functions subserve—i.e., life. True, homeostasis may well be a ubiquitous phenomenon throughout nature; but the combination of all the homeostatic mechanisms which subserve a living system will not of themselves constitute a living system. Again, the holist might argue, "You are confusing parts and wholes." Or the argument might run, "The homeostatic physical system is doing things *like* those which a living system does, but it is not a living thing, no more than the living thing is thereby a mechanism."[10] The objection, then, is that no matter how far we are able to extend the analogy of mechanisms with respect to organic functions, the analogy remains an analogy, and the "identity" (presumably the ontological identity) of mechanisms and organisms is not thereby asserted. At best, we have a partial isomorphism in structures, and therefore a partial isomorphism in accounts of such structures. The "technozoism" which compounds the reduction by talking of mechanisms as organisms suffers the same fate. No matter how far we develop mechanisms which may replace parts of organisms, as in prosthetic devices, each of these is a part, and no combination of such parts can produce more than an artificial organism, the distinction between artifact (as something made by man) and nonartifact remaining forever unimpeachable. (One could argue that men make other men, as "artifacts" in the mechanism of reproduction, but this stretches the sense of *artifact* quite far, albeit in an interesting way.)

On the one hand, then, the mechanist-reductionist may claim that all the distinctive or allegedly biologically specific features of self-regulation may be accounted for in terms of the mechanisms of negative feedback, of a retroactively linked system, of mechanical parts operating wholly within physicochemical laws. On the other hand, the nonreductionist-organicist may argue that all this proves is that the parts of an organism are mechanisms, but what makes the organism an organism is precisely that organization of such parts which gives rise to the qualitatively distinct phenomenon or emergent property of life.

Self-reproduction and growth

The organicist may go a step further here, in pointing to certain homeostatic processes as not really mechanizable, and as distinctive of organic homeostasis. Thus, though thermal regulation of the body and the mechanisms of balance have their analogues in thermostats and gyroscopes, the specific forms of self-regulation which involve growth, adaptation, regeneration of diseased and destroyed tissue, and in general the whole system of endocrine balance and of disease resistance and immunity, are biologically specific processes. These fundamental processes of life are cell processes, on the very lowest level, and do not occur below that level. The cell is thus the irreducible unit of life, even if the organism is not, on this

[10] The analogous argument suggested by M. Bunge concerning computers is that "strictly speaking, computers do not compute, machines do not think, but they perform certain physical operations that we coordinate with certain mental processes." The biomorphism which leads us to talk of machines as organisms, and the anthropomorphism which leads us to think of computers as intelligent is the other side of the coin of that reductionism which leads us to think of organisms or of minds as machines. Bunge's view is that this is "to confuse resemblance with identity." (*Metascientific Queries,* Springfield, Illinois: Thomas, 1959, pp. 151–52.)

view. We may speak of living cells, but not, for example, of living molecules. Again, the "levels" view may countenance physicochemical mechanisms which operate to subserve the homeostasis of the cell, but the living cell is more than the sum or aggregate of these mechanisms, and once again constitutes a "whole" as an integrative level of organization. The reduction from organisms as cell complexes, to unit cells, connotes a concession to the reductionist, on the view of the organic holist. But this does not yet admit an outright mechanism threatening the hegemony of biology in its own domain; rather, this is an internecine issue among biologists, where the intrusion of the physicist would be considered an act of intervention in internal affairs by a foreign power. Still, if the metabolic, regenerative, self-reproductive activities of the cell were also to be challenged by the molecular biologist, on the grounds that all such activities could be explained and reduced to molecular terms, then chemistry at least (if not the "pure mechanism" of physical geometry) would intrude on the biologists' domain.[11]

The most striking challenge to the imperviousness of the cell to reductive explanation comes from contemporary molecular biology, specifically in the areas of genetics, immunology, and virology. For if we leave self-regulation aside now and consider the claim that mechanisms are not self-reproductive, then recent discoveries in genetics raise the issue sharply once more as to whether something taken to be characteristically a physicochemical structure, the molecule, can be said to exhibit features previously reserved to organisms.

The older debate in the 1920's centered around the issue of whether the genetic processes could be said to be located within the cell or were processes of the whole cell, or of the whole organism. If self-reproduction is taken as criterial for living things, then if this process can be shown to be subcellular, there must be a unit of living matter that is smaller than, and a constituent of, the cell and that effects cell reproduction. In general, the process of genetic reproduction centers on cell constituents called chromosomes. The question arises as to what in the chromosome is capable of effecting reproduction, in particular, the growth and division of a single cell into two cells with the same genetic characteristics. Here a distinction needs to be drawn: In mitosis, the chromosomes, visible under a microscope, split and are thus capable of replication. This replication of the chromosomes appears as the effector of cell reproduction. But what controls or effects the replication, or explains how a duplication of features in the new cells takes place, must then be some process in the chromosomes, traditionally associated with entities called genes. The reductionists

[11] All this talk of "intrusion" and "intervention" is of course purely metaphorical, because the scientist in search of truth has nothing to defend (one hopes) except the truth, from whatever quarter it may come, departmental loyalties and commitments notwithstanding.

argued that such a mechanism must be at the level of molecules, whereas the holists (at the cellular level) argued that a molecule could not contain enough structure or information to transmit the complex requirements of reproduction of genetic traits. Discussing the argument as it proceeded in the 1920's, F. O. Schmitt recently characterized it thus:

> Both groups—the molecular reductionists on the one hand and the cellular, organismic or naturalistic holists on the other hand—were right and both were wrong. The molecular reductionists piled up on the Scylla of molecular componentry, because their conceptual models lacked a systems-type organization, in which the stored information might be meaningfully processed; the cellular and organismic holists, on the other hand, foundered on the Charybdis of reliance on mystical emergent properties of systems devoid of demonstrable information—containing molecular components.[12]

In 1923, Schmitt points out, it would have been considered nonsense to suggest that a macromolecule with a weight of 10^6 to 10^9 could exist in the nucleus of the cell. The recent history of the discovery of the relation of viruses to replication, and of the structure of the giant macromolecular polymer DNA (Deoxyribonucleic acid) which is found in cell nuclei (in the chromosomes only) provides the background for the present revolution in biology. We will not recount it here. But the issue comes to this: A molecular structure of enormous size has been discovered in the cell and its structure analyzed. It is such that it provides the model of a genetic "template," complex enough to contain all the information needed to transmit the genetic structure of an organism, and is, furthermore, capable of self-replication. The whole process of storing this information, transferring it (by means of so-called messenger RNA, or ribonucleic acid, which is found outside the nucleus in the cell), and retrieving it can now be explained for a system which contains such large polymeric molecules. The structure envisioned for DNA, in the Watson-Crick model—a double helix with connecting links—permits a reconstruction of the genetic information as a linear sequential array of *codons*—bits of coded information—which may be "read out" and transferred by RNA molecules to the ribosomes, the synthetic centers of the cell which control and direct its growth and development. This genetic coding mechanism, capable of self-replication and effecting cellular and organic reproduction, would certainly seem to be a physicochemical "mechanism" in the full reductionist sense. But the question then arises whether such a molecular structure capable of self-replication is not thereby a living system itself: in short, whether we may talk of a "living molecule." In experiments where the cells containing the

[12] F. O. Schmitt, "The Physical Basis of Life and Learning," *Science,* **149,** no. 3687 (August 27, 1965), p. 932.

DNA were destroyed, there remained, in the disintegrated and dissolved debris of the cells, a factor still capable of transmitting the hereditary characteristics of these killed cells. But the action of DNA is highly specific. It is "dead" except under the specific conditions of its *particular* cell. This same extraordinary specificity is found in the activity of viruses, which are also "dead" or inert substances, except under the conditions of being hosted by their "appropriate" cells. It is as if, for every specific "lock" in the living world of cells, there were only one "key" capable of opening it. Viruses were discovered to be RNA molecules wrapped in a protein sheath, and their replication in host cells became a link in the chain of discoveries and inquiries which led to recent formulations of molecular genetics. The question is asked also, then, whether viruses are "living" or "nonliving." For in one sense, if we can discover a molecular structure which exhibits the criterial characteristic of self-replication, then what is left of the non-reductionist argument but perhaps to claim, *in extremis,* that at least *atoms* are not "living"?

One thing argues against such a simple interpretation and suggests revision of one-sided reductionism and one-sided holism. First, the process of reproduction is not simply a process of replication, but rather, some replicating mechanism is the effector of the self-reproduction of cells. Second, the process of genetic reproduction consists not simply of a molecule of DNA, but of a system: DNA-RNA-protein. The protein molecule is a specific enzyme, formed upon the transfer of the code from DNA via RNA, and it, in turn, controls highly specific chemical reactions. Enzyme specificity is such that there are about 10^5 different enzymes in the human organism, so that growth, adaptation, self-regulation of a system as large and complex as a human organism depends on the systemic interrelation of an extraordinarily large complex of elements. Thus, the notion of system is fully incorporated in the "mechanist" model of the DNA-RNA-protein process. This effective factor of system becomes even more cogent when the specificity of certain molecularly controlled processes is seen to extend to the individual organism. This means, in effect, that something like "self-recognition" occurs at the molecular level of individual organisms. Schmitt calls it "molecular selfness recognition." This occurs strikingly, in the rejection of "foreign tissue," in transplants of organic parts, so that only tissue from a twin or close relation will "take," and even here only with the suppression of this individual specificity by chemical means (cytotoxic drugs, which permit grafts and transplants). It may be left to the holist to argue that the mechanisms of genetic reproduction function only with respect to a system of which these mechanisms are parts, and that life itself is a functional characterization of such wholes. But if it is simply a matter of reiterating "but that's not what *I* mean by life," every time a mechanism is discovered to account for a property of living matter, then assuredly no argument is possible, and holism may then be regarded as the asylum for ignorance. But the mechanist may not simply make the claim that a molecule is "living"; his stronger claim is that more and more living processes can be explained as molecular processes, but as molecular processes in which the element of system plays a major effective role.

This suggests that a system of mechanisms at a certain level of organization will exhibit life-like properties; and further, that at the molecular level of such "mechanisms," it is no longer a matter of an analogy or a model, for the molecules are molecules, whether arranged synthetically in accordance with some model or coming to be arranged naturally, in the course of time and within varying "environments." In short, this suggests the spontaneous generation of life out of the organization of physicochemical structures, or the origin of life out of nonliving matter, as in the hypothesis of Oparin, Wald, and others. At the point of transformation—which is apparently not a "point" at all, for there are intermediate structures of varying degrees of "livingness" and "nonlivingness," in the chemical stages of this development—it is impossible to say "this is life" or "this is nonlife." Leibniz characterized the continuity of nature when he said, "Nature doesn't make any leaps." Recent inquiry into the origin, the structure, and the transmission of life suggest that this continuity between the living and the nonliving goes deeper than we might have guessed.

CHAPTER 14

Mind, Society and History: Some Fundamental Concepts in the Human Sciences

WHY "HUMAN SCIENCES"?

JUST AS A DISTINCTION is drawn between the living and the nonliving, so too an ancient and pervasive distinction has been drawn between man and nature. Man is certainly a physical entity, and as a body moving in space or as a heat-engine his structure and processes are describable in terms of mechanics and thermodynamics. He is certainly a biological entity, however complex and distinctive, and the continuity of human life forms with those of the rest of living nature is a striking fact (brought home by evolutionary theory), which serves as methodologically important guide to scientific study. But there is a clear sense in which man is more than a physical or biological phenomenon. From the dawn of human self-consciousness, in myth, religion, literature, philosophy, there is a persistent attempt to define the distinctively human and to embody the man-nature distinction in some essential or systematic formulation. Aristotle, within his classificatory scheme of genus and difference, defined man as, within the genus *animal,* a *rational* animal. Plato, in the dialogues, has Socrates elicit the tongue-in-cheek definition of man as a "featherless biped" (upon which someone produces a plucked chicken as an instance of "man" thus defined). Man has alternately been described, in other such "essential" definitions, as a value-creating animal, a tool-making animal, a speaking animal, a symbol-making animal, a culture-producing animal. Only man, for example, is said to "work," as distinct from the sheer life activity of other living things. And only man is said to be time-binding, in a culture in which past impinges on present and present on future in the conscious phenomena of memory and in the artifacts of language, art, and technology. Descartes distinguishes human essence as thinking activity, which he conceives as reflective and introspective self-consciousness. In this same direction, the nineteenth-century German philosophers Hegel and Feuerbach fastened on this self-consciousness as unique in being a matter of species-consciousness, man being aware of himself as a species rather than merely as an individual. This fulfills that classic tradition in which the hallmark of thought, or of that distinctly human consciousness we call reason, is that it knows universals. This is also linked to the notion of religious consciousness as uniquely human. ("Animals have no religion," Hegel remarks, by way of making this distinction.) Marx and Engels saw human specificity in the organization of production and in the development of institutional structures, such as the family and society, in which the conjoint activities of production of the means of life and the reproduction of life are carried out. Art, love, cruelty, hope, and sin, among others, have been noted as exceptional and uniquely human phenomena, as have also the features of personality and self-conscious self-identity.

Beyond such philosophical characterizations the development of scientific inquiry into human phenomena has given rise to such disciplines as psychology, sociology, anthropology, and history, each in its way emphasizing some aspect of human activity. The distinction comes to be made, in this context, between the natural sciences (physics, chemistry, biology) and the behavioral and social sciences. Granting the striking continuity of man with all of living nature, it is clear that in essential respects these latter may be called the *human sciences*. An older reductionism, of a generation ago, raised the critical question as to whether such sciences are properly scientific, in the paradigmatic sense in which the natural sciences are said to be scientific; i.e., with respect to the formulability of quantitative laws, the use of experimental method, and the supposedly ideal precision of the "exact sciences." The distinction between "hard" and "soft" sciences, between "exact" and "inexact" sciences, and between "quantitative" and "qualitative" sciences has also been adduced, usually to the derogation of the "soft," "inexact," and "qualitative" sciences. These are methodological questions, but their resolution lies not in some simple adherence to one or another paradigm within this or that science, nor in defensive departmental loyalty. Rather, it lies in an analysis of the concepts and procedures characteristic of the human sciences, and in concrete and specific judgments of the adequacy of method to subject matter within the given disciplines. This field is perhaps the most challenging in contemporary philosophy of science, both for its complexity and the sharp questions it raises concerning the logic and methodology of scientific knowledge. Any adequate treatment, of even an introductory sort, requires more than can be attempted here, and the student is referred to the excellent and rigorous treatment which this subject has elicited in contemporary philosophy of the social and behavioral sciences (see bibliographical note for this chapter). Here, we will do no more than introduce, in the barest way, what some of the conceptual issues are in this framework of the human sciences.

MIND, CONSCIOUSNESS, AND BEHAVIOR: SOME CONCEPTUAL ISSUES IN PSYCHOLOGY

Self-inquiry

The peculiarity of psychological inquiry is that a percipient and conscious organism, whose knowledge is a matter of this very perception and conscious thought, takes these features themselves as the subject of inquiry. Aristotle noted this, writing in his treatise on psychology, "Mind is itself thinkable in exactly the same way as its objects are."[1] This suggests, at the very outset, the problems of methodology in terms of which psychology can come to formulate its subject matter. Initially, "mind thinking itself" suggests a reflective inquiry, best carried out as a matter of self-contemplation and introspection. On such an introspective approach, different investigators might pursue such self-inquiry into the conditions of their own consciousness, and their reports (as "first-person" reports) might then be critically scrutinized, eliciting by comparative analysis such features as would appear to be universal and law-like and eliminating those which would appear accidental and idiosyncratic. Here, in the requirement that reports be given, the very fact of language already sets a certain limit on such a procedure, introducing the "common" framework into what is ostensibly a private inquiry. For the relation of language to consciousness is so intimate that the separation of conscious thought or reflection from expression has sometimes been denied entirely.[2] The utter subjectivity of such an approach to the "immediate data of consciousness" is thus mediated by the condition of linguistic communication, which we saw earlier to be a necessary condition for science, and the means to its objectivity.

Behaviorist reductionism and holist critique

The attempt to go beyond this introspective-subjective limit and to introduce objective observation into psychological inquiry, in the way of establishing public or intersubjective data, turns from introspection to perceptually available outward behavior as the subject matter of psychology. The sharpest expression of this turn from "mind" to "behavior" is the as-

[1] *De Anima,* 430a, 3.

[2] Croce, the great Italian aesthetician, held to a theory of the identity of "intuition" (as immediate consciousness of qualities) and "expression"; and some author somewhere remarks, "How can I know what I think until I see what I say?"

sertion of an ontological reduction, on the basis of this methodological shift. If consciousness is to be studied in terms of the "overt behavior of intact organisms," then the postulation of an invisible and unobservable "mind" or of some internal "mental events" is no longer necessary. At best, *mind* comes to serve only as the name given to that complex of "segments" or "elements" of behavior which we regard as the ultimate entities in terms of which consciousness is to be described; and even *consciousness* is reducible, in these terms, to such manifest behavior. In an early article William James once posed the question, "Does consciousness exist?" And he answered, "no,"[3] qualifying this to mean that consciousness as some entity apart from the processes of perceptual and cognitive activity, which could be empirically investigated, was a useless and misleading hypostatization. The radical thesis of psychological behaviorism, like that of mechanistic reductionism, is that consciousness is a physical fact and that the study of such a fact should proceed in accordance with the procedures of observation, measurement, experiment, i.e., in terms of such variables as lend themselves to such procedures. Thus, physiological psychology investigates the anatomy and functions of the brain and nervous system as a physical complex (or biophysical complex) by means of which perception, memory, thinking, and so on, take place. At the same time, the experimental psychologist studies the behavior of organisms in terms of the discovery and formulation of law-like relations between measurable stimulus and response. In such experimental inquiry, then, the paradigmatic scientific conditions of control of variables, measurement, and so on, become fulfillable.

The distinction between a methodological reduction and an ontological reduction becomes important here, once again. Whereas ontological reductionism makes the claim that there is nothing more than what is investigatable in terms of behavioral variables and that *mind* names an occult entity, a fiction of animistic thought, methodological behaviorism proposes only a method of fruitful inquiry, but does not adduce an "empty" or "mindless" organism.

Yet it becomes clear that in the practical needs of theory construction, and the formulation and the expression of laws, it is helpful to introduce variables which are "unobservables" or "theoretical" or "hypothetical," such as *need, motivation, drive, habit,* and to use the commonsense descriptive language which talks of such states as *anger, fear, pain,* and *pleasure*. On the reductionist thesis, all such terms should ultimately be translatable, without loss of empirical significance, into some "basic" and "behavioral" variables. Whereas motivation, drive, and habit are not observable, but appear as inferences from observation within some language

[3] William James, "Does Consciousness Exist?" reprinted in W. Muelder, L. Sears and A. V. Schlabach, eds., *The Development of American Philosophy* (Boston: Houghton Mifflin, 1960), pp. 380–383.

framework or theory, anger, fear, and so on, are commonsensically observable states, although they are perhaps not quantitatively measurable. Therefore, laws concerning such variables remain merely qualitative and vague, on the behaviorist view. We may, for example, talk of a "law" of anger, such as, "Anger increases with irritation," but plainly this is a crude formulation. And without more precise specification of *anger* and *irritation,* this remains at the level of ordinary common sense and has no claim to science. We want to specify degrees of anger or correlate degrees of some such subjective state either with some objective measurement (e.g., blood pressure, glandular secretion rates, electrical discharge patterns) or with some other subjective state (e.g., feeling of tension). But this requires some technique of correlating such states, in short, some method of measuring. In the case of "unobservable" or "inferred entities," such as *motivation* or *drive,* the case is more complex. For these suggest not some momentary internal state, but an ongoing disposition to act in a certain way under certain conditions. Aristotle asked whether a woodcutter is only a woodcutter when he is cutting wood, or whether a judge is a judge only when he is judging, and concluded that to talk in this way would entirely lose the sense of such dispositional names. Similarly, it would be odd to say that someone is "highly motivated" to achieve some goal only at the times when he is observably striving toward it, but not when he is asleep or doing something else. These strange "entities," such as motivation, drive, and habit, may take their place simply as conceptual "existences," occurring only in our explanations of behavior patterns, as so-called intervening variables. Or it may be held that there really *are* such things as motives, drives, and habits.[4]

The holist and organicist critique of behavioral reduction claims that the distinctive subject matter of psychology—i.e., human consciousness and activity in all of its ramifications—has been lost sight of as a unified "whole," in the concern with the observation of its parts, and with the premature quantification of psychological observation. Although the holist may not question the methodological restrictiveness of the behaviorist's approach as *one* way of approaching the subject matter, he would hold that in interpreting this methodological framework in an exclusive way so as to define psychology in terms of it, the behaviorist has gone beyond the methodological limits of the framework, generalizing it in such a way as to restrict inquiry and to imperialistically appropriate the field of psychology

[4] One may argue for an ontological reductionism which holds, for example, that only physical or physiological states of the organism exist, and that such entities as motives and drives do not. Yet at the same time, it may be held that a methodological holism provides, heuristically, the best way to study the behavior correlated with, or based on such physiological states, conceiving of this behavior as emergent, given the ontological ground. Thus, one may be a methodological holist, and an ontological reductionist. (I owe this suggestion to discussion with Professor Charles Gross of Harvard University.)

to himself. Unfortunately, there is often a plaintive note in holist critiques, that somehow, in giving up the "cognitivist" framework of *mind,* the psychologist has lost his soul. (The old saw is that the reductionist psychologist, having given up first his soul in the nineteenth century, is now losing his mind as well.) The methodological force of the holist critique here, as in biology, is that in respect to this overweening generalization of behaviorism the psychologist may fail to see the forest for the trees, mistaking parts for wholes and entirely losing sight of the part-whole relationship in terms of which alone behavior itself can come to be understood. Such phenomena as do not lend themselves to present behavioral technique are thus lost in psychological inquiry. Although it may be vaguely true and heuristically important to remember that in dealing with particular aspects of conscious phenomena one has to take into account the "whole man," the holist does not remain at this level of vague generality. What, then, are the emphases of holism in psychology which have empirical and methodological force?

(1) The holist may hold that the abstractive requirements of behavioral experimental techniques isolate the very functions of response in such a way as to distort or falsify them. All the modes of conscious response—including sensation, perception, judgment, and emotive response—are organic and situational. If it is in fact the "whole man" (his history and the situation in which he finds himself) which alone provides the adequate framework for investigation, then the operation of such factors as expectation, habit, cultural and ethnic differences, and past experience needs to be retained in inquiry, and it is precisely these features which "drop out" of the typical laboratory situation. Thus, even some such "atomic" behavior as the perception of objects or of sensory qualities is pervaded by the "set," or anticipatory framework, which such factors bring to bear on perception and is more than a simple physiological response. On one approach in recent physiology of perception, even the perceptual activity at the neuronal level is characterized by such "holistic" features, so that the requirements of the whole organism are expressed in the "response" of even a single peripheral nerve. The behaviorist might argue that his approach does not exclude any of these factors, but that to include them in an empirically significant way is to interpret them so that they may be studied by behavioral means. Thus, he might ask, what is the evidence or what are the criteria in behavioral terms for the effect of cultural differences on perception? What is the behavioral reduction of *anticipation,* and what counts behaviorally as "past experience"? If such interpretations cannot be found, then the allegation that such factors are operative remains at the level of unfounded intuition, or hunch, or uncritical commonsense assumption, immune to test and criticism.

(2) The holist might also argue that the *models* of perception, learning, and so on, in terms of stimulus-response—so-called S-R models—are impoverished and fail to account for holist features. Thus, in effect, what one

ends up with is a trivial set of descriptions completely dissimilar from what would count as an adequate scientific explanation. For example, perception is not merely a matter of atomistic bits of stimulus and response; it also involves the active intervention of organizing capacities of the perceptual apparatus itself. On the Gestaltist view, perception tends to be an active process of organizing the input of the sensory field in certain typical configurations, or *Gestalten,* which we may discover in experimental inquiry (e.g., *completeness, good figure*). Furthermore, in addition to this organic "wholeness" of perceptual activity, the *situation* of perception involves a system or unity of subject and object (or field), and not merely an external relation of this "stimulus" to that "response," or of this "thing" to that "perceiver." The interaction of subject and object is seen, on this view, as constituting an "organic unity" in which the separate description of subject and object destroys their character as it exists in the interaction. Thus, *X* is a "beautiful object" when the subject's attitude is aesthetic, or an "expensive item" when the subject's attitude is economic or practical. *Y* is perceived as an object of affection by the husband, as a clinical object by the doctor, and as a deduction by the internal revenue agent. The objection that *X* or *Y* are "really" this, or that, which is then interpreted differently assumes that there is some privileged framework of "thisness" or "thatness." The holist, if he takes the approach of an objective relativism, would hold that the "thisness" or "thatness" of any object of perception is determined within these alternate subject-object relations, and that no one of these has priority over the other, but only differs in different contexts. To take what an object "really" is in terms of its *physical* characteristics would be to choose one among many frameworks, with no special claims except relevance to the directions or requirements of inquiry.

The emphasis in all this is on the activity of the subject in perception. Again, the behaviorist might argue that "response" was never meant to be a simplistic or passive element in his scheme and that all of this "activity" on the part of the subject, all the "dispositions" or "attitudes" or "forms of awareness," can be accommodated in the S-R model, on the elaboration of "response" as complex behavior. He may charge that the holist's argument sets up a straw man.

(3) The holist's most radical argument is that certain features of conscious activity are irreducible to behavioral description in principle, both methodologically and ontologically. The behavioral approach has access only to the physical, but certain features of consciousness are irreducibly mental. Such a radical dualism of the physical and the mental is analogous to the radical dualism of the living and nonliving, in vitalist views, and we may call it *mentalism* here. In particular, the mentalist would charge that such features as *will, intention, purpose, imagination, dreaming,* and the whole array of *belief* contexts elude behavioral description. Similarly, he may argue that all the main features of cognitive activity—the activity of

the imagination, the formation of concepts, the acquisition and use of language—go beyond reduction to segments or sequences of behavior, precisely because these "internal" activities are unobservable. If *observable* is taken in the specified behaviorist sense, then behaviorism cannot even begin to study these features of conscious thought; they lend themselves only to reflective or introspective "mental" examination. There are two alternative replies to this charge, one "behaviorist" but the other involving additional issues concerning the characterization of mind or conscious activity in its relation to its physiological or physical basis.

(*a*) The behaviorist might argue that the so-called internal states or events which the mentalist designates as *intention, will, purpose,* and so on are themselves amenable to behavioral inquiry, just as *motivation* and *habit* are, by virtue of the manifest activity in terms of which such states are operative. And a "will" without action, or an "intention" without effect are ghostly entities better off excised from psychology. The objection here is that the behaviorist overlooks the introspective evidence in terms of which an individual may himself become aware of his will, intentions, and so on as "mental" facts without any outward manifestation. Thus, the simple "observable" fact that Smith's foot connected violently with Jones' shin gives us no clue as to whether Smith was kicking Jones (as a deliberate action), whether Smith's foot accidentally knocked Jones' shin, or whether the foot was mechanically forced to move in such a way, without any action on Smith's part. In this example (from Strawson), it is not clear from the sheer physical description of the event what Smith *might have been doing,* or whether *he* was *doing* anything at all. For these discriminations we need access to the mental events of will, intention, and decision which are irreducible to gross behavioral description. But if such cognition remains entirely private, it cannot become the subject matter for a science of psychology, though it might do to introduce problems and dilemmas for a philosophy of mind. Furthermore, to the extent that such "inner states" are verbalized, then verbal behavior—speech, gesture, the "act" that constitutes verbal communication—itself becomes the observational datum of behavioral inquiry, as verbal utterance (including first-person reports of introspective states) merely replaces gross bodily motion or otherwise physically observable response.

(*b*) The alternative reply to the charge that certain mental states are available only to introspection and are not objectively observable, therefore, is that the "mental" is ultimately identical with physical states of the organism. Thus, for ostensibly private mental states there are physical correlates in the organism, i.e., in the brain or in the whole nervous complex which constitutes the physical basis of consciousness. This introduces a major conceptual issue in epistemology and metaphysics—the so-called mind-body question—which has bearing on these issues in psychology.

MIND AND BODY: DUALIST AND MONIST ALTERNATIVES

Descartes, as we saw, postulated an ontological dualism of two ultimately irreducible substances: the mental and the physical. This formulation raises the problem of how the two are then to be related, for the evidence of the correlation of what we take to be physical events or bodily events and what we take to be mental events is too pervasive, and our conviction that what we perceive is "really there" is too strong for any reasonable belief that the mental and physical are entirely unrelated. This point does not need to be belabored, though the justification and theoretical explanation of our beliefs in this mind-body relation constitutes a lively problem in metaphysics and epistemology.

The point at issue is whether there is some publicly and objectively observable event which we may say is identical with, or the correlate of, what we take to be introspectively known mental states. The question may be rephrased as one concerning the relation between brain and mind, or between organism and mind. In the former case the brain is seen as the organ of consciousness, and in the latter, one may elaborate this to mean that the whole organism is conscious by means of the brain and nervous system. (This is like asserting that it is not my feet which are walking but that *I* am walking by the use of my feet, and also the rest of my body.)

Bodily states are presumably open to scientific investigation by physical means, either directly or indirectly. Such bodily features as temperature, motion, electrical activity, chemical changes, and so on, are straightforward subjects for physical examination. If it is asserted that mind is nothing but "a certain organization of such bodily states," then we have an outright physicalist reduction of mental to physical events or states. If, on the other hand, mind is said to be an emergent property of a certain organization of a physical system, then the basis of conscious activity is seen to be a physical and systemic, but the emergent property itself is seen to be a product of the whole organization and not merely the aggregation of parts. "Mind" is then seen to be not supraphysical but nevertheless irreducible to lower integrative levels of organization of a living system. At the furthest remove from the physicalist reduction, going beyond this emergentism, mind may be said to be nonphysical or supraphysical, and irreducibly "spiritual," in an outright mind-body dualism.

On the physicalist reduction, mental states *are* physical states and are not merely 'based" on them or "derived" from them. The mental state and the physical state are numerically identical. Thus, if there were a way to observe the physical state *p* which appears introspectively as a mental state *m,* we would in effect be "observing" the "mental" state under its other *aspect;* i.e., *'p'* and *'m'* would have identically the same reference, or would be two names for one and the same thing. Spinoza introduced such a double-aspect view of the mental and the physical, describing both as attributes of some underlying substance which was in itself the identity to which the terms *mental* and *physical* applied. Bertrand Russell at one time also held such a view, described as "neutral monism." This identity view of the mind-body relation would resolve the problem of the privacy of mental states, by asserting their publicity, though not as "mental" states. Still the "state" or "event" would be the same one, except that if it were occurring in your brain it would be "mental" to you and if somehow I were observing "it" neurologically it would be "physical" to me. Your introspective report and my neurophysiological report would be about the same event; and presumably these reports could be correlated. With a sufficiently advanced "dictionary" of such correlations I might then be able to tell you "you are seeing red," or "you are thinking of strawberry shortcake," and you would check me out (or check out the dictionary which would thereby be further refined).

On emergentist and mentalist views, the relation of the mental to the physical would not be one of sheer identity, though it may be one of correlation. Thus the emergentist might hold that there is no consciousness without a physical basis, but would refuse to identify the explanatory reduction to physical organization with an ontological reduction or elimination of the mental in favor of nonmental physical description. The outright mentalist would hold that whatever degree of correlation one achieved, one was dealing with two things and not one, so that the description of the mental could be given only in the mentalist language and of the physical in the physicalist language. Thus, at best one would achieve a scheme of partial coordination, but not of identity. At worst, however, the mentalist might argue that there are uniquely mental events without physical correlates, in one or another version of spiritualism or philosophical idealism. If indeed the mental and the physical are related, though irreducible one to the other, the nature of the relation becomes problematic. Descartes, having introduced the sharp dualism, sought the relation in some physiological connection or interaction between brain and mind and hypothesized that this took place in the pineal gland. The utter confusion of such a view led to alternative proposals that body and mind did not interact but were coordinated in parallel.

The difficulties and philosophical muddles to which all this has given rise has led James Thomson to characterize the mind-body problem as the "mind-boggle" problem. But it has become a topic of the liveliest discussion once again, in the context of recent developments in computer technology, in which machines display "artificial intelligence." This analogy to the problem of organisms and machines, which introduces the mechanist alternative into psychology in an almost literal way, we will briefly consider now.

MECHANISMS AND MINDS: CAN MACHINES THINK?

The analogue to the question of whether mechanisms which are self-regulating, self-reproducing, and conceivably self-regenerating can be said to be alive, is the question of whether mechanisms which can make "perceptual" discriminations (e.g., can recognize differences in pattern, shape, color, and so on) and can "compute," "learn," and "carry out" logical operations, can be said to "think." The generous use of quotation marks here suggests that perhaps the computers and automata which carry out such functions are not really doing any of these things at all, in the sense in which conscious human organisms may be said to be doing them. Rather (as Bunge suggests) they may be performing operations *like* those which we perform consciously. But this raises the question of what we mean by *conscious.* If we define consciousness as that which only human beings possess (leaving aside the question of animal consciousness), then, analytically, it follows that automata cannot be conscious, because they are not human. But this begs the question. If, indeed, consciousness is held to have emerged in the course of evolution, as life has, from nonconscious states of organized matter, then in principle the reconstruction by synthetic means of similar states of organization should also produce consciousness.[5] Indeed, automata as electronic mechanisms have been structured as models of the nervous system. The claim that such "nerve-net" models are only abstractive, that only certain features of the brain and nervous system have been modeled, and that therefore the integrative level of consciousness has not been reproduced is a claim concerning practical or engineering limitations. But the rapid development of such machines does not suggest any upper limit to such development, or simulation of the nervous system. (A century ago, Samuel Butler, in his utopian novel *Erehwon,* gave a fanciful account of the "evolution of the machines," in which the Erehwonians destroy the machines once they recognize that this synthetic evolution may overtake and surpass them.) Another and stronger argument is that the imprint of evolutionary and cultural development which has resulted in the "living brain" (to use Grey Walter's striking phrase) cannot be synthetically reproduced. Here again the question becomes one of principle rather than of present engineering technology. Is it impossible to reproduce such a structure and such a history within a finite time, or is it possible but

[5] Cf. J. T. Culbertson, "Since consciousness accompanies brain activity, anyone believing that the brain is a machine or natural cause-effect mechanism of some kind, should have no difficulty in accepting the preliminary working hypothesis that consciousness would accompany the activity of artificial machinery that was sufficiently similar to the brain in its structure." [*The Minds of Robots* (Urbana: University of Illinois Press, 1963), p. 78.] Culbertson begs the question here, but his is a fascinating treatise on the principles and design of "conscious automata."

unimaginably difficult? If the latter, then the conceptual issue is resolved quite differently and it is conceivable to produce a thinking machine.

Almost all cautions from computer theorists, cyberneticians, and philosophers in this regard are of the sort which point out how far short present automata fall of conscious thought. For thought involves more than perception and more than patterned behavior or habit formation, and even more than learning (if we may talk of computer performance in these terms). Presumably, it involves the whole range of self-awareness, feeling, imagination, creative intuition, whose processes are so little understood in the human organism that it is not clear what the criteria would be, much less what the mechanism could be, of a replication of these processes.

It becomes clear that the question of whether machines can think is only in part a technical question of computer-brain analogies. It is, in large part, a matter of semantic and philosophical analysis of what we mean by "thinking." In one standard recent textbook of experimental psychology, the index entry for *thinking* reads, "see problem-solving." On such a reduction of thinking, a computer which "solves problems" (defined in terms of producing a correct answer to a question in accordance with norms of inference and by means of algorisms programmed into the machine) may also be said to think. But then the burden of analysis falls on the term *solve*. Does the computer "solve" or does it do something like what we do when *we* solve. One test, based on Leibniz's "identity of indiscernibles" and on the pragmatic maxim that a difference is a real difference only if it makes a difference, is whether one could distinguish a mechanical solution from a human one. Descartes had already suggested such a test for automata, and Turing reformulated this in contemporary computer terms. In matters such as logical or mathematical operations which have been mechanized, the difference would seem not to exist, for in such a case the very operations of computation which even we perform are "mechanical," just as many other human operations are mechanical or mechanizable. But the additional consideration, that it is we who produce and program the machines by the operations of our human consciousness, has been raised to conclude that even the most sophisticated machine is no different from the crudest hammer or crowbar, in that it is an instrumentality of human use. The machine, in short, does not use itself, but is used by an intelligent, conscious organism. The argument proceeds that without our construction and programming the machine is nothing and its "consciousness" is only the derived and directed activity of a mechanism. The answer may be given that we may program a machine to program itself, or to program a machine to construct a duplicate of itself, or to program one machine to program a second, which in turn programs a third, and so on. In this sense the last machine would regard the prior ones as "conscious" with respect to it. But here is the rub, for the last machine could not "regard" anything unless it were programmed to do so by some prior one, so that consciousness would ultimately be tracked back recursively to its lair in some human engineer's mind. (This is like nothing so much as classical theological arguments concerning the need for a first cause, or a divine intelligence, to avoid the infinite regress of explanations of motion or design in nature.) But on a broad analogy, we too may be conceived of as "programmed machines," in terms of the encoded structures of genetic inheritance, and so programmed as to regard ourselves as conscious by derivation from prior conscious machines (our "parents," for example, or our "teachers"). Such heady speculations suggest, however, that the distinctive element of reflective and speculative thought goes beyond what any programmer could have envisioned for us and raises the question of the "freedom of thought" as its distinctive quality. This "freedom" or "plasticity" enters into the argument in several ways:

(1) The machine is said to be a deterministic mechanism. As a mechanism it is subject to physical laws which do not admit the "free" and non-law-determined activity of thought. The issue here becomes complex, for it depends on an analysis of the concepts of *freedom* and *determinism* in thinking organisms. This leads to the considerations of free will, which machines cannot be said to have. The mechanist answer here might be that if "freedom" means the possibility of action beyond the confines of classical or strict physical determinism, then statistical determinism provides a model of such a degree of freedom, and a machine designed and programmed in terms of such statistical determinism, of probability functions and of a degree of randomness in its operations, can be constructed. Such a "probability machine" or "random robot" could come up with decisions beyond those computable in advance by human beings or other machines, so that if *free will* is defined in terms of a degree of unpredictability (where *determinism* is defined in terms of predictability), such a machine is a "free-will automaton."

Norbert Wiener, the founder of cybernetics, saw in the consequence of this, certain *moral* problems in automation.[6] For if machines are given "decision" powers in increasing degrees, as they are in our national life, then the "decision" which such a machine may make may very well go beyond the predictable ones which its designers can compute in advance or anticipate (though we could always *later* trace back the paths or processes by which such unanticipated "decisions" were reached). But if such decision power were linked to executive power, which is also increasingly allotted to machines, then a catastrophic decision could be effected or executed before we had time to "apply the brakes" (to use Wiener's analogy), because the reaction time of human response and computation would be incredibly long compared to the almost-instantaneous action of elec-

[6] Norbert Weiner, "Some Moral and Technical Consequences of Automation," *Science,* **131:**1355–1358 (1960).

tronic mechanisms. Wiener further posed the following dilemma for the automata of the future: they may be *either* "intelligent" (i.e., capable of "free" and unfettered decision making, and greatly plastic) or "obedient" (i.e., bound within predetermined limits). But they cannot be both "intelligent" and "obedient." Thus, in this conception, an "intelligent" machine could be a "rebellious" machine. The connotations of such an analysıs, when the analogy is reapplied to human beings as automata, functioning as instruments of use, are clearly drawn by Weiner.

(2) Second, the machine may be said to be unfree precisely in the sense of its instrumental function. It is ever a means only, and never an end; it does not use, but is used. That is, the machine does not choose its own goals, but acts only to fulfill some chosen goal. The difference between goal seeking and goal choosing may then be said to mark the difference between free and unfree action, and ultimately, the difference between conscious thought and mere performance. Only human beings choose goals, and machines are never more than instrumentalities which serve, either well or ill, to effect such goals. In this sense, machines are *amoral,* whereas human beings are moral or immoral. Here an ultimate distinction seems to be drawn. Only a free agent can be moral, and only human beings are free in this sense of consciously choosing among alternative goals. Human beings thus create values, whereas machines at best may only "choose" among alternatives on the basis of some norm which is built into them as a computational procedure; they cannot "value" except as directed. The counterargument here may be that human beings are likewise determined by their structure, culture, social group, and so on, to accept such directive norms and to behave accordingly. But against this, it may be argued that human beings may choose wrongly or make mistakes, and no machine may be said to "make a mistake." At most it can only malfunction. Still, a mechanist ethical or social theory might conceive of human error also as such a "malfunctioning," in need of correction, and the therapy in the human case may be no more than a sophisticated sort of "human engineering." Socrates' maxim that "no man errs willingly" and that "ignorance is error" may then be translated into mechanical terms, so that ignorance is interpreted as a malfunction, or as the lack of a proper program-command for a given situation. By the extension of such analogies between human behavior and machine "behavior," programs simulating such complex patterns of behavior as those of economics, politics, or personality, based on the analysis of given human models and translated into the computer language, may be developed. The machine may even be programmed to "learn" from past mistakes and to "improve its game" (as in chess-playing automata, or in the interpretation of complex social behavior in terms of the so-called theory of games). This suggests the great flexibility of machines as analogues to conscious activity. But again, simulation is always partial, and

the holist may argue that no conjoint system of simulations approaches the behavior of the "whole" conscious organism, which is unique precisely because of its plasticity or adaptiveness in the widest variety of contexts. The holist argument here is that each such abstracted aspect of human behavior falls short of the specific property of consciousness, namely its generality. It is the fact that consciousness unifies and integrates these various functions, which the machine may separately simulate, which makes consciousness unique. The argument goes further to claim that consciousness is "free" in its capacity for infinite adaptation in the operations of thought, whereas a machine has, at best, a finite adaptability and cannot be fully generalized in its functions. One automaton may be fitted to simulate mathematical operations, another to simulate economic behavior, a third to simulate perception. But a fully generalized automaton would require an infinite plasticity and adaptability. The reductionist might argue that such a development is limited only by the extent of our knowledge and engineering skill at the present and is not ruled out in principle, so that generalized automata are fully within the scope of human construction and programming.

(3) The freedom of conscious organisms may be said to be distinctive in two other regards, in which machines are not "free": (*a*) in terms of self-consciousness and (*b*) in terms of consciousness of others as like oneself, i.e., in species consciousness. We mentioned these at the outset. Here the "freedom of thought" involves a freedom from self-boundedness, from the brute existence of an organism which merely exists and behaves, but does not yet have a self-identity. It is perhaps odd to raise this in the context of machines and minds. But it is noteworthy that in this present context, the classical epistemological and moral questions of self-consciousness, self-identity, and freedom become focused in a distinctive way.

Grey Walter's automaton (his "turtle" or *Machina Speculatrix*) is endowed with a primitive operation which Walter describes as "self-recognition," and it may also be equipped to "recognize" others of its kind. This amounts to no more than a flashlight bulb built into the head of the "turtle," which when "seen" (by the photoelectric receptors of the turtle) as a reflection in a mirror, or as a similar light in the "head" of another "turtle," leads it to "fascinated attraction." Walter describes this "self-recognition" behavior thus: "The creature . . . lingers before a mirror, flittering, twittering and jiggling like a clumsy Narcissus. The behavior of a creature thus engaged with its own reflection is quite specific, and on a purely empirical basis, if it were observed in an animal, might be accepted as evidence of some degree of self-awareness."[7] Further, when a number of such machines are in each other's presence,

[7] W. G. Walter, *The Living Brain* (New York: W. W. Norton & Co., 1953), pp. 128–29.

they are similarly "attracted" and "cannot escape from one another. . . . In a sense, then, a population of machines forms a sort of community." It is unclear whether "self-awareness" and "community" are metaphors, are to be taken in the sense of simulation, or model, or are veritably instances (albeit low-level ones) of what we ordinarily mean by "self-awareness" and "community." Descartes made self-conscious self-identity the criterion of that consciousness which constituted man's being as *man* (i.e., not as automaton), in the dictum *Cogito ergo sum.* ("I think, therefore I am"; or, it is my thinking activity that constitutes my being, where *I am* has the sense of asserting egohood or selfhood.) Hume based self-identity on a "common center" of all the impressions of sense, requiring here the notion of reflective memory and association to constitute the continuity of such a center as an *I.* The question arises whether machines may ever be said to constitute such "egos." The matter of "self-recognition" in a mirror, as in the case of *Machina Speculatrix,* also raises the question of recognizing an "other," i.e., an object of "awareness," as being somehow *like oneself.* In such a case, *individual* self-recognition presupposes species recognition (a point which Hegel, in *The Phenomenology of Mind,* and Feuerbach, in *The Essence of Christianity,* developed in great detail, in their phenomenological analysis of the "consciousness of consciousness"). The role of communication becomes central here, for mere blind encounter would not in itself constitute recognition. What is distinctively human about human societies is often said to be that they are verbally or symbolically linked organizations. Language constitutes the web of social relation which goes beyond mere common action. (For the machines in a factory may be said to "act" in common, but not to constitute a society, much less a community.) It is by the use of language that self-recognition and the recognition of species-characteristics becomes explicit. If one takes this approach, is it conceivable that by the development of inter-automaton communication, such a "linguistic community," including the development of other- and self-recognition, may be constituted? The counter-argument here may be that machines, no matter how sophisticated, do not use a language, but merely operate with one, as for example a telegraph station, a radio transmitter, or a phonograph might, acting as transformation and transmission devices, but not as "speakers." Such deflationary commonsense comparisons urge us to decline the invitation to conceive of machines as self-conscious language users. But speculation, urged on by wide horizons of automata development, tempts us to entertain the possibility.

It is clear, in any case, that Hilary Putnam is right in claiming recently that "the problem of the Minds of Machines will prove, at least for a while, to afford an exciting new way to approach quite traditional issues in the philosophy of mind. Whether, and under what conditions, a robot could be conscious is a question that cannot be discussed without at once impinging on the topics that have been treated under the headings Mind-Body Problem and Problem of other Minds."[8]

SOCIETY AND HISTORY

Although the foregoing discussion is set in the context of the issue of minds and machines, it also raises the classical questions of the relation of consciousness and sociality. As a complement to his definition of man as a rational animal, Aristotle adds the definition of man as a social (or political) animal. In the *Politics* Aristotle talks of a being who can live outside of a society as "either a beast or a god," but not a man. Theories of society are as old as rational human thought, and it is an irony of conceptual history that where many modern social theories have taken the physical sciences as their model, in a reductive sense, the earliest physical theories drew upon social concepts and models, though for the most part unconsciously (as Cornford and Durkheim, and Marxist scholars such as Farrington have shown, for example). The pervasiveness of the holist-reductionist alternatives in scientific theory construction exhibits itself here once again, both in the consideration of what are the entities of social science and what its methodology should be like. One may therefore divide the consideration of some conceptual issues in the social sciences and history in terms of questions concerning social ontology (what sorts of entities does social theory adduce?) and the methodology of the social sciences (what distinctive issues arise in the consideration of social-scientific observation, measurement, and explanation and of the formulation of laws and models in the social sciences?).

(a) *The entities of the social sciences.* The names of the disciplines suggest that anthropology deals with man and sociology with society. The division of labor here is entirely artificial, for both deal with human interaction, with the social or group structures to which such interaction gives rise, and within which it takes place. Indeed, it seems clear that contemporary sociology and anthropology are no longer sharply distinct disciplines. But given a subject as complex as the social sciences, a division of labor is essential to inquiry. The isolation of certain features of social human existence is prerequisite for scientific study here, as it is in the other sciences. Thus, the separation of fields of study introduces those "entities" characteristic of these alternative emphases and subject matters, and such criterial entities may be said to determine the ontology of the framework of inquiry. What, then, are the appropriate entities to be studied in the social sciences?

Man and *society* are certainly too vague; *human interaction* and *social*

[8] Hilary Putnam, "Robots: Machines or Artificially Created Life?" *The Journal of Philosophy,* **LXI,** 21 (Nov. 12, 1964), p. 669.

structure are at best heuristic, suggesting the broad conceptual frameworks of *action* and *structure* which direct the strategy of investigation and order the formulation of theories. As in other sciences, the reduction of an initially unmanageable complexity comes with the further specification of objects of study, with definition and that process of classification which lies at the foundations of any scientific discipline. Thus, such terms as *persons, groups, roles, functions, institutions,* name the typical entities and emphases in such inquiry.

In one approach, the analysis of society may proceed with the key concept *role,* in the view that man's life is clearly organized, the feature of such organization being differentiation and specialization. Thus, social behavior of individuals may be ordered in terms of "roles" and "role-playing." Thus, too, a role connotes structures within which such role-playing has its significance—e.g., "institutions" or "groups" within a society—and inevitably then, the relation of such groups to each other or to a whole, as well as the "functions" which such "roles" subserve become relevant, as the framework of inquiry is systematically elaborated around such concepts. If the emphasis, alternatively, is on "structures," then perhaps an "anatomy" of society may be pursued, and the relations among structures and the patterns of structural change may occupy the social scientist. If, in one interpretation (analogous to that in biology), *structure* and *function* are taken together as constituting an *organic whole,* the model or entity in terms of which social inquiry may proceed, may be conceived of as an "organism," which "grows," "develops," is "adaptive," or "survives" or "dies"; whose parts then subserve some function of the whole.[9]

Alternatively, an atomist-reductionist approach might relegate such universal terms as *role, institution, function* to the status of abstract names, rather than to approach them as "real" entities of some social reality. In nominalist fashion, such an approach might emphasize the concrete individual, in place of these other "abstract universals," in social science, so that, for example, all "social" entities are reducible to individual behavior or function. In one such reductionist view, sociology reduces to individual psychology. But in another view, because the social scientist is interested in class or group behavior rather than individual behavior as such, it is the statistical properties of the mass or group behavior of individuals (where the individuals are abstractively taken in only some of their features) which characterizes social inquiry.

[9] Such "organic" analogies are classical in social theory and are explicit in such usages as *social organism* and the older *body politic.* This is the primary model, for example, of Plato's *Republic* in which the ideal society is fashioned after the analogy to the human organism (as a "soul"), with its tripartite functions of reason, action, and self-nourishment. It is explicit too in all the classical political theories which, like Hobbes' *Leviathan,* conceive of the state on the analogy to a living animal, with "head," "arms," "legs," and so on.

Another approach is genetic-historical, in holist or "global" fashion. One might argue, on this view, that explanation in the social sciences needs to be in terms of *processes,* i.e., in terms of a causal account of how present social structures and functions develop out of earlier ones. On the analogy here to evolutionary theories in biology, one may then take *social evolution* as the key concept, taking as entities whole "organizations" or social "structures" or social "systems."

Thus are introduced the various entities, models, frameworks, within which social-scientific inquiry develops. And thus, the general ontological models in terms of "things," "events," "processes," "particulars," "universals" are given their social-scientific interpretation, in social "atomism," or "organicism," or "pluralism," and so on. Thus, too, the pervasive problem of the relation of parts and wholes emerges again in this context. In the social sciences the distinction is often made between "global" and reductive approaches, and further elaborated in terms of the "range" of theories having a scale running from the "low" of individual behavior, to so-called theories of the middle range dealing with empirically manageable groups, to the "high" of such global structures as "societies," economic or political "systems" or "periods," and other like high abstractions.

The classical foundations of social theory were largely "global," attempting to establish the widest or most universal frameworks as the "essential" ones within which social phenomena could be meaningfully studied. From the early speculative genetic-sociological theories of Plato, of Seneca, of the great medieval Arabic forerunner of sociology, Ibn Khaldun, to the classic nineteenth- and early twentieth-century theories of such men as Comte, Marx, Spencer, Tawney, Weber, Pareto, Sorel, Spengler, to the contemporary theoretical and historical sociology of Toynbee, Sorokin, Talcott Parsons, and C. Wright Mills, the direction of such sociology has been synthetic and systematic, attempting to establish coherence among the mass of phenomena of human organization and development. The most frequent criticism of such systematic sociology is that it is speculative and not experimental; or that its empiricism is limited to the ordering of accumulated facts, but does not involve the methods of testing and measuring, which alone can eventuate in a science of society. The criticism, in effect, is that such sociology is really a brand of historical scholarship and that history is not a science; specifically in the sense that its purported "laws" are untestable and unfalsifiable, either because they are irremediably vague, or self-fulfilling, or because the facts of history are unique facts and do not offer the prospect of law-like formulation, but only plausible interpretation. Thus, at best, such a developmental and historical sociology, like history, can adduce only "trends," "tendencies," or "directions," or broadly qualitative descriptions of patterns, which have no predictive force, whatever their heuristic value.

At farthest remove from "globalism" is that aspect of the study of man that borders on biology, namely, physical anthropology, which deals with the description, classification, and characterization of the human species as physical organisms. However, such a study impinges (as does evolutionary and ecological study in biology) on the relation of man and environment, on human migrations, diffusion, distribution, on the evolution of *homo sapiens* as a tool-using, speaking organism living within a culture and becoming socialized. The specifically biological study of individual structure thus passes over into social inquiry, especially of early and preliterate societies and cultures, in comparative and cultural anthropology, archaeology, and so on, as the study of human artifacts becomes essential to the study of man.

The fountainhead of empirical methodology in the social sciences is anthropology. For here, once past the eighteenth- and nineteenth-century formulations of a "philosophical anthropology," the anthropologist became a field researcher, seeking out his facts in direct observation and measurement, in comparative and physical anthropology. But even this approach has its "historicist" counterpart, in the older traditions of cultural anthropology. This latter has been criticized as "soft" not because of the lack of rigor of its scholarship, but because it has relied heavily on reconstructions of past facts and lacks an empirical methodology. Nevertheless, the pressure of field research, especially among cultures different from those of the researchers, raised sharply the question of how social-scientific data is acquired, and especially how the "subjective" *set*[10] of the investigator enters into primary data collection, as well as into its interpretation. With the growth of empirical sociology and the development of field-research techniques in anthropological and sociological inquiry, these questions become still sharper, raising methodological issues at the very foundations of the social sciences. When such "entities" of social research as values, customs, and norms arise, then the epistemological and methodological issues become conceptually central to a clarification of exactly what the social scientist is investigating, and how he goes about it.

(*b*) *Observation, measurement, and models in the social sciences.* What exactly is one looking at, and what is one looking for in social-scientific observation? What does one "see" when one observes a "custom" or a "role" or an "institution"? Obviously, as with our earlier missing buttons, eclipses, and theoretical terms in the physical sciences, observation here is within a framework in which certain perceptual data are taken as evidences of "customs" and "roles." The behaviorist-reductionist in the social sciences takes his cue from the psychological behaviorist: terms such as *custom* and *role,* if they are to be empirically significant, ought to be reducible to the overt or manifest behavior of individuals or aggregates of individuals. A group is then defined, perhaps, by common interests, but "interests" are operationally defined as patterns of behavior, or character-

[10] The Gestaltist term *set* (*Einstellung*) calls attention to the general problem of social perception in psychology, as well as to the specific problems of social-scientific observation and research techniques.

istic sequences of segments of behavior. The holist may argue that such characteristics as interests and norms do not make themselves available to behavioral description, and what the latter produces is an emasculated version of social acts. He may argue that we do not come to social research raw, and intellectually naked. Rather, precisely because we are human beings ourselves, we already have a core of initial comprehensions of social realities, by means of which we primitively *understand* certain phenomena in their significance. So, for example, "merely observing" human transactions, I already have an intuitive grasp of such connotative aspects as *intention, motive, goal,* just as from the visible configuration of a face I grasp the physiognomic "qualities" which I intuit as fear, pain, delight, and so on. On this view, such an intuition is not reproducible in behavioral description, but is a recognition of "something more." However subjective this may appear, its objectivity lies in its universality, on this view. Because we are all human together, we have human intuitions of sympathy and empathy, and other modes of affective and aesthetic cognition, which are as much instruments of valid observation as are the microscopes and telescopes of physical science. Kant suggested that there was such a mode of cognition in our judgments of beauty, which he regarded as subjective, but *also* as universal (in the sense that though we cannot demand assent to such judgments on conceptual or logical grounds, we may nevertheless justifiably and plausibly *expect* such assent). Though such "subjective universality" falls short of the evidential support which empirical science demands, neither does empirical science attain to "certain" or *apodeictic* judgments, on Kant's view. Only mathematics does, and thus only it is *a priori.*

The elaboration of this mode of human cognition of human facts, as a method in the social sciences, is called *Verstehen* (*understanding,* as a technical or methodological term) and has strong proponents in the human sciences. The holist emphasis is clear, for here some feature or "physiognomic property" or Gestalt-quality of a "whole" is immediately grasped, without inference or without recourse to reasons or evidence. It has been pointed out, by way of qualification, that though this approach has heuristic value in the social sciences, once beyond this initial "recognition" or "intuition," there is required the follow-up of empirical investigation to support this as more than a hunch or an insight.

This raises the question of the nature of the data of the social sciences. Much of what is collected as data is not physical fact in the raw, nor even gross behavior (as, for example, the motion of organisms in space and time), but consists in artifacts, and especially in that most plastic and elusive of all artifacts, language. For the typical techniques of the social scientist include asking questions, or collecting and describing expressions, judgments, opinions, as well as observing nonverbal behavior. The evaluation of verbal response and of symbolic behavior in general (including here the aesthetic expression exhibited in dance, posture, courtship, and in all the arts and techniques of social life, in manners and mores) becomes a very sticky business indeed. For here the very fact of observation may distort or interfere with the situation being observed. In our earlier discussion of the interference of the observer with the observed situation in physics, we recall Niels Bohr's "mental" analogy, about what happens to a thought when one introspectively "observes" it. This enters here into the nonintrospective and "objective" observation of the behavior of others, to qualify the sense of *objectivity* in social-scientific data collection. This effect of observation involves two variables here:

1. The effect of the observer upon the person, or group observed.
2. The observer's own framework or value-scheme, in terms of which the data may become subjectively interpreted in an idiosyncratic or one-sided way.

That this is not unique to the social sciences is a point we made earlier. But its application to the social sciences is unique, for the responsiveness of human beings to the situational difference between unobserved behavior and deliberately observed behavior is notorious. Where the values or the linguistic framework of the investigator impinge on his observation (as they most clearly may when the value-scheme or language of the subjects studied is alien or strange to the investigator), this introduces another complication concerning objectivity in the social sciences.

(*b*) *Measurement.* If number is the universal language and the ultimate ground of objectivity, then the quantification of social research would appear to be the road toward an objective social science. Such quantification, including the elaboration of scales of measurement especially suited to social variables, has developed quite far in the recent history of the social sciences. Thus, features of social behavior such as preference, avoidance, goal striving, frustration, achievement, and so on, have been interpreted in terms of functional relation and by means of reduction to quantifiable magnitudes (such as income, years of education, and so on). The definition of such "abstract" variables as *social class* has proceeded beyond the naive interpretation in terms of some simple "numbers" (e.g., yearly income) and has been refined by means of nonmetric interpretations of data on occupational status, prestige, expectation of reward, and so on. For example, Parker, Kleiner, Tuckman, Taylor, and others, have been investigating the relation between the incidence of schizophrenia in certain populations and the level of aspiration of members of these populations.[11] They utilize a functional "formula" of Kurt Lewin's as a guide. Simply presented, incidence of schizophrenia is seen to be directly proportional to

[11] R. Kleiner and S. Parker, *Mental Illness in the Urban Negro Community* (New York: Free Press, 1965).

level of frustration and this is in turn defined as proportional to the discrepancy between aspiration and achievement. Clearly, the formula [which is given thus: level of stress = $F[(LA-ACH) \times INT \times PA]$, or stress is a function of the discrepancy between level of aspiration and level of achievement times the intensity of the desire for stated *LA* times the probability of achievement] requires some way of quantifying the variables. And this the authors have done in terms of such interpretations or definitions of the variables as are numerically statable (education level, occupational level in terms of income, and so on) in terms of ordinal or rank-order and interval scales.

Here, as in much of social-scientific and psychological research, the problem arises of "subjective" variables, where quantification or rank ordering of values depends on the subject's own estimation of values (e.g., of prestige or intensity of desire, or in psychophysics, of subjective estimates of relative intensity of brightness, sound, pressure, and so on); on the reference-group in terms of which such social values may be estimated; or on the limitations or constraints of the scale to which the subject's responses are referred. In short, many of the difficulties of social-scientific measurement involve not only so-called intensive magnitudes (such as are nonadditive and therefore cannot make use of the quantitative operations of arithmetic), but magnitudes which would appear to be merely individual responses, or which are narrowly context-dependent. How, then, can meaningful measurement take place when the data may be unique or idiosyncratic, or when it is so relativized to contexts (e.g., reference groups) that there are no valid ways of generalizing from it? For example, even if we test a "large" group, say of 1000 subjects, how strong a basis for inductive generalization can this provide? And if the test is of individuals, how may one relate the subjective responses in one case to those in another? How may one claim to be using quantitative methods, with respect to such elusive and subjective responses as my estimate of the prestigiousness of a certain occupation, and your estimate? Are not the variables of background, family, education, and so on, so divergent as to preclude meaningful generalizations or law-like statements?

Clearly, all the considerations discussed in Chapter 9 are sharpened, for the roles of sampling, error, statistical generalization, and probability here become crucial. It is precisely in terms of such problems that more and more refined methods of sampling and statistical analysis have been developed, in such fields as opinion research, content analysis, voting behavior, and so on, where the subject matter provides mass-phenomena and repeatable events. But more important, measurement begins to stress *nonmetric* techniques, as well as standard correlation techniques. The models of social process become "qualitative," but in terms of the sophisticated mathematical analysis of topology, set theory, and logical calculi suited to this subject matter. And the simulation of such social processes by computers permits a kind of vicarious experimentation in the social sciences whose results may then be tested against actual situations. Thus, the prediction of trends becomes feasible by means of such measurement techniques capable of ordering and analyzing large amounts of data previously unmanageable and unimaginable.

The question of the limited scope of such techniques as are directly quantitative (in terms of interval or ratio scales) raises the problem of "importance" and "triviality" in social-science research strategy. For it may increasingly become the case that central societal facts which do not lend themselves to such analysis will tend to be overlooked or de-emphasized on such narrowly methodological grounds, by virtue of the easy quantification of other, perhaps marginal facts. Social-science research oriented toward empirical-quantitative studies may very well then take the path of least resistance. But the path of least resistance to quantification may be the path of least significance as well, so that data analysis may proliferate precisely where it is least important. The difficulty of judgments as to what is important and what trivial exists in all the sciences, and it is not clear that there is an independent measure of such variables. Such questions of research strategy become increasingly pressing, as techniques often run ahead of imaginative and theoretically significant ideas. But the old objection that the social sciences are not "quantitative" (by contrast to physics as a paradigm of a quantificational science) becomes more anomalous with each passing day.

(*c*) *Models, laws, and theories.* In the social sciences, models have been traditionally plentiful, as in modern physical science they have been relatively sparse. The suggestion has been made that this is because the social sciences are in their infancy, and the empirical constraints on model-construction which will develop with maturity are not yet felt; the early speculative stages of any science, physics included, proliferate models, whereas the demands on a model in a more highly developed science are more rigorous. For example, the developed science is presumably more systematic and its logical structure is more tightly knit, so that the requirements on a new model include consistency with well-established theories or models already existing, and coherent "fit" with a wide range of already systematically connected facts. Such a view, whatever its intuitive plausibility, has several major faults: first, it ignores the nonsystematic or *ad hoc* use of models, which is widespread in even such so-called mature sciences as physics. Second, it suggests that science is a finite enterprise and that the more it is "developed," the more theory devolves upon a unique formulation. This is a thesis in the history of science, and the conditions of its validation are not at all clear. What is more, it is the very people who would most vehemently deny the formulability of "laws" in historical inquiry, who most uncritically adduce such a "law" which has all the appearances of a dogma about the history of science.

Despite this, it does seem to be the case that models abound in the social sciences, that they are often not rigorously conceived, and that they have a qualitative and loose character so that it is not clear on what grounds one should accept or reject a model of this sort. But if one takes a wide-swinging pragmatic view of models as *no more* than *ad hoc* instruments of understanding, or as practical or heuristic aids in suggesting modes of ordering data, and does not regard them as either true or false, then a wide latitude for model construction is preserved.

The criticism of such a view is that such "systematic" models, though incautious in their construction, are often taken dogmatically as reflections of some essential social reality, and thus impose a "premature closure" on empirical research or on more modest theory formation within the "middle-range." Model building may also become a scholastic enterprise relatively empty of significant empirical interpretation and degenerate into a formal exercise, constrained only by the demands of aesthetic satisfaction or imaginative play, or motivated by a penchant for endless elaboration and web spinning. Such a criticism has often been leveled at "global" models, as "speculative" and insufficiently empirical, or at worst "metaphysical" (which is a dirty word in this context) and therefore either meaningless or nonscientific.

The result of positivist criticism in the social sciences has often been an abandonment of theorizing in favor of small-bore data collection and analysis, in narrowly delimited areas, and the wholesale rejection of "theorizing" as an empty activity. The issue remains sharp at present in discussions of the philosophy of the social sciences and provides perhaps the most difficult challenge to critical analysis in contemporary philosophy of science. But it is clear, nevertheless, that the use of models in an experimental way has proceeded quite far in the social sciences very recently. This is in the development of what are in effect *ad hoc* models, as simulations of social situations and processes. Here an abstract model of some conceivable social situation is constructed, as a formal system expressible in a computer language; and under controlled conditions, such a simulation reproduces the abstracted features of such a situation, with various experimental values assigned to the variables. A chess-playing computer is a simulation of an actual game. But the concept of *game* in a more abstract sense has been developed so that many group or two-person situations may be reconstructed as "games," and these "games" can then be "played out," on a computer.

There is nothing conceptually new here, for actual games, like "Monopoly," or the variety of "war" games, or of "detective" games, are in effect "simulations" of actual social situations and processes. So-called ludic (or "play") theories and models in sociology and anthropology derive from the observation that actual socialization and learning often takes the form of simulational play, as in children's games which imitate real-life adult situations. Thus, common practice and the long tradition of "play" theories in aesthetics, biology, anthropology, and sociology provide the background for contemporary *ludic* and *games* models. But it is the formalization and mathematization of such models, in contemporary games theory (as developed by Morgenstern and von Neumann, with special applications to economic behavior) which introduces the present vicarious experimentation of computer simulation of such human and societal features as personality; economic, political, and social behavior; strategy, and so on. The "lessons" learned from such experimentation are, of course, limited in their applications to the much more complex situations of actual social and personal life. But in this respect such simulation is no worse off than is well-established animal experimentation in psychology, sociology, and medicine. The constraints of laboratory abstraction, of "artificial" conditions, of the partiality of the analogies to actual human behavior are present in both cases. What is often overlooked by the partisans of the "really scientific" physical sciences, is that in physical experimentation, analogous constraints also hold, both in the practical "isolation" of physical variables under laboratory conditions and in the formulation of ideal laws. The test of such models and the theories derived from them, in the social sciences, also lies in interpretation and application to real situations, if such vicarious experimentation is not to constitute a closed system which ultimately becomes self-fulfilling and self-validating. Meanwhile, actual "social experimentation" with groups, either under controlled laboratory conditions or in field experiments (as the recent Cornell project, in effecting a controlled social change in a backward Peruvian agricultural community) continues to develop. The more radical notion of large-scale national experiments, in which a whole society is transformed under controlled conditions (as in the Soviet Union in the years following the revolution) or the smaller-scale experiments in economic or financial control or regulation, in accordance with a theory of such controls (as in the influence of Keynesian economic theory, in governmental regulation in finance and in price-support and "pump-priming" spending programs in the United States) all attest to the larger and more dramatic aspects of social experimentation. John Dewey developed a many-sided theoretical approach to such controlled experimentation in social, political, and educational contexts, as the rational application of intelligence to human conduct, fulfilling the philosophical program of pragmatism and instrumentalism. Here the criterion of practical intelligence is the creation of a situation of such plasticity in human affairs that the projects of intelligence are constantly being critically assessed and revised in terms of their testing in experience. In simple terms, this is no more than the interpretation of the method of experimental science in terms of the human sciences, not merely as a theoretical but as a practical undertaking. In this sense, such a project stands to social science as technology and engineering stand to the physical sciences. Here the analogy of "social engineering" or "human engineering" arises, with its two faces: rational intelligence applied to human affairs, for their improvement, and this same intelligence applied for purposes of manipulation by parochial interests. But this bears on the intimate relation to science of values and the choice of goals, which we will discuss later, in Chapter 15.

The crucial criticism of all such experimental procedures in the social sciences is that the human material is too complex, involves too many variables, and that element of human freedom which makes it unamenable to law-like formulations in the social sciences. The companion to this view is the methodological critique which emphasizes the insufficiency of reliable data for generalization or for the validation of theories in social science. On such a view, it is only the relatively isolated and small-scale social situations which may lend themselves to explanation in the rigorous terms of a hypothetico-deductive model, with confirmation-procedures and prediction. For the rest, law-like formulations in the social sciences, as in history, founder on the rocks of the relative uniqueness of social and historical events and processes.

The holist may argue against this that what makes the difference, in the human sciences, is that capacity for "personal knowledge," or of *Verstehen,* or of "social insight" which the investigator brings with him and which is refined by experience and training. As a "clinician" (by analogy to clinical practice in psychology, psychiatry, and medicine), the social scientist himself may thus be the most refined "instrument" of investigation, his intelligence, sensitivity, and human understanding thus compensating for the complexity of the subject matter. But the hard-headed social scientist, or critic of the social sciences, may argue that this is an interpretive art, and not a science, and belongs therefore with such arts as medicine, psychiatry, politics, and history. Models, laws, and theories need to be such, he would argue, that they are empirically interpretable and testable under controlled conditions if the social sciences are to be sciences, if they are to be objective and value-free, and thus more than merely subjective, though plausible interpretations.

(*d*) *History as a science.* The most radical case of a distinction between science and interpretive art is that of history. Here, as in other places, Aristotle's stamp has remained indelible in the discussion of this issue. His distinction in the *Poetics* between poetry and history is that poetry is more "philosophical" than history, because poetry deals with the universal and history with the particular. History, in this context, is regarded as an account of events with no "internal necessity," but simply (and objectively) a sequential account of occurrences in their "accidental" concatenation. Thus it is mere chronicle, or mirror of the past. Unfortunately, the adoption of this view has often gotten the discussion stuck at the level of the historiography of the fourth century B.C. For though the issue of history versus mere chronicle is still alive, the development of the methods and style of historical inquiry has proceeded very far since Aristotle's time, and the alternatives cannot be reconstructed on merely speculative or analytic grounds without taking the concrete practice of historical scholarship into account. In the *Theses on Feuerbach,* Karl Marx remarks that though it is true that man is shaped by history, it is a one-sided view not to acknowledge that man *makes* history as well. One may interpret this in two senses. One, plainly objective, is that history is nothing above and beyond the actions of men, and the product of their striving, goals, needs, character, and so on. But the other sense is that there is no "history" except by the introduction of significance into otherwise brute events and that this "history" is the construction of human interpretation, or the product of human actions, where such actions are "human" precisely because they are humanly significant. Thus, to report as "mere" chronicle, for example, that "The American Revolution began in 1776," is to overlook the fact that the terms *American, Revolution,* and *1776* are not descriptions of brute events or properties, but denote entities which exist only in their significance relations, as human, historical, societal, or institutional facts. Thus, the "facts" of history are significances, and not simply spatiotemporal events. For example, the descriptive or factual report *Napoleon invaded Russia in 1812* already carries with it the meaning of *invaded,* which is not reducible to *French troops crossed the Russian frontier in 1812*. Rather, it means that they crossed without "invitation," or "permission," in "violation" of a "frontier." All the preceding terms in quotation marks (as well as the terms *French, troops, Russian, 1812*) denote societal or historical "facts" which exist only within the framework of history, as an account of humanly significant events or processes.

On such a view the difficult questions of whether there is objectivity in history, whether it exhibits laws, whether a theory or a science of history is possible, all become doubly difficult, for historical observation and data are no longer the straightforward objects of chronicle they were made out to be. As we saw in Chapter 5, this is not a unique characteristic of history. Beyond this complex question of the "entities" of history as acts and meanings, there is the methodological question of the inevitability of interpretation and selection of the "facts" in any historical inquiry. Does this condemn historical scholarship to subjectivity, or to partisanship, whether intended or unconscious? Does the very necessity of selection and generalization—because not all events and actions may enter into any finite account—irremediably distort or falsify some ideal and uninterpreted chronicle? Or are we to take the condition of *significance* for historical facts to mean that, "History exists only in the minds of men," as some ideal entity or construction? And if this irremediable requirement of interpretation and significance is to be met, then how may one talk about any such thing as objective laws of history, or historical explanation? Would not these then be no more than plausible stories, at best, and wishful projections of bias, at worst?

One radical way out of such dilemmas is to deny meaning to history.[12] Depending on one's interpretation of historical "fact," this would reduce the historical account to some recording of "brute facts," or to a fairy tale or a myth. Brute, uninterpreted facts being eliminated by their unavailability, this leaves us with history as some rhetorical, or evocative invention of the historian, or as ultimately ineffable existence to be lived through but not described.

Such a radical critique seems somehow implausible itself, however. For in one sense, all of the content of our descriptive science is "historical," for all of it is a record of the past, in a trivial way, and all of it is selective. Certainly one cannot claim that all of our knowledge of the past is either mythical or ineffable without condemning all of science and all but "the present moment" to utter irrationality. But perhaps the critique delimits its object as history proper, and says only that a science of history is unattainable. This objection would claim that, at best, the historian offers plausible interpretations of past events, insofar as he is more than a chronicler or a collater of diaries. But in the absence of anything like *laws* of history—the universals required by a true science—history remains ultimately ideographic, as Aristotle held, because historical occurrences are unique nonrecurring events or actions about which generalizations cannot be made. Even if one were to interpret laws as rules, such rules would remain without application, for there would in principle be but one instance of the application of such a rule and it would be the one from which the rule itself is derived, so that *rule* would be a senseless term. If it were indeed possible to arrive at certain generalizations about recurring historical processes, the objection would continue (e.g., wars, revolutions, the rise and fall of states), such historical generalizations would be the weakest of inductions, from which no valid or even remotely plausible predictive inferences could be made. Even if historical trends could be meaningfully denoted, Popper points out, "Trends are not laws. A statement asserting the existence of a trend is existential, not universal."[13] Thus scientific explanation in history is in effect ruled out. More crucially, such a critical view seems to rule out forever the possibility of learning from history, because "history never repeats itself."

This is certainly a gloomy view, especially by contrast to those views of history which see in it the great teacher of humanity and the guide to the future. Whatever the merits or dangers of such a romantic rationalism,

[12] As, for example, Karl Popper does, baldly asserting, "History has no meaning," *The Open Society and its Enemies,* (London: Routledge and Kegan Paul, 1945), vol. II, p. 256.

[13] Karl Popper, *The Poverty of Historicism* (London: Routledge and Kegan Paul, 1957), p. 115.

which seeks both truth and salvation in historical knowledge, one need not go this far in rejecting the astringent skepticism of the critics of history. They are not all historical nihilists, first of all; for although history may not be science, on this view, it need not be myth or nothing. The feasible role of historical interpretation does offer the full prospect of understanding, but without the fringe benefits of prediction or of law-like explanation. But, on this view, it is a matter of true interpretation to abjure such gifts, which at their worst clothe prophecy and religious or messianic inevitabilism in the garments of science—a disguise that is fraught with danger. The critic would argue that the error here is in taking history for what it is not, and thus, of using it in a way it is not meant to be used.

This modified skepticism may still be argued against, on the grounds that it counterposes an emasculated history to an idealized science. If historical research and reconstruction enters into that same rational critique which characterizes philosophy and science, and if canons of empirical evidence operate for the historian, as they assuredly do (and as anyone who is acquainted with the rigors of establishing historical evidence will attest), then the matter of predictive law cannot in itself be used to deny history a scientific character. For there are large (and perhaps the largest) areas in acknowledged sciences (e.g., in evolutionary theory in biology) where the function of prediction is likewise absent or only nascent. Furthermore, contrary to the standard formulation of the nomological model of explanation, it may be argued that explanation and prediction are not symmetrical (p. 267), and that general laws in history may be formulated with plausibility appropriate to the subject matter. On the matter of the nonrepeatability of historical events, or their uniqueness, it may be argued that the criterion of repetition used here has been lifted bodily from the natural sciences and inappropriately applied to historical events. Though in ideal physical laws, and under the conditions of experiment, physical events of a certain type may be said to be recurrent, strictly speaking, no two events may be said to be identically recurrent, but recurrent only with respect to certain abstracted features. The judgment of recurrence in terms of the abstraction of certain features or type-or class-characteristics of events may be said to function similarly in history and the human sciences, and in physics; and it is only the features which are abstracted which distinguish the two cases. It is not clear, then, why history may not be judged a science. Here a problem arises, however, which is akin to one in the social sciences. It is not clear how far one may abstract the features of historical events in the interest of producing evidence for laws in history, without destroying the significance of the event as historical, i.e., without eliminating its historicity and turning it into a brute fact. One may trivially assert that after every major war, there follows a period of *détente* and of reconstruction of destroyed areas. Or one may say that revolutions succeed only where there are weak ruling classes. Anything so general has all but lost its historical significance, and certainly its historical interest, as characterizing the specificity which makes the description of an historical event or process more than an empty and unenlightening platitude. The soul of historical reconstruction is detail and concreteness. Yet it is also significance, and the isolate and accidental particulars of mere chronicle (if indeed such chronicle is even possible) do not constitute history. The balance between the factually empty and hypothetical ideal type and the bare particular event or action would seem to require some art of the historian. But it is not a matter of *a priori* judgment, "in principle," that a reasonable abstraction of certain features of historical events cannot be made or that general laws in history wtih genuine empirical relevance cannot be formulated. Rather, it involves the critical-empirical judgment of the historian, as a scientist in the community of scientists, where rigor, criticism, and canons of evidence and inference are as much his concern as they are the concern of the physicist, the biologist, or the psychologist.

PART IV

Coda

CHAPTER 15

Science, Values, and the Humanistic Understanding

TOWARD THE CLOSE of the *Critique of Pure Reason,* Kant summarizes, "The legislation of human reason . . . has two objects, nature and freedom, and therefore contains not only the law of nature, but also the moral law, presenting them at first in two distinct systems, but ultimately in one single philosophical system. The philosophy of nature deals with all *that is,* the philosophy of morals with that which *ought to be.*"[1] This classical expression of the relation of scientific knowledge to knowledge of the good exhibits at once the division of fact and value, and the project of their coherence which underlies the history of philosophical thought. Kant contrasts them as two worlds, equally "real" or objective; and with the full power of his rigorous rationalism he sets out to analyze the conditions of our knowledge in both, and the conception under which they may come to be synthesized. The two realms, of nature and of human freedom, are both subject to the legislation of reason, in Kant's view; both may come to be known under the aspect of law, and thus each is the subject matter of science. The pervasive and difficult question of the relation of natural scientific knowledge to human values and to human freedom thus presents itself as a question for "science" (in that broad and humane sense in which Kant conceived of it, as critical and systematic knowledge). But the question is not clear, and to the same degree that it remains a matter of deep

[1] I. Kant, *Critique of Pure Reason,* tr. Norman Kemp Smith (New York: St. Martin's Press, 1961), pp. 658–59.

public concern and not merely a philosophical puzzle, it remains also a matter of profound public and private confusion. The separation of the two "worlds" of fact and value raises such questions as that of the moral neutrality of science, the relation of ends to means, and the possibility of the scientific study of values. The synthesis of the two raises even sharper questions concerning the relation of *is* and *ought* and of what exactly we mean by *value*.

THREE QUESTIONS IN PLACE OF ONE

We ordinarily take as valuative all that has to do with *right* action; with the *good* in human life (or in the cosmos, for that matter), and with what is *evil* as well; with what is *pleasing* or *estimable* or *beautiful* or *obligatory* or *well done;* in short, all those things which entail attitudes of approval or disapproval, feelings of obligation and duty, of assent and consent, the beliefs in virtue of which we take such attitudes, the reasons by which we justify them, and the actions which exemplify them. It is obvious that the study of such values, value situations, and of the judgments concerning them is extraordinarily complex. It constitutes the domain of one of the most difficult and rigorous of the philosophical disciplines, value theory, and as such is not a part of philosophy of science. But the fundamental questions which arise here impinge on the philosophy of science in a crucial way, for they have to do with the relation of scientific knowledge to such valuation, with the status of valuative facts, or whether there are such facts at all, and with the question of whether the domain of values and of value claims is one in which cognitive judgments are possible, or consists instead of noncognitive expressions of attitude, feeling, desire, and so on.

The general question of the relation of science to value may be divided into three quite separate questions:

1. Is value amenable to scientific study, and may the object of such study be taken as either natural, or human or societal fact? Is there a science of value?
2. What values are exhibited *in* science? This is a question concerning the sociology of science or the study of the *ethos* of science.
3. What is the value of science? What larger interests does it subserve or subvert?

We may also distinguish between reflection, analysis, or criticism of the concepts of value, and the use of such concepts in prescriptive, persuasive, and judgmental ways. Thus, we may distinguish between ethical analysis and moral precept or exhortation, between the criticism of the concepts of morality, which is philosophical analysis, and the criticism of social and individual morality, which is the domain of the moral teacher, the social critic, the prophet. We may distinguish between aesthetic analysis, which examines the concepts of art and beauty, and the reasons and conditions which characterize aesthetic judgment, on the one hand, and aesthetic judgment itself, which proceeds to evaluate or to exhort to valuation, on the other. It is not always clear that one may separate one of these functions from the other, and this becomes the concern of the analysis of ethical and aesthetic discourse.

(*a*) *Descriptive and normative.* If we want to give an account of what, as a *matter of fact,* someone believes, or what his attitude is, without ourselves making a valuative judgment concerning this, such an inquiry may be called descriptive. If we intend not only to describe, but to account for the reasons or causes of such beliefs or attitudes, still without valuative judgment on our part, then our inquiry may be called explanatory. Thus far, we may be said to be dealing with valuative facts, and the description and explanation of facts is after all the object of scientific inquiry. But this raises the question of the sorts of facts these are.

Suppose that some value investigator, doing field research in some society not his own, were to "observe objectively" that murder is regarded as wrong in the given society. He would not simply report the "fact" that murder is wrong, but that in a society *S,* murder is *regarded* as wrong. What fact, exactly, would he be observing and reporting? If the investigator himself took it to be a fact that murder is wrong, then presumably he would be judging that wrongness is a factual or natural property of an act of murder; for certainly an "act of murder" is a fact, and the statement that such an act took place is either true or false, therefore. But the term *murder* itself connotes a wrong act, if we take it in anything like the ordinary sense. In such a sense, *wrong* is already contained in the concept *murder,* and if we knew that what we were observing "factually" were a murder taking place, then the wrongness of the act would then seem to be a property of that fact, as some naturally describable property, if the appropriate conception of this fact of murder contains this as part of its meaning. We might then conclude that murder is "naturally or factually wrong." Or we might instead conclude that the statement *murder is wrong* is simply analytic, like *circles are round,* so that if one were to construe an act as an act of murder, this would entail that it is wrong. But thus far we have had our investigator telling us, in effect, what, upon observation, he would take to be an act of murder; and that, in his sense of *murder,* such an act is wrong. Now his observation that in society *S,* murder is regarded as wrong may be effected in one of two ways. He either observes what he construes as an act of murder and then observes that the members of society *S* behave in a way which shows that they regard this act as wrong, or he interrogates the *S*ians concerning their beliefs, he studies their laws and moral code, and discovers that the act he would construe as an act of murder is regarded as wrong. So far, no problems.

But now suppose that he observed that "in society *S*, murder is regarded as right," and that what he construes as *murder,* the *S*ians construe as *necessary social therapy*. Are the *S*ians and the investigator talking about the same fact? Or are there two different facts? Is the fact *murder* or *necessary social therapy?* One might evade this by saying, "What we would regard as murder (and wrong) is regarded by the *S*ians as necessary social therapy (and right)," alleging that a truly *factual* report would merely describe the act and circumstances of one man killing another. In effect, the investigator would be giving us the correlation between his usage and that of the *S*ians, with regard to the "brute" fact of homicide. But then it would appear that *murder* is not a fact, but a construal of a fact; no one is ever "murdered" then, but only killed, and this is construed differently according to the usage (not simply linguistic, but social or moral or legal usage) of particular societies. But this gives the odd result that murders never take place, except as "interpretations of fact," or as opinions or feelings in the minds of observers. Murder, however, is not an opinion or a feeling, but rather some sort of thing *about* which one opines or feels. We might relativize this, and have our observer say that, "In the context of the social laws and rules of society *S,* an act which in our own context we would construe as murder and wrong, is regarded as right." Following this lead, we might set up a peculiar class of facts, called "societal" or "institutional" facts, which exist, or are what they are only by virtue of their social or institutional contexts. Suppose further that such contexts confer valuative properties upon their peculiar facts (as previously, it was suggested that historical contexts confer significance upon "historical facts"). We would then have to say that in the institutional context of society *S,* a homicide took place, but not a murder, and that the alleged "fact" of a murder which the investigator observed simply never occurred.

The situation is not so far-fetched, for the determination of whether a murder has taken place in our own society is a matter of construal according to rules and norms prescribed by our legal system. We sometimes get into the peculiar situation of claiming, in a "miscarriage of justice," that the murderer got away scot-free. But if someone is legally adjudged innocent of the crime of murder, on what independent grounds would one allege that a murder was in fact committed? If the "fact" of murder is in effect a context-determined fact, then the context of law which defines murder, and the mode of judgment that a murder was committed, would all determine, in our instance, that a murder never really took place.

It is with such "strange" facts that a science of values would have to deal, and even the apparently simple "descriptive" task of reporting on the "valuative facts" or the usages of individual or social belief and value judgment becomes enmeshed with the normative. This issue, as we saw, arises sharply in the social sciences, and recent studies of the methodology of anthropological and sociological research into norms and values have recognized and begun to cope with such difficulties, going beyond an earlier simplistic view. All this is by way of raising the problem of objectivity which arises in a purported science of values.

One conclusion from all this may be that the subject of valuation is so irremediably subjective that a scientific study is impossible. The most radical form of such a view would claim that there can be no science of values, because there simply are no facts with which such a science would deal. That is, the kinds of concepts and actions which are the subject of valuative inquiry are not "factual," to begin with, and all discourse which preserves the valuational nature of the subject of inquiry is irreducible to factual or descriptive discourse. The *ontological* claim would be that values and facts are unique and distinct entities, and just as facts cannot constitute values, so values are irreducible to factual components. The methodological and logical-linguistic claim would be that one cannot derive "ought" statements from merely factual premises, nor can one reduce "ought" statements to "is" statements. In effect, one cannot base judgments of value on matters of fact (where *fact* is taken in the sense of the objects of empirical-scientific knowledge, propositions concerning which are either true or false). On such a view, a *descriptive* science of value may be possible, in the limited sense of reports on the expressions of belief, or opinion, or attitude of individuals or of social groups. Such a purely descriptive science might be pursued as a part of descriptive anthropology or sociology, or descriptive linguistics. Or a purely formal science of valuative discourse may be possible, in terms of logical and linguistic analysis of meaning and inference in valuative discourse and argument. Thus, any scientific approach to values is either a part of descriptive social science or a logical-linguistic formal science. But these deal with the facts of expressions of value, and not with the "facts" of value itself, so that a normative science of value is impossible.

The absoluteness of the descriptive-normative distinction is usually illustrated by some such case as the distinction between the statements *x believes that murder is wrong* or *y feels that z is beautiful* and the statements *murder is wrong* and *z is beautiful.* It seems plain that such statements as *x believes – – –* or *y feels – – –* are true or false in some straightforward and ascertainable way, and that we may discover this empirically or matter-of-factly. But *that murder is wrong,* or *that z is beautiful* are not assertions whose truth and falsity may be established by empirical research, or by taking an opinion poll, for example. Nor is it clear that they are the sorts of statements which can be true or false at all. In short, it is not clear that these are statements at all, if we take statements to be expressions of propositions which are either true or false. Some such analysis has led to the view that these are "pseudostatements" and are neither true nor false. They constitute, instead, a class of expressions which serve a different function in discourse, though they have the form of statements. In fact, they are imperatives; prescriptions; rules; expressions of attitude, belief, or desire. That is, they convey the state of feeling of the speaker rather than information about some "objective" fact, and as such stand outside the domain of factual expressions which constitutes empirical science. (In some versions, this is called the "emotive theory" or the "prescriptive theory," but these earlier versions have been so modified that such names are misleading.)

An alternative view takes a decidedly different approach to value and value statements. Here no distinctive realm of value as such is held to exist apart from the actual processes of valuation; and these are natural processes characteristic of human activity, such as desiring, willing, approving, and so on. In this sense, things have value because of their being valued. To use an analogy, the value of a commodity is whatever one is ready to exchange for it, so that its market price, or its desirability, constitutes the only value it has. There is no "real" or "intrinsic" value which it has outside such "institutional" contexts (as in our earlier case of murder). Thus something would be of value because it is desired; being an object of desire is what confers value upon it. It is the fact of desiring that confers value upon such an object, therefore. Against such a view, it has been argued that the distinction between what is desired, as a matter of fact, and what *ought* to be desired, has been ignored. For if there is any sense at all to moral imperatives and moral ideals, it must be the case that some things which are desired ought not to be, and other things not desired ought to be. The conflating of the descriptive and the normative, in such a case, has been labeled the "naturalistic fallacy," for the value theory which alleges that values are "natural facts," in the sense of the facts of desiring, willing, believing, and so on, is called naturalism. Among such naturalistic theories are those which seek the sources of valuation in the conditions of the organism itself, so that although it is the valuation of some subject which confers value upon an object, this "subjective" valuation is not arbitrary. Rather, it has objective grounds in the "nature" of the valuing subject (e.g., in human nature) or in the objective relations between some organism and the environment. The good is then that which fulfills best, or realizes to the fullest, the needs, desires, capacities of an organism or species. The "biological" tone of such a theory is not accidental, for the "highest good" in the variety of such naturalistic theories is that which supports, preserves, or enhances life and growth. "Growth itself is the only moral 'end,'" says Dewey.[2] The burden falls on the naturalist in value theory to make clear what such ends as "growth" or "self-realization" come to, if they are more than honorific, rhetorical terms. Given this, in terms of what we may come to learn about the optimal conditions of "growth"

[2] J. Dewey, *Reconstruction in Philosophy* (Boston: Beacon Press, 1957), p. 177.

or "self-realization" (suitably defined), the naturalist might argue that even the assertion of matter-of-fact propositions involves some normative element, in terms of the criteria of truth and falsity, just as assertions of value involve conditions of evidence and factual reference, if they are to be more than empty, or trivial, or "transcendental" statements about some ideal realm. In giving reasons for valuative judgments, one does not trivially adduce prior definitions, or rest content with appeal to "necessary intuitions of the mind." If I assert that murder is wrong, on such a view, my reasons may be that ultimately I regard as wrong whatever is destructive of the social order. Then it is a matter of empirical fact (though not simply so) to establish or disestablish the proposition *Murder is destructive of social order.* But then the preservation of social order itself needs its reason, which the naturalist may give as *human life is possible only in a social order, and human life ought to be preserved.* From such a premise, one might deduce that social order ought to be preserved, and that if murder is destructive of such order, it is wrong. But the critic of naturalism will be quick to point out that in the major premise of such a chain of inference, there is an "ought" statement, and not a descriptive or factual one.

One reply would be to reject the sharp descriptive-normative distinction altogether, or to question the status of the statement which asserts this dichotomy in the first place. Is the statement that *ought cannot be derived from is* itself a factual statement? Or a normative one? If it is itself "irreducibly normative," as it seems, then is it a prescription, or a rule of use, or a self-evident proposition? What justifies it? Is it analytic? Synthetic *a priori?* And is it not the case that such a bifurcation glosses over the range of "facts" which statements (or propositions) may describe? It is true that at either end of the range we cannot simply assert that goodness is a natural property in the sense that the mass of a body is. Here, analogously to the cases we examined in biology and the human sciences, one may take an emergentist position as well: value is neither reducible to the "natural facts" of physics, nor is it a non-natural property, as "life" and "mind" are in vitalist or mentalist theories. Rather, the emergentist may hold that value is the characteristic "fact" which emerges at a certain level of organization, namely that of self-conscious human society, and simply does not exist at "lower" levels. The emergentist thus seeks to have it both ways; value is a natural property but is not reducible to "physical" or "biological" fact. On such a view, a science of value is one of the human sciences and is at least no worse off than they are.

The various claims concerning fact and value are properly the study of such disciplines of philosophical analysis as ethics and aesthetics. But only such analysis can make sense (or nonsense) of talk about a science of value. It is here that these considerations become germane to the philosophy of science.

THE VALUE OF SCIENCE: "GOOD" SCIENCE, "BAD" SCIENCE

The question of the value of science may also be divided. (1) On the one hand, we may consider the scientific enterprise as a whole, or in its several aspects, in terms of the value or disvalue it produces. This concerns the effect of science on national life, on the economy, on politics, on peace and war, and on every aspect of human life and survival with which it has become so closely linked. This is primarily the subject matter for political and sociological study, for the moralist, the strategist, the policy maker, the moral and social critic. Recently such a discussion has centered around C. P. Snow's critique of "the two cultures," and such technological-political studies as those of P. M. S. Blackett, J. D. Bernal, Lewis Mumford, Robert Merton, Herman Kahn, and Irving Horowitz.

(2) On the other hand, we may consider how the very activity of scientific work generates certain norms of value concerning truth, right conduct, and aesthetic satisfaction. Here the concern is for what one may call the ethics and aesthetics of science. Such questions as the following arise: Do the norms of scientific objectivity, of critical and skeptical attitudes toward belief, of evidence and experimental testing, of scientific modesty and rigorous self-criticism tend in themselves to constitute a distinctive scientific ethic?[3] Do the standards of economy of formulation, of systematicity and well-ordered form, and do the aspects of creative intuition in scientific discovery suggest a distinctive scientific aesthetic? At their best such features of science indeed show a high and humane ideal of human conduct, and of intellectual temperance and open-mindedness. Since Plato's time science has provided the model of the rational man. Renaissance and Enlightenment thinkers took the man of science as the paradigm of the man of reason and high purpose; and Emerson's ideal of the American scholar whose proper condition is "man thinking" seems to have no more adequate embodiment than the scientist at work. Indeed, through much of its history, science was broadly defined *as* rational thought. But the ambivalence about science, described in the opening pages of this book, expresses itself also in the image of the scientist as archfiend, as amorally rational, as the Frankenstein who produces the monster who will destroy him, and all of us with him. And to the extent that this too has its grounds in the antihuman practice of some scientists who, like the Nazi doctors,

[3] C. S. Peirce writes, on objectivity in sciences as an ethical norm, "The logic which observational science uses is not, like the logic which the books teach, quite independent of the motive and the spirit of the reasoner. There is an ethics indissolubly bound up with it—an ethics of fairness and impartiality—and a writer, who teaches, by his example, to find arguments for a conclusion which he wishes to believe, saps the very foundations of science by trifling with its morals." [In J. Buchler, *The Philosophy of Peirce* (London: Routledge & Kegan Paul, 1940), p. 313.]

forgot that they were human beings, it compromises the rosy and pious view of a scientific ethic. Robert S. Cohen remarks, in a recent address on science and ethics, that,

> The full truth is bitter. Science is no longer the wholly enlightening ally of human progress that it once seemed to be, and humane men will look warily at any model of a scientifically rationalized social order, at too strict a devotion to facts, at too concentrated a focus of intellectual resources upon the very technical fields which have enabled the mechanization of human life and culture. . . . We come to realize again that science is morally neutral. It has not automatically been a force for good. . . . Furthermore, the extension of science to the study of society and history is no guarantee of a humane commitment within the scientific community, nor of moral wisdom within scientific knowledge.[4]

However qualitatively vague a matter it may be to assess "too strict a devotion to fact," or however one may interpret the "moral neutrality of science," it is clear that for all the methods and standards of scientific thought have to offer in the way of an ethical model, the older romanticized view of a scientific reason as intrinsically humane requires the negative qualifications which Cohen suggests. For the "good science" view is the other side of the same coin which bears the "bad science" view (i.e., that classical romantic critique of science which saw it as intrinsically inhumane and amoral).

The relation between scientific knowledge and the use of this knowledge for human ends thus poses most sharply the practical question of the rela-

[4] Robert S. Cohen, "Science and Ethics," presented at the International Conference on Science and Technology, Herceg Novi, Jugoslavia, 1964. Perhaps the classic formulation of the ethos of science is Robert K. Merton's. In "Science and Democratic Social Structure" [in *Social Theory and Social Structure,* rev. ed. (New York: The Free Press, 1957), pp. 550–561], Merton writes, "The ethos of science is that affectively toned complex of values and norms which is held to be binding on the man of science. The norms are expressed in the form of prescriptions, proscriptions, preferences and permissions. They are legitimized in terms of institutional values. These imperatives, transmitted by precept and example and reinforced by sanctions are in varying degrees internalized by the scientist, thus fashioning his scientific conscience or, if one prefers the latter day phrase, his superego. Although the ethos of science has not been codified, it can be inferred from the moral consensus of scientists as expressed in use and wont, in countless writings on the scientific spirit and in moral indignation directed toward contraventions of the ethos."

Merton suggests that four sets of "institutional imperatives" comprise the ethos of modern science: *Universalism* (the canon that truth claims, whatever their source, are to be subjected to preestablished impersonal criteria), *Communism* (the view that scientific findings belong to the community at large and are the product of social collaboration), *Disinterestedness,* and *Organized Skepticism.* For a sharp contemporary critique of Merton's view, see Daniel A. Greenberg, "The Values of Science," 1966 (unpublished manuscript, forthcoming).

tion of fact and value. On one view, science is knowledge of fact, and this knowledge serves merely as the instrument for the achievement of ends. But the choice of ends to be achieved is not the domain of the scientist but of the moralist, the artist, the citizen. When he makes value judgments, the scientist takes off his scientist hat and puts on his moralist hat, or his citizen hat (thus going through that transformation usually reserved for metamorphic insects). The relation of means and ends thus focuses the relation of science and values upon what appears as a dichotomy between cognitive knowledge and valuative judgment. When the scientist is wearing his scientist hat, he is no more than the effectuator of chosen ends, or the critic of the feasibility of such ends, on this view. He can, for example, tell you how to control atomic processes, or whether a manned flight to Mars may be undertaken. He is concerned with truth and valid knowledge, but also with the utilization of such knowledge as an instrument. But *how* and *whether* are not the same as *why,* in the sense of reasons for choosing this or that goal. It is true that the choice of relative ends as themselves means to further ends may be a matter of scientific knowledge. Suppose one asked whether one should choose to build a bridge across a certain river. One could decide this question in terms of some larger or more ultimate goal, say, the facilitation of transportation between two cities. This goal, in turn, may have its reasons in some further goal to be achieved, with respect to which it is instrumental. Such values as are relative to the achievement and consummation of other values are called instrumental values, and it seems clear that decisions on instrumental values are within the province of applied scientific study and judgment (once the ends, for which these instrumental values are means, have been chosen). The applied scientific judgment in such contexts is technology. The theory of such judgments is studied in so-called *decision-theory,* and in what the Polish theoretician Kotarbinski calls *Praxiology.* Its logical framework is the hypothetical judgment: "If you want to achieve *B,* then do *A.*" But whether one should want to achieve *B* in the first place seems to require some categorical judgment ("*B* ought to be achieved"). Otherwise, we are caught in an infinite regress (*B* for the sake of *C, C* for the sake of *D* . . .). If indeed science has to do with *what is,* and if *ought* may not be derived from *is,* then certainly the prescriptive functions of science are subordinate to some ultimately extrascientific value judgments. On such a view, science is morally or valuatively neutral with respect to such decisions, because they lie outside of its scope.

The counterargument here is that scientific activity is not merely an abstracted matter of "knowledge-in-itself," but constantly involves the use of this knowledge. It is an analytic statement to say that science is morally neutral, if one means by *science,* "knowledge abstracted from its use." But then one is not talking about real science, in its concrete activity. The scientist is always more than disembodied mind, or inquirer, though his relative isolation may be a condition for proper work. But this condition itself may be said to be an instrumental value, and there is no non-normative reason for scientific neutrality, except that it subserves the end of scientific progress, taken as an end in itself. Thus, the very condition of neutrality presupposes some end or choice of goals, ultimately valuative. If we ask, "Why should science be regarded as morally neutral?" We must invoke some such premise as "knowledge is an intrinsic good, and its pursuit is best served by the instrumental belief that science ought to be morally neutral." Thus neutrality is a policy that is justified by some intrinsic value. If we relativize this, we may argue hypothetically, "*If* you want science to make progress and succeed in its tasks, and *if* the condition for this is freedom to pursue its course wherever this leads, apart from all ideological and moral restrictions, *then* you ought to support scientific neutrality." But this makes the moral neutrality of science itself a matter of choice, of determining by empirical inquiry whether such neutrality does or does not subserve the end of scientific progress.

It is also clear that norms operate within science. Examination of the place of values within scientific inquiry raises the question of whether ultimate human concerns are not mirrored in the very practice of science as human activity, for such norms of science as truth, consistency, and confirmation may themselves be the highly refined reflection of profound human imperatives. The argument is that such norms are universal and are not colored by the immediate and partial interests of human beings or states. Thus, by virtue of the universality of its norms, science transcends local prejudice and narrow interest. The values of science become part not of the facts which science investigates, but of science itself, that is, a characteristic of its procedure and its rationality.

SCIENCE AS RATIONAL ACTION

In the broadest sense we may characterize science as rational action; and whereas the sources of this action may be need, intellectual adventure, or personal satisfaction, its guide and judge in all things is critical and reflective intelligence. Such intelligence judges not only intentions but results, and not only immediate success and failure but the qualities of vision and insight. This critical reason, this rational intelligence, has at the same time been the model of rational belief and rational action which Socrates, Plato, Aristotle, Kant, and Dewey, among others, sought in their ethical theories. As guides to rational action, science and ethics have a common ancestry and a common interest; their division, insofar as it is substantive and not merely a division of intellectual labor, is a sign of deep trouble.

But it is not enough to establish some vague and pious identity of science and ethics on these grounds. What is needed is some hardheaded analysis of the relation between the rationality of science and human freedom, that consummation which Kant so devoutly sought. This is subject for a separate inquiry. But Cohen, in the paper previously cited, neatly outlines some of the content of a democratic ethic which the rational action of science exhibits,

> The life of science, the ways we live with each other when we are true to the unimpeded knowledge-seeking goal of science, is characterized by an ethic with notable positive features. We form a democracy whose citizens decide what shall be the policy, what accepted as truth for guiding the commonwealth. . . . We scientists do not have formal elections, much less regularly scheduled ones, but we do have that plausibility of a true democratic practice: we give an idea, or a theory, or a technique, a test; we choose some men and their proposals and let them run the affairs which are on our agenda and after a while, we test them against our experience, and decide whether they are right or wrong, wise or foolish, the best likely or the least likely to succeed. And usually we replace them. . . . And while Einstein replacing Newton does so with the greatest respect for Newton, there is yet psychological interest in the manner by which science utilizes the revolt of young generations against the old, for positive ends. In any case, this scientific democracy has an additional quality which should demand respect: the social collaboration which I have stressed is combined with an extraordinary respect for individual work. If ever the conflicting claims of classic bourgeois individualism and of classic socialism will be reconciled in a fully healthy society, it will, I believe, reflect this beautiful legitimacy of *independence* and *interdependence* within science. . . . In science, we combine subjective attitudes with objective demands, for example, an esthetic delight with a demanding reasonableness. We combine beauty with utility. We combine pride with modesty. We combine authority and leadership with private judgment and constant individual criticism. And we treat each other with respect. Despite violation by pride and other weaknesses, the ethic of the international community of scientists is known and persists. And the ethic of science is the democratic ethic of a cooperative republic.[5]

Cohen adds all the qualifications on an ideally rational practice introduced by the social functions of science as a subordinate instrument of power and as a commonwealth with its share of human weaknesses. But as a human activity, science has contributed a model of rational and free action and has exhibited it as one of its highest achievements.

[5] For sharp criticisms of such a view, and of Merton's, see Daniel A. Greenberg, *op. cit.*

SCIENCE AND THE HUMANISTIC UNDERSTANDING

The aim of this inquiry has been to examine the origins and growth of scientific thought, its structure and methodology, and some of its fundamental concepts, with a view to examining it as a humane study. But what exactly is such a humane study? What kind of understanding may be characterized as a humanistic understanding of science? Not simply the understanding of science as a human activity, though this is an aspect of such an understanding and is the subject of scientific study in its own right in the sociology, psychology, and history of science. Nor simply the understanding of science as one of the liberal arts, marked by its quest for rational knowledge and truth, beyond their utility or technological import. Nor does a humanistic understanding mean an understanding of generalities in some superficial overview. But it does mean a *general* view which at the same time embodies a deep sense of the direction and character of the sciences, their interrelationships, and their relation to what lies outside them. It does not therefore deal with generalities but with the deep structures of science, as matters of intellectual comprehension, of a sense of the enterprise which goes to its foundations. Such foundations are not "in" the particular sciences as a pea is in a pod; but they are exemplified only in the sciences, as humanity is exemplified only in particular human beings and their concrete activities. To realize the humanity of a person is to do more than to know how he acts, and even more than to know how to judge or estimate his actions. It is to have a grasp of what his character is, what his sources of humanity are; to know him, as one knows oneself, to be a child of man. To come to a humanistic understanding of science then is to come to achieve, and recognize in oneself, that mode of conceptual understanding exemplified in science itself; to effect that rapport between one's own understanding and the sort of understanding which science exhibits, which makes it possible to realize the full humanism of scientific thought.

This is not a matter of sudden intuition, but of study and of that discovery which is sometimes the reward of study. Such discovery comes piecemeal, for science is a complex, and not a simple, "whole." That sense of the unity of science which grows out of the conceptual analysis of its methodology and its fundamental ideas is itself complex. In the best and deepest sense of philosophy, a humanistic understanding of science is a philosophical understanding of science.

Appendixes

APPENDIX A

ALL FALL DOWN: The Development of the Concept of Motion from Aristotle to Galileo

A CASE STUDY IN THE CONCEPTUAL FOUNDATIONS OF SCIENTIFIC THOUGHT

INTRODUCTION

THIS CASE STUDY in the evolution of the concept of motion is intended to exemplify the several issues raised in the preceding chapters of this book. Thus, it attempts to interweave discussion of the genesis of science, the methods of science, and the substantive philosophical questions relevant to the concept of motion. At the outset, we deal with the genesis of the ordinary concepts of motion, in what is called here "the primary experience of motion" (what might be called a phenomenological account of motion-as-experienced). From the matrix of this common experience and commonsense concepts of motion, there develops that characteristic Greek philosophical speculation and critique on the questions of motion and change. The deliberate restriction and abstraction of the concept of motion as change of place or of the position of bodies in space leads to the first formulation of the specific subject matter of physics. Aristotle's kinetics (dealing with change of place, or local motion) and his dynamics (involving an explanatory theory of motive forces) is scrutinized in the context of previous Greek thought, and some of the problems he leaves are examined in terms of the alternatives and criticisms brought forth by his successors and commentators. The all-important advance in medieval mechanics is examined, principally in terms of the development of the Merton Rule or the Mean Speed Theorem by the fourteenth-century "calculators" at Oxford. The analysis proceeds to show how Galileo finally resolves the problem of the mathematical analysis of the motion of falling bodies. The contemporary translation of Galileo's formulation, in terms of the calculus and the concept of limit, is introduced in elementary form and explained, to show the function and significance of formal systems and their interpretation in empirical science.

The interrelated aspects of observation, hypothesis, experiment, and formal mathematical inference are seen in relation to the metaphysical and epistemological frameworks within which the concept of motion developed.

Thus, this brief, introductory case study seeks to exhibit the *Problematik* of philosophy of science, to show its many-sided aspects in the living form of a historical scientific problem and its (partial) resolution. At best, it can whet the appetite for further study and for involvement in the scientific adventure as participant as well as critical onlooker.

Sources of additional case studies, in greater detail than the one which is presented here, are suggested in the bibliographical note. The student is encouraged to examine this literature for a sense of the living activity of science, contact with which is the source of the strength and relevance of philosophy of science.

THE PRIMARY EXPERIENCE OF MOTION

London bridge is falling down
Falling down, falling down
London bridge is falling down
My fair lady

Here we go round the mulberry bush
The mulberry bush, the mulberry bush
Here we go round the mulberry bush
All fall down

Interwoven with our early experience of motion is our experience of the *language* of motion. Our lived experience of motion is thus bound up with our concepts of motion, as they are expressed in language. Once we are past that early enculturation in which we acquire language and the ways of experiencing, these enter into our having the experience as well. Thus our culturally inherited ways of talking about motion form part of that complex of perceiving and judging which shapes our experience to our thought as much as it exhibits the way in which our thought has been shaped by our experience. Our empirical knowledge of the world is not simply acquired by looking and seeing, but by *looking at* and *seeing as;* what it is we choose to notice, and what escapes our attention even when it stares us in the face, and what we take whatever it is we notice to *be,* is a function, in large part, of that framework of concepts into which we enter when we are weaned from our mother's breast. This very metaphor of separation from the mother—first in the cutting of the umbilical cord, then in weaning—has found many interpretations in terms of the process of our coming to know the world. Cognitive knowledge requires the separation of the subject from the object of knowledge; a certain distance, therefore, between ourselves and nature, a disjunction in space and time from the flow and push of goings-on.

This separation from the mother-nature is itself a natural process: we acquire the means of separation from the mother, primarily, in acquiring language in the "mother's way," as some linguists describe the primary acquisition of language. As we begin to speak, we are disunited from that symbiosis which keeps us mute, and as we become articulate, we articulate the world of our experience. We re-enter the world armed, disabused, our initial innocence gone. No longer symbiotic, we approach the world more nearly as objective, as material for our fashioning, with tools suited to construct this world to our needs and interests.

With our articulateness we acquire also mobility. From the infant's head-turning and eye-rolling, we advance to turning over, to crawling, to walking. What was seen at a distance, what could be touched by reaching, now becomes an object to be gone around, and past. Our early projectile play involves learning the delight of reaching beyond our reach, the complex motor processes of throwing; learning therefore the coordination of muscular effort and direction. Arriving at a place converts a *there* to a *here,* as the complexities of locative vocabulary are learned. *Faster, faster!* cues an additional exertion, usually with a reward at the end. Running beats walking, as any toddler knows. And there are two sorts, besides—there is running *to* and running *away from,* very different in temper. The cessation of motion is important too. It means being stopped, held back by some force, blocked, but also it means fatigue and the final arrival at the state and place of rest, home plate, or bed—in each case, a place of satisfaction and surcease.

The day's activities provide rich empirical material. The references for a host of commonsense concepts of motion are ready to hand, to be formulated into that space of motion which our own mobility and activity inhabits. The concepts *up, down, from, to, fast, slow* are ingeniously related and subtly interwoven with kinesthetic sensations, visual cues, sounds at hand and distant, desires and aversions. Characteristic of this primary experience of motion, then, is its affective quality, the way in which its empirical content is permeated with personal expressiveness.

We recognize also the motions of things around us from the vantage point of our own mobility. Things approach and recede; tops, wheels, and phonograph records spin around, as we sometimes also do. We feel the speed of our own motion, being carried or transported, watching things whiz or slide past us. We notice the position of things: the dresser *next to* the bed, the plate *on* the table, the sun *above* our heads, then *behind* a rooftop, and always *in front of,* or *behind, above or below, to the right* or *to the left* of that center which we come to articulate as our selves.

Position is learned as relation—things out there in relation to each other, and all of them in relation to ourselves. And in this richly textured fabric the whole philosophical lexicon of motion is already laid out before us: the stuff of all the concepts of motion, from the commonsense ones by which we orient our action in the world, to the philosophical and scientific accounts of this motion. The questions of how to describe this motion and how to explain it still remain. But however complex and sophisticated these questions become, they have their sources in and return to this primary world of our experience of motion and of the concepts of motion; to the space of our motor activity, and to that other space, that conceptual and linguistic "space" in which we learn to manipulate and formulate the ideas which represent the space of motion for us.

There is of course a prior framework: our sensory apparatus is of a certain structure. Our neurons, differentiated and specialized in their responses, and distributed complexly at our receptive surfaces, have their thresholds, their selective activity, their own "choosing" and "judging" to do, prior to our acquisition of concepts. The eye has strictly set degrees of freedom: its musculature, its position, and its neural capacities determine motions up and down and side to side, focus, accommodation. Our whole kinesthetic frame, involving the fine adjustment of tension and release, is adapted to gravity, to pressure, to balance. Our heads are on top of our bodies, our feet beneath. We swallow down and breathe in and out; and the even pulsing of our blood requires the pumping action and valve system which frees us to move about and change position, without having the blood rush out of our toes, thus orienting us uniquely to terrestrial gravity. When we are placed upside down, here on earth, we feel the potent pressure of the blood in our heads and see the flush of its concentration. In space, freed from weight, we would also be abandoned to directionlessness, were it not for the cues of stars, sun, moon, earth. Without such cues all that is left is the most primitive (and perhaps most basic) of coordinate systems: *me-ward* and *away-from-me; left, right, in front of, behind, head-ward* and *foot-ward.* Fixed in a directionless space, without the cues of visual and kinesthetic orientation, deprived of sensory contact with the familiar world of pressures, sounds, and images, our very self-orientation disintegrates too, and hallucination and loss of identity ensue, as recent experiments in sensory deprivation have shown. Residually, we could rely on our own organic motions—for example, click our teeth, feel our pulse, flex and relax our muscles, and save at least this world of internal sensation and proprioception. We could try counting to ourselves or reviewing American League pennant winners from 1910–1950; but with sensory deprivation this eventually goes too. Stripped bare, what we have lost is all sense of motion: the motion of body through space, the motion of thought, the motion of change of quality of feeling; in an undifferentiated void, we become undifferentiated.

So much of our experience is tied up with motion that it would have been odd indeed if this had not early become the subject of philosophical and scientific thought, as earlier, it was the subject of myth. But motion is not a simple concept, with a single unequivocal meaning. Ordinary usage retains the variety of senses which language has extruded from our primary experience. Our dictionaries list separately 'motion' and 'motive.' But between the two, the full range of early conceptions is still preserved. Thus we have for *motion,* the "act or process of moving," "passage of a body from one place to another," "the act of moving the body or any of its parts," "gesture," "the ability to move," "an impulse, inclination" and in music, "melodic progression, as a change from one pitch to another." Under *motive,* we add to this list, "Some inner drive, impulse, intention, etc., that causes a person to do something or act in a certain way; incentive; goal." And we are advised, among the synonyms, to consider *incentive* and *inducement,* and to see also *cause.*

With appropriate additions this could well serve as the basis for a philosophical lexicon of the concept of motion. For here is that variety, first systematically classified by Aristotle, of the concepts of motion out of which scientific thought had to distill its appropriate description of motion.

THE ABSTRACTION OF MOTION: THE CONCEPT OF MOTION AS CHANGE OF PLACE

From this complex primary experience of motion, and from the great variety of the ordinary and richly metaphorical uses which language provides, the deliberately restricted conception of motion as change of place, abstracted and subjected to sustained analysis, served as the basis for the development of the fundamental concepts of classical physics. The reasons for this singling out for fuller development are complex. One, at least, is that the rational analysis of spatial relations, in geometry, lent itself to applications to such motion. In particular, one of the two forms of geometrical analysis, so-called generative geometry, defined its figures not in the static representation of place and distance alone, but in terms of the *motion* of points, planes, and solids. Thus, on such a "static" definition (i.e., one in terms of positions and distances), a circle's circumference is that curve any point on which is equidistant from a given point. But on a "generative" account, it is that curve generated by the motion of a point at a given distance from some given point, taken as the center. This generative geometry itself may have had its sources in the experience of motion which lends itself to abstraction in these terms. For although *geometry* has its etymological and historical roots in earth measurement, (i.e., of fixed or static distances), it is the heavens that display the ideally simple motion of point-like entities in a homogeneous space. Not that this is immediately evident. The Pythagorean arithmetic, with its geometric representation of arithmetic relations and operations, owed much, no doubt, to reckoning with markers, pebbles, fingers. The identification of the unit with a point-like geometrical entity, of the concept *one* with one *thing,*[1] and the abstraction of this *thing* as a sign ideally simple and homogeneous, is itself a product of human action: of handling, and counting, of picking up and laying down, of distributing amorphous quantities (oil, wine, wheat) into shaped and countable containers. But the heavens display a purity not found here below. So uncomfortable is the emptiness and abstractness of the night sky, by comparison with the solidity and hustle of the world of nature and man, that myth filled in the spaces with beings, battles, and artifacts. Philosophy followed suit, avoiding the void by postulating—as Aristotle did, for example—a fifth element, a "quintessence" as the medievals literally named it, a rare and subtle "ether" which filled the celestial sphere, as the four earthly elements, air, earth, fire, and water, filled the terrestrial spheres. This ether was different from the four terrestrial elements, but was a substance nevertheless.

Only in the severe and abstract imagination of the mathematicians did substantiality give way to the pure conceptual space of the realm of reason itself. The geometrical space of the Greek geometers was unprivileged as to direction. But attaining to this abstraction required its conceptual precedents as well. One cosmological tradition served well here. Heraclitus, exulting in the *Logos* which loved to hide beneath appearances, said, "The way up and the way down are the same way," and the Parmenidean *One* was a sphere alike in all directions. This serves the development of the concept of an *isotropic* space, i.e., a space alike in all directions. But it does not square with all our experience; for up and down are different, in our experience of direction. The neutral space, which has no favorites and will take whatever is placed in it indifferently, is the kind of *nonbeing* which the Greek mind had great difficulty in conceiving. Yet geometrical construction did manage to free itself from such considerations, postulating finally a space we have come to call *Euclidean,* after its fundamental presentation in Euclid's *Elements.* Consider the sensible correlate to this space in the visual aspect of the heavens. Abstracting the components of myth and cosmology, the stars are relatively alike in aspect. Larger or smaller, their size and brightness become features related to recognition of the *identity* of the same stars night after night. But more important is the abstraction concerned with position and motion. The stars "move" in the sense that their position relative to us (or better, to a fixed point on the

[1] The Pythagoreans defined the *unit* as a "point without position" and contrasted this arithmetic "point" with the geometrical one, which had position. See, for example, T. L. Heath, *A Manual of Greek Mathematics* (Oxford: Oxford University Press, 1931); later reprinted (New York: Dover Publications, 1963), p. 38.

horizon) changes. "A point," Poincaré says somewhere, "is what is at the end of my finger." Such a homocentric geometry would do, perhaps, for a percipient organism fixed to a spot. But we move about, and so we "fix" the stars by reference to what we regard as fixed in our own space of motion: a tree, a mountain top, a space between two rocks (as at Stonehenge). So this relative motion of the stars is a motion through a space coordinated to our own space of motion and to its fixed points.

Yet there is a more fundamental relative position discernible here: the position of the stars relative to each other. We identify the same stars, night after night, not merely by their size and brightness (because these features are not, on the whole, distinguishable enough), but by the configurations into which they fall and in which they appear to remain fixed. We mark these configurations, or constellations, mnemonically by making pictures in which these point-like entities figure familiarly: the belt of Orion, Cassiopeia's chair, and so on. What we have then is the motion of whole configurations through space, in fixed relative position. The problem of "vagabondage," of "wanderers" through this fixed configuration, arises with the planets. (See Appendix B, p. 477.) But their motion, again, is a motion of change of position relative to some configurations taken as fixed. By repeated observation the relative motion of the whole system of configurations itself is seen to be referent to some fixed point: the heavens revolve nightly, in a circle about a fixed point, as time-exposure photography or the long observation of shepherds and astronomers of antiquity shows. This fixed point, this pole of the axis of rotation, has a fixed reference to our own space of terrestrial motion. The stars move but this pole remains on a line directly above the end of a finger pointed toward a fixed horizon mark, or some other suitable fixed terrestrial direction line, which we label *North.*

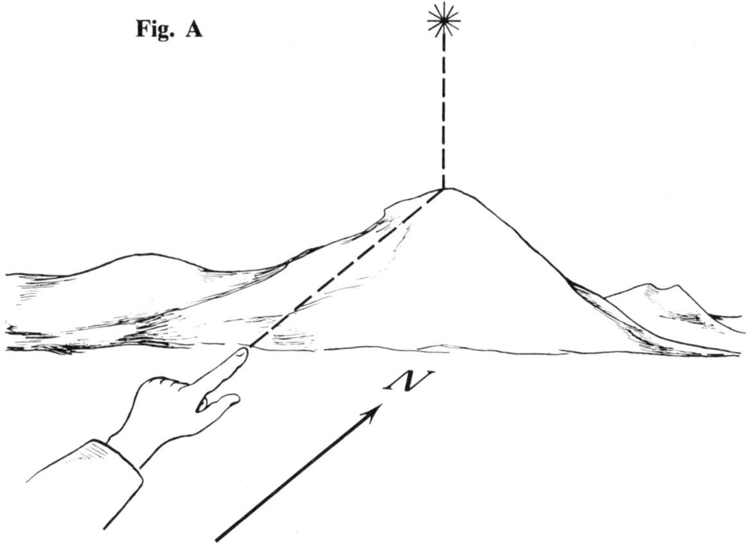

Thus, all motion is seen, in this abstract yet perceivable model, as a change of place, of position in space. The geometrical unit, as a "point with position," moves by change of position, by local motion. The path of its motion in the heavens is a circle. The unceasingness of this motion, neither speeding up nor slowing down, and its circularity, as well as the esteemed place of its motion, beyond the terrestrial spheres, all lend it those attributes of perfection partly derived from religious adoration of the heavens, partly from the intellectual pride which man felt in the perfection of geometric thought itself. In Greek thought, this uniform and circular motion of the heavens bespoke a realm of perfection, which projected the perfection of rational geometry and which geometry itself was taken to represent, as an image of an ideal and perfect universe. For the sphere of fixed stars, there is no up, no down, no falling and no rising. Even this is a sophistication to be remarked. For relative to us, the stars rise and fall with the progress of night. Yet, in the astronomical model of concentric spheres developed by Eudoxus (see Appendix B, p. 477), this is already taken as an apparent rising and falling, relative to our own position on a spherical earth. Thus motion, as local motion, is defined geometrically in terms of position, and change of position relative to some fixed point.

This shift from the space of our self-centered local motion to the space coordinated to some fixed landmarks, in terrestrial motion, and then, further still, to the space of celestial revolution about some fixed point, brings with it an increasing objectivity, and increasing elimination of self-reference and of the subjective perspective of such reference. Finally, in the purely conceptual space of geometry, the fixed points are arbitrarily chosen in a space whose qualitative homogeneity permits them to be placed anywhere at all without prejudice.

But along with the abstraction of the space of motion there is an abstraction of the qualities of our experience of motion as well. By delimiting itself to position and change of position, the geometric-kinematic description eliminates also all reference to the effort of motion, all the experience of exertion, and all the differentiations of rate of motion which we come to know as differences in exertion or direction. It retains them only by introducing another mathematization of experience, in the arithmetic concept of time, as itself constituted of identical units, in additive sequence, such that two are twice as "long" in duration as one, and four twice as "long" as two. In addition to the timeless "generation" of curves in rational geometry, the time of this generation is added to the kinematic account, and with it, the concept of *rate,* i.e., of the time rate of motion, in which distance is measured against time. Without up and down, without push and pull, the kinematic framework makes of motion an abstract ballet of weightless elements, a completely insubstantial cinematographic sequence in three dimensions.

For purposes of description of the ethereal celestial sphere, this is just right; the abstraction is so close to the image it abstracts that no difficulties arise, as long as a picture is all that is wanted (albeit a symbolic and elegantly computable picture, taking full advantage of the "economy of thought" of mathematics). So Eudoxus' model of concentric spheres presents a geometric construction whose purpose is to order the visual aspect of our experience of motion, to "account for the appearances."

Our experience of motion is insistent, however, and demands a fuller treatment, in which up and down, weight and force receive full recognition. Similarly, the inquiring intellect demands its due. Given the kinematic description of motion, what explains it? Given differing time rates of change, what accounts for them? The neutral isotropy of the heavens is heavenly; but here on earth, there is privileged direction. The motion of fall, as we learn when we learn to use the term *fall,* is down. But why? Facetiously, we could answer *"Because* the usage 'falling up' is ungrammatical," in that sense of grammar which has to do with use, with the idiom of language. But things do not fall down to observe grammatical use. They fall down, as we are prone to say, because they are heavy, because nothing is holding them up. But what makes them heavy, and why should they need to be held up? Besides, other things rise, if they are not held down. One of the earliest physical experiments, complementing Strato's experiment of dropping a rock into a container of water (see Appendix B, p. 478), is releasing an air bubble under water, to watch it rise. Steam and mist rise, and fire always rises. "Because they are light," we say. But we do not weigh them to discover that they are light; rather, we say they are light because they rise. Thus, our experience of up and down, and our experience of the effort in moving things and throwing them (and watching them fall), as well as our natural observation, makes the kinematic account of motion incomplete. We need the additional account that takes all these things into consideration. In short, we need to add a dynamic account in terms of forces to the kinematic one in terms of changes of position. Between these two, presumably, our account of both celestial and terrestrial motion will be complete, and the range of our experience of motion will have found its adequate conceptual expression. Thus, we approach the conceptualization of motion armed with the full range of our primary experience, the idiom of our ordinary language, and the already refined analytic instrument of geometry.

EARLY VIEWS OF MOTION IN GREEK PHILOSOPHY AND SCIENCE

Some of the earliest conceptions of motion, in the natural philosophy of the Ionians, concern the original motion of the universe, out of which all things arose. Motion is thus given the primary place in the order of existence; it is the originating activity, and all other things have their source or genesis in this motion. This was conceived, as we have seen (see Chapter

4, pp. 72–73), as a whirling or vortex motion (in Anaximander, for example), out of which the four elements separated. This generalized conception of motion as activity linked it closely to the conception of active beings, of the sorts of things which moved "by themselves" without push or pull from without. The nature of this self-activity was thus conceived to be an inherent or innate motion.

Motion is life, in our common experience. What moves of its own accord is a living being, or akin to living beings. Its motion is thus conceived to be its principle of life, as the "end" or purposiveness of its motion is the purposiveness of its activity and thus of its life. Such motion is therefore conceived of as the "nature" of the thing itself. Thus, all derives from the original motion, every thing has *its* motion, and hence everything in nature comes to be thought of as self-active, or living. The view that everything, being in motion, is therefore a kind of life, that the material stuff of nature is all infused with its degrees of self-motion, its own life activity, is called *hylozoism* (by combination of the Greek words for *matter* and *life*). Yet some things seem not to move of their own accord, but seem to be naturally at rest. A rock may be moved, but it does not move by itself. Yet the notion of *being moved,* by derivation from our experience of motion, requires a mover who acts continually on the object. When his motive action ceases, then the moved object also ceases to move and remains at rest. The distinction between such things as move by themselves and those which require to be moved is an early, but already problematic distinction, if everything is taken to be in motion originally.

The original mode of self-activity of any kind of thing, its directive and regulative energy, was taken by Aristotle to be its *form,* or that which "actualizes" it, makes it become the kind of thing it is. This form-energy, the source and pattern of the self-motion of things, this actualization of a thing's potentiality Aristotle called its *energeia;* its potentiality, the innate capacity to become formed or actualized in an individual way he called its *dynamis.* In this general framework, motion is *change,* and is defined as the *passage* from potentiality to actuality of a thing, according to its nature; thus, it is *natural motion.* The Aristotelian view is that the way we come to form concepts of things, to explain and understand them, is by grasping their essential nature, their individuality, or class character, i.e., those features which make them members of a certain class of things, and thereby individuals of a certain kind. According to Aristotle, reason, as distinct from sense perception, knows universals. To understand a particular thing is therefore to come to recognize it as an individual, that is, as an *instance* of a class (or of all the classes) of which it is a member. This universal form, as it is exhibited in the thing's activity, reveals itself as the characteristic natural motion of that thing, so that it is this natural motion which is the concrete embodiment of the rationally comprehensible form of the thing, or its "intelligible nature." That all things have intelligible natures does not mean that the things themselves are "rational," but rather that they are capable of being understood rationally. Aristotle's fundamental epistemological claim here is that nature is fully accessible to reason, that it can be known *scientifically,* and science is defined as this knowledge of universals in their concrete embodiment in natural processes.

However, the commonsense distinction between living and nonliving things complicates this picture. For there are things which, in the framework of Aristotelianism, are naturally inert, and whose motion therefore is only the passage from some *un*natural or artificially induced state, back to the natural state. Within the biological analogy which is evident in so much of Aristotle's thought, not only organisms but all things whatever tend to maintain themselves in their "natural state," i.e., the state which is in accordance with their nature, or form. Even the passage from potentiality to actuality, is itself a motion whose end is to realize this so-called "natural state." Thus, all natural motion is end-directed, or teleological, and thus "purposive" in this limited sense of tending toward the maintenance of the laws of a thing's nature.[2] All natural motion therefore tends toward that natural homeostasis, which is the thing's "right functioning."[3]

Now things which are inert, or tend toward a state of rest, are inert by nature, and if this inertia is violated by some motion forced on the thing from without, then as soon as the motive force ceases to act, the natural inertia will bring the thing to rest. In Aristotle's view, it is nonliving things, things not self-animated, which are inert, or naturally at rest. Living things, having their principle of motion within themselves, have a natural motion in the fulfillment of their life needs, and this both Aristotle and Plato called *psyche,* developing a biological, psychological, and social theory around this concept.[4]

[2] Pittendrigh introduces the term *teleonomy* for such law-directed, or "programmed" activity, to distinguish it from "Aristotelian teleology," as outright purposiveness. (C. S. Pittendrigh, in A. A. Roe and G. G. Simpson, eds., *Behavior and Evolution* (New Haven: Yale University Press, 1958), p. 394. But see the excellent discussion by Ernst Mayr, who realizes that Aristotle already had this sense of teleology in mind—E. Mayr, "Cause and Effect in Biology," *Science,* **134:**1501–1506 (November 10, 1961).

[3] So wide is Aristotle's application of this principle, that in his analysis of human action, he defines its end, which is "happiness," to be "activity in accordance with man's nature." (The usual translation of "nature" here is "virtue," but in Greek terms, a thing's "virtue" is its nature.) But just as human activity is teleologically oriented toward the fulfillment of human nature, so is the activity of any kind of thing whatever also the fulfillment of its nature. Of course, this is not *any* activity whatever, but *right* activity or *proper* functioning of a thing, and thus this is a normative (and problematic) formulation, analogous to that we have discussed earlier (in Chapter 10) concerning *nomological* and *accidental* universal (law-like) statements.

[4] We take our word psychology from this, and take it in a more restricted sense as pertaining to mind. But for the Greeks it meant the life principle of self-activity. The Latin *anima,* used in translation for *psyche,* soon acquired the connotations which Christian theology added to Greek and other Eastern views, and which our English

ARISTOTELIAN PHYSICS: THE ANALYSIS OF "NATURAL MOTION" AND OF SPACE

Conceiving of physics as the science of bodies in motion, Aristotle developed a scientific system in which he attempted to analyze and explain physical motion. Aristotle's theory is principally oriented toward the explanation of motion, i.e., he is concerned not only with a descriptive account of how motion takes place (though he gives some of the first quantitative descriptions of motion) but with why it takes place as it does.

This explanatory account of the motion of bodies requires as part of its conceptual framework a certain concept of *body* and of the *space* of the motion of bodies, and the corollary concept of *place* or *location*.

The theoretical account which Aristotle gives derives in part from the tradition of mathematical-cosmological construction of the Pythagoreans and the Platonists. In the Pythagorean scheme, adopted and developed by Plato and his students Eudoxus and Callippus, the heavenly bodies were ordered in concentric spheres, whose distances from each other were taken to be in harmonic ratios (as in the mathematical relations of pitch to lengths of string, which the Pythagoreans had discovered in their investigations of harmonic ratios in acoustics).

The Pythagorean account was not simply mathematical: it involved certain value considerations of an aesthetic and religious sort. Plato elaborated on this in the context of his theory of ideal forms. The heavens represent the visible workings of divine rationality, the ideal of reason at work. Divinity, in this Platonic context, connotes the universal, essential, and immutable form of that reality which appearances merely mask. Still, the heavenly bodies do appear to the senses (i.e., to sight). How then can this appearance directly reveal the perfection of form which all other appearances distort? Here we have both the dichotomy and the bridge in Platonic thought between the earthly and the divine, between the world of ordinary sense and perception and the intelligible world of pure forms. Plato accomplishes this by separating the earth from the heavens, by making the heavens both metaphorically and literally the realm of the forms. What we see are mere perceptual motions but what we understand rationally is the perfection of these motions, as circular and uniform. Divinity reveals itself to us in its perfection in the heavens. Therefore, the physics of heavenly motion is a divine physics, whereas the physics of earthly motion is an earthly physics, and thus we have two physics instead of one. Heaven and

---

translation of the term, as "soul," still carries. The incongruous version of Aristotle which medieval Christianity bequeathed to us thus combines these elements to result in the odd picture of little "souls" inside of things moving them about. The view that everything is thus ensouled is called *panpsychism,* and is analogous to *hylozoism,* according to which all matter is living.

earth are sundered physically as the rational world of forms and the confused, changing, and imperfect world of sense are sundered epistemologically. Plato accounts for this problematic separation by distinguishing between divine imitation of the ideal forms (which gives us a *true* copy) and human imitation of the divine forms, particularly in art (which gives us at best an incomplete copy, and in the fine arts, a distorted and false copy).

For Aristotle too, as an heir and student of Plato, there is the perfect realm of heavenly physics, with its perfect circular motion, and the more problematic realm of earthly motion which is not uniform but changes, begins, and ends.

The construction of the concentric spheres as a geometric model of the universe by Eudoxus, and its modification by Callippus, was concerned to "save the appearances," to account for the observed positions of celestial bodies by some abstract geometrical schema. The centrality of the earth was a requirement of visual perspective, and was privileged only as the place from which observation took place (at least in the purely mathematical construction; beyond this, religious, intuitive, and traditional elements also played a part). For Aristotle however, the centrality of the earth became a qualitative feature, concerned not primarily with kinetic but dynamic considerations and related to the framework of natural motion. Aristotle's cosmology enters here. The terrestrial realm consists of four concentric spheres, i.e., all those below the sphere of the moon, which is the first of the celestial spheres. In this sublunary realm of coming-to-be and passing away, there is constant alteration and change, as the four elements which constitute all earthly bodies combine, dissolve, and recombine. The four are, from the center out, earth, water, air, and fire, each with its appropriate sphere. Each of these has paired qualities associated with it, from among the paired opposites dry-wet, hot-cold (which we recognize from the earlier Ionian cosmologies). All the combinations of these paired qualities give us the elements: *dry* + *cold* is earth, *cold* + *wet* is water, *wet* + *hot* is air, and of course, *hot* + *dry* is fire.

Now the question is, how are these four elements to be arranged in the concentric spheres? Again, common intuition and observation suggests that what is heavier is naturally below, and what is lighter is naturally above. On a concentric model, earth is below (i.e., at the center), water lies on the earth, air surrounds or lies above the water, and although fire is found here below, it tends to rise, and is thus the outermost sphere. Even the natural experience of seeing lightning set fire to a tree suggests its natural habitat in the upper regions; and in Greek myth, Prometheus brings fire *down* from the home of the gods on Olympus, to make a gift of it to man.

Thus, with the four elements neatly ordered into concentric sublunary spheres, we have a natural place for each element. And we have further associated with this natural place the dynamic intuitions of heavy and light, associated with the directions up and down. Heaviest is earth, and *down* therefore means, on the spherical model, toward the center. Water is less heavy, but also tends down to its sphere. Air and fire are light, in increasing degree, so that "lightness" and the tendency to rise are associated, and *up* therefore means away from the center. Thus *down* is a centripetal vector and *up* is a centrifugal vector.[5]

Because natural bodies are compounds of the four elements, their natural motion will be the motion toward its natural place of the dominant element. Notice that questions of density or rarity do not play a role here in their ordinary sense. A compound body is more densely earth if it has more of earth in a given volume than it has of another element. But Aristotle's cosmology is like Empedocles' here. There is no void, no vacuum, or any place at which body is not: there is instead a *plenum* made up of varying compounds of the four elements. Relative "density" therefore depends on the distribution of the heavy and the light elements, rather than the distribution of an element in some empty space. (Not being an atomist, Aristotle does not give us any quantitative notion of units of an element in a given volume—a notion which was to play an important part in Newton's conception of mass as "quantity of matter," defined as "bulk and density taken conjointly.")

From all this, we can derive Aristotle's dynamics almost deductively. The natural motion of any body as a compound of elements is the natural motion of the *dominant* element in the compound. But since all natural places are concentrically arranged, the only natural motions are up and down, i.e., toward and away from the center of the spheres. There is no natural lateral motion within the spheres, because these are the natural locations

[5] The kinds of motion which Aristotle describes as up, down, and circular are strictly speaking two kinds of (natural) motion: *rectilinear,* or in a straight line, and *circular.* But all motion is with respect to a center, according to Aristotle, perfect circular motion being motion at a uniform rate around a center, at a fixed distance, and rectilinear motion being either toward or away from a center, or what we might quite literally describe as centripetal and centrifugal motion. Thus *down* is not the naively conceived intuitive downward motion, though it is related to this concept. Rather, it is centripetal, or center-seeking, motion, as *up* is centrifugal, or center-fleeing motion. Up and down are therefore described by Aristotle in his work *On the Heavens,* in the framework of the four concentric sublunary spheres.

That takes care of *up* and *down.* But perfect circular motion is characteristic of the fifth element, *ether,* and being perfect, such motion suffers neither increment nor diminution and goes on forever. It has no up or down, but proceeds eternally in the celestial spheres in which, in proper order, are fixed the moon, sun, planets, and stars. Thus Aristotle maintains the principle of "each according to its nature," while establishing the distinction between the terrestrial and heavenly natures. The Platonic heritage is clear here, as is that older Greek tradition which regards change and the transitory nature of worldly phenomena as somehow lower or less perfect than permanence.

of the elements, and their places of rest, therefore. Water at its own level does not move, nor does earth, or fire, or air. They can however be moved by something else, by some motion which overcomes their inertia and *re*-moves them from their natural location or place. This unnatural or antinatural motion is forced, or in the usual term, violent, motion. Such violent motion displaces bodies, by action upon them. Once the force of displacement ceases, then *natural* motion takes over and actualizes the potentiality of the body, fulfilling its nature. Thus natural motion is the motion of return to the natural condition of rest; and since this has a place as its condition, it is the motion of return to an element's natural place. Thus, when a stone is thrown *up,* it is displaced by violent motion. When the violent motion ceases to act, the stone's natural motion takes it to its "natural location," i.e., *re*places it at the location where it is naturally *at rest.* Thus, the stone "naturally" falls *down.*

The geometry of this space of motion is thus a geometry of privileged place and privileged direction, for natural motion is always directed motion whose goal is the natural location of the element dominant in a physical body. In the spherical geometry of the model (sometimes called *homocentric,* but more accurately, *geocentric*) natural motion is always along some radius of the spheres whose center is common. For the heavy elements, it is motion toward the center, coming to rest in its proper sphere (of earth or water); for the light elements it is motion away from the center, also coming to rest in its proper sphere (air, fire). These, according to Aristotle, are the only simple terrestrial motions, all other natural motion being a compound of these, depending on the composition of bodies. All natural motion of bodies composed of the four elements is therefore *rectilinear,* and all composites analyzable into rectilinear components. Aristotle notes that there is another simple motion, which is irreducible to rectilinear elements and which is more "perfect" than rectilinear motion. This is of course circular motion, the motion of celestial bodies.

Aristotle's introduction of forces acting on terrestrial bodies complicates the initially simple geometry of *up* and *down* in several ways. First, a force acting on a body can make it move in directions other than its natural direction, thus introducing the notion of change of direction. Further, differences in force result in different velocities of motion. Aristotle introduces the notion of velocity as time-rate of motion, and also the first formal treatment of velocities, or speeds of motion, into physics. In effect, he introduces the first equations of motion. He also introduces the notion of changes in velocity, or changes in rate of motion, or acceleration.[6] The kind of equations Aristotle uses are not the modern sort we are familiar with, but an earlier form, characteristic of Greek mathematics and devel-

[6] We also regard change of direction as acceleration, but the relation between these two is not established until the concept of inertia is clarified and corrected.

oped most fully in Book V of Euclid's *Elements,* on the Theory of Proportions.[7] In this formulation, ratios are always between *like* qualities (i.e., of the same "species"). Thus ratios between distance and time are not expressed directly, but by proportions between ratios of distances and ratios of times.

First, Aristotle introduces the notion of differing velocities in a discussion of the concepts *quicker* and *slower.* This applies only to terrestrial motions, because the perfect motion of the celestial spheres is unchanging, and suffers no increase or decrease. In his discussion, Aristotle makes an interesting logical point concerning the abstraction of that quality in terms of which comparisons of motion are to be made. It must be, he says, the "same" quality, without "specific differences." (Akin to the grammar school injunction against adding apples to pears—this bears on the Greek use of proportions as made up of ratios between like qualities.) By "specific differences" Aristotle alludes to differences in species of motion. He distinguishes between four species of the genus motion: alteration; increase and decrease; coming-to-be and passing away; and locomotion, or change of place. It is this local motion that concerns us here, and the quality which is common to this species, and in terms of which comparisons of local motion are to be made, is "magnitude traversed," or distance, with respect to time. Velocity of this motion is defined, in the proportional formulation, as a ratio of velocities with respect to ratios of distances and ratios of times. Equal velocities are defined by equal distances traversed in equal times, and quicker and slower are likewise defined by the ratios of two motions, in which one traverses a greater distance in equal time, or an equal distance in a shorter time, or a greater distance in a shorter time. Borrowing Clagett's formulation, this may be represented as (where v = velocity, s = distance, and t = time):

1. $v_2 > v_1$ if $s_2 > s_1$, when $t_2 = t_1$
2. $v_2 > v_1$ if $s_2 = s_1$, when $t_2 < t_1$
3. $v_2 > v_1$ if $s_2 > s_1$, when $t_2 < t_1$

In our notation, this comes to something like our definition of average velocity as

$$\bar{v} = \frac{s}{t}$$

This gives us a formalization of the concept of quicker and slower motion and permits the comparison of velocities. Thus far the account is purely kinematic. Now Aristotle introduces the notion of moved bodies and movers, or motive forces. Again, it is suggested that two forces are equal if they can move equal bodies equal distances, but this does not stand by

[7] See T. L. Heath, *op. cit.*, pp. 226 ff., for a summary.

itself. Two complicating factors enter. First the question arises, are two forces equal if they move equal bodies with equal velocities (where distances and times may vary, but the ratio of distances and times remains the same)? Aristotle holds (as we might, intuitively) that it takes a greater force to move the same body a greater distance than it takes to move it a lesser distance. This introduces the other complicating factor. Why should it take a greater force over a greater distance? Aristotle proposes that for any terrestrial motion, in the plenum filled by the four elements or composites of them, there is a *resistance* to motion offered by the medium. Thus heavier elements resist motion through them more than do light ones. The velocity of a body or the distance it is moved in a given time therefore is not merely proportional to the force of motion impressed on it, but to the ratio of force to resistance. Thus, it would take a greater force to move the same object through a more resistant medium, for the resistance acts contrary to the force of motion. The rate of motion in a medium is determined by two contrary forces, the *motive force* (or *vis viva* in the latin form in which this has come down to us) and the *resisting force* (or *vis inertiae*). The equation for the relation of force to velocity is therefore

$$v = k\frac{F}{R} \qquad \text{(where } k \text{ is the constant of proportionality)}$$

In a much discussed passage, Aristotle also considers forces acting through different distances and times. He says that if a given force of motion A moves B a distance C in a time D, then the same force A will move $\frac{1}{2}B$ twice the distance C in the same time D, and that in $\frac{1}{2}D$ it will move $\frac{1}{2}B$ the whole distance C, thus maintaining the proportionality already adduced in the velocity equations (or proportions, strictly speaking). This means that different forces acting in the same time and on the same bodies and with the same resistance of the medium will result in different velocities, because a greater force, all other things being equal, will move a body a greater distance than a lesser force or will in a lesser time move the body the same distance as a lesser force. But, he continues, it does not follow that if a force E moves a body F a distance C in time D, that E can move twice F half the distance C in the same time; for E may not be able to move $2F$ at all. Now this conjures up all sorts of ideas of rest-mass and inertia, of which Aristotle had no conception. He just knew from common observation that some bodies are too heavy to be moved at all by the available force, whereas if we divided these bodies, their parts may be moved at a certain rate. Now heaviness or the relation of weight to force enters the picture, and with it the doctrine of natural place. In natural motion, the cause of motion is the tendency to return to the natural place. And here Aristotle introduces that feature of his dynamics, his treatment of forces, which is central to our discussion.

We need to return for a moment to the notion of composite bodies. Aristotle says that the preponderant or dominant element will determine the natural motion of a composite body. If earth is preponderant, the body will move down, toward the center; if fire, then it will move up, and so on. But now we add another consideration: How much of an element is present in a body. For to predominate means for there to be more of one element than another. But of one element, even by itself, there may be more or less. And more of a heavy element is heavier, as more of a light one is lighter. Aristotle takes this weight to be additive—twice as much being twice as heavy. But because elements have natural motion as their feature, he takes natural motion to be additive as well; the *more* of an element there is, the *more* natural motion in the appropriate direction. Natural motion being the result of this natural tendency, which is its motive force, the greater the motive force within the body, by reason of its heaviness, the greater its velocity through a given medium (if the medium is the same in all its parts). Thus the natural velocity of a heavier body will be greater than the natural velocity of a lighter body. It will move faster, therefore, because its force of motion will be greater.

This is a conclusion arrived at by reasoning from certain premises of the theory, and so it is a systematic and rationally arrived at conclusion. But it is false, as we know, in the case of freely falling bodies in a vacuum. Yet Aristotle took it to be true, it would seem, and furthermore, even seems to allude to experience as evidence for his conclusion. He says, "We see that bodies with a greater impulse either of weight or lightness, if they are alike in other respects, move faster over an equal space, and in the ratio which their magnitudes bear to each other."[8]

One standard view is that Aristotle fitted what he saw to what he conceived; that he was bound to rationalist and *a priori* dogmas, and failed to test his theories against observation. This seems less credible now than it did by an earlier and simpler view of "good" (empirical) and "bad" (speculative) science. At least one critic of the standard view[9] argues that Aristotle has been misread and mistranslated, and that he is not talking about freely falling bodies here. If, on the other hand, the analysis is of ballistic motion, then clearly the analysis is of impulse or impressed motion, and Aristotle's view is then borne out by observation of such motion.

In any case, Aristotle's analysis was taken, more often than not, to be concerned with falling bodies, and even so astute a scientist as Hero of Alexandria, who wrote on mechanics, held that in natural motion, the force of attraction downward is greater in heavier than in lighter bodies.

[8] *Physics,* 216a, 14–16.

[9] Lane Cooper, *Aristotle, Galileo, and the Tower of Pisa,* (Ithaca, N.Y.: Cornell University Press, 1935).

POST-ARISTOTELIAN ANALYSES OF MOTION AND ACCELERATION

Aristotle's successors raised certain crucial questions about his formulation, some of which were not pursued for centuries thereafter but others of which continued that tradition of conceptual criticism which marks the growth of science. One ingenious alternative to Aristotle's explanation of increased velocity in falling bodies emphasized Aristotle's own formulation of the relation of velocity to resistance of the medium. In our previous discussion we have held the resistance of the medium constant, dealing only with differences in weight and distance. But if motive forces (in natural falling motion, weight) were held constant, because velocity then varies inversely with the density or resistance of the medium, increasing velocity could be accounted for by a decrease in the resistance. This view held that because a body higher up had a greater column of air beneath it than one lower down, this offered a greater resistance proportional to the height of the body. As it fell, therefore, the amount of air retarding its downward motion would decrease, and thus its velocity would increase proportionately with the distance of fall. Ingenious but false. Yet the advantage of this view is that it held weight constant, foreshadowing the concepts of the constancy of mass which lay at the foundation of modern physics. But the proportionality of increase in velocity to distance was to remain a hurdle for a long time yet.

Directly contrary to Aristotle's view was that of Hipparchus (perhaps the greatest astronomer of ancient times, who discovered the precession of the equinoxes and calculated the length of the lunar month to within less than a second of the present reckoning). In a lost work (cited by Simplicius) called *On Bodies Carried Down by Weight,* Hipparchus holds that bodies are heavier the further they are from their natural place, rather than the closer, as Aristotle held. Simplicius points out the absurd results of the latter view. For example, a weight in a balance, if it moved down, would get lighter. This is now an appeal to an experiment to decide the issue, although the experiment is simply a commonsense observation in that commonsense context already familiar with weights and balances. Simplicius also suggests that the same object be weighed at different altitudes, to see whether in fact there is any difference in weight, varying with distance from the center. He concludes that there would not be any difference "unless it is claimed that the difference between the two cases is imperceptible." Most interesting, perhaps, is the work of Aristotle's follower and head of the Lyceum after Theophrastus, Strato, whose work *On Motion* (also lost, and cited by Simplicius) deals in part with accelerated motion. He offers an observational instance of acceleration in watching water falling from a roof. The flow at the top is seen to be continuous, but at the bottom of the fall it is discontinuous, from which Strato infers that the water "traverses each successive space more swiftly," thus "completing the last stage of its trajectory in the shortest time." Using Aristotle's definitions of quicker and slower, we can then account for accelerated motion as successive (equal) distances traversed in shorter times, or successively greater distances in equal times. This explication of the Aristotelian concept of quicker becomes fundamental for later analysis, as we shall see.

CRITICISMS AND ALTERNATIVES

The atomists, in the meantime, had a fundamentally different view. Most important, the space of motion of the atoms of Democritus, Epicurus, and Lucretius was not a plenum, but a void. Only atoms in motion and void existed. But this void space was the undifferentiated space of the geometers, and therefore location in it could have no effect on motion. Thus the velocity of bodies in the void was taken to be the same for all bodies, regardless of differences of weight—the correct view, in terms of classical physics, but certainly not the product of observation and experiment. Still, Lucretius talks of atoms moving downward through the void, because they are all "body," and body is heavy. (Even fire atoms thus have weight, and fire tends upward because it is "pushed" by air.) Because all atoms would then fall downward (although downward seems difficult to conceive in a directionless and unlimited void), they would fall in parallel paths and there would be no interactions among them. In order to account for these interactions by means of which all things come to be and pass away, Epicurus introduces a spontaneous "swerve" (*clinamen*) in the atomic paths, which takes place by chance. This kind of random motion would not have been admissible in Aristotle's universe.

Still other alternatives to the Aristotelian account give evidence of the style of reasoning and conceptual criticism that was to be pursued in the analysis of motion. The Aristotelian commentator John Philoponus (sixth century A.D.) argued against Aristotle's view that the conception of motion in a void led to the absurdity of instantaneous motion or infinite force. Remember that Aristotle believed velocity to be proportional to force and inversely proportional to resistance, or proportional to the ratio of force to resistance. But Philoponus argued, on Aristotelian grounds, that every body has its own "natural weight," and thus also its characteristic natural motion and its characteristic natural velocity, intrinsically and apart from the resisting force of the medium. The time of traverse of a given distance at this natural velocity Philoponus called "original time," and even in a void different bodies would move with differing natural velocities, over a given distance in this original time, contrary to Aristotle's claim that there can be no motion in a void. [According to Aristotle there can be no differences in "nothing" (the void), and so no differences in motion; but because all motion is differentiated, according to differences in body or weight, there can be no motion in a void. Also, because the void offers no resistance, motion would be infinite and there would be instantaneous transport between points; but because all motion takes place in a finite time, there can be no motion in a void.] According to Philoponus, in a medium some additional time would be added to the original time taken to traverse a given distance at the natural velocity, and this additional time would be proportional to the resistance of the medium (longer in a denser medium, offering greater resistance, and shorter in a rarer one). Reconstructing this view, if v_o is taken as the natural velocity of a body b in the void and t_o as the original time in which a distance s is traversed; and if v_m is taken as the velocity of this same body b in a medium m and the resistance of this medium as r_m, and Δt as the additional time postulated by Philoponus, then we have

$$(1)\quad v_o = \frac{s}{t_o}$$

and

$$(2)\quad v_m = \frac{s}{t_o + \Delta t}$$

where

$$(3)\quad \frac{\Delta t}{r_m} = k$$

Thus, for any media m and n, where $r_m > r_n$, then $\Delta t_m > \Delta t_n$ and obviously $(t_o + \Delta t_m) > (t_o + \Delta t_n)$, and we have, from (2), $v_n > v_m$.

In a careful analysis of the theory of proportions, the fourteenth-century investigator Thomas Bradwardine draws certain conclusions from this formulation and rejects it in favor of a reinterpretation of Aristotle's ratio of force to resistance. Because, as Philoponus states, in a void the velocities of bodies are proportional to their innate motive force of natural motion, the subtraction of the additional time required in a medium from the total time of motion in this medium gives the original time. But then, Aristotle's formulation (in modern symbolism) $v = k(F/R)$ is changed so that the proportion holds between the velocity and the difference between force and resistance $(F - R)$. Thus when force equals resistance, $v = 0$, and there is no motion. Bradwardine points out that in the original Aristotelian formulation, where $F = R$, the ratio is not equal to zero, but equal to 1, which means that even if the resisting force were equal to the motive force, there would still be motion, which is absurd. Thus, Bradwardine looks for a ratio whose relation will be such that when $F = R$, the *velocity* will be zero, thus avoiding the formulation in terms of a simple arithmetical difference. This he finds in the formulation that as the ration F/R increases *geometrically,* the velocity increases *arithmetically*. Although Bradwardine does his calculation in the cumbersome language of proportions, and does not have available the concepts of exponent and logarithm (the latter not introduced until the seventeenth century by Napier, the former even later), the relation he proposes in modern terms is

(1) $$(1)\ v = \log a \frac{F}{R}, \qquad \text{where } a = \frac{F_1}{R_1}$$

Thus two ratios (F_1/R_1), (F_2/R_2), stand to each other in the exponential relationship

(2) $$\left(\frac{F_2}{R_2}\right) = \left(\frac{F_1}{R_1}\right)^n \qquad \text{where } \frac{F_1}{R_1} > 1 \quad \text{and} \quad n = \frac{v_2}{v_1}$$

Therefore, when $v_1 = v_2$, the exponent is 1 and the two ratios are equal. Further, where $(F_2/R_2) = 1$, i.e., when $F = R$, the exponent is 0, and, in (1), $v = 0$, since the log of 1 is always 0, to any base.[10]

MEDIEVAL MECHANICS: THE CALCULATORS AND THE MERTON THEOREM

This takes the original Aristotelian discussion quite far in its emphasis on the mathematical analysis of the relations between the postulated forces and resistances, in accounting for the motion of bodies. The remarkable extent to which this calculation proceeded, side by side with the philosophical discussion on the nature of motion, is best seen in the work of two fourteenth-century schools, at Paris and Oxford. Until the pioneering historical studies of Duhem, the stages of the transition from Aristotelian to Galilean physics were not clear; but with the publication of his *Études sur Léonardo da Vinci* (1906–1913), the precursors of Galileo in the fourteenth century were brought to light, and the historical interplay of conceptual criticism, in both philosophical and mathematical terms, emerged more clearly. In pursuing the analysis of motion to Galileo, we will examine first the mathematical analysis of motion, the *kinetic* analysis from which came the so-called *Merton Theorem,* and then see how its applications to the motion of falling bodies finally emerged in Galileo's famous formulation of uniformly accelerated motion.

While the qualitative discussion of the reasons for the acceleration of

[10] For the full discussion on which this account depends, see M. Clagett, *The Science of Mechanics in the Middle Ages* (Madison: University of Wisconsin Press, 1961), chap. 7, esp. pp. 438 ff. The text of a medieval abridgement of Bradwardine's *Book of Proportions* is also given here (Document 7.3) and is worth reading to see how the fourteenth-century "Calculators" developed the ancient theory of proportions into an instrument of mathematical analysis of mechanical problems before the introduction of modern algebraic notation.

falling bodies continued, the quantitative and geometrical analysis of "successively quicker" motions followed as well, but along a different path. Among other ingenious qualitative modifications of Aristotle's views were those of his Arabic commentator, Averroës, and the criticism of these innovations by the French philosopher-physicist, John Buridan. Averroës proposes an aerodynamic hypothesis that as a body falls through the air, it heats the air in proportion to its velocity. This *calefaction* makes the air less dense beneath a falling body, and proportionately less dense the faster the body falls, so that resistance of the medium diminishes in proportion to the increase in velocity, and reflexively, the velocity increases in proportion to the decrease in resistance, in a sort of positive feedback loop. Thus as the ratio of force to resistance increases, the body's velocity increases, in accelerated motion. Buridan argued, *per experimentum* (and probably wryly), that if this were true, things would fall faster in the summer, when the air is warmer, than in the winter. And further, that the air resists before it is heated, so that the time sequence of events alleged here does not hold.

The clue to the quantitative analysis of motion was the geometrical representation of motion, which developed in the fourteenth century. The precursors of this approach were the Greek geometers and physicists, and in particular Archimedes in his work on statics. But it was only with the conceptual formulation of certain distinctions concerning motion that this geometrical representation achieved its power.

Most important was the distinction between the quality and the quantity of motion. In medieval terms this was taken as a distinction between the velocity or speed of a motion, without regard to how long the motion proceeded, and the quantity of motion, in terms of the time through which a motion of a given velocity proceeded. This is a distinction like the one between intensity of heat (or temperature) and quantity of heat, and also between so-called intensive weight (or specific gravity) and total weight. As we have seen, the characteristic velocity of a body, in the Aristotelian framework, depended on its nature or "form"; thus differing degrees of this "quality of motion" were spoken of, in terms of their increase or decrease, as *the intension and remission of forms* (e.g., in the proportional increase of weight and velocity, with diminution of distance from the center). The measurement of intensive qualities posed a problem, however, which was resolved by translating intensive into quantitative, or extensive, magnitudes. (We do this when we read a temperature on a scale; for here, the intensive quality, degree of hotness, or temperature, is translated into a variable quantity, namely, a gradation on a scale in terms of length of an interval, for example, the height of a column of mercury.)

Thus, William of Heytesbury (one of the fourteenth-century innovators of mathematical physics, at Merton College, Oxford), writes that the quality of motion, which he conceives of as "the velocity at any given instant" can be determined quantitatively by "the path which would be described by the most rapidly moving point if, in a period of time, it were moved uniformly at the same degree of velocity with which it is moved in that given instant, whatever given instant be assigned." The measure of motion introduced here is one in which what were earlier called "virtual quantities" are translated into "corporeal," or "dimensive," quantities. In short, not only quantity of motion but also instantaneous velocity of a point are made numerable. The qualitative discussion of "quicker" or "successively quicker" now can proceed in terms of a quantitative analysis. Aristotle had given a quantitative measure for equal velocities in terms of equal distances in equal times, and of quicker and slower, likewise. But what now became conceivable (though it was not yet clearly worked out) was the notion of a rate of change of velocity, not only through succeeding spaces, or times, but at the limit of such spaces and times, i.e., a notion of instantaneous rate of change of velocity, or what we would call an instantaneous acceleration.

The geometrization of motion proceeded then, along the lines of this distinction. The two variables, quality of motion and time, were conceived geometrically as lengths of two lines, and plotted against each other, by analogy to the lines of latitude and longitude in maps. The "latitude" of a quality, or of a form, was therefore the measure of its intensity, along a vertical line (so we might speak of degrees of temperature as measuring latitudes of the intensity of heat), and the duration in time of this quality, or degree of velocity, was given in a longitudinal measure along a horizontal line. These are the precursors of our x-y axes in a two-dimensional Cartesian coordinate system. But only one of these coordinates (time) is quantitative here, in the strict metrical sense of being numerable ("dimensive" in the medieval terminology), whereas the other (velocity) is conceived of in terms of degrees of intensity of a quality (i.e., of "more" and "less").

We may catch the flavor of the medieval-Aristotelian conception if we think of qualities such as anger, pleasure, or mercy. This would be like representing degrees of anger, pleasure, or mercy by lengths of line, without yet having established a unit magnitude or unit interval of actual empirical measurement to distinguish twice as much, say, from three times as much. Yet one could distinguish greater, or less, or the same, in a qualitative sense. As long as one remains angry at the same intensity, or as long as a degree of pleasure is maintained, or as long as one's mercy does not flag, or one does not become more merciful, the quality of anger, pleasure or mercy may be said to remain uniform; but it may vary in duration, so that one may have the same degree of pleasure, say, for one-half hour or for three hours, and the *amount* of the quality, pleasure, would presumably be six times as great in the second case.[11] The physical analogues, e.g., in-

[11] That subjective magnitude estimation, of such variables as pleasure, happiness, and so on, is not simply a linear function of time is suggested by psychophysical scaling. See the references to the work of S. S. Stevens, in the bibliographical note for Chapter 14.

tensity of heat (temperature) or of weight (specific weight) were conceived in the same way, and so too was the quality, velocity. The linear representation does not represent units therefore, except in the imaginative conceptual sense that suggests equal degrees, or equal increases or decreases in the quality, without yet having established a way of measuring these equalities or of establishing whether or not they are additive. Now it is true that Aristotle, in his definitions of quicker, slower, and equal motion did propose a quantitative measure in terms of ratios of distances in proportion to ratios of times, but the coordination of this metrical concept with the qualitative concept of intension and remission of forms had to be made in an explicit step of concept formation, in terms of an interpretation of the geometric formalism.

Thus with the geometric representation of *quantity of a quality,* we may compare two equal qualities of motion (represented by the equal altitudes of the rectangles *ABCD* and *ABEF,* in Fig. B) in terms of the differences between their quantities, where quantity is interpreted as duration in time (represented by the base lines *AD* and *AF*). Because, for a uniform or unchanging intensity of the quality, the altitude *AB* would remain the

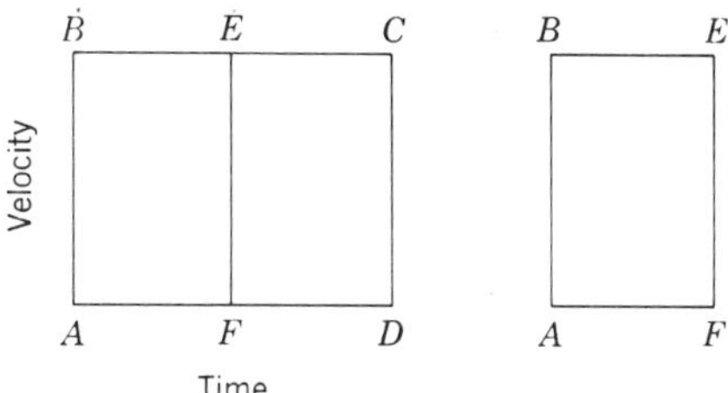

Fig. B

same through time, the geometrical figure produced by this representation would plainly be a rectangle. This is therefore a representation of uniform velocity. But then it can be seen that the representation of the quantity of this quality, which is algebraically given by $(AB \times AD)$ in the first case, and $(AB \times EF)$ in the second, is equivalent to the area of the rectangle. As small and obvious a step as this is, it is an important one, as we shall see. Thus, at a given velocity *AB,* through time *AD,* the "amount of motion" is $(AB \times AD)$ or the area of *ABCD;* for the same velocity through *AF,* the amount is $(AB \times EF)$ or the area of *ABEF*. If $AF = \frac{1}{2}AD$, then $ABEF = \frac{1}{2}ABCD$, and if we then add the considerations of quantitative definition of different (velocities $\times$ times) in terms of the proportions of the distances, as Aristotle suggested, we may then say that a body whose motion is represented by *ABCD* will move twice as far as a body whose motion is represented by *ABEF*. The implicit formula for uniform velocity is $s = vt$. The relation of this to average velocity [in modern notation given as $s = \bar{v}t$ or $\bar{v} = (s/t)$, where $\bar{v}$ (v-bar) stands for average velocity] is a refinement which also provides a small but crucial step in this development. But average velocity, where velocity is still conceived of as an intensive quality and the relation of velocity, time, and distance is not yet explicit in the representation, would presumably be the arithmetic average of the sum of the velocities through finite and equal time intervals of *AD*. But we cannot add velocities, because they are not dimensive, or quantitative in this scheme. However the geometric representation (fallaciously) suggested the additivity of equivalent or unit degrees of velocity, since a line of a given length is taken to represent the degree of a quality; thus we may represent equal increments of a given velocity by equal lengths of the line. Because we may compare different amounts of the same quality in terms of duration in time, it suggested itself that we may also compare different degrees of quality by the differences in the lengths of the vertical, not as representing actual measurable magnitudes but as representing proportions. The constants required to translate these proportions into numerical magnitudes are discovered only by empirical measurement, and this did not enter into the consideration of the calculators of the fourteenth century. Yet free of such considerations, they could envison a unit degree of a quality, a double degree, a half degree, and so forth, in terms of proportions. Thus changes in velocity could be represented by differing heights of the vertical, and a uniform change of velocity by equal increments of velocity in equal increments of time. (This foreshadows Galileo's definition, which is precisely the same).

Now the question of how to represent all this arises. Within the framework of our rectangular areas we might mark off the finite equal time intervals along *AD,* and indicate the change in velocity by step-like increments along *AB,* assuming for each equal time interval a uniform velocity within that interval, and then a "jump" of increment Δv in the next interval, as in Fig. C_1 below. But suppose now that we wanted to consider the representation of *continuously* changing velocity, without any jumps at all. This would mean that for any instant through *AD* the velocity would be given by the height of the vertical at that point. Thus, in previous Fig. B, because the motion is uniform, all altitudes raised at any point whatever along *AD* are equal and each of them represents the instantaneous velocity at that instant which Heytesbury had defined. Since by definition there is no change of velocity in uniform motion, the instantaneous rate of change of velocity of such motion is zero or the motion undergoes zero acceleration. But if the rate of a continuous acceleration were to be represented, it would be by a rising line with no step-like jumps, and the instantaneous velocity at any successive point, no matter how close to the one preceding it, would differ by increments taken as small as one wanted. The figure representing this continuously accelerated motion would then no longer be a series of rectangles but a triangle (or a triangle atop a rectangle, if the acceleration were taken to begin at a given velocity >0). (Fig. C_2.)

As the intervals of time become smaller, that is, as Δt approaches zero as

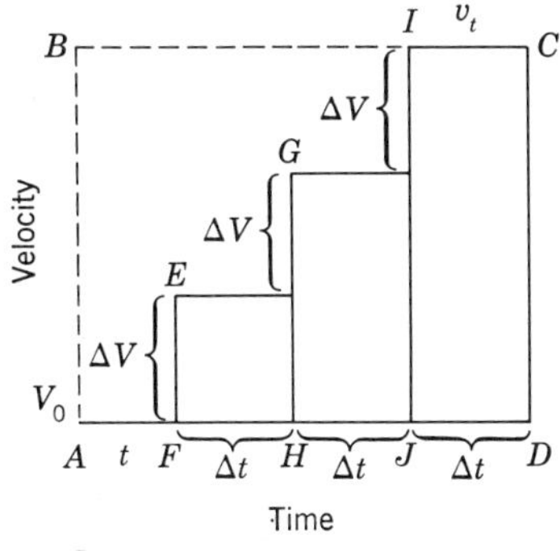

Fig. C_1

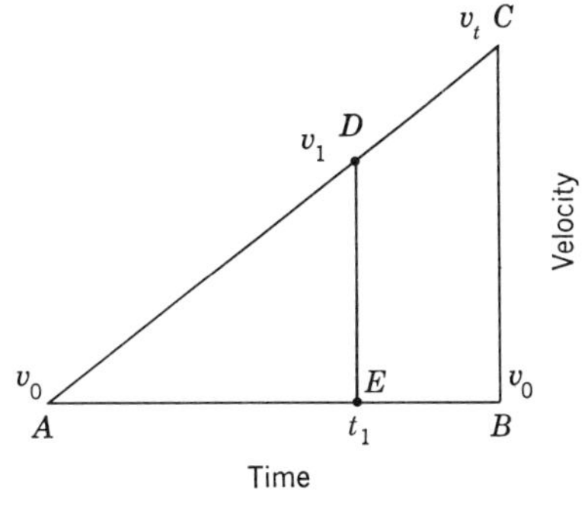

Fig. C_2

a limit, diagram C_1 approaches diagram C_2. As the time intervals approach a limit, the increments of velocity Δv also do, getting smaller and smaller. In modern notation this ratio of the increment of velocity to the increment in time, as the increment in time approaches zero, is expressed as

$$\lim_{\Delta t \to 0} \frac{\Delta v}{\Delta t} = \frac{dv}{dt}$$

(the differential expression which is the definition of acceleration in modern physics).

The fourteenth-century students of mechanics did not have this in mind when they constructed their diagrams; but the later concepts of the calculus, by means of which instantaneous rates of change can be expressed, are contained in germ in the geometrical "pictures" which display the intuitive sense of instantaneous rate of change of velocity which the Mertonians and the Parisians attained. The method of constant approximation is ancient, however, and was known to the Greeks as the method of exhaustion, involved in the problems of quadrature of curves.

The medievals distinguished uniform motion (at constant velocity) from what they called *difform* motion (at changing velocities). Where the change in velocity was itself continuous, i.e., where the rate of change was constant or uniform, they called this *uniformly difform* motion (and as one might guess, *difformly difform* when the rate of change of velocity was not constant). The triangle represented uniformly difform motion (when interpreted for the quality velocity) or, therefore, uniform acceleration. But here the comparison of "quantities of a quality" in terms of the area of geometric figures comes into play. For it can be seen that the triangle ABC is equal in area to a rectangle $AFGB$, where the altitude of the rectangle $AF = \frac{1}{2}AC$ (by elementary geometry, since the triangles EFC and EGB are equal (Fig. D). On the geometric interpretation, this means that the quantity of the quality (velocity) is the same in both figures. The triangle ABC gives this quantity in terms of uniformly accelerated motion, whereas

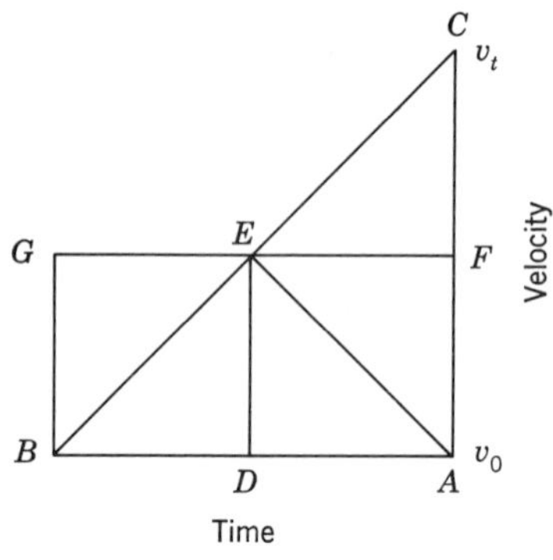

Fig. D

the rectangle *AFGB* gives it in terms of uniform motion. Thus the two *quantities* of the motion, one at a uniformly changing velocity, the other at a constant velocity, are the same. But, as can be seen from the diagram, the degree of velocity marked by the line *AF,* is the *mean* degree between the extremes, at *A* and at *C* (the first, in this case being 0, and the second, marked by the line *AC*). Thus, if *A* is taken as the initial velocity v_o, starting from rest, and *C* as the terminal or final velocity v_t, after acceleration through time *BA,* then *F* represents the *mean* velocity, or mean speed $[(v_o + v_t)/2]$.[12] This is, in effect, Oresme's geometrical proof of the so-called Merton Mean-Speed Theorem (sometimes called the Merton Rule), which, as we shall note, was repeated and used by Galileo in much the same form.

Earlier, at Oxford, William of Heytesbury, Richard Swineshead, and John Dumbleton had formulated the Merton Theorem, and offered a number of algebraic proofs (albeit in the language of proportions, in large part). But it was Oresme's geometric proof that Galileo finally arrived at (though in a different version derived from Casali). In the earliest ascertainable statement of the Merton Theorem (1335) Heytesbury formulates it thus,

> With respect . . . to the distance traversed in a uniformly accelerated motion commencing from zero degree [of velocity] and terminating at some finite degree [of velocity] . . . the motion as a whole, or its whole acquisition, will correspond to its mean degree [of velocity]. The same thing holds true if the latitude of motion is uniformly acquired from some degree [of velocity] in an exclusive sense, and is terminated at some finite degree [of velocity].[13]

But then Heytesbury goes on to present a corollary, which he states thus,

[12] On the distinction between velocity and speed and between vector and scalar magnitudes, see p. 470, and any introduction to vector algebra.

[13] William of Heytesbury, *Rules for Solving Sophisms,* in M. Clagett, *op. cit.* Document 5.1, p. 272.

> From the foregoing, it can be sufficiently determined for this kind of uniform acceleration or deceleration *how great a distance will be traversed other things being equal, in the first half of the time, and how much in the second half. For when the acceleration of motion takes place uniformly from zero degree* [*of velocity*] *to some degree* [*of velocity*], *the distance it will traverse in the first half of the time will be exactly one-third of that which it will traverse in the second half of the time.*[14] [Italics inserted.]

This is an extremely important passage, and its full significance is realized only when Galileo applies an extension of this analysis to the kinetics of falling bodies, three centuries later. It is alluded to as the *Distance Theorem,* and it has two significant aspects. First, it indicates a shift from the Aristotelian-dominated philosophical framework, permitting a translation of degrees or amounts of a quality into the quantitative language of distances, the proportions between the "quantities of a quality" now stateable as proportions between distances. Second, it suggests an important generalization which we shall see is mathematically fundamental in formulating the law of uniformly accelerated motion $s = \frac{1}{2}at^2$, as Galileo arrives at it. In a work attributed to Heytesbury, a proof of the Merton Theorem is offered in terms of distances traversed, which depends on the proportionality of degree of velocity to distance, a mistake which we shall see repeated in Galileo. Yet the relation of the distances through successive portions of time of uniformly accelerated motion is correctly given here too (for the two halves of a given time) as 1:3. A generation later Nicholas Oresme generalizes this relation, in his *Questions on the Elements of Euclid,* stating that the successive distances through equal intervals of time of uniformly difform motion stand to each other in the relation 1:3:5, and so on, or as the series of odd numbers beginning with one. The geometric interpretation, using Oresme's diagram, yields a simple geometric demonstration of this proportion, which depends on taking the areas of the triangles as proportional to distances of uniformly accelerated motion. The areas, we remember, were originally taken to represent "quantities of a quality," or a total amount of velocity through a given time.

The summability or additivity of velocities is problematic, as we shall see, and its representation as the simple product of a degree of velocity and time involves an error (because degrees of a quality are intensive, and do not take a simple numerical or geometric expression, such as length of a line). Oresme himself cautions on the limits of geometric spatial representation of qualities, saying that the line representing the degree of a quality (the "line of intension") in a body at a particular point "is not extended outside of the point in actuality, but only in imagination."[15]

[14] *Ibid.*, p. 272.

[15] Oresme, *Questions on Euclid's Elements,* cited by Clagett, *op. cit.*, p. 362.

Nevertheless, he asserts that proportions between intensive degrees of a quality may be expressed in similar proportions between lengths of lines, and this is the crucial step in the geometrization of the concept of motion. The Distance Theorem depends on the Mean Speed Theorem, for geometrically the triangle can be taken to represent the total quantity of velocity (proportional to distance) of uniformly accelerated motion on the grounds that its area is equal to that of a rectangle representing uniform motion at the mean speed (or mean "degree" of the initial and terminal velocities), as we have seen.

If we examine Fig. D once more, and now take the areas of the figures as distances, then triangle *ABC* represents the distance through which a body uniformly accelerated will pass in the time *BA*. The distance through the first half of that time will then be represented by the triangle with base *BD* (the velocity increasing along the hypotenuse *BC*, the "line of ascent"); the distance through the second half of the time *DA* will be represented by the total area *ADEC*, which consists of the three triangles *ADE, AEF, CEF*. But it can be shown geometrically that $BED = ADE = AEF = CEF$, or (in the interpretation) that each represents the same distance. The total distance in the second half of the time ($ADE + AEF + CEF$) is thus three times as large as the distance in the first half of the time (*BED*). Clearly, by dividing the time intervals further, we could continue this reasoning and demonstrate the ratio of the distances in successive equal intervals of time, as 1:3:5:7. . . . As we shall see, Galileo used a version of this proof in his formulation of the laws of uniformly accelerated motion.

THE MOTION OF FALLING BODIES

Though this geometric representation lends itself to physical interpretation, being generally concerned with changes in quality through time, and specifically with the physical quality, velocity, only two centuries later do we have evidence that the Merton Theorem is specifically applied to the motion of falling bodies and of projectiles, although it is likely that it had occurred to others earlier that it was applicable. In 1545, Domingo de Soto, a Spaniard who had studied at Paris, proposed that the Mean Speed Theorem was properly to be applied to two sorts of "uniformly difform" motion, (1) the natural motion of fall and (2) projectile motion, saying ". . . when a body falls through a uniform medium, it is moved more quickly at the end than at the beginning. On the other hand, the movement of projectiles [upward] is less quick in the end than in the beginning. And so the first is uniformly increased, while the second is uniformly decreased."[16]

As we have seen earlier, it was a basic premise of Aristotelian dynamics that falling motion increased in velocity, but it was not entirely clear what

[16] Domingo de Soto, *Questions on the Eight Books of the Physics of Aristotle,* cited by Clagett, *op. cit.,* pp. 555–56.

the description of this increase should be, nor what its causal account should be. As we have seen (pp. 437–38), Strato is already cited as giving an observational argument for this proportional increase for falling water. But the ambiguity remains whether *toward the end of its fall* means *later,* in terms of the time of fall, or *further along,* in terms of the distance of fall, or *closer to the end* in terms of distance from the natural location. Common sense plainly relates distance and time here, because the same object certainly takes longer to fall further, and common sense would rebel at any notion that the same object could fall twice as far in the same time that it would fall a given distance (an argument Galileo was to use; see p. 457). Common sense would also suggest some proportionality, therefore, between increase in velocity, distance of fall, and time of fall. But there, common sense would have gone as far as it can go.

A contemporary common sense, used to concepts of measurement and experimentation, might suggest the further step. Why not just go ahead and measure the times taken in various distances of fall, or measure the changes in velocity as the distance and time increase. Then, as good empiricists, we could inductively generalize from all the observations and come up with a law of fall. One could argue that we would need accurate ways of measuring time and distance, and how indeed could we measure increase in velocity, unless we had some very fast stop-motion photographs sharply and accurately marked at different instants. But suppose all this were available, or that some of the ingenious machines for exhibiting these relations were available (like the early ones of Atwood, Morin, Laborde, Lippich, Von Babo, Wheatstone, Hipp). They would be of very little use (and in the case of the machines, would not have been invented in the first place) unless it were conceptually clear what it was we were looking for. This kind of conceptual clarification, even with the conceptual elements of the Mean Speed Theorem, the Distance Theorem, and their application to the motion of falling bodies and projectiles, took until well into the seventeenth century, and taxed the best intellects of the time. So obvious is the step from common sense to scientific formulation, after the fact, that any first-year physics student, or even the student with no formal knowledge of physics, but some elementary geometry and algebra, sees the scientific formulation as almost obvious. But, as Norwood Hanson and others have pointed out, it is something like finding the hidden figure in visual puzzles: it's been there all along, hidden only by one's set, or visual attitude. When the hidden figure "clicks" into focus, then one says, "Of course, it's obvious." To make the application of Mertonian and Parisian kinematic representations to the motion of freely falling bodies clear was no less a step than to found modern physics.

DISTANCE, VELOCITY, AND TIME: GALILEO'S ERROR AND ITS RESOLUTION

A major conceptual confusion had to be overcome, and it turned out to be difficult partly because common sense was persuasive in hiding a distinction; but also partly because the very method of geometrical representation carried with it certain dangers of misrepresentation, or misinterpretation, of the geometric picture. Because it is plain that the longer things fall, the further they fall, and that they fall faster the longer and further they fall, it seems natural to assume that velocity can be conceived of as depending either on distance or time of fall, and that increase of velocity is indifferently proportional to either one of these two related measures. We have seen that a causal explanation of this increasing velocity was sought in the Aristotelian theory of weight and its relation to velocity. Velocity was seen to be a function of weight, and change of velocity a function of change of weight. With the modifications of this dynamics, especially in projectile motion—the "forced" motion of bodies thrown from a height or into the air—there developed the notion of *mixed motions,* natural plus forced, which gave rise to theories of impetus. But even with the modifications which provided the transition to the modern concept of inertia, the description of these motions was not yet adequate. Whatever the causes of the change in velocity in falling bodies or in projectiles, the account of this change, without regard to the *forces* involved—i.e., the kinematic account—was a matter of mathematically relating distances, times, and velocities.

The confusion inherent in the commonsense view becomes explicit only when the relations of time, distance, and velocity are made explicit in terms of proportional or geometric analysis. Leonardo da Vinci states it most clearly in a passage in his *Notebooks,* when he says,

> The heavy body which descends at each degree of time acquires a degree of movement more than in the degree of time preceding, and similarly, a degree of swiftness greater than the degree of the preceding movement. Therefore at each doubled quantity of time the length of descent is doubled and also the swiftness of the movement.[17]

Thus velocity increases proportionately to time *and* distance of fall. The mistake is repeated in the famous letter of Galileo to Paolo Sarpi, in 1604, in which the geometric representation of distance of fall is used. Here Galileo seeks an axiomatic principle which will serve as the premise from which two already formulated laws can be derived. These are (1) that the distances of fall are to each other as the squares of the times and its corollary (2) that the spaces, in successive equal times, are to each other as the

[17] Leonardo da Vinci, *Notebooks,* in Clagett, *op. cit.,* Document 9.4, pp. 572–73.

series of odd numbers beginning with one. (We shall see below how Galileo later gives proofs of these laws as theorems in his *Discourses,* but from premises radically different from the one he gives here.) The principle, as Galileo states it, is this,

A
B
C
D

> The speed of a body in natural motion increases with its distance from the point of departure; thus, for example, if a heavy body falls from point A along $ABCD$, I hypothesize that the degree of speed that it has at C is to the degree of speed it had at B as the distance CA is to the distance BA, and consequently, that its degree of speed at D will be greater than that at C in the same measure that the distance DA is greater than the distance CA.[18]

The strange thing is that the geometric representation helped to reinforce this error. It served to give a spatial picture of the fall of a body through space, using a vertical line to represent the trajectory and different line segments to represent parts of this trajectory. But here a crucial shift from our earlier diagram takes place. Whereas in the previous diagrams, degree of velocity was being measured against time, here it is being measured against distance. On the assumption that the proportionality holds *indifferently* for both time and distance of fall, the logic of the diagram is blithely transferred from the time representation to the distance representation, in the following way. Whereas in our previous diagram, the area represented the quantity of motion, or total quantity of velocity during a given *time,* here (in Fig. E) the area represents this quantity over a given *distance* of fall. In Galileo's earlier, and mistaken, interpretation, then, he interprets the proportionality between the line segment AB, representing distance of fall, and the line segment BC, representing the velocity at the point B of fall as representing the proportionality of velocity to distance of fall. Because, for a given angle θ ($\measuredangle BAC$), the ratio between opposite and adjacent sides of the triangles ABC, ADE, and so on, remains constant —what we would call in trigonometry tan θ—then for the uniform slope AI, the velocity remains in the same ratio to the distance at any point of fall, or degree of speed is proportional to distance of fall. Further, because the areas of the triangles are to each other as the squares of the sides, geometrically ($ABC : ADE :: AB^2 : AD^2 :: BC^2 : DE^2$), then the sum of all the instantaneous velocities through all the points from A to B is represented by the area of the triangle ABC, on Galileo's interpretation in 1604. But this assumes that the summation of velocities, at each point of fall is equivalent to the summation of velocities at each instant of fall. And since this summed velocity is proportional to the square of the distance, it would

[18] Galileo to Paolo Sarpi, Padua, Oct. 16, 1604, *Opera,* Vol. X, p. 115, cited in Koyré, *Etudes Galiléennes* (Paris: Hermann & Cie, 1939), Vol. II, pp. 78–79.

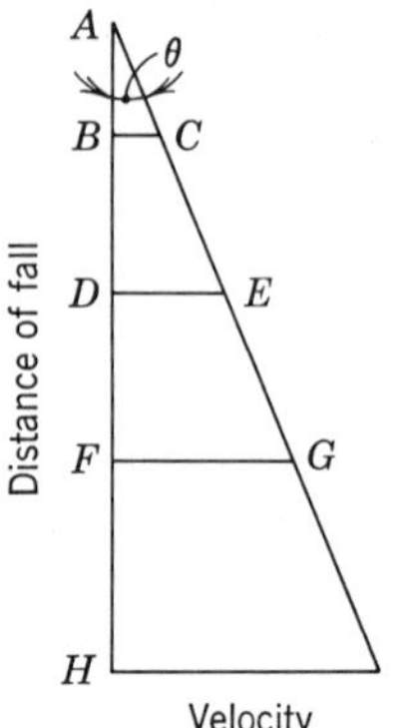

Fig. E

also be proportional to the square of the time. But if $ABC : ADE ::$ $AB^2 : AD^2 :: t_1^2 : t_2^2$, then it cannot be that the distances $AB : AD ::$ $t_1^2 : t_2^2$, which Galileo also alleges (and which is correct). For the increases of velocity at each point, if they are infinitesimally small, or if they are as small as one wishes to take them, toward a limit, may be summed only by a process of integration of these differential increments, and not by simple linear addition. And the area of the triangle thus represents the area under a curve (in this case AC) which in turn represents the instantaneous changes or differences in quantity expressed by the differential expression dy/dx (or in this case, where v = velocity and s = distance, dv/ds or $\lim_{\Delta s \to 0} \frac{\Delta v}{\Delta s}$). Though the concepts of integration were already anticipated in the classical methods of exhaustion (used in the quadrature of curves) developed by Eudoxus, Hipparchus, and Archimedes, and the concept of instantaneous velocity was anticipated in the picture of velocity at an instant, as we have seen in the previous diagrams and in Heytesbury's definition, still Galileo still did not have a working vocabulary nor a working method for the clear expression of these concepts. The calculus, first developed by Newton and Leibniz into a formal method, in the seventeenth century, was already anticipated by many students of the subject, and Galileo, in his later work, made important contributions to its development. But here, in 1604, the mistake still persists, of treating the sum of increments of velocity in time as equivalent to treating the sum of these increments through distance of fall.[19]

[19] To complete the argument, there is, of course, an algebraic relation between distance of fall and velocity, though not the mistaken "proportionality" alleged to hold indifferently for both distance and time in the early views. The equation, as every physics student knows is $v^2 = v_0^2 + 2as$. This may be derived from the definition of acceleration, $a = (v - v_0)/t$ and the mean-speed theorem, $c = \frac{1}{2}(v + v_0)t$. Multiplying these, we get $a \cdot s = \frac{1}{2}(v^2 - v_0^2)$, which reduces to $v^2 = v_0^2 + 2as$.

Koyré suggests, in his great study of the development of the concepts of the fall of bodies, that Galileo, as well as his predecessors (such as Leonardo da Vinci, Benedetti, Michel Varron, and the great mathematician-philosopher Descartes) all made the same mistake for the same reason, "It is easier—and more natural—to *see* (that is, to *imagine*) in space, than it is to *think* in time."[20] Koyré also points out that this "ease" also relates to Galileo's rejection of the causal account of change of velocity, in Aristotelian dynamics and in the impetus theories, and to his attempt to discover the axiom or principle from which the laws of fall could be deduced. "It is not surprising, therefore," writes Koyré, "that the renunciation of causal explanation reinforces the tendency to geometrization, and thus to spatialization. Instead of *thinking* motion, Galileo represents it to himself. He sees the line, the space traversed at variable speed. And it is this line—the trajectory—that he takes as the argument of the function, velocity."[21]

Galileo corrects his error concerning the fundamental principle from which the laws can be derived, but not without great difficulty. What now appears simple to a college freshman was difficult for Galileo; and so difficult that although Galileo finally recognized his error, Descartes never did. The correct principle—increase in velocity is proportional to time of fall—does not involve a correction of the geometrical reasoning. There is no error here, for the geometry is a strictly formal system, uninterpreted as to physical relations of velocity, time, and distance. Yet it is taken to represent physical relations, and thus the use of this formalism depends on its proper interpretation in physical terms. But underlying any interpretation, there is a deeper philosophical or meta-mathematical thesis, which we have already encountered. It is the view that the physical world is mathematically ordered, that it is composed in the language of mathematics. This was, as we have seen, the Platonic-Pythagorean world-view, and it was revived in the Platonism of the Italian Renaissance, which profoundly influenced Galileo. Thus, Galileo writes, in 1623, in criticism of his critic Sarsi, "Philosophy is written in this grand book, the universe, which stands continually open to our gaze. But the book cannot be understood unless one first learns to comprehend the language and read the letters in which it is composed. It is written in the language of mathematics, and its characters are triangles, circles and other geometric figures without which it is humanly impossible to understand a single word of it; without these, one wanders about in a dark labyrinth."[22]

The certainty that the natural motion of fall and projectile motion lent themselves to mathematical analysis was not based on accumulated empirical evidence (unless one regards mathematical intuitions as somehow de-

[20] Alexandre Koyré, *op. cit.,* Vol. II, p. 88.

[21] *Ibid.,* Vol. II, p. 95.

[22] *The Assayer,* tr. Stillman Drake, in *Discoveries and Opinions of Galileo* (New York: Doubleday Anchor Books, 1957), pp. 237–38.

rived from the centuries-long experience of the human race), but rather on the rational conviction that nature was orderly, and that mathematics was the language for the expression and the discovery of this order. There was as yet no experimental check on the geometric hypotheses, and it required none to critically re-evaluate the principle of the proportionality of velocity to distance of fall. What occurred was partly a compounding of confusions, partly a rational critique of initial assumptions, and the discovery of an error, one which Galileo thought led to an absurd consequence unacceptable to ordinary common sense: namely, that the same body would fall a shorter and a longer distance in the same time. Some time between 1604 and 1632, Galileo had reconsidered his earlier formulation, revised it, and come up with the correct one, that instantaneous velocity is proportional to the time of fall in uniformly accelerated motion, and that the distance traversed is proportional to the square of the time. The earlier error, as Galileo recognized, lay not in geometry or mathematics but in the physical interpretation given to the formal calculation. He writes, "The errors, then, lie not in abstractness or concreteness, not in the geometry or the physics, but in a calculator who does not know how to make a true accounting."[23]

THE MATHEMATIZATION OF MOTION: GALILEO'S DISCOURSES AND THE BIRTH OF MODERN PHYSICS

The "true accounting" was given by Galileo in his *Discourses on Two New Sciences* (1638). In the Dialogue of the Third Day, Galileo gives his final version of the analysis of uniform and uniformly accelerated motion, with which we close this account of his analysis of motion. His method, starting from axioms and definitions, and proceeding by analysis of the concepts of motion, to certain additional "assumptions" and to theorems, geometrically proved, and to their corollaries, gives the ideal construction of a science that Galileo hoped for. In short, the science of motion was to be reduced to the clarity and certainty of a mathematical science, its laws stateable in mathematical form, and derivable by formal inference from axioms or postulates previously set forth. These laws then yield, on interpretation, empirically testable predictions, in terms of direct measurement of distances and times—the famous inclined plane experiments in which Galileo allegedly "proved" the physical validity of his formal analysis. Nature agreed with the hypothesis. But Galileo knew—in the sense of knowledge which considers nature as mathematical, and the laws of nature as rationally necessary inferences from true premises—Galileo knew *without* experiment that his formulation was correct. The experiment he regarded as a way of demonstrating the truth of his mathematical discoveries

[23] Galileo, *Dialogues Concerning the Two Chief Systems of the World*, tr. Stillman Drake (Berkeley: University of California Press, 1953), p. 208.

to others. The senses are, in the Platonic view, finally illusory and deceptive, and at best give only approximations to the underlying reality, once the subjective and fluctuating evidences of perception are stripped away and the rational kernel alone remains, in terms of geometric shapes, magnitudes, and the relations among them.[24] In his rational construction, approximating to the form of a geometrical system, Galileo therefore begins his account with a definition of uniform motion, which he gives as follows:

> *Definition*: By steady or uniform motion, I mean one in which the distances traversed by a moving particle during any equal intervals of time, are themselves equal.

The four "Axioms" which follow are then given (in abbreviated form here, where s = distance, t = time, and v = average speed or velocity)

Axiom I: (In one and the same uniform motion) if $t_1 > t_2$, then $s_1 > s_2$
Axiom II: If $s_1 > s_2$, then $t_1 > t_2$
Axiom III: (In one and the same interval of time) if $v_1 > v_2$, then $s_1 > s_2$
Axiom IV: If $s_1 > s_2$, then $v_1 > v_2$

Thus Galileo sets out what seem perfectly obvious truths, given the commonsensical definition of uniform motion. (Compare these with Aristotle's definitions of quicker and slower, p. 434.) We may "hold these truths to be self-evident," but here they are explicated in a form which permits them to be explicitly appealed to in the steps of a proof, as the arguments for a step of inference, or a move from one statement to another. The self-evidence of these "axioms," as Galileo calls them, is in effect the explication of the meaning of the term *uniform motion* as Galileo defines it. But the more relevant problem is the one which concerns uniformly accelerated motion. Here, Galileo is heir to that long history of conceptual criticism and reformulation which we have examined. He already knows the Mean Speed Theorem and the Distance Theorem, and has at hand the method of geometric representation (which he inherits in a variant form attributed to Casali, in which Oresme's representation is "turned over," and the axes are interchanged, the vertical, in this version, now representing time and the horizontal representing velocity). Galileo begins with certain methodological considerations, which he claims derive from the most natural way of considering the problem.

> . . . We have decided to consider the phenomena of bodies falling with an acceleration such as actually occurs in nature and to make this definition of accelerated motion exhibit the essential features of observed ac-

[24] See, for example, Galileo's passage on the evidence of sense perception, in which he makes the classical distinction between primary and secondary qualities, in *The Assayer*, in Drake, *op. cit.*, pp. 274 ff.

> celerated motions. . . . In this belief we are confirmed mainly by the consideration that experimental results are seen to agree with and exactly correspond with those properties which have been, one after another, demonstrated by us. Finally, in the investigation of naturally accelerated motion we were led, by the hand as it were, in following the habit and custom of nature herself, in all her various other processes, to employ only those means which are most common, simple and easy. . . . When therefore, I observe a stone initially at rest falling from an elevated position and continually acquiring new increments of speed, why should I not believe that such increases take place in a manner which is exceedingly simple and rather obvious to everybody?[25]

Thus does Galileo rhetorically reduce the long conceptual struggle to achieve an adequate formulation of acceleration to something "exceedingly simple and rather obvious to everybody." The puzzle picture has clicked into focus, and now it appears to Galileo (or he would have it appear) as unproblematic from the start. For us, it appears unproblematic too, and it takes an effort of historical empathy and some knowledge of the history of the concept to realize how unsimple and unobvious Galileo's "simple" definition is. For one thing, the claim to having observed a falling stone acquiring new increments of speed is fatuous: it requires the observation already shaped by the concept of acceleration in terms of increments of speed, i.e., by an additive concept of acceleration and the quantificational concept of increment. For another, the methodological claim to "follow nature" in her simplicity is a profound philosophical assumption—that nature is economical in her action, taking the simplest among alternative paths (whatever "simple" means in such a case), and further, that in our account of nature, therefore, we follow the principle of economy—or the "law of parsimony," sometimes called *Ockham's razor*—which urges that we make no more assumptions than are necessary to explain something; that the fewest principles or entities be adduced, therefore. Thus, because Galileo had already defined uniform motion in terms of equal distances in equal times, he concludes that the definition of uniformly accelerated motion partake of this same simplicity and this same form: "A motion is said to be uniformly accelerated, when starting from rest, it acquires during equal time intervals, equal increments of speed," or $(\Delta v/\Delta t) = k$; the rate of change of velocity is uniform, through equal intervals of time, or the time rate of change of velocity is constant. Here, Galileo introduces that error which he thinks he has discovered in the earlier formulation, that change of velocity is proportional to distance traversed. But he introduces it in a charming and Platonic way, emulating the dialectical criticism ex-

[25] Galileo, *Dialogues Concerning Two New Sciences* tr. H. Crew and A. De Salvio (New York: Macmillan, 1914), pp. 160–61. This is the text referred to here by the alternate title, *Discourses*.

hibited in the Platonic dialogues. He has the sympathetic listener, Sagredo, say,

> So far as I see at present, the definition might have been put a little more clearly perhaps without changing the fundamental idea, namely, uniformly accelerated motion is such that its speed increases in proportion to the space traversed; so that for example, the speed acquired by a body in falling four cubits would be double that acquired in falling two cubits and this latter speed would be double that acquired in the first cubit.[26]

This is, of course, Galileo's earlier and mistaken opinion, and he has his spokesman in the dialogue, Salviati, comment that "our author himself admitted . . . that he had for some time shared the same fallacy." The *reductio ad absurdum* is this: If velocities are proportional to spaces traversed, then these spaces are traversed in equal periods of time (the greater space being traversed at a greater velocity in the same time as a lesser space at a lesser velocity). The outcome is, for example, that a body falling eight feet would therefore have a velocity double that of the same body falling four feet, and thus it would fall eight feet and four feet in the same time. And thus also, for the same body falling a thousand feet or a thousand miles. Now this is not logically impossible, or logically absurd; it is *empirically* inconceivable on the grounds of ordinary commonsense observation. Galileo has Salviati say, "Observation however shows that the time required for fall from the greater height is longer." But Galileo thought he had revealed a logical self-contradiction, whereas in fact, his reasoning about this fallacy is itself fallacious.[27] Galileo now proceeds to make one "assumption," namely, "The speeds acquired by one and the same body moving down planes of different inclinations are equal when the heights of the planes are equal." Thus, in Fig. F, on the different inclinations or slopes *CA, CD,* and *CB* of the plane *ABC,* the initial velocity v_o at *C* will be the same in each case, and the terminal or final velocity v_t at *A, D,* and *B* will also be the same. Now plainly, the distances *CA, CD,* and *CB* are different, and by the relation of distances to the squares of the times, the times will be different as well. Thus a body falling freely from *C* to *B* will reach the line *AB* sooner than a body rolling (ideally, without friction or any resistance of the medium) from *C* to *A* (or indeed, from *C* to some point *P* along the line *AB* extended as far as one wishes). But the maximum velocity acquired at any of these terminal points will, according to Galileo's

[26] *Ibid.,* p. 167.

[27] See, for a discussion of Galileo's fallacious reasoning here, and his confusion of average with instantaneous velocity, Ernst Mach, *The Science of Mechanics* (Chicago: Open Court, 1893), pp. 247–48, and I. B. Cohen, "Galileo's Rejection of the Possibility of Velocity Changing Uniformly with Respect to Distance," *Isis,* Vol. 47 (1956), pp. 231–38.

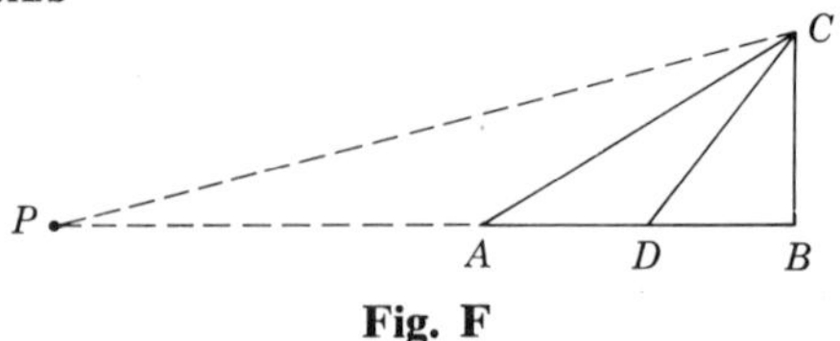

Fig. F

assumption, be the same. Now there is nothing obvious or simple about this assumption. It involves, indeed, some very fundamental additional assumptions involving the conservation of mechanical energy and the concept of inertia. But here, Galileo appeals to the function of this assumption, or postulate, within the systematic structure of his whole argument, and uses it to justify his experiments which are to *confirm* the laws (or theorems) of uniformly accelerated motion, which he reports on later in the Dialogue. *"Let us then, for the present, take this as a postulate, the absolute truth of which will be established when we find that the inferences from it correspond to and agree perfectly with experiment."*[28] Thus Galileo has Salviati propose a postulate while formulating a fundamental *methodological* principle of the hypothetico-deductive method of theory construction. The methodological principle, in simple terms, is this: one hypothetically sets forth propositions, which serve as premises (conjointly with other premises already established) from which one can then deduce other propositions concerning experimentally or observationally ascertainable facts. They are then justified *systematically* as providing the grounds for empirical inference. But Galileo is not content with this alone. He offers an experiment which bears on this postulate and serves to support its use empirically, exhibiting the conservation of momentum in a freely swinging body. (This is easily accessible in editions of the *Discourses* and in many excerpted versions, and will not be given here.)

Now Galileo is prepared to offer his theorems and to prove them, using some theorems already proved, and his definitions. But, as we shall see, he uses the geometric constructions with which we have already become familiar, and which represented the language of mathematical argument then current. His first theorem is, in effect, the Mean Speed Theorem, which he states thus:

> *Theorem I, Proposition I*: The time in which any space is traversed by a body starting from rest and uniformly accelerated is equal to the time in which that same space would be traversed by the same body moving at a uniform speed whose value is the mean of the highest speed and the speed just before acceleration began.

His proof is by means of the following interpretation of the diagram in Fig. G. The distance of fall is represented by the line *CD*. The triangle *AEB* represents the uniform increase of velocity, from *A* to *EB*, each of

[28] *Ibid.*, p. 172.

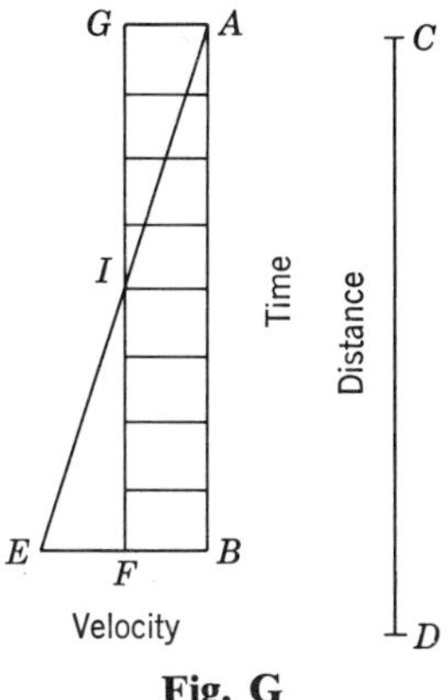

Fig. G

the increasingly long parallel lines drawn at equal intervals along *AB* representing the increasing velocity, at equal intervals of time marked off along *AB*. In this diagram, unlike the similar one used in the 1604 argument (p. 451), velocity is measured against time, as in the original diagram of Oresme (the diagram now turned around so that the vertical represents time, and the horizontal, the degrees of velocity, but otherwise the same). The proof is essentially the same as Oresme's, as well. The areas are now referred to by Galileo as representing the "values of the velocities" or the "momenta of the moving body." Plainly, if we draw a vertical from the midpoint of *EB*, (*F*), this will represent half of the highest velocity represented by *EB*. Uniform motion is represented, as in the fourteenth century, by a rectangle, formed by the base *FB*, representing the constant velocity of uniform motion, and the altitude *AB* representing the time. Because *AB* is also the altitude of *AEB*, the times of both motions are the same. Also, because the area of the rectangle $ABFG =$ the area of the triangle *AEB*, the value of the velocities during the time *AB*, at uniform motion or constant velocity $FB = \frac{1}{2}EB$, will be equal to the value of the velocities at the uniformly changing rate represented by the hypotenuse *AE*, through the same time. The translation of "values of velocities" or "momenta of the moving body" into comparisons of distance assumes that distances of motion are proportional to some "quantity of motion." The simple reading off of areas as representing distances was never attained by Galileo, though it is implied by the proportionality assumed.

Now Galileo is ready to undertake the proof of the basic theorem.

> *Theorem II, Proposition II*: The spaces described by a body falling from rest with a uniformly accelerated motion are to each other as the squares of the time intervals employed in traversing these distances.

The translation of the theorem into geometric form proceeds as follows (in Fig. H): the time of fall is represented by the vertical *AB* and the uniformly accelerated motion of the body by the slope *AC*, the increasing

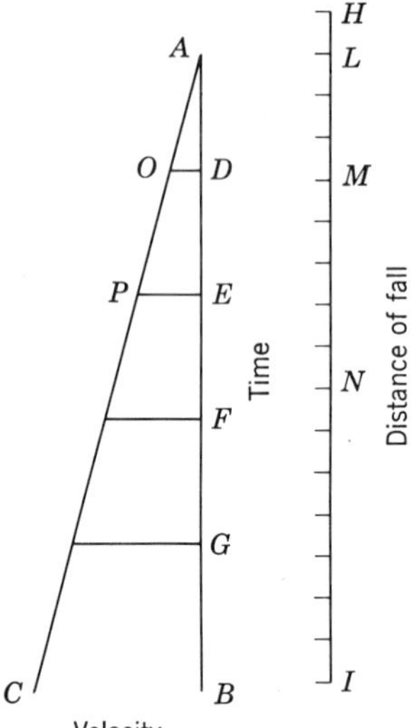

Fig. H

degrees of velocity at equal intervals of time being marked off by the parallels at equal intervals along AB. Thus, the definition *equal increments of velocity in equal times* is visually represented here as in Fig. C_2. Again, this is not Galileo's innovation, but merely the use of an already common convention. The distance of fall is represented separately by the line HI, along which equal intervals have been marked. The first, fourth, ninth, and sixteenth have been marked by the letters L, M, N, and I (following Galileo's notation in all of this). These are obviously the squares of the integers 1, 2, 3, and 4. The theorem then states that the distances HL, HM, HN, HI stand to each other as AD^2: AE^2: AF^2: AG^2, or in a more convenient notation: $HL/HM = AD^2/AE^2$. This then is what has to be proved.

The parallel lines (at equal intervals along AB) DO, EP represent the maximum velocities attained at instants D and O of the time of fall (say, after one second, and after two seconds). But Theorem I has just stated that the distances traversed at uniformly accelerated motion are the same as the distances traversed at uniform motion at the mean speed attained during the same times. Thus, HL and HM represent distances traversed during uniform motion at $\frac{1}{2}DO$ and $\frac{1}{2}EP$, respectively. Here Galileo calls into play another proposition, previously proved, on the basis of the definition and "Axioms" of uniform motion, namely, that two different spaces traversed by two bodies stand to each other in the same ratio as the product of the ratios of their respective velocities and the ratios of their respective times, that is

$$(1) \qquad \frac{s_1}{s_2} = \frac{v_1}{v_2} \times \frac{t_1}{t_2} \qquad \text{since } s_1 = v_1 t_1 \text{ and } s_2 = v_2 t_2$$

But in the diagram, because the velocity of the falling body after one interval of time is represented by *DO,* and after two intervals, by *EP;* because the distances of fall through these two periods are *HL* and *HM;* and because, in addition, the same distances would be traversed at uniform velocities $\frac{1}{2}DO$ and $\frac{1}{2}EP$, in the time periods *AD* and *AE,* substituting in (1) we get

$$(2) \qquad \frac{HL}{HM} = \frac{\frac{1}{2}DO}{\frac{1}{2}EP}\,\frac{AD}{AE}$$

But $\frac{1}{2}DO/\frac{1}{2}EP = DO/EP$; and because triangles *ADO* and *AEP* are similar, the ratios of the respective sides are equal, or $AD/AE = DO/EP$. Substituting once more, in (2), we get

$$(3) \qquad \frac{HL}{HM} = \frac{(AD)}{(AE)}\frac{(AD)}{(AE)}, \quad \text{or} \quad \frac{HL}{HM} = \frac{AD^2}{AE^2}$$

which is what we set out to prove: namely, that the distances of fall *HL, HM* are to each other as the squares of the times of fall *AD, AE*. In more modern notation, this may be expressed as $s = kt^2$ in uniformly accelerated motion, i.e., where $\Delta s/\Delta t = k$ for average velocity $(v_o + v_t)/2$; and where

$\lim\limits_{\Delta t \to 0} \Delta s/\Delta t = ds/dt$ for instantaneous velocity, and $s = f(t)$, and the

function of t is t^2. Given any value of s or of t, we can then compute the other. Where t increases by equal increments 1, 2, 3, 4 . . ., then s increases as the square of t increases, namely 1, 4, 9, 16. . . . If we put these in a column, for values of s and t, something else becomes readily apparent. The *differences* between each of the squares increase in a series, as the odd numbers, beginning with 1. And if we proceed one further step (which Galileo does not do), we perceive that the difference between the differences is a constant (2). We will return to the significance of this later on.

Table I

t(*time*)	s(*distance*)	*differences* $(s_1, s_2 \ldots s_n)$	*difference between differences* $(s_1, s_2 \ldots s_n)$
0	0	1	2
1	1	3	2
2	4	5	2
3	9	7	2
4	16	9	.
5	25	.	.
.	.	.	.
.	.	.	.

Given the Mean Speed Theorem (Theorem I) and the theorem relating time and distance of fall (Theorem II) derived with the help of Theorem I, Galileo is now prepared to prove the Distance Theorem as a corollary of Theorem II. He states it thus:

> *Corollary I*: While . . . during equal intervals of time the velocities increase as the natural numbers, the increments in the distances traversed during these equal time intervals are to one another as the odd numbers beginning with unity.

He thus uses the definition of uniformly accelerated motion (equal increments in velocity in equal time intervals), which as we saw is represented in Fig. H as the proportionality $DO/EP = AD/AE$. And now the significance of the equal intervals along the distance line *HI* becomes clear; $HM:HL$ as 4:1. But the distance *LM* (traversed through the time *DE*) is to the distance *HL* (traversed through the time *AD*) in the ratio 3:1; and $MN:ML = 5:3$, and so on. Mathematically (or here geometrically), the Corollary does not tell us anything *new*; it just *restates* Theorem II in a different way, much in the same way as $3 \times 6 = 18$ may be restated in the form $6 = 18/3$, or generally $xy = z$ may be restated as $x = z/y$. But just as these transformations follow a rule, and may be proved (though we are taught the operations and take them for granted), here too, the corollary may be proved. If we look at Table I, we may discover *on inspection*, that the corollary is true, at least for the numbers given. To prove, however, that it is true for any numbers whatever requires an additional postulate of arithmetic (see Chapter 6, p. 147, on *mathematical induction*). Galileo proves the Corollary geometrically in the following way (see Fig. I).

The line *AO* represents time once more, and the intervals *AC, CI, IO* are equal intervals of time. The parallel lines *BC, FI,* and *PO* represent the increasing degrees of velocity acquired at times *C, I,* and *O,* from motion starting from rest at *A,* the velocity increasing in proportion to the time (definition). Once again the areas of the triangles *ABC, AFI, APO* are taken as representing the total of the momenta during *AC, AI,* and *AO,* and the distances being taken proportional to these momenta, the areas thus represent also the distances fallen through these times. The conversion to distances traversed at uniform velocities is accomplished once more, as in the Mean Speed Theorem, by taking one half of the maximum velocity at the time *C,* which is $\frac{1}{2}BC$ or *EC,* the distance traversed through *AC,* now given proportional to the area of the rectangle *ACED.* (Area $ABC =$ area $ACED$.) By constructing equal rectangles through the remaining figures *BCIF* and *FIOP,* which are proportional to the distances traversed in intervals *CI* and *IO,* Galileo then shows that, since the rectangles are in each case equal in area to the whole figures (*BCIF, FIOP*), and these figures represent the distances in equal successive time intervals *CI, IO,*

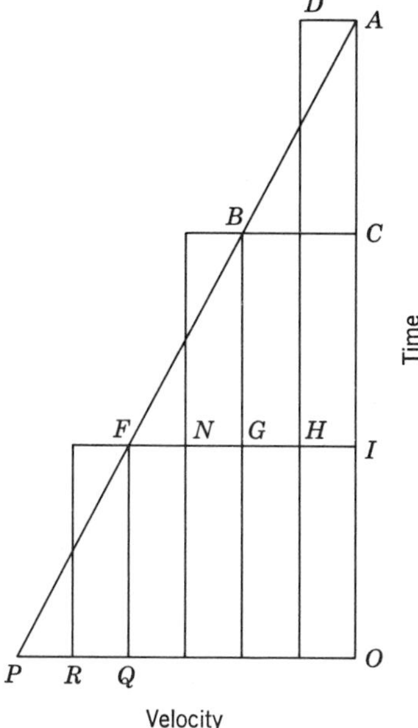

Fig. I

that the distances are to each other in the ratios 1:3:5. By extending the construction, we would then see that the corollary is proved, namely, that the distances traversed through successive equal time intervals of a body falling from rest are to each other as the series of odd numbers beginning with unity, *or* that the distances are to each other as the differences between the squares of the times. This latter form is the more general statement.

At the end of the *Dialogue* Galileo interprets these findings experimentally. That is, he uses the formal reasoning, the theorems, and the assumption concerning inclined planes to produce a prediction concerning observed times and distances. This is where the inclined-plane assumption figures significantly. For, in effect, the inclined plane permits one to slow down the motion conveniently, by extending the plane, or by making its inclination less. Thus, if the assumption is valid and if the whole interpretation of the relation between times, distances, and velocities is valid, all together they provide a systematic network from which one may derive particular statements referring to *observable* measurements of time and distance. Thus, what the experiment will confirm (if observed measurements are in agreement with predictions) or disconfirm (if they are not) is not this or that theorem, but the whole system of theorems, definitions, assumptions which constitute the "machinery" which produces the predictions.

Galileo proceeds to recount the famous inclined-plane experiment then, measuring the time of "fall" (because rolling down a plane at any inclination is equivalent to falling vertically from the same height, in terms of the maximum velocity attained at "ground level", according to the assumption). The distances should then be proportional to the squares of the times of fall (or roll). Galileo reports the experiments thus:

> A piece of wooden moulding or scantling, about 12 cubits long, half a cubit wide, and three finger-breadths thick, was taken; on its edge was cut a channel a little more than one finger in breadth; having made this groove very straight, smooth and polished, and having lined it with parchment, also as smooth and polished as possible, we rolled along it a hard, smooth and very round bronze ball. Having placed this board in a sloping position, by lifting one end some one or two cubits above the other, we rolled the ball . . . along the channel, noting, in a manner presently to be described, the time required to make the descent. We repeated this experiment more than once in order to measure the time with an accuracy such that the deviation between two observations never exceeded one tenth of a pulse beat. Having performed this operation, and having assured ourselves of its reliability, we now rolled the ball only one-quarter the length of the channel; and having measured the time of its descent, we found it precisely one half the former. Next we tried other distances comparing the time for the whole length with that for the half, or with that for two-thirds, or three-fourths, or indeed for any fraction; in such experiments repeated a full hundred times, we always found that the spaces traversed were to each other as the squares of the times. . . . For the measurement of time, we employed a large vessel of water placed in an elevated position; to the bottom of this vessel was soldered a pipe of small diameter giving a thin jet of water, which we collected in a small glass during the time of each descent . . . the water thus collected was weighed, after each descent, on a very accurate balance; the differences and ratios of these weights gave us the differences and ratios of the times, and this with such an accuracy that although the operation was repeated many, many times, there was no appreciable discrepancy in the results.[29]

This experiment has for many years been the source of much discussion among historians of science, philosophers of science, and "plain" scientists. It established a crucial relation between formal reasoning and empirical testing, between theory and practice which has been taken, justifiably or not, as a model of scientific method. And it does have these paradigmatic features. But there is much of interest to a critical view, regarding the concepts of experimentation, measurement, and confirmation, which we have discussed at length in Chapters 7, 8, and 10. Briefly, we may note that much depended upon idealizing the experiment, abstracting those physical features which were not taken into account in the conceptual formulation of the theorems: resistance of the air, surface friction, the limits of ob-

[29] *Ibid.*, pp. 178–79.

servational accuracy and of error. In addition, the measurement of time intervals itself was grounded in theory, as well as in the relative accuracy of the apparatus. Time was measured indirectly in terms of weight; intervals of time were taken as proportional to the respective weights of water collected during each interval. The manual operation of the water clock did not take reaction time into account. The theory of weights and of the balance—of that part of physics called *statics*—was adduced here, but not explicitly. (The development of the physical-mathematical theory of weights, of the lever, and of the balance from Archimedes, through the Middle Ages, to Galileo's time had gone quite far.) The quaintness of Galileo's appeal to accuracy, talking of a "very straight channel" and a "very round bronze ball" (how much rounder is "very round" than "round"?) is also notable. The repetition of the experiment "a full hundred times" is an appeal to some sort of weight of confirmation, the significance of which we have examined in Chapter 9. Even in the reasoning itself, Galileo proceeded with imagination, not always supported by full clarity of conception. In interpreting the areas of triangles as proportional to, and therefore representing distances, he took, as A. R. Hall[30] says, "a great intuitive leap" (as did his predecessors, in geometrizing the Merton Theorem), not yet having at his command the conceptions of the calculus which would justify such a move (which requires integration). Also, Galileo's originality, now that some of the earlier sources of his ideas are known, seems not as great as it once did. The two fundamental theorems were already known, and the proportionality of velocity to time had at least been considered earlier. Galileo may have done no more than popularize and systematize already existing knowledge, as one dour view would have it.

But having said all this, it still remains clear that Galileo's was a prodigious feat. He arranged already existing knowledge, it is true; but he arranged it in such a way, and used it to such effect, that what was hidden appeared to view, what was obscure became clarified. And more than this, he formulated, in an initial way, such concepts of momentum, of the conservation of momentum, of inertia, of the geometric analysis of projectile motion that he established that systematic approach to science and to natural knowledge which culminated in what we now call "mathematical physics."

FROM GEOMETRIC TO ALGEBRAIC REPRESENTATION OF MOTION

A central question in both the strife and the mutuality of the Platonic-Pythagorean and Aristotelian systems of thought was the role of abstract

[30] A. R. Hall, *From Galileo to Newton 1630–1720: The Rise of Modern Science*, Vol. III (New York: Harper & Row, 1963), p. 68.

reason and its relation to the role of sense perception and practical experience. Galileo's thought, and that of the great system builders of modern physics who followed him, is similarly concerned with such questions and such fundamental concepts. They often lie under the surface, in the actual reasoning and criticism and experiment that produce a scientific advance; but as often, they become explicit and become themselves the direct objects of reflection and criticism. Aristotle's space of motion was not Galileo's, nor was it Plato's, nor that of the atomists. Aristotle's dynamics was not Galileo's, for the concept of force underwent a major transformation in the new science. When Newton formulated his three laws of motion, he inherited not only a physical-mathematical tradition, but a philosophical tradition in which lively consideration and criticism of fundamental concepts went hand in hand with mathematical analysis and experimental work.

In all of this development a crucial feature, relevant to the clarification of concepts, is the clarification of language, of meaning and usage. As the analysis becomes increasingly mathematical, the inadequacy of ordinary natural language to express economically and rigorously the newly elucidated concepts becomes more evident. The use of geometric figures as aids to reasoning was an important innovation, but as we have seen, it had its dangers, working the magic of the picture upon the concept-forming activity of the thinker. Once the formal system is interpreted for purposes of kinematic representation, and beyond that for dynamical representations, its visual character becomes increasingly symbolic, and the meanings of geometric representation becomes more and more metaphorical (in much the sense of poetic metaphor) and more conventional. A kinetic-dynamic geometry, conceived of in terms of paths of a point, or areas swept out by a curve, involves a motion imagined, but not exhibited by the geometric figures. But as we have seen from Aristotle's first definitions of *quicker* and *slower* through the great development of the fourteenth-century calculators, another algebraic language develops, in which magnitudes are represented by letter symbols and proportions among magnitudes by appropriate notational innovations. The algebra we all learn in high school derives, in name and fact, from Arabic innovations in the Middle Ages, and its extension and development in connection with geometric representation enlarges also the scope of the geometric metaphor. Number is for counting; but measuring also involves counting, and when proportions become metricized, and the representations not only of length (a principle geometric parameter) but of time, and even of such problematic magnitudes as velocity, heat, and force are also given a visual interpretation, then geometric length and arithmetic number, as well as more general relations among properties of things, become geometrically more conventional. We may talk of a "long time" but hardly of a "long force" or a "short heat." The more general concepts, more qualitatively ambiguous, such as *greater* and *lesser* and *the same* become refined, in their particular applications; but also the conceptualization becomes more abstract, and a more general theory of relations among magnitudes develops as the conventionalism of geometric representation is abstracted in the pure conventions of algebra. The algebraization of Galileo's quasi-algebraic, quasi-geometric instrument of reasoning reveals still more clearly the nature of the relations being investigated. And here the choice of language becomes almost crucial. With the invention of the calculus, by Newton and Leibniz, the algebraic instrument comes into its fullest use and serves to explicate concepts of motion until then hidden from view by the cumbersome language itself. Therefore it will be useful to summarize what we have so far examined, in terms of the shift in linguistic representation and expression of the concepts of motion.

First, we have often noticed that change of some property (distance, time, velocity) involves the term *increment*. This means the change in the state or magnitude of that property from a previous state or magnitude. Algebraically, for a finite increment or change, which is itself a certain magnitude, we adopt the symbol Δ ("delta"). But operationally, we may also express this change as the difference in magnitude from one state to another, so that for a change in velocity Δv, we may also write $(v_2 - v_1)$. In talking about instantaneous speed or velocity at a point, we saw that there are *two* ways of talking about this. One talks of infinitesimal change of state, and the other of a change of state (or magnitude) as small as one wishes to make it, *approaching a limit*. The line of distinction between nothing and something is maintained in both expressions, but as it turns out, more clearly in the latter. Thus, when a change is taken as small as one wishes, we take it as approaching a limit, 0, and write (for example, in the case of time intervals, or increments of time taken as small as one wishes) $\lim_{\Delta t \to 0}$, as we have seen. We also saw that average speed or velocity, represented by $\bar{v}$, through some finite period of time t, is different from instantaneous velocity, through some increment or change in t taken as small as one wishes; so that where average velocity would be given by $v = s/t$, where s would be the distance $(s_2 - s_1)$, and t the time interval $(t_2 - t_1)$, and our equation would read $v = (s_2 - s_1)/(t_2 - t_1)$. For instantaneous velocity, at some given point, we would reformulate the expression for the intervals or increments Δs and Δt, as Δt approached a limit. For instantaneous velocity, v, our equation would then read $v = \lim_{\Delta t \to 0} (\Delta s/\Delta t)$.

But this is for a given instantaneous velocity, which if it remained the same from one instant to the next would give us a uniform motion or uniform velocity. Our conceptual problems, however, had much to do with changes in velocity, or changes in instantaneous velocity from one instant to the next—what we discussed as a uniform acceleration, or a uniformly accelerated motion, when the change in velocity took place so that there were equal increments of velocity in equal increments of time. This change in velocity we may then also express as Δv, and when it is an instantaneous change, in an increment of time Δt approaching a limit, it may be written as $\lim_{\Delta t \to 0} (\Delta v/\Delta t)$, which is then our expression for a uniform or constant acceleration. In both cases, for instantaneous velocity and for instantaneous change in velocity or acceleration, we may use the differential expressions, so that

$$v = \lim_{\Delta t \to 0} \frac{\Delta s}{\Delta t} \quad \text{is replaced by} \quad v = \frac{ds}{dt} \quad \text{and}$$

$$a = \lim_{\Delta t \to 0} \frac{\Delta v}{\Delta t} \quad \text{is replaced by} \quad a = \frac{dv}{dt}$$

Let us see how, in this algebraic way, we may derive Galileo's Theorem II, without geometrically conceived aids to reasoning. We need first to algebraize in the modern form of equations certain definitions previously given only verbally or in the older "algebra" of proportions. First, the definition of uniform motion, as equal distances in equal times, may be given as

$$(1) \quad v = \frac{s}{t} \quad \text{(which, in uniform motion, is the same as } \bar{v} = \frac{s}{t}\text{)}$$

Second, we may define constant acceleration in terms of equal changes of velocity in equal times. But since in constant acceleration, *average* and *instantaneous* acceleration are the same, we may write our definition as

$$(2) \quad a = \frac{v_t - v_o}{t} \quad \text{or } v_t = v_o + at$$

where v_o is initial or original velocity at the beginning of interval t, and v_t is the final or terminal velocity at the end of interval t.

Now, by the Mean Speed Theorem, we know that the terminal velocity v_t through a time t will move a body the same distance s in uniformly accelerated motion, as will the mean velocity in uniform motion. The mean velocity may be expressed as

$$(3) \quad \frac{v_o + v_t}{2} \quad \text{which may be rewritten as } v_o + \tfrac{1}{2}(v_t - v_0) = \bar{v}$$

Since $v = s/t$ for uniform motion (1), we may substitute, and obtain

(4) $\frac{s}{t} = v_o + \frac{1}{2}(v_t - v_o)$, which we may rewrite for s as

(5) $$s = v_o t + \tfrac{1}{2}(v_t - v_o)\, t$$

Rewriting our definition of acceleration (2) as $at = (v_t - v_o)$, and substituting in (5), we finally get

(6) $$s = v_o t + \tfrac{1}{2}\,(at)\; t \text{ or } s = v_o t + \tfrac{1}{2}\, at^2$$

and where the initial velocity is zero, or the motion starts from rest, the term $v_o t$ drops out, leaving

(7) $$s = \tfrac{1}{2}at^2$$

Because, in uniformly accelerated motion, or at constant acceleration, a remains constant, and because $\frac{1}{2}$ is a numerical constant in the equation, substituting k for the combined constant $(\frac{1}{2}a)$, we may then get

(8) $$s = kt^2$$

which states the proportionality of distance traversed during uniformly accelerated motion to the square of the time, which is Galileo's Theorem II, rewritten algebraically. In other words, comparing the two notations,

(9) $\frac{HL}{HM} = \frac{AD^2}{AE^2} \equiv s = kt^2$ (where $\equiv$ means "is equivalent to")

Thus, we have derived *algebraically* the equivalent theorem to Galileo's, expressed differently. They are expressions in different languages, and so we may say that both of these languages mirror or express the same relations among entities, but in different ways; in fact, we may say, that these two languages are isomorphic or may be "mapped" on each other.

FORCE, MASS, ACCELERATION: THE DERIVATIVE

Once the dynamics of modern physics replaces the Aristotelian dynamics, the concepts of force, acceleration, and mass become central. Without going into the development of these concepts here, the central notion of inertia permits a reformulation of the Galilean kinematics. The motion of a body no longer depends on a force to sustain it, but only to change it. Thus, unlike Aristotelian dynamics, it is not velocity which is proportional to force, but change of velocity or acceleration. In Newton's formulation of his First Law, this is expressed as: *If a body is not acted on by a net (or unbalanced) force, then if it is at rest, it will remain at rest, and if it is in motion, it will continue in motion at a constant velocity in a straight line* (i.e., without change of direction). A change of motion will then be either a change in speed or a change in direction (or both since velocity is a vector) and will require the action upon the body of a net force. (Two equal and opposite forces may act on a body, but as vectors, they will counteract each other, so that there is no net effect, and the motion of the body will be unchanged.) But then, any force vector, of any magnitude > 0, will effect a change in velocity (speed and/or direction) i.e. an acceleration due to this net force. We may write this as

$$F = ka \tag{10}$$

i.e., Force is proportional to acceleration. With the new concepts of inertia, and of weight and mass, the Aristotelian concept of change of weight with change of velocity is replaced by the concept of a constant *mass,* to which is proportional the *weight* of a body, in a certain gravitational field. Where the earth is taken as the gravitational field, its measure is given by the acceleration produced on bodies falling freely, and for a constant field, this acceleration is constant and is given by the letter g, called the gravitational constant. If we substitute in (10), we see that

$$F = kg \tag{11}$$

which, because k and g are both constant, means that F is constant. Obviously, then, for bodies of whatever weight, a constant force will produce a constant acceleration, so that all bodies will fall with the same acceleration. Contrary to Aristotle's view that heavier bodies would fall faster, then, all bodies under a constant acceleration would fall at the same rate (ideally, in a vacuum, disregarding the different coefficients of friction, which would make for some variation). Thus, in the common experiment in a vacuum jar, a feather and a ball of lead dropped from the same height at the same time reach the bottom of the jar at the same time. But because it takes more force to move a heavier body than a lighter one, in projectile motion—i.e., to change its velocity or direction—the proportionality between force and acceleration is given by the mass of the body moved, a larger mass having greater inertia than a smaller one, but for any given mass, the inertia remaining constant. The force required to overcome this inertia, i.e., to produce a given acceleration, is thus proportional to the mass. For a given acceleration a, the force will be proportional to the mass m, as for a given mass m; the acceleration will be proportional to the force. This is expressed in Newton's second law, which restates (10), giving the constant of proportionality in terms of a constant inertia of a mass m of any given body.

$$F = ma \tag{12}$$

and for bodies of mass m under constant acceleration g due to the action of a constant force F of gravitation, this gives

$$F = mg \tag{13}$$

Substituting g for a, in (7), for bodies falling from rest, we get

$$s = \tfrac{1}{2}gt^2 \tag{14}$$

the equation of motion for terrestrial bodies falling freely from rest. For instantaneous change of velocity or instantaneous acceleration, we had $a = dv/dt$, so that for the instantaneous acceleration due to gravity, we may rewrite (13) replacing g, or (12) replacing a in the general case as

$$F = m\frac{dv}{dt} \tag{15}$$

Now we introduce one more notion, and a new notation. Since the instantaneous velocity is the limit approached as the increment in time Δt approaches zero, the relation between distance and time, in the expression $v = ds/dt$ which gives this instantaneous change of distance or space traversed at $\Delta t \rightarrow 0$, is given in Galileo's Theorem II, or in our equation $s = kt^2$ (8). Where distance in one dimension, or along a straight path is given by the x-coordinate, $\lim_{\Delta t \rightarrow 0} (\Delta x/\Delta t)$ or dx/dt replaces ds/dt, and the change in x with respect to t where x is a *function* of t [$x = f(t)$] is given by Table I (p. 461), namely, $x = t^2$, then the expression dx/dt is called the derivative of the function, or the derivative of x with respect to t, where $x = t^2$. The derivative of x with respect to t turns out to be, by computation according to the definition, $2x$, where the coefficient 2 remains constant for all values of x and t (expressing the constant proportion $s = kt^2$ for all values of s and t). We have seen, earlier, that arithmetically, this is equal to the *differences between the differences between* the squares, in Table I. This is called the first derivative of x with respect to t. Let us interpret this notation, and this notion of derivative, physically. In uniform motion, at constant velocity, the ratio of change in distance traversed to change in time remains constant. In one unit of time, one unit of distance will be traversed, and in two units of time, two units of distance, and so on. Thus, in accordance with our definition (equal spaces in equal times) the ratio will remain constant. The rate of *change of this ratio* (of change in distance to change in time) will be *zero*. The derivative of x with respect to y will also be zero, or for uniform motion at constant velocity, $dx/dt = 0$. In general, it can be shown, by the definition of *derivative,* that the derivative of a constant ratio of some value with respect to another (or, for short, the derivative of a *constant*) is always zero. We may then suspect that, in general, the derivative expresses a rate of change in the ratio between two changing values. If, where the ratio is constant, the derivative is zero, we might suspect that when this ratio changes, the derivative is some value greater than zero, in some proportion to the rate of change of the ratio. In uniformly accelerated motion, the velocity changes at a constant rate in accordance with our definition (equal increments of velocity in equal times), and we have seen that this rate may be expressed as a proportion between distances and times, namely $s = kt^2$. Thus, for the first unit of time we have a unit distance, but for the second unit of time we have the square of this second unit as our distance, so that the ratio changes as $1/1$, $4/2$, $9/3$ . . . or at the uniform *rate* of change represented by the progression 1, 2, 3. . . . The coefficient of x, in this derivative $dx/dt = 2x$, for uniformly accelerated motion may be seen to be the exponent in the proportion between x and t, where $x = kt^2$. Thus, the derivative expresses the rate of change of the ratio of x to t at the *limit,* with a positive value > 0 where the rate of change is not zero. But as we have seen that in uniformly accelerated motion, the *ratio* between distances and times changes; we can now show that the *ratio* between velocities and times remains constant, that is, the acceleration is constant. The definition gives us this (equal increments of velocity in equal times). Thus, the rate of change of the ratio of velocity with respect to time will be zero, and thus the derivative of v with respect to t will be $dv/dt = 0$ for uniformly accelerated motion, or for constant acceleration. But because instantaneous velocity is defined as *the instantaneous rate of change of distance with respect to time,* the rate of change of velocity (by substituting the definition) becomes the (instantaneous) rate of change of the (instantaneous) rate of change of distance with respect to time. This is the *second* derivative of x with respect to t, and is written d^2x/dt^2. Now we may see that whereas, for uniformly accelerated motion, the first derivative is $dx/dt = 2x$, the second derivative is $d^2x/dt = 0$ which is the equivalent expression, in terms of *distance* with respect to time, for $dv/dt = 0$, in terms of *velocity* with respect to time. Substituting, now, because acceleration is defined as rate of change of velocity,

$$a = \frac{dv}{dt} = \frac{d^2x}{dt^2} \tag{16}$$

and substituting again in (11), we get the form in which Newton's Second Law sometimes appears:

$$(17) \qquad F = m\frac{d^2x}{dt^2}$$

[or sometimes $\vec{F} = m(d^2\vec{x}/dt^2)$ to indicate that as a second derivative, representing change in velocity, which is a vector, x has direction, as F has direction.]

This is familiar to most students, from first-year physics or first-year calculus. It is available in fuller and more formal presentation in any introductory textbook, and the student adopts the language as his own with familiarity after little effort. But notice what has happened here. The purpose of presenting (or *re*-presenting) this "manner of speaking" here is to show that the physical analysis of motion, including all the definitions and theorems painfully reached over the centuries, now takes place in a completely algebraic context, once the concepts find their expression in this new language. The algebra is a formal game without physical significance until the physical concepts are clearly interpreted in this language. The action is mutual. The calculus develops as an instrument of physical analysis; but, then, physical analysis itself becomes transformed by the availability of the power of this language. (It might be added that the development of the concept of the *limit,* in mathematics, is as complex and great an achievement as the development of the physical concepts of motion, though it is simply taken for granted in this account.) In the economical calculating device of the derivative, and of equations using differential expressions such as the ones we examined here, complex relations are expressed with elegance and economy, and the effects are not only aesthetic (for they are surely that) but conceptually clarifying. What is more, they liberate the intellectual energy of the scientist, making calculation swift and precise and permitting the inquiry into phenomena of a complexity unmanageable in the older languages. The very concept of motion, still bound to the experience of motion which we all acquire, is now refined in such a way that this experience itself becomes infinitely richer in scope, more clearly ordered in thought, and significant with respect to domains that were hitherto unexpected. For now we not only *have* the range of ordinary commonsense experience of motion, but we begin to dominate it, by predictions of great accuracy and by the control over the phenomena of motion which underlie much of our technology. We are no longer the passive experiencers of motion, but makers of motion, rational fabricators of a wider experience. We not only order the experience of motion, as passive observers, we produce a new environment of experience under our control and suited to our needs. The rational analysis of concepts thus directly affects the use of concepts, in that use discussed in Chapter 2 in considering science and human survival.

APPENDIX **B** *Appendix to Chapter 4*

THE GROWTH OF SCIENCE: Some Developments in Greek Science After Plato and Aristotle

PLATO AND HIS STUDENT Aristotle represent major philosophic and scientific syntheses of the achievements of several generations of observers, theorizers, craftsmen, and discoverers, not only in Greece and the Greek cities of Ionia, Sicily, and Italy, but also in Egypt, Babylonia, and other ancient centers of scientific thought and technological advance. The schools which they founded—Plato's *Academy* and Aristotle's *Lyceum*—which we have characterized as research institutes, inherited a complex and vital scientific-philosophical tradition. Some of the developments in scientific thought are given here to suggest the vitality of the spirit of inquiry and of criticism which characterized the successors of Plato and Aristotle; and to suggest the close interplay between scientific and philosophical considerations which typified the research and theorizing of the scientists of antiquity.

MODELS OF THE UNIVERSE: ASTRONOMY AND THE STRUCTURE OF THE HEAVENS

One of the central ideas in the growth of scientific thought is that concerning the astronomical model of the universe which the Greeks conceived. It would be more accurate to say astronomical *models,* because there were several, all of which repudiated to one degree or another the earlier mythical accounts of heavenly bodies. Astronomy as an observational science concerned with charting the positions and motions of the sun, moon, stars, and planets goes back to dim antiquity, and the refinement of such observation in the ancient cultures of Egypt, Babylonia, China, and among the Maya and Aztecs in America is remarkable. But observations do not yet constitute a theory which explains or orders these observations according to laws or by means of a model.

What concerns us here is the sort of explanatory model which Platonic and Aristotelian astronomical theories proposed. (How this model was interpreted within the Aristotelian framework of motion of bodies in space is dealt with in particular in Appendix A.)

The Ionian nature philosophers had already considered in their cosmological theories how the appearances of the sun, moon, and stars could be accounted for within their various physical theories. The main contribution here was to consider the heavenly bodies as physical bodies, and in particular, as made up of one of the four elements which constituted all things—in this case, fire. Anaxagoras went further, in giving a physical interpretation of heavenly phenomena, in conceiving of the sun and of the heavenly bodies as solid physical bodies—perhaps by inference from observing a large meteor which had fallen at Aegospotami—and talking of them as "flaming stones." This teaching was regarded as impious by the Athenians, in whose religious and theological considerations the heavenly bodies were considered divine entities, and not merely physical. Anaxagoras' impiety almost cost him his life, and he was banished from Athens. A half century later, when Socrates was put to death by the Athenians for alleged impiety, part of his defense consisted in disclaiming views such as those of Anaxagoras concerning the physical nature of heavenly bodies. We may infer that although such physicalist views were acceptable and common in certain circumstances, in the Athens of Socrates, and of Plato and Aristotle after him, such views ran counter to strongly held beliefs and were regarded as dangerously atheistic.

But there was, apart from this question of *what* constituted the sun, moon and stars, the question of how their apparent motions could be explained. In one sense, this could be taken as a purely geometrical problem, because the considerations could be reduced or abstracted to those concerning only position and change of position in space. The stars lent themselves to this sort of abstraction very neatly, appearing so much like the point particles with which Pythagorean mathematics was already familiar. The sun and the moon, being larger and involving such phenomena as the phases of the moon and lunar and solar eclipses, provided additional problems. Anaxagoras had already provided an account of lunar eclipses in terms of the earth's shadow, which the Pythagoreans accepted and which served then (as it still does in all of our elementary science courses) as evidence for the sphericity of the earth. The Pythagoreans added a still more advanced notion, derived in part from mathematical considerations in explaining the motions of the heavenly bodies, and in part from religious or theological considerations: namely, that the earth, which was spherical, rotated on its axis and that it revolved in a circular orbit about a central point in the universe.[1]

[1] This central point was the holy "central fire" or the so-called hearth of the universe, watchtower of Zeus, or mother of the gods (among other like names). Fire was regarded as the purest of the elements, and its central place was therefore

The Pythagoreans, thus, did not attribute central position to the earth, which they considered to be in motion, both rotating and orbiting. The nine heavenly bodies also moved in circular orbits about this central fire at different distances, these distances arranged according to the harmonic ratios which the Pythagoreans had discovered in their studies of acoustics. The Pythagorean arrangement (perhaps because 10 was a magic and religiously significant number in the Pythagorean system of belief,[2] perhaps for ex-

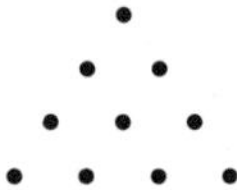

Fig. J The Tetractys of Decad

planatory reasons in accounting for eclipses) included the so-called *counter-earth* as the tenth body revolving about the central fire. This moved along with the earth but was invisible, facing always the presumably uninhabited hemisphere on the "other side of the sphere." This counterearth was the nearest to the central fire. The earth came next, followed by the moon, sun, and the then known five planets. Outermost was the sphere of the fixed stars, making a total of ten orbital spheres. It was the interrelated motions of these spheres that accounted for the apparent motions of the heavenly bodies.

The important conceptual feature of the Pythagorean scheme was one which developed from the mathematical and aesthetic considerations of this philosophical view. According to the Pythagoreans, as we have seen, all was number, and number meant rational order and harmony. This went so far as the speculation that the distances between the spheres were in harmonic ratios, so that the motion of the spheres produced harmonic "tones," the so-called music of the spheres. Now the most mathematically perfect and pleasing conception of the motion and the configuration of these spheres, in the Pythagorean view, was one which conformed to the sense of regularity and symmetry, of perfect well-ordering, which always played

---

a function of its purity or sanctity. This notion of the centrality of the noblest or purest or most important of the elements has various sources—social, religious, biological—and it was destined to play a major role in astronomical concept formation up to the seventeenth century.

[2] As a mystery cult, the Pythagorean brotherhood invested numbers and number properties with all sorts of powers. The sum of the first four integers (1, 2, 3, 4, 10), for example, was given mystical significance and was regarded as having sacred power, because it represented the totality of "points" needed to construct a world (generating lines, planes and solids with 2, 3 and 4, 1 being the generator of number). This sacred number 10 was represented as an equilateral triangle with a base of four points— the so called Tetractys of the Decad (10)—and the Pythagoreans swore their most binding oaths by it.

such a large role in these conceptions. The motion was therefore *uniform,* not sometimes fast and sometimes slow; the spheres were "perfect" circles rather than some more "irregular" and less symmetrical form. This requirement of uniform motion and "perfect" circles was not a requirement made by the observational data, but rather a hypothesis based on mathematical and aesthetic intuitions and deeply grounded religious beliefs. The role of the circle in human conception, as representing the perfect or the god-like, is very ancient and widespread, and its hold on the human imagination is so strong that more than mere convention or tradition is needed to account for it. In any case, this model of geometric circularity introduced by the Pythagoreans had a profound influence on Plato, who modeled his geometry on that of the Pythagoreans.

It was a student of Plato, Eudoxus, who further developed this model of concentric spheres and made a major addition to the original notion; this, because of the disturbing *irregularity* (and therefore apparent imperfection) of the motions of the planets. The planets, as we know, are not so-called fixed stars and the very term *fixed stars* distinguishes the (relatively) stable positional relations of these stars *to each other,* which we recognize in the configurations we call constellations. The planets were in fact called planets because they wandered—the word *planet* meaning *wanderer* in Greek. Indeed, the word means something less innocuous in another context; it means *vagabond* or *tramp.* One interpreter, Benjamin Farrington, even has it that the attempt to "fix" or regularize these "wanderings" in the heavenly sphere was a projection of a contemporary social problem in Greece, that of vagabondage, which Plato's contemporary Isocrates had studied. Isocrates proposed solving the problem of vagabondage and beggary by forcibly enlisting these "irregulars" into the army and using them to fight the Persians. Whether or not this attempt at social order parallels the contemporary interest in making "regulars" out of the planets or whether all of these parallel interests expressed a deeper concern for order in Greek life, the astronomical-geometrical problem of accounting for these irregular wanderers in terms of perfectly uniform and circular motion remained. Eudoxus resolved it by elaborating a theory of concentric spheres with *different* axes, different directions, and different rates or periods of rotation. The revolution of a heavenly body was therefore accounted for by its being fixed in position on some (one or more) of these spheres, each sphere being perfectly spherical and moving uniformly, but the combination of these motions accounting for the apparent irregularity of planetary motion. This was a unique feat of hypothetical-geometrical reasoning, and Eudoxus required no less than 26 spheres to account for all the planetary motions and the regular motions of the sun, moon, and stars. It seems clear that Eudoxus proposed this scheme as a mathematical hypothesis, "to save the appearances" as the Greeks were prone to say, for he did not extend this to a physical interpretation of the spheres, in terms of what they were "made of," or what accounted for their motion, or how they were connected to each other. His model of twenty-six spheres was elaborated further by Callippus, to gain accuracy at a cost of additional complexity, and seven more spheres were added. When Aristotle got through with a further elaboration, he ended up with fifty-five concentric spheres. But it is Aristotle's considerations that are of special interest here. He did not need the additional spheres to refine the account of the apparent motions, but rather to establish a coherent explanatory *physical* model of the interconnections among the spheres thus far adduced. Thus, spheres were connected by spheres, in that complex construction which found its final form in Ptolemy's "Great Mathematical Syntax of Astronomy" (known to us more familiarly by the Arabic name *Almagest*) which served as the scientific model of astronomical structure and motion up to the Copernican revolution.

THE ARISTOTELIAN SCHOOL: THEOPHRASTUS, STRATO, AND ALEXANDRIAN SCIENCE

Aristotle's school, the Lyceum, gave rise to a rich development in the sciences and in mathematics. The remarkable fact is that the two great successors of Aristotle in the Lyceum, Theophrastus and Strato, were not only almost as productive and powerful thinkers as Aristotle himself, but in the spirit of scientific criticism, revised some of Aristotle's basic views. In particular, Theophrastus questioned the value of teleological explanation, saying critically, "With regard to the view that all things are for the sake of an end and nothing is in vain, the assignation of ends is in general not easy, as it is usually stated to be," and further, "We must try to set a limit to the assigning of final causes. This is the prerequisite of all scientific inquiry into the universe, that is, into the conditions of existence of real things and their relations with one another." In this tempered and skeptical approach to the use of teleological explanation, Theophrastus showed himself (as he did also in his masterful works on botany, and in the fragment of his study *On Fire*) a keen empirical observer. One recent historian of science calls Theophrastus' botanical studies "the most important products of botanical investigation until well into modern times."[3] Theophrastus' successor as head of the Lyceum, Strato, devoted himself to the study of physical theory, as an "investigator of nature," like the Ionian *Physiologoi*. With Strato, the long-term myth that Greek science had no experimental tradition is finally shattered. There were of course elements of deliberate experimentation, beyond mere observation, earlier, in the Pythagorean studies of the relations of lengths of string to pitch, in Empedocles' early

[3] Marshall Clagett, *Greek Science in Antiquity* (New York: Abelard-Schuman, 1955), p. 52.

experiment to show that air, though invisible, was corporeal. And there is clear evidence of much good controlled experimentation in the Hippocratic medical writings. Similarly, contrary to popular vulgarizations of Greek philosophy and science, both Plato and Aristotle conceived of their theories as accounts of observed phenomena, which would explain them coherently. Thus, the charge that their theories were somehow "unscientific," that they were sheer *a priori* speculations, or "metaphysical dogmas," is one which assumes that the true scientific enlightenment has finally come in our time and that the Greeks neither observed nor experimented but simply "speculated." Still, Strato may be said to be an experimentalist *par excellence,* to the point of constructing experimental apparatus specifically concerned to give evidence with respect to a hypothesis (namely, that there is a discontinuous vacuum). His report on the experiment, cited by another great scientist of antiquity, Hero of Alexandria, shows the astuteness of Strato's experimental sense.

With the rise of the Macedonian empires of the Ptolemies in Egypt, after the death of Alexander the Great, the great inheritors of the Aristotelian tradition shifted their center to the new scientific institute established in Alexandria—the famous Alexandrian Museum—and the continuity of Greek scientific thought was preserved under the patronage of the Ptolemies. Although this institute degenerated after a while, under the influence of mystical and magical functions assigned to the priests and scientists, in support of the state religion (an invented state theology centered around a deliberately manufactured god, called *Serapis*), the first centuries of the Museum's achievements are enough to mark it as one of the major organizations of scientific thought. In mechanics—the study of moving bodies and of the action of forces on bodies which plays the central role in the development of physics—in medicine, in astronomy, in engineering, and in mathematics, pure and applied, in geography, and in the study of grammar the Museum of Alexandria organized scientific research of the most fundamental importance.

It was here that the Greek mathematical tradition, inherited from Plato's Academy and from the work of such followers of Aristotle as Eudemus (who undertook to write a history of mathematics), reached its full flowering. Here Euclid put together that model of Greek rational thought, the *Elements,* which has been characterized as the greatest scientific textbook in history. Here Archimedes, a generation or so later, wrote on the measurement of the angular diameter of the sun, calculated approximations of the value of π, and of the areas and volumes of curved surfaces and spheres, invented the science of hydrostatics, and in general showed the application of mathematical analysis to physics in such a way that he may be considered the founder of mathematical physics. In his application of the method of "exhaustion," he introduced a technique which in essence is that of integration in the calculus. He was noted also for his mechanical inventions and as a military engineer. In Alexandria too, Apollonius of Perga wrote the basic treatise *On Conic Sections,* introducing the geometrical analysis of the ellipse, the parabola, and the hyperbola. The mechanical applications of all this mathematical analysis gave rise to a theoretical mechanics, in Archimedes' work on the lever and the principles of statics (dealing with bodies or masses or forces in equilibrium or at rest), and in the comprehensive work *Mechanics* by Hero of Alexandria. Hero describes the principles of the five simple machines—the wheel and axle, the lever, the pulley, the wedge, and the screw—reducing them all to the principle we learn in elementary physics concerning the inverse proposition of force to distance in moving a given weight by means of a machine.

The method of demonstration which Archimedes and Hero use is a classic one in science: a complex problem is *reduced* by analysis to its elements, each of which presents a soluble, or an already solved problem, or represents a postulate or axiom of the system. The first approaches to the axiomatic method, in which theorems are derived by rules of inference from axioms or postulates and from already proved theorems, are here applied to problems of theoretical and applied mechanical physics. The revolutionary nature of this innovation was not appreciated fully until the late medieval period, when physicists and "calculators" turned to Archimedean principles and techniques of mathematical analysis to replace the unwieldy qualitative mechanics of the Aristotelians.

Alexandrian astronomy arrived at a most significant alternative to the Eudoxian-Aristotelian model of concentric spheres with the earth at the center. Aristotle had rejected the Pythagorean idea of the earth revolving about a central fire as, in his words, "not seeking for theories and causes to account for observed facts, but rather forcing their observations and trying to accommodate them to certain theories and opinions of their own." (*On the Heavens,* Bk. II, 293^{a} 25–28.) This is an interesting and significant remark, for it brings into focus the uncommonsensical character of the notion of terrestrial motion. After all, what we observe is the motion of the heavenly bodies, in our ordinary framework which still talks of the sun rising in the morning and setting at night. Nevertheless, among the alternative hypothetical models in Aristotle's own time was one devised by a student of Plato, Heraclides of Pontus. Although it retained the centrality of the earth, it had the earth rotate on its axis to account for the rising and setting of sun and stars. But more interesting still, it had two of the planets, Mercury and Venus, the so-called inferior planets closest to the sun, revolving about the sun, in a modified heliocentrism. A generation later, the Alexandrian astronomer, Aristarchus of Samos proposed a completely heliocentric model, thus foreshadowing the Copernican system by almost twenty centuries. In Archimedes' account of Aristarchus' views, he tells us that in this model, both the sun at the center and the sphere of the fixed stars, at the outermost perimeter of the universe, are at rest and that the earth revolves about the sun. To account for the lack of parallactic displacement of the fixed stars (by then available measurement—this parallax was not observed until the nineteenth century, and Copernicus did not have it to go on as an argument for earthly motion in an orbit) Aristarchus argued that the sphere of the fixed stars was so far away that no parallax is noticeable—an ingenious argument, which vastly extended the distance at which the fixed stars were supposed to be.

Aristarchus' proposal remained an isolated one, however, and as far as we know, only one other astronomer of antiquity, the Babylonian Seleucus, who lived a century later, supported Aristarchus' heliocentric hypothesis, and expanded on it, taking it not merely as a mathematical hypothesis but also as a physical conjecture.

It is an indication of the character of abstract rationalism in Greek thought that the constructions of thought could be thus separated from the considerations of perception and practical belief. But we have also seen (in Chapter 4) that in Platonism the rational objects of thought and the mathematical constructs were taken to be more eminently real than their perceptual or physical appearances. Along with the penchant for close observation and empirical study exhibited in much of Greek science, e.g., in the biological works of Aristotle and his successors and in the medical treatises of the Hippocratic school, there yet remained evidences of a distaste for practical application or for the value of physical experiment. Archimedes, renowned for his great ingenuity in mechanical invention and in engineering, as well as for his theoretical work in geometry and in statics, nevertheless disdained to write a textbook on engineering, as a subject unworthy of scientific treatment.

The Alexandrian school produced, as we have seen, many innovations and discoveries in a wide range of sciences. In addition to the fields we have mentioned, the work in medicine and anatomy, culminating in the contributions of Galen at the end of the first century A.D., the geography of Strabo, at the end of the first century B.C., and the grammatical studies of Dionysius of Thrace in the first century B.C. all mark the scope of Alexandrian science.

These and many more were the innovations and scientific discoveries that the Alexandrian school produced. In effect, the major conceptual formulations of an earlier period, in the work of Plato and Aristotle and their schools, were elaborated, interpreted, and brought to bear on specific scientific problems. Nor was this merely a matter of elaboration and extension, as we have seen. Conceptual alternatives were tried out; abstract thought experiments, hypotheses, models were developed; the flowering of the Greek genius for geometry found its outlet not only in the rigorous development of methods of proof and demonstration, of high sophistication, but also in applications to mechanics, to engineering, and to the invention of such ingenious machines, as Ctesibius' water clock. The rationalization of the physical world picture proceeded by leaps and bounds, with periods of rapid and explosive development. But the rate of scientific, theoretical progress was not even, nor were the conditions of scientific growth always optimal. Local superstition, narrow religiosity, and the opportunist use of science as a wonder-working and awe-inspiring handmaiden of theology and of state policy and ideology often served to blunt the critical edge of scientific thought. A great scientist like Archimedes was killed in war, during the Roman seige of his home city, Syracuse. The ordinary grey fortunes of history provided anything but a smooth and uninterrupted foundation for the growth of scientific thought. Yet in periods of high prosperity and great culture, the schools and research institutes flourished, the Academy lasting some 900 years, the Lyceum some 600. The great center at Alexandria was disrupted several times by the persecution of the Greek scholars by Ptolemy IX (reigned 146–117 B.C.), which resulted in the dispersion of the scientific heirs of Plato and Aristotle to new centers of learning, east and west; then by a great fire in 47 B.C. which destroyed the library (which was later reconstituted); and finally by the destruction of the Museum, and the burning of the library by the Mohammedan general Amrou in 640 A.D. A century before, the emperor Justinian had closed the Platonic Academy in Athens (529 A.D.). The great collection of the library at Alexandria, estimated at some 700,000 volumes, was lost forever, and the reconstruction of classical learning and science remained the task of countless thinkers, translators, and scribes: during the Arabic and Jewish renaissance of the eighth through eleventh centuries (including the centers of learning and science in Persia), during the early Christian Middle Ages (in the Benedictine monasteries, and later in the great university centers and cathedral schools in Paris, Oxford, Bologna, Padua), and finally in that glorious humanistic renaissance of the sixteenth and seventeenth centuries, which looked back to the Greek models of reason and order as the foundation on which to reconstruct their own ideal world view.

APPENDIX C

LOGICAL NOTATION

ELEMENTARY NOTATIONS

THE REPRESENTATION of the form of propositions or statements and of arguments, in the notation of symbolic logic, utilizes alphabetic symbols for variables and constants, and special symbols for logical connectives.

Individual constants are represented by the lower-case letters at the beginning of the alphabet ($a, b, c \ldots$). Individual variables are represented by the lower-case letters at the end of the alphabet (x, y, z).

Predication is represented, in the functional notation borrowed from mathematics, by capital letters which represent predicate variables and constants; and the terms which take the predicates—the individual constants and variables—are placed within parentheses. Thus, the form of the predicate statement *Aristotle is Greek,* which assigns the property *Greek* to the individual Aristotle, is written as $G(a)$. The capital letters P, Q, R are generally used as predicate variables. Thus, a general expression assigning a predicate variable to an individual variable would appear as a functional expression in mathematics, e.g., $P(x)$ (read "P of x" or sometimes simply "Px"). An interpretation of predicates as classes or sets gives the alternative notation of class membership given in Chapter 7 (pp. 155 ff.). Thus, $P(x)$ would be interpreted as $x \in P$, or as "x is a member of the class or set P."

Statements or propositions, e.g., *The table is brown* or *The second door on the right leads to the attic,* are represented by capital letters, and again the early letters in the alphabet ordinarily stand for constants. $P, Q, R,$ and S ordinarily stand for variables. These are so-called atomic statements. Statements formed by compounding or connecting atomic statements are called "compound" or "molecular statements." The statement *The table is brown and the second door on the right leads to the attic* is such a molecular statement, connected by the conjunction *and*. The statement connectives in logic derive from the connectives in natural language but are explicitly defined by means of truth tables, because the concern with statements in logic is with their truth values. The main logical statement connectives (or "logical connectives," for short) are roughly equivalent to the connectives: *and, or* (or *either–or*), *if–then, if and only if,* in ordinary speech. But the exact sense of the connectives rests in their truth-functional definition. For example, the conjunction of the propositions *P* and *Q*—i.e., the compound statement *Aristotle is Greek and the table is brown*—is a true statement as a whole, only if the atomic statements *Aristotle is Greek* and *The table is brown* are both true, and is false if either one or both of the atomic statements is false. In this sense, the negation of a statement, which changes its truth value, is also regarded as a logical connective. That is to say, the prefix *not* before a statement makes a true statement into a false statement and vice versa. Thus, if the statement *Aristotle is Greek* is true, then the statement *It is not the case that Aristotle is Greek* (or *Aristotle is not Greek*) is false.

The representation of truth-functional connectives in symbolic logic is as follows:

1. Negation: "$\sim$" (or *tilde*) so that "$\sim P$" is read "not-*P*."
2. Conjunction: " $\cdot$ ", so that "$P \cdot Q$" is read "*P* and *Q*."
3. Alternation: "$\vee$" (or *vel*), so that "$P \vee Q$" is read "*P* or *Q*."
4. Material Implication: "$\supset$" (or *horseshoe*); (sometimes given as "$\rightarrow$", as in this text), so that "$P \supset Q$" is read, "If *P* then *Q*," or sometimes (to avoid the confusion of ordinary usage with the special logical definition) "*P* horseshoe *Q*." (This is not to be confused with the similar set-theoretical notation for class inclusion.)
5. Equivalence: "$\equiv$" or sometimes "$\leftrightarrow$" to indicate that this is a case in which the material implication connective holds both ways, i.e., for "$P \leftrightarrow Q$," we may write "$(P \rightarrow Q) \cdot (Q \rightarrow P)$," or abbreviating as a "biconditional," "$P \leftrightarrow Q$," which is read "*P* if and only if *Q*" (or "*Q* if and only if *P*"). (Note that parentheses are used here to separate the two compound statements "$P \rightarrow Q$" and "$Q \rightarrow P$," so that one will not mistakenly take "$Q \cdot Q$" as a separate compound statement.)

The truth table definitions of these connectives are as follows:

(1) *Negation*

P	P
T	F
F	T

(2) *Conjunction*

P	Q	$P \cdot Q$
T	T	T
T	F	F
F	T	F
F	F	F

(3) *Alternation*

P	Q	$P \vee Q$
T	T	T
T	F	T
F	T	T
F	F	F

(4) *Material Implication*

P	Q	$P \rightarrow Q$
T	T	T
T	F	F
F	T	T
F	F	T

(5) *Equivalence*

P	Q	$P \leftrightarrow Q$
T	T	T
T	F	F
F	T	F
F	F	T

It may be seen that the truth table for the compound connective "$\sim(P \cdot \sim Q)$" is the same as the one for "$P \rightarrow Q$." In such a case, tables (4) and (6) are truth-functionally equivalent; or we may say that the connective "$\rightarrow$" may be defined in terms of the connectives "$\sim$" and "$\cdot$" (and thus eliminated if we wish).

(6) *Material implication in terms of negation and conjunction*

P	Q	$\sim Q$	$(P \cdot \sim Q)$	$\sim (P \cdot \sim Q)$
T	T	F	F	T
T	F	T	T	F
F	T	F	F	T
F	F	T	F	T

This table [(4) or (6), because these are truth-functionally equivalent] is especially important in the discussion of rules of inference. A fundamental rule of inference, the so-called *Modus Ponens* rule, is given by this table, which states in effect, where *P* is a premise or the antecedent of an argument and *Q* is the conclusion (as in "If *P*, then *Q*"), that a true premise cannot yield a false conclusion. This is, in effect, a definition of valid inference and is exhibited in the table. The only instance in which the last column of the truth table shows an F is the one in which *P* is true and *Q* is false.

QUANTIFICATION

The representation of the traditional *all, some, none* prefixes in logic is replaced in symbolic logic by *quantifiers,* i.e., operators placed at the beginning of a quantified statement, which indicate for what range of the variables the statement holds. Thus, if by the statement *Bees are insects* I mean *Anything which is a bee is an insect,* or *All bees are insects,* then the *universal quantifier* is placed at the head of the expression, and "binds" all instances of that variable in the expression. For example, if I intend to say *For anything* x, if x *is a bee then it is an insect,* I would write $(x)[B(x) \rightarrow I(x)]$.

If, on the other hand, I want to assert that no bee is an insect, or equivalently, that for anything x which is a bee, it is not an insect, I would write $(x)[B(x) \rightarrow \sim I(x)]$. Thus, the symbol "$(x)$" placed at the head of a statement, with the whole statement in parentheses, is the universal quantifier, which binds all occurrences of x within the parenthesized statement.

If I want to state that there is some bee which is an insect, or at least one, the quantifier is an *existential quantifier,* represented symbolically by a backwards E, thus "$(\exists x)$." This is read, *For some* x, or, *There is at least one* x *such that. . . .* The statement *Some human beings are females* would thus be represented: $(\exists x)[H(x) \cdot \mathrm{F(x)}]$, or *There is at least one* x *such that* x *is a human being and a female.*

This note can do no more than introduce the notation. Any further discussion must enter more fully into the matters of logic and quantification theory. There are several excellent introductory texts which treat these matters in a clear and detailed way. These should be consulted for further discussion. We may recommend the following few among many:

W. V. Quine, *Methods of Logic,* New York: Holt, 1950.
P. Suppes, *Introductory Logic,* New York: Van Nostrand, 1957.
I. Copi, *Symbolic Logic,* New York: Macmillan, 1954.

Bibliographical Notes

BIBLIOGRAPHICAL NOTES

GENERAL WORKS IN PHILOSOPHY OF SCIENCE

THIS AND SUCCEEDING bibliographical notes offer references to selected books and periodical articles which pertain to the subject matter of each chapter. At the outset, however, it will be useful to mention some of the main general works in philosophy of science, almost all of which deal substantively with the whole range of issues presented in this work.

Among the older works (roughly, those antedating World War II) are A. C. Benjamin, *An Introduction to the Philosophy of Science* (New York: Macmillan, 1937); C. D. Broad, *Scientific Thought* (New York: Humanities Press, 1952); M. R. Cohen, *Reason and Nature* (New York: Harcourt, Brace, 1931); A. G. Ramsperger, *Philosophies of Science* (New York: F. S. Crofts, 1942); B. Russell, *The Scientific Outlook* (New York: Norton, 1962); M. Schlick, *Philosophy of Nature* (New York: Philosophical Library, 1949); W. H. Werkmeister, *A Philosophy of Science* (New York: Harper & Row, 1940). The classical and long-lived text by M. R. Cohen and E. Nagel, *An Introduction to Logic and Scientific Method* devotes Book II (pp. 191–403) to "Applied Logic and Scientific Method," dealing with a wide range of problems. The much older work of Karl Pearson, *The Grammar of Science,* 2nd ed. [London: Dent, 1906 (reissued, 1937)] still offers a vital account from the viewpoint of one of the founders of positivism. Of special value, for its account of laws and theories, is N. R. Campbell, *What Is Science?* [London: Methuen, 1921 (reprinted, New York: Dover, 1952)]. Several of the works of A. N. Whitehead offer a complex and rich introduction to the philosophy of science, especially in terms of its relations to the history of philosophy and to general culture, as well as to the formal disciplines of logic and mathematics and to the physical sciences. Among these are his *The Concept of Nature* (Ann Arbor: University of Michigan Press, 1957); *An Introduction to Mathematics* (New York:

Galaxy, 1958); *Science and the Modern World* (New York: New American Library, 1959); and the more technical work *Foundations of Natural Knowledge* (Cambridge: Cambridge University Press, 1955).

Among the more recent general works are J. Bronowski, *The Common Sense of Science* (Cambridge, Mass.: Harvard University Press, 1953), and *Science and Human Values* (New York: Messner, 1956); C. W. Churchman and R. Ackoff, *Methods of Inquiry* (St. Louis: Educational Publishers, 1950); J. B. Conant, *Science and Common Sense* (New Haven: Yale University Press, 1951); P. Frank, *Philosophy of Science—The Link Between Science and Philosophy* (Englewood Cliffs, N.J.: Prentice-Hall, 1957); C. G. Gillispie, *The Edge of Objectivity* (Princeton, N.J.: Princeton University Press, 1960); D. Hawkins, *The Language of Nature* (San Francisco: Freeman, 1964); A. Kaplan, *The Conduct of Inquiry—Methodology for Behavioral Science* (San Francisco: Chandler, 1964) which, despite its special focus, contains much on general philosophy of science; J. G. Kemeny, *A Philosopher Looks at Science* (Princeton, N.J.: Van Nostrand, 1959), a good elementary text; H. Mehlberg, *The Reach of Science* (Toronto: University of Toronto Press, 1958), notable for its section on measurement and its tough-minded empiricism; E. Nagel, *The Structure of Science* (New York: Harcourt, Brace, 1961), the outcome of many years of intellectual activity in the forefront of contemporary philosophy of science and perhaps the most comprehensive of the recent general works, especially in its treatment of explanation and of the biological and social sciences, and history—a second volume is forthcoming; Leonard K. Nash, *The Nature of the Natural Sciences* (Boston: Little, Brown, 1963), a distinctive and unorthodox treatment, especially rich in references to the natural sciences and to the history of science; F. S. C. Northrop, *The Logic of the Sciences and the Humanities* (New York: Macmillan, 1947); A. Pap, *An Introduction to Philosophy of Science* (New York: The Free Press, 1962), which is the posthumously published work of a leading young American philosopher. It copes most systematically and clearly with the relation of theories of meaning and verification to philosophy of science, and is notable for its sustained analysis of probability and induction, and the notion of causality—an analytic work in the best sense; H. Reichenbach, *Introduction to Scientific Philosophy* (Los Angeles and Berkeley: University of California Press, 1951), a largely nontechnical work on substantive questions in philosophy of science, by one of the most prolific and influential of the "first generation" of contemporary philosophers of science, introducing the distinction between justification and discovery in science; A. D. Ritchie, *Scientific Method* (Paterson, N.J.: Littlefield-Adams, 1960); B. Russell, *Human Knowledge—Its Scope and Limits* (New York: Simon and Schuster, 1948); S. Toulmin, *The Philosophy of Science—An Introduction* (London: Hutchinson's, 1953), and *Foresight and Understanding—An Enquiry into the Aims of Science* (Bloomington,

Ind.: Indiana University Press, 1961); and H. Weyl, *Philosophy of Mathematics and Natural Science* (Princeton, N.J.: Princeton University Press, 1949).

ANTHOLOGIES: READINGS IN THE PHILOSOPHY OF SCIENCE

In the last few years there have appeared a number of anthologies designed to serve as source books or as readings in philosophy of science. These are not always clearly distinguishable from source books in the history of science or in the philosophy of nature. The most important ones are H. Feigl and M. Brodbeck, eds., *Readings in the Philosophy of Science* (New York: Appleton-Century-Crofts, 1953); P. P. Wiener, ed., *Readings in Philosophy of Science* (New York: Scribner's, 1953); E. Madden, ed., *The Structure of Scientific Thought* (Boston: Houghton Mifflin, 1960); A. Danto, and A. Morgenbesser, eds., *Philosophy of Science-Readings* (New York: Meridian, 1960); H. J. Koren, ed., *Readings in the Philosophy of Nature* (Westminster, Md.: The Newman Press, 1961). Material from the history of scientific discovery and experiment, relevant to philosophy of science may be found in J. B. Conant, ed., *Harvard Case Histories in Experimental Science* (Cambridge, Mass.: Harvard University Press, 1950), two volumes; M. Shamos, ed., *Great Experiments in Physics* (New York: Dryden, 1959); G. Schwartz and P. Bishop, eds., *Moments of Discovery* (New York: Basic Books, 1958); J. R. Newman, ed., *The World of Mathematics* (New York: Simon and Schuster, 1956); R. H. Herrnstein and E. G. Boring, eds., *A Source Book in the History of Psychology* (Cambridge, Mass.: Harvard University Press, 1965). A number of illuminating articles are collected in J. R. Newman, ed., *What Is Science?* (New York: Simon and Schuster, 1955), e.g., see those by B. Russell, J. Huxley, Condon, Whittaker. Other recent collections include A. Beiser, ed., *The World of Physics* (New York: McGraw-Hill, 1960); R. Kahl, ed., *Studies in Explanation—A Reader in Philosophy of Science* (Englewood Cliffs, N.J.: Prentice-Hall, 1963), especially broad in its coverage.

SYMPOSIA, COLLOQUIA, AND COLLECTIONS OF CURRENT DISCUSSIONS IN PHILOSOPHY OF SCIENCE

Much of ongoing publication in philosophy of science is in periodicals, such as *Philosophy of Science* (U.S.), *The British Journal for the Philosophy of Science* (England), *Synthese* (Holland), *Voprosi Filozofii* (U.S.S.R.), and in the whole range of philosophical journals here and abroad, as well as occasionally in some of the general scientific and special disciplinary journals, such as *Scientific American, Science, American Scien-*

tist, Psychological Review, (U.S.), *Nature* (England), and *Isis* (on the history of science, U.S.). More recently a significant part of such publication has been collected in special volumes, which publish the proceedings of congresses, symposia, seminars, colloquia, and institutes devoted to topics in philosophy of science, or are offered as *Festschriften* to honor senior contributors to the philosophy of science. Among such publications are the three volumes, *Minnesota Studies in the Philosophy of Science:* Vol. I, H. Feigl and M. Scriven, eds., *The Foundations of Science and the Concepts of Psychology and Psychoanalysis;* Vol. II, H. Feigl, M. Scriven, and G. Maxwell, eds., *Concepts, Theories and the Mind-Body Problem;* Vol. III, H. Feigl and G. Maxwell, eds., *Scientific Explanation, Space and Time.* All three are the results of collaborative research at the Minnesota Center for the Philosophy of Science and are published by the University of Minnesota Press (in 1956, 1958, and 1962, respectively). Also R. Colodny, ed., *Frontiers of Science and Philosophy* (Pittsburgh: Pittsburgh University Press, 1962); B. Baumrin, ed., *Philosophy of Science—The Delaware Seminar* (New York: Interscience, Vol. I, 1962, Vol. II, 1963); M. Wartofsky, ed., *Boston Studies in the Philosophy of Science* (Dordrecht, Holland: Reidel, 1963); R. S. Cohen and M. Wartofsky, eds., *Boston Studies in the Philosophy of Science—Essays in Honor of P. Frank,* Vol. II (New York: Humanities Press, 1965); Vol. III (forthcoming); H. Feigl and G. Maxwell, eds., *Current Issues in the Philosophy of Science* (New York: Holt, 1961); A. Tarski, P. Suppes, and E. Nagel, eds., *Logic, Methodology and Science—Proceedings of the International Congress for Logic, Methodology and Philosophy of Science* (Stanford: Stanford University Press, 1960); *Proceedings of the 1964 International Congress for Logic, Methodology and Philosophy of Science* (Amsterdam: North-Holland Publishing Co., 1966). Among the *Festschriften* (in addition to that for P. Frank) are the important volumes of the Library of Living Philosophers, edited by P. Schilpp, on Albert Einstein, Bertrand Russell, A. N. Whitehead, John Dewey, and C. D. Broad. The latest volume, *The Philosophy of Rudolf Carnap* (La Salle, Ill.: Open Court, 1964), appearing after a long delay, is exceptionally important. So too, it is expected, will be the forthcoming volume on *The Philosophy of Karl Popper* in this series. Two briefer *Festschriften,* one in honor of R. Carnap's seventieth birthday issued as a special issue of the journal *Synthese,* **12,** December 1960 and the other in honor of Karl Popper, M. Bunge, ed., *The Critical Approach in Science and Philosophy* (New York: Macmillan, 1964), add to the discussion of the work of these philosophers of science. Another such volume in honor of Herbert Feigl has just appeared: P. K. Feyerabend and G. Maxwell, eds., *Mind, Matter and Method—Essays in Philosophy and Science in Honor of Herbert Feigl* (Minneapolis: University of Minnesota Press, 1966). No doubt many more such volumes will continue to appear and serve as a major means of publishing contemporary work in philosophy of science.

Additional symposia volumes include the series edited by S. Hook, N.Y.U. Institute of Philosophy Symposia, especially *Determinism and Freedom in the Age of Modern Science; Psychoanalysis, Scientific Method and Philosophy;* and *Dimensions of Mind* (New York: New York University Press, 1958, 1959, 1960, respectively) and P. Frank, ed., *The Validation of Scientific Theories* (New York: Collier Books, 1961).

CHAPTER 1

The question of the relation of science to philosophy is discussed in almost all the listed general works, in one or another way. It has preoccupied philosophers and scientists from the time of Plato and Aristotle (when the distinction was not yet made explicitly, but the problem was nevertheless present) to the rise of contemporary positivist and empiricist philosophy (in which the distinction was attempted as an absolute one). Some relevant discussions on aspects of this question are in the following books: J. Bernal, *The Social Function of Science* (London: Routledge and Kegan Paul, 1949); M. Brodbeck, "The Nature and Function of Philosophy of Science," in H. Feigl and M. Brodbeck, eds., *Readings in the Philosophy of Science* (New York: Appleton-Century-Crofts, 1953); J. B. Conant, *On Understanding Science* (The Terry Lectures) (New Haven: Yale University Press, 1947), and the much expanded and revised treatment, *Science and Common Sense* (New Haven: Yale University Press, 1951); J. Dewey, *Logic: The Theory of Inquiry* (New York: Holt, 1938); H. Dingle, *Through Science to Philosophy* (Oxford: Clarendon, 1937), and *The Scientific Adventure* (New York: Philosophical Library, 1953); P. Duhem, *The Aim and Structure of Physical Theory,* tr. P. Wiener (Princeton, N.J.: Princeton University Press, 1954); H. Feigl, "The Scientific Outlook—Naturalism and Humanism," in H. Feigl and M. Brodbeck, *op. cit.* (an especially cogent brief treatment), and also his "The Philosophy of Science" in R. Schlatter, ed., *Humanistic Scholarship in America* (Englewood Cliffs, N.J.: Prentice-Hall, 1964). Philipp Frank deals with the problem at length and gives its recent historical background in the introductory sections of his *Philosophy of Science—The Link Between Science and Philosophy* (Englewood Cliffs, N.J.: Prentice-Hall, 1957) and especially in his *Modern Science and its Philosophy* (Cambridge, Mass.: Harvard University Press, 1949) and in the essay (reprinted there) "The Origin of the Separation Between Science and Philosophy," *Proceedings of the American Academy of Arts and Sciences,* **80**:115–139 (1952). An older work is J. S. Haldane's *The Sciences and Philosophy* [The Gifford Lectures, University of Glasgow, 1927–28 (London: Hodder, 1929)]. See also R. Oppenheimer, *Science and the Common Understanding* (New York: Simon and Schuster, 1954); and E. Schrödinger,

Science and the Human Temperament (New York: Norton, 1935). Further references on the relation of science to society are in the bibliographical note for Chapter 15. Obviously, C. P. Snow's controversial essay *The Two Cultures and the Scientific Revolution* [The Rede Lecture, Cambridge University (Cambridge: Cambridge University Press, 1961)] belongs here as well.

The separation of science from philosophy, with respect to criteria of meaning and verification, or of testability, is dealt with in A. J. Ayer, *Language Truth and Logic* (London: Gollancz, 1936); H. Reichenbach, *The Rise of Scientific Philosophy* (Los Angeles and Berkeley: University of California Press, 1951); and preoccupies Karl Popper, as the "demarcation question," in many of his writings, including *The Logic of Scientific Discovery* (London: Hutchinson, 1959) and especially in the essay "The Demarcation Between Science and Philosophy," in his *Conjectures and Refutations* (New York: Basic Books, 1962). A systematic treatment of alternative philosophical frameworks and their relation to science is in S. Pepper, *World Hypotheses—A Study in Evidence* (Berkeley: University of California Press, 1942).

CHAPTERS 2–3

The most sustained treatment of science as human activity is perhaps in the works of John Dewey. The thesis is nowhere stated in one piece, but runs through many of his works, in which the relations among habit, intelligence, cognitive knowledge in its dual aspect as theoretical and practical, are explored and framed in Dewey's larger concern with the relation of human experience to the natural world and to society. The principal works here are *Reconstruction in Philosophy* (New York: Holt, 1920), an overview and an introduction to Dewey's major concerns; *Human Nature and Conduct* (New York: Modern Library, 1930); *Logic: The Theory of Inquiry* (New York: Holt, 1939), especially Chapters 3 and 4; and the most thickly textured of these, *Experience and Nature* (New York: Norton, 1925). The collection, edited by J. Ratner, *Intelligence in the Modern World* (New York: Random House, 1939), and the volume *The Philosophy of John Dewey,* in the Library of Living Philosophers, edited by Paul Schilpp (New York: Tudor, 1939) are also important.

Works dealing with knowledge and perception, relevant to the discussion in this chapter, include F. C. Bartlett, *Thinking* (London: Allen and Unwin, 1958); Sir Russell Brain, *The Nature of Experience* (London: Oxford University Press, 1959); H. Dingle, *Science and Human Experience* (London: Williams and Norgate, 1931); J. J. Gibson, *The Perception of the Visual World* (Boston: Houghton Mifflin, 1950); S. Körner, *Conceptual Thinking—A Logical Inquiry* (New York: Dover, 1959), especially Part I,

Chapters 1–7 and Part III, Chapters 25–33; the article by E. C. Tolman and E. Brunswik, "The Organism and the Causal Texture of the Environment," *Psych. Review,* **42**:43–77 (1935) and Tolman's famous article "Cognitive Maps in Rats and Men," *Psych. Review,* **55**:189–208 (1948). An early article by the forerunner of the pragmatist movement, Chauncey Wright, is still significant in this context: "The Evolution of Self-Consciousness," in E. H. Madden, *The Philosophical Writings of Chauncey Wright* (New York: Liberal Arts Press, 1958). The work cited in the text is H. Werner and B. Kaplan, *Symbol Formation—An Organismic-Developmental Approach to Language and the Expression of Thought* (New York: Wiley, 1963), especially Parts I (Theory) and II (Ontogenesis).

Herbert Mead's *Mind, Self and Behavior* (Chicago: University of Chicago Press, 1934) provides a unique philosophical framework for considering the interaction of man with his environment and with other men. Mead represents a view akin to Dewey's interactionism, and both derive from German nineteenth century philosophy, their work relating clearly to Fichte, Hegel, and Schopenhauer, as well as to the influences of Marx and Darwin. The psychological investigation of the activity of perception and the role of cognitive structures as "hypotheses" or "set" in perceptual activity is represented in contemporary work perhaps best by Jerome S. Bruner and his collaborators. Some principal works here are J. Bruner, J. Goodnow, and G. Austin, eds., *A Study of Thinking* (New York: Wiley, 1956); J. Bruner, *On Knowing* (Cambridge, Mass.: Harvard University Press, 1962); and in such articles as J. Bruner and L. Postman, "Symbolic Value as an Organizing Factor in Perception," *Journal of Soc. Psych.,* **27**:203–208 (1948); J. Bruner, "On Perceptual Readiness," in D. C. Beardsley and M. Wertheimer, eds., *Readings in Perception* (Princeton, N.J.: Van Nostrand, 1958); J. Bruner, "The Act of Discovery" and "Learning and Thinking," both in R. C. Anderson and D. P. Ausubel, eds., *Readings in the Psychology of Cognition* (New York: Holt, 1965). An excellent introduction to the psychology of perception of J. Hochberg, *Perception* (Englewood Cliffs, N.J.: Prentice-Hall, 1964).

Related work in developmental psychology is the corpus of writings of J. Piaget. Its relevance here, and much of its philosophical interest rests on the thesis that ontogeny recapitulates phylogeny in concept formation and that the historical evolution of concepts may be traced in the child's process of concept formation (a thesis which Herbert Spencer propounded in the nineteenth century and which has found adherents in contemporary developmental psychology). Among Piaget's numerous works, those of special interest here include *The Language and Thought of the Child* (New York: Meridian, 1955); *The Child's Concept of the World* (New York: Harcourt, Brace, 1929); *The Child's Conception of Physical Causality* (New York: Harcourt, Brace, 1930). Some special studies of animism, relevant here, are Margaret Mead's early "An Investigation of the Thought of Primitive

Children with Special Reference to Animism," *J. R. Anthrop. Inst.*, **62**:173–90 (1932), and the studies by R. W. Russell and W. Dennis, "Studies in Animism, I–IV," *Journal of Genetic Psych.*, 1939–40 and W. Dennis, "Animism and Related Tendencies in Hopi Children," *J. Abn. Soc. Psych.*, **38**:21–36 (1943).

The reconstruction of the life, the society, the art and modes of thought of early man is both a careful science and a speculative art. Relevant works include F. Boas, *The Mind of Primitive Man* (New York: Macmillan, 1938); V. Gordon Childe, *Man Makes Himself* (London: Watts, 1936), and *Social Evolution* (London: Watts, 1951); E. Durkheim, *The Elementary Forms of the Religious Life—A Study in Religious Sociology,* tr. J. W. Swain (London: Allen and Unwin, 1915); and his *De la Division du travail social,* sixth edition (Paris: Alcan, 1932). The work cited in the text, H. Frankfort et al., *Before Philosophy* (originally titled *The Intellectual Adventure of Ancient Man*) (Baltimore: Penguin, 1949) deals with early thought in Egypt, Babylonia, and Greece. Sir James Fraser's classic study in cross-cultural similarities in myth and ritual, *The Golden Bough* (New York: Macmillan, 1922) is available in a one-volume abridgment which makes marvelous in-between reading on subways and street cars. It was reissued as a paperback by Macmillan in 1963. See also Melville Herskovits, *Man and His Works* (New York: Knopf, 1948); Hans Kelsen, *Society and Nature* (London: Routledge and Kegan Paul, 1946); J. Maringer, *The Gods of Prehistoric Man* (New York: Knopf, 1960); Milton Munitz, ed., *Theories of the Universe—From Babylonian Myth to Modern Science* (New York: The Free Press, 1957); J. Needham, *Human Law and the Laws of Nature in China and the West* [Hobhouse Memorial Lecture (London: Oxford University Press, 1951)]; A. R. Radcliffe-Brown, *Structure and Function in Primitive Society—Essays and Addresses* (New York: The Free Press, 1952); Paul Radin, *Primitive Man as a Philosopher* (New York: Appleton, 1927); R. Redfield, *The Primitive World and Its Transformations* (Ithaca, N.Y.: Cornell University Press, 1953); S. L. Washburn, ed., *The Social Life of Early Man* (Chicago: Aldine, 1961). On early art, see G. Weltfish, *The Origins of Art* (Indianapolis: Bobbs-Merrill, 1953); P. Graziosi, *Paleolithic Art* (New York: McGraw-Hill, 1960); and the sumptuously illustrated S. Giedion, *The Eternal Present: The Beginnings of Art,* Bollingen Series XXX·6·1 (New York: Pantheon, 1962).

CHAPTER 4

Discussions of common sense and its relation to science are to be found in many of the introductory general texts listed in the bibliographical note for Chapter 1. One may specially note the discussion in J. Dewey, *Logic: The Theory of Inquiry* (New York: Holt, 1938), especially Chapters 2–4;

E. Nagel, *The Structure of Science* (New York: Harcourt, Brace, 1961), Chapter 1; L. Nash, *The Nature of the Natural Sciences* (Boston: Little, Brown, 1963), Chapters I and II. The writings of Charles Sanders Peirce, the founder of pragmatism, abound in what amounts to a theory of common sense, of a subtle and elaborate sort, related to his evolutionary thought. Two introductory essays here are his "The Fixation of Belief" and "Critical Common-Sensism," in J. Buchler, *The Philosophical Writings of Peirce* (New York: Dover, 1955). Bertrand Russell, in *The Analysis of Matter* (London: Allen and Unwin, 1927), considers this matter in Chapters XV and XVI. An explicit philosophical position based on common sense is developed by the school of Scottish Common-Sense Realists in the eighteenth century (e.g., Thomas Reid's *Essays on the Intellectual Powers of Man* and Dugald Stewart's *The Philosophy of the Active and Moral Powers of Man* and *Elements of the Philosophy of the Human Mind*), and more recently in the common-sensism of G. E. Moore, e.g., his "A Defense of Common Sense" in *Philosophical Papers* (London: Allen and Unwin, 1959). Wittgenstein's philosophy of language, his concern for ordinary use and its relation to "forms of life" exhibits another approach to common sense, by way of the analysis of "ordinary language," e.g., his *Philosophical Investigations* (New York: Macmillan, 1953).

The literature on Greek philosophy and science is vast, and no more can be attempted here than the barest sketch of relevant works. Among more general works on the origins of science and philosophy in Greece are F. M. Cornford, *Principium Sapientiae: The Origins of Greek Philosophic Thought* (Cambridge: Cambridge University Press, 1952) and his earlier *From Religion to Philosophy in Ancient Greece* (New York: Harper Torchbooks, 1957); also his essays in *The Unwritten Philosophy* (Cambridge: Cambridge University Press, 1950) and in *Before and After Socrates* (Cambridge: Cambridge University Press, 1932); E. R. Dodds, *The Greeks and the Irrational* (Berkeley: University of California Press, 1951); H. Frankfort et al, *Before Philosophy—The Intellectual Adventure of Ancient Man* (Baltimore: Penguin, 1949); W. K. Guthrie, *The Greeks and Their Gods* (London: Methuen, 1950) and also his *In the Beginning* (Ithaca: Cornell University Press, 1957); J. Harrison, *Prolegomena to the Study of Greek Religion* (Cambridge: Cambridge University Press, 1922); W. A. Heidel, *The Heroic Age of Science* (Baltimore: Williams and Wilkins, 1933) (an original and important interpretation) and his *Hippocratic Medicine, Its Spirit and Method* (New York: Columbia University Press, 1941); E. H. Hutten, *The Origins of Science* (London: Allen and Unwin, 1962); W. Jaeger, *The Theology of the Early Greek Philosophers* (Oxford: Clarendon, 1947); H. Kelsen, *Society and Nature* (London: Paul, Trench, Trubner, 1946); G. Misch, *The Dawn of Philosophy* (London: Routledge and Kegan Paul, 1950); L. Robin, *Greek Thought and the Origins of the Scientific Spirit* (London: Paul, Trench, Trubner, 1928);

E. Schrödinger, *Nature and the Greeks* (Cambridge: Cambridge University Press, 1954); S. Sambursky, *The Physical World of the Greeks* (New York: Macmillan, 1956) and *The Physical World of Late Antiquity* (New York: Basic Books, 1962); G. de Santillana, *Origins of Scientific Thought* (Chicago: Chicago University Press, 1961); B. Snell, *The Discovery of the Mind—The Greek Origins of European Thought* (Cambridge, Mass.: Harvard University Press, 1953); G. Thomson, *Studies in Ancient Greek Society, II: The First Philosophers* (London: Lawrence & Wishart, 1955). See also the critique by F. M. Cornford, "The Marxist View of Ancient Philosophy," in *The Unwritten Philosophy, op. cit.*

Thomson, like Farrington, whose works we will next list, is a British Marxist scholar who has contributed (e.g., his *Aeschylus in Athens*) much to the understanding of the social context of Greek thought and literature, from the point of view of historical materialism. Benjamin Farrington's work in this area is distinctive and often controversial (see Cornford's critical essay in *The Unwritten Philosophy,* listed previously). He attempts to relate philosophic and scientific thought to the social and political context of ancient Greece. His main works here, all exceptionally readable, are *Science in Antiquity* (London: Oxford University Press, 1936), *Science and Politics in the Ancient World* (London: Allen and Unwin, 1936), *Greek Science,* revised ed. (Baltimore: Penguin, 1961); and *Head and Hand in Ancient Greece* (London: Watts, 1947).

Translations of the extant fragments of the Pre-Socratic philosophers are available in several editions. An earlier one is J. Burnet, *Early Greek Philosophy* (New York: Macmillan, 1930), which contains Burnet's distinctively "positivistic" interpretation. Relatively complete sources are in K. Freeman, *Ancilla to the Pre-Socratic Philosophers* (Oxford: Blackwell, 1952) and in her *Companion to the Pre-Socratic Philosophers* (Oxford: Blackwell, 1953). A handy one-volume collection with interpretation and the Greek texts is G. S. Kirk and J. W. Raven, *The Pre-Socratics* (Cambridge: Cambridge University Press, 1957) and also M. Nahm, *Selections from Early Greek Philosophy* (Appleton-Century-Crofts, 1962). Special studies include C. Bailey, *The Greek Atomists and Epicurus* (Oxford: Clarendon, 1928); J. Beare, *Greek Theories of Elementary Cognition* (Oxford: Clarendon, 1906); D. Greenberg and D. Gershenson, *Anaxagoras* (New York: Blaisdell, 1964), a systematic and critical reconstruction of the ancient sources; H. C. Kahn, *Anaximander and the Origins of Greek Cosmology* (New York: Columbia University Press, 1960); P. Wheelwright, *Heraclitus* (Princeton, N.J.: Princeton University Press, 1959). See also the article by G. S. Kirk, "Natural Change in Heraclitus," *Mind,* **60**:35–42, 1951. Karl Popper, among contemporary philosophers of science, has returned to the pre-Socratics in his much discussed paper "Back to the Pre-Socratics," *Proceedings Aristotelian Soc.,* N.S. **59**:1–24 (1958), reprinted in K. Popper, *Conjecture and Refutations* (New York: Basic

Books, 1962). In this volume see also his discussion of Plato and the Pythagorean problem of the irrational in "The Nature of Philosophical Problems and Their Roots in Science," especially Sections IV–VIII.

Among the many histories of Greek philosophy, the old standby, W. Windelband, *History of Ancient Philosophy* [New York: Dover, 1956 (not to be confused with his two-volume *History of Philosophy*)] still seems one of the best works tracing the development of Greek philosophical thought, as a dialectic of problems and criticisms. Among the classical German histories of philosophy available in translation, E. Zeller, *Outlines of the History of Greek Philosophy* (New York: Meridian, 1955) is very useful. The modern histories include J. Burnet, *Greek Philosophy, I: Thales to Plato* (London: Macmillan, 1914); F. Copleston's *History of Philosophy,* Vol. I (Garden City, N.Y.: Doubleday, 1963); T. Gomperz, *Greek Thinkers* (New York: Scribner, 1912); F. Thilly and L. Wood, *A History of Philosophy* (New York: Holt, 1957); J. H. Randall's distinctive *The Career of Philosophy,* Vol. I (New York: Columbia University Press, 1962) and the relevant portions of the perennial *The Making of the Modern Mind* (Boston: Houghton Mifflin, 1940).

Works on Plato and Aristotle abound, and only a few will be listed here: A. E. Taylor, *Platonism* (New York: Longmans-Green, 1927), and his *Plato, the Man and his Work* (London: Methuen, 1926). Plato's works are available in many selections, and complete in the two-volume edition (New York: Random House, 1937) and in the more recent one-volume edition (at a remarkably reasonable price) by E. Hamilton and H. Cairns (New York: Bollingen, 1961). On Aristotle, see W. D. Ross, *Aristotle* (New York: Meridian, 1959) and the interpretation by J. H. Randall Jr., *Aristotle* (New York: Columbia University Press, 1960). Among the one-volume selections, the most complete is *Basic Works of Aristotle,* ed. R. McKeon (New York: Random House, 1941). The works of Hippocrates are available in the Loeb Classical Library, in the translation of W. H. S. Jones. See *Hippocrates,* Vol. I, [London: Heinemann, 1923 (New York: Putnam's)], especially the works "Ancient Medicine," "Airs, Waters, Places," and "Percepts," included here. On the Socratic method of dialectic, the so-called Socratic dialogues of Plato are the vivid source. See especially the dialogues *Euthyphro, Crito, Phaedo, Euthydemus,* and *Laches* in this regard. The development of Socrates' theory of knowledge by Plato is especially clear in the dialogues *Meno, Theatetus,* and Books VI and VII of *The Republic.* On the dialectic as instrument of criticism, see the essay by K. Popper, "On Dialectics," in his *Conjectures and Refutations* (New York: Basic Books, 1962), pp. 312–335.

Greek science and its relation to philosophic thought is fully treated in a very wide literature, a selection of which follows: P. Brunet and A. Mieli, *Histoire des sciences: Antiquité* (Paris: Pagot, 1935); M. Clagett, *Greek Science in Antiquity* (New York: Abelard-Schuman, 1955); the first-rate selection, M. R. Cohen and I. Drabkin, *Source Book in Greek Science* (New York: McGraw-Hill, 1948); J. L. Heiberg, *Mathematics and Physical Science in Classical Antiquity* (Oxford: Oxford University Press, 1922); O. Neugebauer, *The Exact Sciences in Antiquity* (Princeton, N.J.: Princeton University Press, 1952); the relevant sections of J. L. Partington, *The Origins and Development of Applied Chemistry* (London: Longmans, Green, 1935); J. Precope, *Iatrophilosophers of the Hellenic States* (London: Heinemann, 1961); A. Reymond, *History of the Sciences in Graeco-Roman Antiquity* (New York: Dutton, 1927); A. D. Ritchie, *Studies in the History and Methods of the Sciences* (Edinburgh: The University Press, 1958), especially Chapters II–VI); G. de Santillana, *The Origins of Scientific Thought, from Anaximander to Proclus, 600* B.C. *to 300* A.D. (Chicago: Chicago University Press, 1961); C. Singer, *Greek Biology and Greek Medicine* (Oxford: Clarendon, 1922); and also his *A History of Biology* (London: Abelard-Schuman, 1962); H. Sigerist, *A History of Medicine,* Vol. I (New Haven: Yale University Press, 1951); George Sarton, *Ancient Science and Modern Civilization* (New York: Harper Torchbooks, 1954), see especially the essays on Euclid, Ptolemy, and the end of Greek science; also Sarton's *A History of Science,* Vol. I (Cambridge, Mass.: Harvard University Press, 1952); P. Tannéry, *Pour l'Histoire de la science héllène* (Paris: F. Alcan, 1887); L. Thorndike, *A History of Magic and Experimental Science,* Vol. I (New York: Macmillan, 1923); S. Toulmin and J. Goodfield, *The Architecture of Matter* (New York: Harper & Row, 1962), especially Chapters 1–6. For special studies, see d'Arcy Thompson, *Aristotle as a Biologist,* C. Bailey, *The Greek Atomists and Epicurus* (Oxford: Clarendon, 1928); A. G. von Melsen, *From Atomos to Atom* (New York: Harper Torchbooks, 1960); S. Sambursky, *The Physics of the Stoics* (London: Routledge, 1958); and B. Mates, *Stoic Logic* (Berkeley: University of California Press, 1961). Collections of studies in Greek Science include R. M. Palter, ed., *Toward Modern Science—Studies in Ancient and Medieval Science,* Vol. I [(New York: Noonday Press, 1961), includes d'Arcy Thompson's essay listed above, and essays by Neugebauer, Heath, Singer, and Drabkin, among others)]; R. Taton, ed., *History of Science: Ancient and Medieval Science —from the Beginnings to 1450,* A. J. Pomerans, tr. (New York: Basic Books, 1963), especially good sections on ancient science in the East (Egypt, Mesopotamia, Phoenecia and Israel, India and China) and on Greek, Hellenistic, and Roman science by Michel, Bourgey, Bloch, Beaujeu. A. Haudricourt and J. Needham's essay on ancient Chinese science is a good introduction to Needham's epochal work, *Science and Civilization in China* (Cambridge: Cambridge University Press), Vols. I–IV, 1954–1962 (will go to seven volumes when completed). The special issue of the Danish journal *Centaurus,* Vol. II, nos. 1–2, (1953–1954) *Essays on the Social History of Science* includes V. G. Childe's essay "Science in Preliterate and Ancient Oriental Civilizations" and B. Farrington's "The Rise of Abstract Science among the Greeks." An excellent collection of essays is in P. P. Wiener and A. Noland, eds., *Roots of Scientific Thought—A Cultural Perspective* (New York: Basic Books, 1957). Part I ("The Classical Heritage") includes J. E. Boodin, "The Discovery of Form," L. Edelstein's exceptionally important essay, "Recent Trends in the Interpretation of Ancient Science" (Edelstein writes, p. 91, "The quantitative approach to the analysis of phenomena as well as the method of experimentation were well-known to the ancients. This is often denied even nowadays; the evidence available should settle the debate once and for all."); Heinrich Gomperz, "Problems and Methods of Early Greek Science," T. S. Hall, "Scientific Origins of the Protoplasm Problem"; R. McKeon, "Aristotle's Conception of Scientific Method." On the matter of experimentation, see also O. Blüh, "Did the Greeks Perform Experiments?" *Am. J. of Physics,* **17**:384–388 (1949) for positive evidence.

In addition to the treatments of Greek mathematics in the works listed, and the readily available accounts in general histories of mathematics, see T. Dantzig, *The Bequest of the Greeks* (New York: Scribner, 1955), a well-illustrated, brief, and eminently readable book with a very useful chapter on the various proofs of the Pythagorean Theorem (pp. 95–107); J. Gow, *A Short History of Greek Mathematics* (New York: Stechert, 1923); the classic works of Sir Thomas Heath, *Aristarchus of Samos* (Oxford: Clarendon, 1913); *A History of Greek Mathematics* (Oxford: Clarendon Press, 1921); and *A Manual of Greek Mathematics* [London: Oxford University Press, 1931 (reprinted, New York: Dover, 1963)]; G. Milhaud, *Les Philosophes géomètres de la Grèce* (Paris, F. Alcan, 1934); B. L. Van der Waerden, *Science Awakening,* tr. A. Dresden [Groningen: P. Noordhoff, 1954 (deals also with the background in Egyptian and Babylonian mathematics)]; E. Carrucio, *Mathematics and Logic in History and in Contemporary Thought,* tr. I. Quigley (Chicago: Aldine, 1964), gives a compact account relating mathematics to philosophical thought, especially Chapters 1–7.

CHAPTER 5

Some of the classical discussion of observation, sense perception, and knowledge of the external world, in Greek philosophy, may be approached by reading Plato's dialogues *Theatetus, Phaedo, Symposium,* and the allegory of the cave in *The Republic,* Book VI; and Aristotle's work on psychology, *De Anima.* For a full account, beyond that given in the general works on Greek philosophy listed in the bibliographical note for Chapter 4, see J. Beare, *Greek Theories of Elementary Cognition* (Oxford: Clarendon, 1906). An overview of philosophical theories of perception is given in D. W. Hamlyn, *Sensation and Perception* (London: Routledge, 1961).

Some main works in modern philosophy which provide the background for contemporary discussion are René Descartes, *Meditations* (New York: Liberal Arts, 1951), and the writing of the British empiricists, especially John Locke, *An Essay Concerning Human Understanding* (Oxford: Clarendon, 1894), David Hume, *A Treatise on Human Nature* (Garden City, N.Y.: Doubleday, 1961), and George Berkeley, *Principles of Human Knowledge* and *Three Dialogues Between Hylas and Philonous* (New York: Bobbs-Merrill, 1954). The Scottish commonsense realists are represented best in Thomas Reid, *Inquiry into the Human Mind* and *Essays on the Intellectual Powers of Man,* especially Essays II, IV, and V; and Dugald Stewart, *Elements of the Philosophy of the Human Mind,* especially Chapters I–IV. Emphasis on the organic and physiological elements in perception is represented by the works of David Hartley, *Observations on Man* (1749) and Erasmus Darwin, *Zoonomia, or the Laws of Organic Life* (1794). On the role of hypothesis and the relation of observation to explanation, see William Whewell, *Philosophy of the Inductive Sciences* (London: Parker, 1847), especially Vol. I, Book I, "Of Ideas in General," and Book XI, "Of the Constructs of Science," Chapters 3–4, "Of Facts as the Materials of Science" and "Of the Colligation of Facts."

Much of the contemporary discussion of observation derives from the problems and formulations which Immanuel Kant presented in his *Critique of Pure Reason.* Kant's well-known formula, "Concepts without percepts are empty, percepts without concepts are blind," sets out the interdependence of sense perception and frameworks of conception. See on this the opening section of the *Critique,* "Transcendental Aesthetic" in which Kant sets forth the notion of "*a priori* forms of perception." (A terminological difficulty here is that the standard translations render Kant's *Anschauung* as *intuition,* in the sense of what is given to thought "in immediate relation," as Kant says. I have used *perception* here instead, though this has notorious difficulties too, as the discussion in the chapter suggests.) The late nineteenth century discussion on perception was profoundly influenced by Kant, as well as by Hume. Early positivist notions of the nature of perception and observation in science are exemplified in Ernst Mach, *Analysis of Sensation* (Chicago: Open Court, 1906), especially Chapters I–IV, XIV, XV, and in the important treatment in his *The Science of Mechanics,* Chapter IV, Part iv, "The Economy of Science" (Chicago: Open Court, 1893), pp. 481–494. See also the discussion by P. Frank in his *Modern Science and Its Philosophy* (Cambridge, Mass.: Harvard University Press, 1949). Mach's major work on epistemological questions, *Erkenntnis und Irrtum,* has thus far not been translated into English. (There is, however, a French translation.) Poincaré's discussion of these matters is in many of his essays, particularly in "Is Science Artificial?" in *The Value of Science* (New York: Dover, 1958) Chapter X, and in "The Selection of Facts," in *Science and Method* (New York: Dover, n.d.). Pierre Duhem treats of the relation of hypothesis, law, and observation from a positivist viewpoint in *The Aim and Structure of Physical Theory,* tr. P. P. Wiener (Princeton, N.J.: Princeton University Press, 1954) especially Part II, Chapters 5, 6, and 7.

American philosophers focused on this and related problems, especially during the formative period of American pragmatism. See, for example, C. S. Peirce's essay "How to Make Our Ideas Clear," in J. Buchler, ed., *Philosophical Writings of C. S. Peirce* (New York: Dover, 1955), and also Questions Concerning Certain Faculties Claimed for Man," in P. P. Wiener, ed., *Values in a Universe of Chance—Selected Writings of C. S. Peirce* (New York: Doubleday—Anchor Books, 1958). See also William James, *Pragmatism and four essays from The Meaning of Truth* (New York: Meridian, 1955). John Dewey's discussion runs through many works, especially *Experience and Nature* (New York: Norton, 1925), Chapters 4 and 5; *Logic—The Science of Inquiry* (New York: Holt, 1939), Chapters 7–9, 12, 13; and with A. Bentley, *Knowing and the Known* (Boston: Beacon, 1949). In the pragmatist tradition, but with a distinctive and subtle analysis of his· own, C. I. Lewis deals with these matters in his *Mind and the World Order* and in the Carus Lectures, *An Analysis of Knowledge and Valuation* (Lasalle, Ill.: Open Court, 1946), especially Chapters 1, 2, and 7. The best representative of American realism is Roy Wood Sellars, who deals at length with the question of perception and error. [see, e.g., his *Critical Realism* (New York: Rand, McNally, 1916), and *The Philosophy of Physical Realism* (New York: Macmillan, 1932.] For a thick-textured and critical analysis of these issues in recent philosophy up to the 1930's, see A. O. Lovejoy, *The Revolt Against Dualism* (New York: Norton, 1930).

Sense-datum theory has had an active philosophical history in the last half-century. Some principal works here are G. E. Moore, *Philosophical Studies* (New York: Harcourt, Brace, 1922), especially the essays "Refutation of Idealism," "The Nature and Reality of Objects of Perception," "The Status of Sense Data," and "Some Judgments of Perception"; B. Russell's essays "The Relation of Sense-Data to Physics" and "Knowledge by Acquaintance and Knowledge by Description" in *Mysticism and Logic,* (New York: Doubleday, n.d.) and Chapters 15–22 in his *The Analysis of Matter* (London: Allen and Unwin, 1927). Also, for an elaborated theory of "sensa," see C. D. Broad, *Scientific Thought* (London: Routledge, 1949); *Perception, Physics, and Reality* (Cambridge: Cambridge University Press, 1914); and *Mind and Its Place in Nature* (New York: Harcourt, Brace, 1925).

The most systematic attempt to construct a theory of sense data is H. H. Price, *Perception* (London: Routledge and Kegan Paul, 1932). The argument for a phenomenalist sense-datum view is in A. J. Ayer, *Foundations of Empirical Knowledge* (New York: Macmillan, 1940), and the sharpest criticisms of this view are G. Ryle, *The Concept of Mind* (New York: Barnes & Noble, 1949), especially Chapter VII. See also his *Dilemmas* (Cambridge: Cambridge University Press, 1954); and J. Austin, *Sense and Sensibilia* (London: Oxford University Press, 1962). A critical review of the arguments, and the case for a representationist theory of perception, is in R. H. Hirst, *Problems of Perception* (London: Allen and Unwin, 1959). For the approach to observation and perception from the standpoint of ordinary language, see L. Wittgenstein, *Philosophical Investigations* (New York: Macmillan, 1953), and J. Austin, *op. cit.*

The relation of language to perception has been studied widely in the last years. Notable here are L. Vygotsky, *Thought and Language* (Cambridge, Mass.: M.I.T. Press, 1962); Roger W. Brown, *Words and Things* (Cambridge, Mass.: M.I.T. Press, 1957); R. W. Brown and E. H. Lenneberg, "A Study in Language and Cognition," *J. of Abnormal and Social Psych.,* **49**:454–462 (1954); E. H. Lenneberg, "The Relationship of Language to the Formation of Concepts", in M. Wartofsky, ed., *Boston Studies in the Philosophy of Science* (Dordrecht: Reidel, 1963) and N. Chomsky, "Perception and Language" (in the same volume); and *Aspects of the Theory of Syntax* (Cambridge, Mass.: M.I.T. Press, 1965). The controversial thesis that linguistic structure shapes our perception of reality is propounded by Benjamin Lee Whorf, *Language, Thought and Reality,* ed. J. B. Carroll, (Cambridge, Mass.: M.I.T. Press, 1956). A radical behaviorist theory of meaning and reference is in W. V. Quine, *Word and Object* (Cambridge, Mass.: M.I.T. Press, 1961). See also the readings in S. Saporta, ed., *Psycholinguistics* (New York: Holt, 1961), and C. Morris, *Foundations of the Theory of Signs,* Vol. I, no. 2, *International Encyclopedia of Unified Science* (Chicago: Chicago University Press, 1938).

On what the organism brings to perception, in terms of its sensory apparatus, and native dispositions or structures of perception, see J. Y. Lettvin, H. R. Maturana, W. S. McCulloch, and W. H. Pitts, "What the Frog's Eye Tells the Frog's Brain," *Proc. Inst. Radio Engnr.,* **47**:1940–1951 (1959), and by the same authors, "Two Remarks on the Visual System of the Frog," in W. Rosenblith, ed., *Sensory Communication* (Cambridge, Mass.: M.I.T. Press, 1961). Also R. L. Fantz, "The Origin of Form Perception," *Sci. Am.,* **204**:66–72 (1961); T. G. R. Bower, "The Visual World of Infants," *Sci. Am.,* **215**:80–92 (1966); and D. H. Hubel, "The Visual Cortex of the Brain," *Sci. Am.,* **209**:54–62 (1963).

On the distinction between knowledge of matters of fact, and what is known *a priori* by reason alone, see D. Hume, *Inquiry into Human Understanding,* esp. Book I, Part I, Sections 1–7, Part IV, Sections 1–4; and on Kant's introduction of the analytic-synthetic distinction, see *The Critique of Pure Reason,* Introduction, Sections iv and v [in the translation by

N. Kemp Smith (New York: St. Martin's Press, 1961), pp. 48–58]. Also see Book II (Analytic of Principles) First Division (Transcendental Analytic), especially Chapter iii, on Phenomena and Noumena, pp. 257–275. For contemporary versions of the analytic-synthetic distinction, see R. Carnap, "Formal Science and Factual Science," in H. Feigl and M. Brodbeck, *Readings in the Philosophy of Science* (New York: Appleton-Century-Crofts, 1953), and also his "Testability and Meaning" in the same volume, which deals with the reduction question. See also his essay "Empiricism, Semantics and Ontology," reprinted in P. P. Wiener, *Readings in Philosophy of Science* (New York: Scribner, 1953), and as an appendix to the second edition of Carnap, *Meaning and Necessity* (Chicago: Chicago University Press, 1956). The long discussion on the so-called verifiability principle or the verifiability criterion of meaning, through the past three decades, would require a separate bibliographical note. We mention here only M. Schlick, "Meaning and Verification" and C. I. Lewis' critical "Experience and Meaning," both reprinted in H. Feigl and W. Sellars, eds., *Readings in Philosophical Analysis* (New York: Appleton-Century-Crofts, 1949); A. J. Ayer, *Language, Truth and Logic,* revised ed. (New York: Dover, 1946); C. Hempel's "The Criterion of Cognitive Significance: A Reconsideration" in *Proc. of the Am. Acad. of Arts and Science,* 1951, "Problems and Changes in the Empiricist Criterion of Meaning," in *Rev. Int. de Philos.,* **IV** (1950), reprinted in R. R. Ammerman, ed., *Classics of Analytic Philosophy* (New York: McGraw-Hill, 1965), and his discussion throughout *Aspects of Explanation* (New York: The Free Press, 1965). See also A. Pasch, *Experience and the Analytic—A Reconsideration of Empiricism* (Chicago: University of Chicago Press, 1958), and the excellent full discussion by A. Pap in *An Introduction to the Philosophy of Science* (New York: The Free Press, 1962), Part I (Meaning and Verifiability), Chapters 1–4, in which Pap considers the questions of reduction to observational and operational terms, the verifiability criterion of meaning, and the limits of operationism. The full bibliography in P. Edwards and A. Pap, *A Modern Introduction to Philosophy* (New York: The Free Press, 1965) Revised Edition, Part VIII, Selected Bibliography, pp. 756–760, gives an excellent account of the relevant literature on this topic. In the volume, *The Philosophy of Rudolf Carnap,* ed. P. Schilpp, the following articles are relevant: N. Goodman, "The Significance of *Der Logische Aufbau der Welt*" [on Carnap's early work on a reconstruction of the world picture in terms of primitive observation predicates and observation statements; recently translated as *The Logical Structure of the World,* tr. R. A. George (Berkeley and Los Angeles: University of California Press, 1967)], P. Henle, "Meaning and Verifiability," A. Pap, "Reduction Sentences and Disposition Concepts." Nelson Goodman's *The Structure of Appearance* (Cambridge, Mass.: Harvard University Press, 1951), is a rigorous and elaborate reconstruction in terms of "qualia," which C. I.

Lewis took as the "givens" in perception. The critical discussion includes M. White, "The Analytic and the Synthetic—An Untenable Dualism," in L. Linsky, ed., *Semantics and the Philosophy of Language* (Urbana, Ill.: University of Illinois Press, 1952); W. V. Quine, "Truth by Convention," in H. Feigl and W. Sellars, *Readings in Philosophical Analysis* (New York: Appleton, 1949), and the important, much discussed critique, "Two Dogmas of Empiricism," in W. V. Quine, *From a Logical Point of View* (Cambridge, Mass.:. Harvard University Press, 1953). See also H. Putnam, "The Analytic and the Synthetic," in H. Feigl et al., eds., *Minnesota Studies in the Philosophy of Science* (Minneapolis: University of Minnesota Press, (1962), vol. III, reprinted in A. Rorty, ed., *Pragmatic Philosophy* (Garden City, N.Y.: Doubleday, Anchor, 1966). On the *synthetic a priori,* see W. Sellars, "Is There a Synthetic a Priori?" *Proceedings of the Aristotelian Society,* Supplement vol. 15, pp. 102–117 (1936); H. Hahn, "Logic, Mathematics and Knowledge of Nature," in A. J. Ayer, ed., *Logical Positivism* (New York: The Free Press, 1959). See also P. Frank, "Introduction to the Philosophy of Physical Science on the Basis of Logical Empiricism," *Synthese,* **8**:28–45 (1950).

Operationism, the methodological thesis that proposes that the meaning of scientific terms be reducible or interpretable in terms of unambiguously specified "operations," e.g., instrumental procedures, is closely akin to the logical empiricist notions of reduction to a basic language. Relevant discussion in the works of the physicist P. W. Bridgman, the leading exponent of operationism, includes his *The Logic of Modern Physics* (New York: Macmillan, 1927); *The Nature of Physical Theory* (Princeton, N.J.: Princeton University Press, 1936); "Operational Analysis," *Phil. Sci.,* **5**:114–131 (1938); "The Operational Aspect of Meaning," *Synthese,* **8**:251–259 (1950–1951); "The Nature of Some of Our Physical Concepts," *Brit. J. for the Philos. of Sci.,* **1**:257–272 (1951). An early argument is in G. Boas and A. Blumberg, "Some Remarks in Defense of the Operational Theory of Meaning," *J. Phil.,* **28**:544–550 (1931). A recent symposium on "The Present State of Operationalism" is in P. Frank, ed., *The Validation of Scientific Theories* (New York: Collier Books, 1961), and includes discussion by H. Margenau, G. Bergmann, C. Hempel, R. B. Lindsay, P. W. Bridgman, R. Seeger, and A. Grünbaum. A. Danto and S. Morgenbesser, eds., *Philosophy of Science* (New York: Meridian, 1960), includes Hempel's "Operationism, Observation and Scientific Terms," as well as articles by R. L. Goodstein, "Language and Experience," R. Carnap, "Elementary and Abstract Terms," and I. Scheffler, "Theoretical Terms and a Modest Empiricism," all relevant to the observation-reduction question, as is also the selection from Susan Stebbing's *Philosophy and the Physicists* (London: Methuen, 1937) contained here as "Furniture of the Earth." Especially useful is the selection in Danto and Morgenbesser from

Galileo's *The Assayer,* on "Two Kinds of Properties," which deals with the distinction between what later came to be called primary and secondary qualities.

Problems of reference are dealt with in J. G. Frege's classical paper "On Sense and Nominatum," reprinted in Feigl and Sellars, *op. cit.* W. V. Quine carries on in the Fregean tradition in a series of works which deal with reference: in the collection *From a Logical Point of View* see especially "Notes on the Theory of Reference," "Ostension, Identity and Hypostasis" and "Meaning and Reference," and also the lead essay, "On What There Is." Quine's extended treatment of observation and reference is in *Word and Object* (Cambridge, Mass.: M.I.T. Press, 1960), especially Chapters I–IV. See also P. F. Strawson, "On Referring," in A. Flew, ed., *Essays in Conceptual Analysis* (London: Macmillan, 1960), and his contribution to the Symposium on "Truth," *Proceedings of the Aristotelian Soc. Supplement,* **24**:129–156 (1950). The issue is joined with Strawson by J. Austin in the essay "Unfair to Facts," in his *Philosophical Papers,* ed. J. O. Urmson and G. J. Warnock (London: Oxford University Press, 1961). See also, P. Herbst, "The Nature of Facts" in the Flew volume, and Poincaré's "The Selection of Facts"' in his *Science and Method* (New York: Dover, n.d.).

The realist alternatives to and criticisms of phenomenalism include N. Lenin's critique (leveled at Duhem, Poincaré, P. Frank, and in particular against Ernst Mach) in *Materialism and Empirio-Criticism* (New York: International Publishers, 1927), especially Chapters 1–3 [in turn criticized by G. A. Paul, "Lenin's Theory of Perception," in M. MacDonald, ed., *Philosophy and Analysis* (Oxford: Blackwell, 1954)]; W. Sellars, "Empiricism and the Philosophy of Mind," in Feigl et al., *Minnesota Studies,* Vol. I (Minneapolis: University of Minnesota Press, 1956); and in his *Science, Perception and Reality* (New York: Humanities Press, 1963) which includes the previously noted essay; and the critique of sense-datum theories, "The Language of Theories" as well as the article noted earlier, "Is There a Synthetic A Priori?" See also P. K. Feyerabend, "An Attempt at a Realistic Interpretation of Experience," *Proc. of the Artist. Soc.,* **58**:143–170 (1959) and his "Materialism and the Mind-Body Problem," *Rev. Metaphysics,* **17**:49–66 (1963). For an account of the view which sees all observation as "theory laden," i.e., as framework-dependent, see N. R. Hanson's *Patterns of Discovery* (Cambridge: Cambridge University Press, 1958). Going beyond this in emphasizing the subjective and irrational components in the contexts of scientific observation, are the works of M. Polanyi, esp. *Personal Knowledge* (Chicago: University of Chicago Press, 1960), and T. Kuhn's controversial essay, *The Structure of Scientific Revolutions, Encyclopedia of Unified Science,* Vol. 2, no. 2 (Chicago: University of Chicago Press, 1964). See also S. Körner, ed., *Observation* *and Interpretation,* Colston Research Society Proceedings [London: Butterworth, 1957 (reprinted, New York: Dover, 1962)], especially the sixth session, W. Kneale, "What Can We See?" and G. Ryle, "Predicting and Inferring."

CHAPTER 6

The nature of formal systems is discussed in M. Cohen and E. Nagel, *Introduction to Logic and Scientific Method* (New York: Harcourt, Brace, 1934), Chapter vii. ("The Nature of a Logical or Mathematical System"), reprinted in H. Feigl and M. Brodbeck, eds., *Readings in the Philosophy of Science* (New York: Appleton-Century-Crofts, 1953); and at length, by A. Pap, *Introduction to Philosophy of Science* (New York: The Free Press, 1962), Part Two: "Mathematics, Logic and Experience," including discussions of arithmetic, the laws of logic, and geometry, Chapters 5–8. See also the same author's full discussion in his *Semantics and Necessary Truth* (New Haven: Yale University Press, 1958). Carnap gives a comprehensive introduction to these matters in *Foundations of Logic and Mathematics,* Vol. I, no. 3, *International Encyclopedia of Unified Science* (Chicago: University of Chicago Press, 1939), and discusses them in many other writings, including "Formal and Factual Science," reprinted in H. Feigl and M. Brodbeck, *op. cit.*; *Philosophy and Logical Syntax* (London: Routledge and Kegan Paul, 1935); *Logical Syntax of Language* (London: K. Paul Trench, 1937); "The Old and the New Logic," in A. J. Ayer, ed., *Logical Positivism* (New York: The Free Press, 1959); *Introduction to Symbolic Logic and Its Applications* (New York: Dover, 1958); and on issues related to the logical status of meaning and of intensions, in *Meaning and Necessity* (Chicago: University of Chicago Press, 1956), 2nd ed. (In the appendix to this edition, see also his essay, "Meaning Postulates.") Philipp Frank, *Philosophy of Science* (Englewood Cliffs, N.J.: Prentice-Hall, 1957) discusses geometry as a formalized system (Chapter. 3). See also C. Hempel, *Fundamentals of Concept Formation in Empirical Science,* Vol. II, no. 7, *International Encyclopedia of Unified Science* (Chicago: University of Chicago Press, 1952), and the same author's "Geometry and Empirical Science," *Am. Math. Monthly* **52**:7–17 (1945), reprinted in H. Feigl and W. Sellars, eds., *Readings in Philosophical Analysis* (New York: Appleton-Century-Crofts, 1949); H. Reichenbach, *Elements of Symbolic Logic* (New York: Macmillan, 1947), Chapter 7, § 3, discusses the question of object language and metalanguage in an introductory way, as well as other questions concerning formal systems, not always treated in logic texts (e.g., Chapter VII, § 51, on the tenses of verbs). On the relation of language to representation, see C. S. Peirce, "How to Make Our Ideas Clear," in J. Buchler, ed., *The Philosophy of*

Peirce [New York: Harcourt, Brace, 1940 (reprinted, Dover, 1955)]; and in the same volume, Peirce's "Logic as Semiotic: The Theory of Signs"; also C. W. Morris, *Foundations of the Theory of Signs,* Vol. I, no. 2, *International Encyclopedia of Unified Science* (Chicago: Chicago University Press, 1938) and his *Signs, Language and Behavior,* (Englewood Cliffs, N.J.: Prentice-Hall, 1946). On some modern approaches to the theory of linguistic structure, see N. Chomsky, *Syntactic Structures* (The Hague, Holland: Mouton & Co., 1957) and *Aspects of the Theory of Syntax* (Cambridge: M.I.T. Press, 1965), as well as the articles in R. D. Luce, R. R. Bush, and E. Galanter, eds., *Handbook of Mathematical Psychology,* Vol. II, (New York: Wiley, 1963): "Introduction to the Formal Analysis of Natural Languages," and "Formal Properties of Grammars." See also the collections: L. Linsky, ed., *Semantics and the Philosophy of Language* (Urbana, Ill.: University of Illinois Press, 1952) and J. Katz and J. Fodor, eds., *The Structure of Language–Readings in the Philosophy of Language* (Englewood Cliffs, N.J.: Prentice-Hall, 1964), especially the articles by Quine, Chomsky, Carnap, and Katz and Fodor. For a discussion of models, see H. Freudenthal, ed., *The Concept and the Role of the Model in Mathematics, and Natural and Social Sciences* (Dordrecht, Holland: Reidel, 1961), especially Leo Apostel, "Towards the Formal Study of Models . . . ," A. Kuipers, "Model and Insight," P. Suppes, "A Comparison of the Meaning and Uses of Models in Mathematics and the Empirical Sciences," and J. B. Ubbink, "Model, Description and Knowledge"; P. Duhem, *The Aim and Structure of Physical Theory,* tr. P. Wiener, (Princeton, N.J.: Princeton University Press, 1953), Chapters 1 and 4; N. Campbell, *Physics —The Elements* (Cambridge: Cambridge University Press, 1920), Chapters V and VI; E. Nagel, *The Structure of Science* (New York: Harcourt, Brace, 1961), Chapters 6 and 7; R. Braithwaite, *Scientific Explanation* (Cambridge: Cambridge University Press, 1953), Chapter 3, and his article "Models in the Empirical Sciences" in E. Nagel, P. Suppes and A. Tarski, eds., *Logic, Methodology and Philosophy of Science,* Proceedings of the 1960 International Congress of Philosophy of Science (Stanford: Stanford University Press, 1962). In the same volumn, see N. Chomsky, "Abstract Models in Linguistics," Yuen-Ren Chao, "Models in Linguistics and Models in General", and P. Suppes, "Models of Data." On the use and nature of mathematical models in the behavioral and social sciences, see H. Simon, *Models of Man* (New York: Wiley, 1957) and H. Borko, ed., *Computer Applications in the Behavioral Sciences* (Englewood Cliffs, N.J.: Prentice-Hall, 1962), which contains a summary of recent approaches to "simulation" and computer models, especially the articles by Feldman, Ashby, Culbertson, and Sprowls. See also, for applications to specific subject matters, the papers by W. Pitts and W. McCulloch, "How We Know Universals," *Bull. Math. Biophysics,* **9**:127–47 (1947) and the articles on nerve-net theories in C. Shannon and J. McCarthy, eds., *Automata Studies*

(Princeton, N.J.: Princeton University Press, 1956); J. T. Culbertson, *The Minds of Robots* (Urbana, Ill.: University of Illinois Press, 1962) and J. Z. Young, *A Model of the Brain* (Oxford: Clarendon Press, 1964). Mary Hesse discusses alternative approaches to models in *Models and Analogies in Science* (London and New York: Sheed and Ward, 1963), and in Chapter I of her *Forces and Fields* (London: Nelson 1961). See also the discussion by P. Achinstein, "Models, Analogies and Theories," *Phil. of Sci.,* **31**:328–350 (1964), and "Theoretical Models," *Brit. J. for Phil. of Sci.,* **16**:102–120. N. Wiener draws the distinction between "operative" and "pictorial" images, in *God and Golem* (Cambridge, Mass.: M.I.T. Press, 1964) pp. 30ff. On the notion of mapping and of functional models as accounts of cognitive behavior, see E. C. Tolman, "Cognitive Maps in Rats and Men," *Psych. Review,* **55**:189–208 and G. Miller, K. Pribram, and E. Galanter, *Plans and the Structure of Behavior* (New York: Holt, 1960). The questions concerning language as a representation of the facts are raised in L. Wittgenstein, *Tractatus Logico-Philosophicus* (London: Macmillan, 1922); B. Russell, "The Philosophy of Logical Atomism," *Monist* **28**:495–527 (1918); **29**:32–63, 190–222, 345–380 (1919). Criticisms of the so-called picture theory of meaning are in E. Daitz, "The Picture Theory of Meaning," in A. Flew, ed., *Essays in Conceptual Analysis* (New York: St. Martin's Press, 1960); N. Goodman, "On Likeness of Meaning," *Analysis* 10:1–7 (1949). An elaborated theory of mapping, based on a phenomenalist language of qualities, or *qualia,* is in N. Goodman's *The Structure of Appearance* (Cambridge, Mass.: Harvard University Press, 1951). An interesting treatment of the problem of representation, with respect to the history of art but with clear relevance to the general problem, is in E. Gombrich, *Art and Illusion* (New York: Bollingen Foundation, 1961).

A theory of representation, in a different tradition, is in E. Cassirer's three-volume work, *Philosophy of Symbolic Forms* (New Haven: Yale University Press, 1953–57), and a summary of this thesis may be found in his *Essay on Man* (New York: Doubleday, 1956), Chapter 2. See also Susan Langer, *Philosophy in a New Key* (New York: New American Library, 1958), and her treatment of formal representation in the arts, in *Feeling and Form* (New York: Scribner, 1956). On the nature of mathematical-logical systems and the question of interpretation and representation, see M. Black, *The Nature of Mathematics* (New York: Harcourt, Brace, 1933); H. Castañeda, "Arithmetic and Reality," *Australasian Journal of Philosophy,* **37**: 91–107 (1959); D. A. T. Gasking, "Mathematics and the World," *Australasian J. of Phil.,* **18**:97–116 (1940); the symposium "Why are the Calculuses of Logic and Mathematics Applicable to Reality?" with G. Ryle, K. Popper, and C. Lewy, *Arist. Soc. Proceedings,* Supplement, **20**:20–29 (1946); K. Menger, "The New Logic," *Phil. of Science,* **4**:299–336 (1937); H. Jeffries, *Scientific Inference* (Cambridge: Cambridge University Press, 1931); W. S. Jevons, *The Principles of Science* (New York: Macmillan, 1900); W. E. Johnson, *Logic,* part I, *Demonstrative Inference* part II, and *Logical Foundations of Science* (Cambridge: Cambridge University Press, 1921); J. Jørgenson, *A Treatise of Formal Logic* (London: Oxford University Press, 1931); and the recent essay by Jørgenson, "Some Remarks Concerning Languages, Calculuses and Logic," in *Logic and Language—Studies Dedicated to Prof. R. Carnap on the Occasion of His 70th Birthday* (Dordrecht, Holland: Reidel, 1962), pp. 27–38; F. Klein, *Elementary Mathematics from an Advanced Standpoint* (New York: Dover, 1939); J. S. Mill, "Mathematics and Experience," selection from Chapters V and VI of Book II of *A System of Logic* (1843), reprinted in P. Edwards and A. Pap, *A Modern Introduction to Philosophy* (New York: The Free Press, 1965), revised edition, pp. 624–637; [also in E. Nagel, ed., J. S. Mill, *Philosophy and Scientific Method,* abridged ed., of *A System of Logic* (New York: Hafner, 1950), pp. 1–365]; J. Nicod, *Foundations of Geometry and Induction* (New York: Humanities Press, 1950); H. Poincaré, "On the Nature of Mathematical Reasoning," in *Science and Hypothesis* (New York: Dover, 1952), pp. 1–16; F. P. Ramsey, *Foundations of Mathematics* (New York: Humanities Press, 1950); L. Rougier, *La Structure des théories déductives* (Paris: F. Alcan, 1921); F. Waismann, *Introduction to Mathematical Thinking* (New York: Ungar, 1951); H. Weyl, *Philosophy of Mathematics and Natural Science* (Princeton, N.J.: Princeton University Press, 1949), especially Chapters 1–2.

On the philosophy of mathematics and the formal sciences, the collection of P. Benacerraf and H. Putnam, eds., *Philosophy of Mathematics* (Englewood Cliffs, N.J.: Prentice-Hall, 1964), contains much basic material as well as a good introduction. See also S. F. Barker, *Philosophy of Mathematics* (Englewood Cliffs, N.J.: Prentice-Hall, 1964) for a brief introduction, and S. Körner, *The Philosophy of Mathematics* (London: Hutchinson, 1960). Very important is the fundamental work *The Foundations of Arithmetic* by G. Frege, tr. J. L. Austin, (New York: Philosophical Library, 1950), and B. Russell's exceptionally clear little book, *Introduction to Mathematical Philosophy* (London: Allen and Unwin, 1919). See also C. Hempel, "On the Nature of Mathematical Truth," reprinted in H. Feigl and M. Brodbeck, *op. cit.,* and the selections in part A of P. Wiener's *Readings in the Philosophy of Science* (New York: Scribner, 1953), which include A. N. Whitehead, "The Abstract Nature of Mathematics," C. S. Peirce, "How Mathematics Generalizes" and C. Hempel's essay (noted previously), "Geometry and Empirical Science." The selections in Section VII of P. Edwards and A. Pap, *A Modern Introduction to Philosophy, op. cit.,* on *"A Priori* Knowledge" (including the Mill selection noted previously) are also relevant to the general question of the status of mathematical or logical truths. On axiomatic method, see L. Henkin, P. Suppes and A. Tarski, eds., *Axiomatic Method with Special Reference to Geometry and Physics—Proceedings of an International Symposium, 1957–58* (Oxford: Blackwell's, 1959); O. Veblen, "A System of Axioms for Geometry," *Transactions of the Am. Math. Soc.,* **5**:353–384 (1904); A. Tarski, *Introduction to Logic and to the Methodology of the Deductive Sciences* (London: Oxford University Press, 1941) and *Logic, Semantics, Metamathematics—Papers from 1923 to 1938:* tr. and edited by J. H. Woodger (Oxford: Clarendon Press, 1956), especially "The Concept of Truth in Formalized Languages." On the logic of Relations, see, for an introductory account, P. Suppes, *Introduction to Logic* (Princeton, N.J.: Van Nostrand, 1957); and for a more technical treatment, W. V. Quine, *Mathematical Logic,* rev. ed. (Cambridge: Harvard University Press, 1951), Chapter 5.

CHAPTER 7

Philosophical discussion of the nature of measurement, and logical analysis of the structure of measurement systems run through the many treatments of this topic, even where the emphasis is on applications of measurement theory. An excellent introductory account is C. Hempel, *Fundamentals of Concept Formation in Empirical Science,* Vol. II, no. 7, *International Encyclopedia of Unified Science* (Chicago: Chicago University Press, 1952), Part III, pp. 50–78. So too is E. Nagel, "Measurement," in A. Danto and S. Morgenbesser, eds., *Philosophy of Science* (New York: Meridian, 1960) [reprinted from *Erkenntnis,* **II,** 5:313–33 (1932)], and the more elementary account in M. R. Cohen and E. Nagel, *Introduction to Logic and Scientific Method* (New York: Harcourt, Brace, 1934), Chapter XV. See also N. Campbell's account in *What Is Science?* (New York: Dover, 1952), Chapters VI and VII, and the very influential and full treatment in Campbell's *An Account of the Principles of Measurement and Calculation* (London & New York: Longmans Green, 1928). The fundamental formulation of scales of measurement, which has occasioned much critical discussion and further elaboration is S. S. Stevens, "On the Theory of Scales of Measurement," *Science,* **103**:677–80 (1946), reprinted in Danto and Morgenbesser, *op. cit.,* 141–149, and the fuller account in "Mathematics, Measurement and Psychology" in S. S. Stevens, *Handbook of Experimental Psychology* (New York: Wiley, 1951). Stevens' continuing work on the theory and applications of measurement in psychophysics constitutes an important body of publications, a partial bibliography of which may be found at the end of his article (cited in Chapter 6), "Quantifying the Sensory Experience," in P. Feyerabend and G. Maxwell, eds., *Mind, Matter and Method* (Minneapolis: University of Minnesota Press, 1966). Especially important is his article "On the Psychophysical Law," *Psych. Review,* **64**:153–181 (1957). A. Pap summarizes some of the basic questions in Chapter 8 ("The Logical Analysis of Measurement") of his

Introduction to Philosophy of Science. Also important for its discussion of measurement and magnitude in the physical sciences is H. Jeffries, *Scientific Inference,* second ed. (Cambridge: Cambridge University Press, 1957), Chapters V–VI. On the formal structure of systems of measurement, a pioneering work of the nineteenth century is H. von Helmholtz, *On Counting and Measuring,* tr. C. L. Bryan (Princeton, N.J.: Van Nostrand, 1930). Recent work includes P. Suppes, "A Set of Independent Axioms for Extensive Quantities," *Portugaliae Mathematica,* **X**:163–172 (1952); D. Scott and P. Suppes, "Foundational Aspects of Measurement," *J. of Symbolic Logic,* **23**:113–128 (1958); and the very extensive treatment by P. Suppes and J. L. Zinnes, "Basic Measurement Theory," in R. D. Luce, R. R. Bush, and E. Galanter, eds., *Handbook of Mathematical Psychology,* vol. I (New York: Wiley, 1963). The collection by C. W. Churchman and P. Ratoosh, eds., *Measurement: Definitions and Theories* (New York: Wiley, 1959), includes C. W. Churchman "Why Measure?" J. L. McKnight, "The Quantum-Theoretical Concept of Measurement," K. Menger, "Mensuration and Other Mathematical Connections of Observable Material," A. Pap, "Are Physical Magnitudes Operationally Definable?" and S. S. Stevens, "Measurement, Empirical Meaningfulness and Three-valued Logic." Churchman's article, "A Materialist Theory of Measurement," in R. W. Sellars, V. J. McGill, and M. Farber, eds., *Philosophy for the Future* (New York: Macmillan, 1949), contains a distinctive view. See also G. Bergmann and K. Spence, "The Logic of Psychophysical Measurement," *Psych. Review,* **51**:1–24 (1944), reprinted in H. Feigl and M. Brodbeck, *op. cit.;* P. Bridgman, *The Logic of Modern Physics* (New York: Macmillan, 1927) and also *Dimensional Analysis,* rev. ed., (New Haven: Yale University Press, 1931); J. Dewey, *Logic—The Theory of Inquiry* (New York: Holt, 1939), Chapter 11; the series of articles by B. D. Ellis, "Some Fundamental Problems of Direct Measurement," *Australasian Journal of Philosophy,* **38**:37–47 (1960), "Derived Measurement, Universal Constants and the Expression of Numerical Laws," in B. Baumrin, ed., *Philosophy of Science—The Delaware Seminar,* vol. II (New York: Interscience, 1963), and his article "Measurement," in P. Edwards, ed., *International Encyclopedia of Unified Philosophy* (forthcoming); also, by B. D. Ellis, the recent book, *Basic Concepts of Measurement* (Cambridge: Cambridge University Press, 1966). In S. Körner, ed., *Observation and Interpretation* [London: Butterworth, 1957 (reprinted New York: Dover, n.d.)], see P. K. Feyerabend, "On the Quantum Theory of Measurement," and G. Süssman, "An Analysis of Measurement," and especially the discussion following on pp. 137–147. R. D. Luce and E. Galanter, "Psychophysical Scaling" in *Handbook of Mathematical Psychology,* vol. I, *op. cit.,* give a refined and detailed account of applications of measurement and various scales used in psychophysics. See also, on methods of measurement in the behavioral and social sciences, J. P. Griffin, "Chronology and Dating Processes," in W. L.

Thomas, ed., *Current Anthropology* (Chicago: University of Chicago Press, 1955), especially interesting on techniques of pollen, buried soils, trace metals and radiocarbon dating, linguistic chronology and tree-ring dating. An account of the application of tree-ring dating, or Dendrochronology, as well as of other anthropological techniques of ordering data is in H. M. Wormington, *Prehistoric Indians of the Southwest* (Denver: Denver Museum of Natural History, Popular Series no. 7, 1959). See also B. Phillips, *Social Research: Strategy and Tactics* (New York: Macmillan, 1966), especially Parts III and IV; H. Solomon, *Mathematical Thinking in the Measurement of Behavior* (New York: The Free Press, 1960) and W. S. Torgerson, *Theory and Methods of Scaling* (New York: Wiley, 1958). Further accounts are given in S. A. Stouffer, et al., eds., *Measurement and Prediction* (Princeton, N.J.: Princeton University Press, 1950); H. Weyl, *Philosophy of Mathematics and Natural Science* (Princeton, N.J.: Princeton University Press, 1960), especially pp. 139–145; and A. N. Whitehead, *The Concept of Nature* [Cambridge: Cambridge University Press, 1920 (reprinted Ann Arbor: University of Michigan Press, 1957), Chapter VI].

CHAPTER 8

The classic account of experimental method and the testing of hypotheses is Francis Bacon's *Novum Organum* (1620), which proposed turning away from speculative and deductive methods–"anticipations of the mind"–to "genuine induction" based on sense observation of particulars, which he called the "interpretation of nature." The work gives the original account of the experimental methods of agreement and difference (later reformulated by J. S. Mill—see discussion in Chapter 9) and argues for the role of so-called crucial experiments—"experiments of the cross"—as means of deciding upon alternative hypotheses. A recent argument for such a method is J. R. Platt, "Strong Inference," *Science,* **146**:347–352 (1964). In the nineteenth century, William Whewell's *Philosophy of the Inductive Sciences* emphasized the role of hypotheses in the sciences, characterizing the function, in discovery, of conjectures, "clearly conceived and brought into rigid contact with the facts," and which "perpetually show their vigor by overshooting the mark." Especially useful here is the discussion in Part II, Book XI ("Of the Construction of Science"). Whewell's work was first published in 1840, and later in a revised and enlarged edition (London: John Parker, 1847). The discussion of hypothesis and experiment around the turn of the century and thereafter includes the important contributions of Mach, Duhem, and Poincaré, as well as of the Americans, Peirce and Dewey. Mach's discussion of the "Economy of Science," in his *Principles of Mechanics* (La Salle, Ill.: Open Court, 1893), Chapter IV, Section iv., and of the "Unity of Science" in *The Analysis of Sensations* (reprinted, New York: Dover, 1959), Chapter XIV, are crucial here. See also his essay, "On the Part Played by Accident in Invention and Discovery," in E. Mach, *Popular Scientific Lectures,* tr. McCormack (LaSalle, Ill.: Open Court, 1943). See also H. Poincaré, "Hypotheses in Physics," in his *Science and Hypothesis* [New York: Dover (reprint), 1952]; P. Duhem, *Aim and Structure of Physical Theory,* tr. P. Wiener (Princeton, N.J.: Princeton University Press, 1954), Chapter VI ("Physical Theory and Experiment"), reprinted in Feigl and Brodbeck, eds., *Readings in the Philosophy of Science* (New York: Appleton-Century-Crofts, 1953). J. S. Mill's analysis of scientific method in his *System of Logic* (1843) is an important work in this context. An available (abridged) edition is E. Nagel, ed., *John Stuart Mill's Philosophy of Scientific Method* (New York: Hafner, 1950). See especially Book III, Chapters vii-ix, xiv. Mill's influence on the founders of pragmatism was large, and the work of Chauncey Wright, Charles Sanders Peirce, William James, and John Dewey is, in effect, a systematic elaboration of a philosophy of hypothesis and experiment. See E. Madden, ed., *The Philosophical Writings of Chauncey Wright* (New York: Liberal Arts Press, 1958); [Wright's essay, "The Origins of Modern Science" is reprinted in E. Madden, ed., *The Structure of Scientific Thought* (Boston: Houghton Mifflin, 1960)] C. S. Peirce, "The Logic of Abduction," in V. Tomas, ed., *C. S. Peirce: Essays in the Philosophy of Science* (New York: Liberal Arts Press, 1957); J. Dewey, *Logic—The Theory of Inquiry* (New York: Holt, 1939), Chapters VI, XXIII. Recent works include C. W. Churchman, *Theory of Experimental Inference* (New York: Macmillan, 1948), especially Chapters 10–13; H. Jeffreys, *Scientific Inference* (Cambridge: Cambridge University Press, 1957); V. Lenzen, *Procedures of Empirical Science,* Vol. I, no. 5, *International Encyclopedia of Unified Science* (Chicago: University of Chicago Press, 1938); K. Popper's major work, *The Logic of Scientific Discovery* (London: Hutchinson, 1959), as well as some of the essays in K. Popper, *Conjectures and Refutations* (New York: Basic Books, 1962), especially 1. Sources and case histories from the history of hypothesis and experiment in science include the excellent series, J. B. Conant, ed., *Harvard Case Studies in Experimental Science* (Cambridge, Mass.: Harvard University Press, 1957), two volumes; M. Shamos, *Great Experiments in Physics* (New York: Holt, 1959); A Beiser, *The World of Physics* (New York: McGraw-Hill, 1960). See also, for a discussion of relevant methodological questions, E. Madden, ed., *Theories of Scientific Method from the Renaissance to the Nineteenth Century* (Seattle: University of Washington Press, 1959); and the discussion of the role of hypothesis in scientific discovery in R. N. Hanson, *Patterns of Discovery* (Cambridge: Cambridge University Press, 1958).

The discussion of Galileo's formulation of the law of falling bodies, in Appendix A at the end of this volume, bears on the whole matter of hypothesis and experiment as it is discussed in Chapter 8.

CHAPTER 9

Most of the general texts in philosophy of science (listed in the bibliographical note for Chapter 1) include discussions of probability and induction. One of the fullest and best discussions is in A. Pap, *Philosophy of Science—An Introduction* (New York: The Free Press, 1962), Part Three, Chapters 9–13. Among the collections of articles and excerpts on this topic, E. Madden, ed., *The Structure of Scientific Thought* (Boston: Houghton Mifflin, 1960), Parts 5 and 6 contain an excellent selection of classic and contemporary discussions, including P. S. LaPlace, "Probability and its Principles," J. Venn, "Difficulties of the Classical View of Probability," R. Carnap, "Statistical and Inductive Probability," C. S. Peirce, "Induction as Experimental and Self-Corrective," and the discussion of Reichenbach's view of induction by J. Lenz, "The Pragmatic Justification of Induction." The collection edited by M. H. Foster and M. L. Martin, *Probability, Confirmation and Simplicity—Readings in the Philosophy of Inductive Logic* (New York: Odyssey Press, 1966) gives the full range of contemporary views on this subject and includes most of the important recent articles. It also has a good selected bibliography, for further study. Other important collections include H. E. Kyburg, Jr., and E. Nagel, eds., *Induction: Some Current Issues* (Middletown, Conn.: Wesleyan University Press, 1963), and H. E. Kyburg, Jr., and H. Smokler, eds., *Studies in Subjective Probability* (New York: Wiley, 1964), which contains selections from J. Venn, E. Borel, F. P. Ramsey, B. de Finetti, B. O. Koopman, and L. J. Savage, on the notions of so-called subjective or personalistic probability. There is also an excellent bibliography at the end of this volume. Some major works are S. Barker, *Induction and Hypothesis* (Ithaca, N.Y.: Cornell University Press, 1957); R. Carnap's many works, which include *Logical Foundations of Probability* (Chicago: University of Chicago Press, 1950); *Probability and Induction* (Chicago: University of Chicago Press, 1950); *The Nature and Application of Inductive Logic* (Chicago: University of Chicago Press, 1951); and *The Continuum of Inductive Methods* (Chicago: University of Chicago Press, 1952); (major articles by Carnap and discussion of his views follow in the listing of periodical literature); R. F. Harrod, *Foundations of Inductive Logic* (New York: Harcourt, Brace, 1957); H. Jeffries, *Theory of Probability* (Oxford: Clarendon Press, 1939); J. M. Keynes, *Treatise on Probability* (London: Macmillan, 1921); W. Kneale, *Probability and Induction* (Oxford: Clarendon, 1949); H. E. Kyburg, Jr., *Probability and the Logic of Rational Belief* (Middletown, Conn.: Wesleyan University Press, 1961); P. S. LaPlace, *A Philosophical Essay on Probabilities*, tr. F. W. Truscott and F. L. Emory (New York: Dover, 1951); H. LeBlanc, *Statistical and Inductive Probabilities* (Englewood Cliffs, N.J.: Prentice-Hall, 1962) R. von Mises, *Probability, Statistics and Truth* (New York: Macmillan, 1939); E. Nagel, *Principles of the*

Theory of Probability, International Encyclopedia of Unified Science, Vol. I, no. 6 (Chicago: University of Chicago Press, 1939); J. Nicod, *Foundations of Geometry and Induction* (London: K. Paul, Trench, Trubner, 1930); H. Reichenbach, *Theory of Probability,* 2nd ed., (Berkeley: University of California Press, 1949); and *Experience and Prediction* (Chicago: University of Chicago Press, 1938); J. Venn, *The Logic of Chance,* 4th ed. (New York: Chelsea, 1962); D. C. Williams, *The Ground of Induction* (Cambridge, Mass.: Harvard University Press, 1947); G. H. von Wright, *A Treatise on Induction and Probability* (London: Routledge and Kegan Paul, 1951); *The Logical Problem of Induction* (New York: Macmillan, 1957). Important alternative views of probability and induction and a lively critical discussion are represented in such essays and discussion articles as R. Carnap, "The Two Concepts of Probability," *Philosophy and Phenomenological Research,* **5**:513–532 (1945), reprinted in H. Feigl and M. Brodbeck, eds., *Readings in the Philosophy of Science* (New York: Appleton-Century-Crofts, 1953); H. Reichenbach, "On the Justification of Induction," *Journal of Philosophy,* **37**:97–103 (1940), which follows I. P. Creed, "The Justification of the Habit of Induction," in the same issue, **37**:85–97, and is reprinted in H. Feigl and W. Sellars, *Readings in Philosophical Analysis* (New York: Appleton-Century-Crofts, 1949); K. Popper, "The Propensity Interpretation of Probability," *British Journal for the Philosophy of Science,* **10**:25–42 (1959); C. Hempel, "Inductive Inconsistencies," *Synthese,* **12**:439–469 (1960); N. Goodman, "On Infirmities of Confirmation Theory," *Philosophy and Phenomenological Research,* **8**:149–151 (1947–1948), "A Query on Confirmation," *Journal of Philosophy,* **43**:383–385 (1946) and *Fact, Fiction and Forecast* (Cambridge, Mass.: Harvard University Press, 1955), Chapters 3 and 4.

The discussions of probability and induction by the founder of American pragmatism, C. S. Peirce, are especially important. See, for example, the essays "The Doctrine of Chances," "The Probability of Induction," "The Order of Nature," "Deduction, Induction and Hypotheses," "Uniformity," and "The Doctrine of Necessity Examined" [all in V. Tomas, ed., *C. S. Peirce: Essays in Philosophy of Science* (New York: Liberal Arts Press, 1957)]. The recent periodical literature includes M. Black, "The Justification of Induction," in his *Language and Philosophy* (Ithaca, N.Y.: Cornell University Press, 1949), " 'Pragmatic' Justifications of Induction," in his *Problems of Analysis* (Ithaca, N.Y.: Cornell University Press, 1954), and "Can Induction Be Vindicated?" *Philosophical Studies,* **10**:5–16 (1959); C. E. Bures, "The Concept of Probability," *Philosophy of Science,* **5**:1–20 (1938); A. W. Burks, "The Presupposition Theory of Induction," *Philosophy of Science,* **20**:177–197 (1953); G. Buchdahl, "Induction and Scientific Method," *Mind,* **60**:16–34 (1951); among R. Carnap's many works on probability and induction, and in addition to those already mentioned: "What is Probability," *Scientific American,* **189**:128–138 (1953), "Probability as a Guide in Life," *Journal of Philosophy,* **44**:141–148 (1947), "Truth and Confirmation," in H. Feigl and W. Sellars, *op. cit.,* "Statistical and Inductive Probability," in E. Madden, *op. cit.* On Carnap's views, see the discussions in P. A. Schilpp, ed., *The Philosophy of Rudolph Carnap* (LaSalle, Ill.: Open Court, 1964), especially J. G. Kemeny, "Carnap's Theory of Probability and Induction," A. W. Burks, "On the Significance of Carnap's System of Inductive Logic for the Philosophy of Induction," H. Putnam, " 'Degree of Confirmation' and Inductive Logic," E. Nagel, "Carnap's Theory of Induction," and Carnap's replies to these discussions (Section V, pp. 966–998). See also C. W. Churchman, "Probability Theory," Parts I, II, III, *Philosophy of Science,* **12**:147–173 (1945) and "A Pragmatic Theory of Induction" in P. Frank, ed., *The Validation of Scientific Theories* (New York: Collier Books, 1961); C. Ducasse, "Some Observations Concerning the Nature of Probability," *Journal of Philosophy,* **38**:393–403 (1941); H. Feigl, "De Principiis non est Disputandum . . . ? On the Meaning and Limits of Justification," in M. Black, ed., *Philosophical Analysis* [Ithaca, N.Y.: Cornell University Press, 1950 (reprinted, Englewood Cliffs, N.J.: Prentice-Hall, 1963)], and also Feigl's "The Logical Character of the Principle of Induction," *Philosophy of Science,* **1**:20–29 (1934) (reprinted in H. Feigl and W. Sellars, *op. cit.*) and "On the Vindication of Induction," *Philosophy of Science,* **28**:212–216 (1961); P. E. B. Jourdain, "Causality, Induction and Probability," *Mind,* **28**:162–179 (1919); W. Kneale, "Probability and Induction," *Mind,* **60**:310–317 (1951); R. D. Luce and P. Suppes, "Preference, Utility and Subjective Probability," in R. D. Luce, R. R. Bush, E. Galanter, eds., *Handbook of Mathematical Psychology,* Vol. III (New York: Wiley, 1965); E. Nagel, "A Frequency Theory of Probability," *Journal of Philosophy,* **30**:533–554 (1933), and "Probability and Non-Demonstrative Inference," *Philosophy and Phenomenological Research,* **5**:485:507 (1945). This same issue contains a symposium on probability, in which D. Williams, H. Margenau, F. Kaufmann, and G. Bergmann are among the other contributors. See also Nagel, "Probability and the Theory of Knowledge," *Philosophy of Science,* **6**:212–253 (1939) [reprinted in E. Nagel, *Sovereign Reason* (New York: The Free Press, 1954)]. Also see O. Neurath, "Prediction and Induction," Analysis, **3**:5ff. (1946). Karl Popper, whose views on the method of conjecture and of refutation in science argue against "inductivist" approaches, develops his position on probability and induction in *The Logic of Scientific Discovery* (London: Hutchinson, 1959), especially Chapters 1, 8–10. See also his essays, "Three Views Concerning Human Knowledge," "Truth, Rationality and the Growth of Scientific Knowledge" (especially Sections x-xxii), and "The Demarcation Between Science and Metaphysics" (especially Section 6). All of these are in K. Popper, *Conjectures and Refutations* (New York: Basic Books, 1962). For a recent criticism of Popper's view, see R. Carnap, "Probability and Content Measure" in P. Feyerabend and G. Maxwell, *Matter, Mind and Method* (Minneapolis, Minn.: University of Minnesota Press, 1966). See also H. Reichenbach, "The Logical Foundations of the Concept of Probability," in H. Feigl and M. Brodbeck, *op. cit.*, and for a critique of Reichenbach's view, see J. Katz, *The Problem of Induction and its Solution* (Chicago: University of Chicago Press, 1962). See also W. Salmon, "The Predictive Inference," *Philosophy of Science,* **24**:180–190 (1957) and "Inductive Inference," in B. Baumrin, ed., *Philosophy of Science—The Delaware Seminar,* Vol. II (New York: Interscience, 1963); F. L. Will, "Is There a Problem about Induction?" *Journal of Philosophy,* **39**:505–513 (1942) and "Will the Future Be Like the Past?" *Mind,* **56**:332–347 (1947).

CHAPTER 10

Perhaps there is no better place to begin considering the problem of understanding and explanation than with a reading of Plato's dialogue *Theatetus,* which concerns itself with the conditions of knowledge. Plato's distinction between scientific knowledge and mere opinion is elaborated in many other dialogues, constituting a main issue in his so-called theory of forms. See, for example, *The Republic,* Books VI and VII, and especially those sections in VII which deal with the education of the rulers. Aristotle's discussion of scientific knowledge and explanation in Book A of the *Metaphysics* also pursues this theme, with a different emphasis. A recent introductory treatment of epistemological questions of knowledge and belief, which bears on the broader questions of scientific explanation, and of rationality in general is I. Scheffler, *Conditions of Knowledge* (Chicago: Scott, Foresman, 1965). Chapter 1 of Nagel's *Structure of Science* (New York: Harcourt, Brace, 1961), also gives an introduction to questions of scientific explanation. The matter of understanding which has in large part been ignored in discussions of scientific explanation because of its psychological tinge, does rise in some recent works. See, for example, D. Bohm, "On the Problem of Truth and Understanding in Science," in M. Bunge, ed.,*The Critical Approach to Science and Philosophy* (New York: The Free Press, 1964); J. J. C. Smart, "Philosophy and Scientific Plausibility," in P. Feyerabend and G. Maxwell, eds., *Matter, Mind and Method,* (Minneapolis, University of Minnesota Press, 1966); S. Toulmin, *Foresight and Understanding* (New York: Harper & Row, 1963); L. K. Nash, *The Nature of the Natural Sciences* (Boston: Little, Brown, 1963), Chapter XI; N. R. Hanson, *Patterns of Discovery* (Cambridge: Cambridge University Press, 1961); T. S. Kuhn, *The Structure of Scientific Revolutions, International Encyclopedia of Unified Science,* Vol. II, no. 2 (Chicago: University of Chicago Press, 1962); M. Polanyi, *Personal Knowledge* (New York: Harper & Row, 1960).

The nature of scientific laws and the role of theories in science are questions which are dealt with extensively in the literature. The classic older formulations are in W. Whewell, *The Philosophy of the Inductive Sciences* (London: John W. Parker, 1847), two volumes, especially Vol. II, Books XI, XIII; E. Mach, "On the Economical Nature of Physical Inquiry," in *Popular Scientific Lectures,* tr. T. J. McCormack (LaSalle, Ill.: Open Court, 1943), and also in his *Root of the Principle of the Conservation of Energy* (LaSalle, Ill.: Open Court, 1911), and *The Principles of Mechanics,* tr. T. J. McCormack (LaSalle, Ill.: Open Court, 1902); H. Poincaré, "Is Science Artificial?" and "Science and Reality," in *The Value of Science* [New York: Dover, 1958 (reprint)]; P. Duhem, *The Aim and Structure of Physical Theory,* tr. P. P. Wiener (Princeton, N.J.: Princeton University Press, 1953); E. Meyerson, *Identity and Reality,* tr. K. Loewenberg [New York: Dover, 1962 (reprint)] and the important but as yet untranslated *De l'Explication dans les sciences* (Paris: Payot, 1927); J. B. Stallo, *The Concepts and Theories of Modern Physics,* ed., P. W. Bridgman (Cambridge, Mass.: Harvard University Press, 1960); and N. R. Campbell, *Physics—The Elements* (Cambridge: Cambridge University Press, 1920), and also the introductory text by Campbell, *What Is Science?* [New York: Dover, 1952 (reprint)].

More recent discussion includes P. W. Bridgman, *The Nature of Physical Theory* (Princeton, N.J.: Princeton University Press, 1936); M. Bunge, *Metascientific Queries* (Springfield, Ill.: Thomas, 1959), Chapter 4; E. Cassirer, *Determinism and Indeterminism in Modern Physics* (New Haven: Yale University Press, 1956), especially Part 2, Chapters 4–5; S. Körner, "On Laws of Nature," *Mind,* **62**:218–229 (1953); J. A. Passmore, "Prediction and Scientific Law," *Australasian Journal of Philosophy,* **24**:1–33 (1946); R. E. Peierls, *The Laws of Nature* (New York: Scribner, 1956). In A. Danto and S. Morgenbesser, eds., *Philosophy of Science* (New York: Meridian, 1960), Part Two, there is a good selection of readings, including Mach and Duhem, and selections from Hempel and Oppenheim's "The Logic of Explanation," C. F. Presley, "Laws and Theories in the Physical Science," W. H. Watson, "On Methods of Representation" and L. Boltzmann, "Theories as Representations" (from his *Fundamental Principles of Mechanics*). See also M. Schlick, "Are Natural Laws Conventions?" in H. Feigl and M. Brodbeck, *Readings in the Philosophy of Science* (New York: Appleton-Century-Crofts, 1953); and the more technical discussion, E. Wigner, "Events, Laws of Nature, and Invariance Principles," *Science,* **145**:995–998.

The question of explanation and prediction, and the issues in the deductive or covering-law model of explanation are discussed in C. Hempel's writings, the principal ones of which have been collected in the recent volume *Aspects of Scientific Explanation* (New York: Macmillan, 1966). The central work is perhaps "The Logic of Explanation" by C. Hempel and

P. Oppenheim, which appeared in *Philosophy of Science,* **15**:135–175 (1948) and is reprinted in large part in H. Feigl and M. Brodbeck, *op. cit.* See also the discussion in R. Carnap, "The Methodological Character of Theoretical Concepts," in H. Feigl and G. Maxwell, eds., *Minnesota Studies in the Philosophy of Science* (Minneapolis: University of Minnesota Press, 1958), Vol. II; C. Hempel, "The Theoretician's Dilemma"; and M. Scriven, "Definitions, Explanations and Theories" in the same volume. In Volume III of *Minnesota Studies* (*Scientific Explanation, Space and Time,* 1962), there is a series of articles on these questions, including C. Hempel, "Deductive-Nomological vs. Statistical Explanation," M. Scriven, "Explanations, Predictions and Laws," M. Brodbeck, "Explanation, Prediction and 'Imperfect' Knowledge." In B. Baumrin, ed., *Philosophy of Science—The Delaware Seminar,* Vol. II (New York: Interscience, 1963), Part I contains discussion of scientific explanation, prediction and theories by P. K. Feyerabend, "How to Be a Good Empiricist—A Plea for Tolerance in Matters Epistemological"; N. Rescher, "Fundamental Problems in the Theory of Scientific Explanation"; W. Sellars, "Theoretical Explanation"; Sylvain Bromberger, "A Theory about the Theory of Theory and about the Theory of Theories"; and M. Scriven, "The Limits of Physical Explanation." See also, I. Scheffler, "Explanation, Prediction and Abstraction," *British Journal for the Philosophy of Science,* **7**:293–309 (1957) and the full discussion in his *The Anatomy of Inquiry* (New York: Knopf, 1963), and his "Prospects of a Modest Empiricism," *Review of Metaphysics,* **10**:383–400, 602–625 (1957); S. Bromberger, "An Approach to Explanation," in R. J. Butler, ed., *Studies in Analytical Philosophy* (Oxford: Blackwell, 1962); P. Frank, "Mechanical 'Explanation' or Mechanical Description?" Chapter 6 of his *Modern Science and its Philosophy* (Cambridge, Mass.: Harvard University Press, 1949); D. L. Miller, "Explanation vs. Description," *Philosophical Review,* **56**:306–312 (1947); J. Hospers, "On Explanation," *Journal of Philosophy,* **43**:337–356 (1946); A. Pap, *Introduction to the Philosophy of Science* (New York: The Free Press, 1962), Part 5, Chapter 18, "Logical Analysis of Explanation," pp. 343–357; G. Schlesinger, *Method in the Physical Sciences* (New York: Humanities Press, 1963); J. W. Yolton, "Explanation," *British Journal for the Philosophy of Science,* **10**:194–208 (1959).

In R. S. Cohen and M. Wartofsky, eds., *Boston Studies in the Philosophy of Science* II (New York: Humanities Press, 1965), there is a symposium on current issues in Explanation which includes J. J. C. Smart, "Conflicting Views About Explanation," W. Sellars, "Scientific Realism or Irenic Instrumentalism," H. Putnam, "How Not to Talk About Meaning" and P. K. Feyerabend, "Reply to Criticism." In the same volume, see also the historical treatment by E. Mendelsohn, "Physical Models and Physiological Concepts: Explanation in Nineteenth-Century Biology" and the Comments by E. Mayr. In M. Wartofsky, ed., *Boston Studies in the Philosophy of*

Science, Vol. I (Dordrecht, Holland: Reidel, 1963) see A. Grünbaum, "The Falsifiability of Theories: Total or Partial? A Contemporary Evaluation of the Duhem-Quine Thesis" and L. Tisza, "The Logical Structure of Physics" and the discussion following. See also H. Feigl, "Some Remarks on the Meaning of Scientific Explanation," in H. Feigl and W. Sellars, eds., *Readings in Philosophical Analysis* (New York: Appleton-Century-Crofts, 1949).

Discussion on the nature of scientific theories, of theoretical entities, and of models includes L. W. Beck, "Constructions and Inferred Entities," in H. Feigl and M. Brodbeck, *op. cit.;* R. B. Braithwaite, *Scientific Explanation* (Cambridge: Cambridge University Press, 1953), especially Chapters iii, iv, and ix; M. Bunge, "Phenomenological Theories," in M. Bunge, ed., *The Critical Approach to Science and Philosophy—Essays in Honor of Karl Popper* (New York: The Free Press, 1964); H. Feigl, "Existential Hypotheses," *Philosophy of Science,* **17**:35–62 (1950); P. K. Feyerabend, "Attempt at a Realistic Interpretation of Experience," *Aristotelian Society Proceedings,* **58**:143–170 (1958); and also his "Explanation, Reduction and Empiricism," in H. Feigl and G. Maxwell, eds., *Minnesota Studies in the Philosophy of Science,* Vol. III (Minneapolis: University of Minnesota Press, 1962), and "Realism and Instrumentalism—Comments on the Logic of Factual Support," in M. Bunge, ed., *The Critical Approach to Science and Philosophy* (New York: Free Press, 1964). See also P. Frank, "Comments on Realistic vs. Phenomenalistic Interpretations," *Phil. of Sci.,* **17**:166–169 (1950) and "Metaphysical Interpretations of Science," *Brit. Journal for the Phil. of Sci.,* **1**:60–91 (1950). The volume edited by H. Freudenthal, *The Concept and the Role of the Model in Mathematics and Natural and Social Science* (Dordrecht, Holland: Reidel, 1961) contains a number of important papers on this issue, for example, L. Apostel, "Towards the Formal Study of Models in the Non-Formal Sciences," H. J. Groenewold, "The Model in Physics," A. Kuipers, "Model and Insight," P. Suppes, "Meaning and Uses of Models in Mathematics and the Empirical Science," and J. B. Ubbink, "Model, Description and Knowledge." See also, on this, the Symposium on Models in the Empirical Sciences, in E. Nagel, P. Suppes, and A. Tarski, eds., *Logic, Methodology and Philosophy of Science* (Stanford, Calif.: Stanford University Press, 1962), which contains contributions by R. B. Braithwaite, L. Hurwicz, P. Suppes, H. Putnam, and J. Vigier; and in the same volume, the "Symposium on Theoretical and Empirical Aspects of Science," with contributions from J. Kotarbinska, H. Mehlberg, K. Popper, and J. H. Woodger. There is a sustained treatment of this question in M. Hesse, *Models and Analogies in Science* (Notre Dame, Ind.: University of Notre Dame Press, 1966), and in her *Forces and Fields* (London: Nelson, 1961), Chapter 1; also, in E. Nagel, *The Structure of Science* (New York: Harcourt, Brace, 1961) Chapters V and VI; E. H. Hutten, "The Role of Models in Physics," *British*

Journal for the Philosophy of Science, **4**:284–301 (1953); M. Wartofsky, "The Model Muddle—Proposals for an Immodest Realism" (forthcoming). See also W. Kneale, "Induction, Explanation and Transcendent Hypotheses," in H. Feigl and M. Brodbeck, *op. cit.,* and in the same volume, K. McQuorquodale and P. E. Meehl, "On a Distinction Between Hypothetical Constructs and Intervening Variables [reprinted from *Psychological Review,***55**:95–107 (1948)]; G. Maxwell, "The Ontological Status of Theoretical Entities," in H. Feigl and G. Maxwell, *op. cit.,* Vol. III, which discusses the issues raised in R. Carnap's influential papers which are relevant here: "Empiricism, Semantics and Ontology" and "Testability and Meaning," both reprinted as Appendices to the revised edition of R. Carnap, *Meaning and Necessity* (Chicago: University of Chicago Press, 1956). See also W. Rosenblith and N. Wiener, "The Role of Models in Science," *Philosophy of Science,* **12**:316–322 (1945); S. Stebbing, "Constructions," *Proceedings of the Aristotelian Society,* **34**:1–30 (1933–34) and also her "Logical Constructions and Knowledge through Description," *Proceedings, 7th International Congress of Philosophy* (1930), in which the position of Russell and others, on the matter of substituting logical constructions for inferred entities, is discussed. On Russell's view, see his "The Relation of Sense Data to Physics," in *Mysticism and Logic* (New York: Doubleday Anchor, n.d.), and in the recent symposium on the philosophy of Bertrand Russell, with W. V. Quine, C. Hempel, and H. Wang, *Journal of Philosophy,* **63**: 657–673 (1966). On theories and models in the social sciences, see A. Kaplan, *Conditions of Inquiry—Methodology for Behavioral Science* (San Francisco: Chandler, 1964) especially Chapters vii, viii, and ix; also H. A. Simon and A. Newell, "Models: Their Uses and Limitations" in L. D. White, ed., *The State of the Social Sciences* (Chicago: University of Chicago Press, 1956) and H. A. Simon, *Models of Man* (New York: Wiley, 1957).

CHAPTER 11

Causality is a central issue through the history of modern philosophy and science. Some major and seminal treatments are those of Leibniz, in *The Discourse on Metaphysics and The Leibniz-Clarke Correspondence,* ed., G. H. Alexander (Manchester: Manchester University Press, 1956); Kant, in the *Critique of Pure Reason,* tr. N. Kemp Smith (New York: St. Martin's Press, 1961), especially Chapter II, Section 2, Part 4, "The Second Analogy" and "The Third Antinomy"; Hume, *Treatise of Human Nature,* Selby-Bigge, ed. (London: Oxford University Press, 1941), Book I, Part III; and *An Enquiry Concerning Human Knowledge* (Indianapolis, Ind.: Bobbs-Merrill, 1955). [For some of the many discussions of Hume's view of causality, see A. N. Whitehead, *Process and Reality* (New York: Macmillan, 1929, pp. 263 ff.), C. A. Mace, "Hume's Doctrine of Causality," *Aristotelian Society Proceedings* **32**:301–328 (1932), and the essays by J. A. Robinson, T. J. Richards and J. W. Lenz in V. C. Chappell, ed., *Hume—A Collection of Critical Essays* (New York: Doubleday, Anchor, 1966)]. Important works devoted mainly to this question are J. D. Bernal, *The Freedom of Necessity* (London: Routledge and Kegan Paul, 1949); É. Borel, *Le Hasard* (Paris: Presses Universitaires Françaises, 1948); É. Boutroux, *De la contingence des lois de la nature* (Paris: Alcan, 1898); D. Bohm, *Causality and Chance in Modern Physics* (London: Routledge and Kegan Paul, 1957), especially Chapters I–III, in which Bohm sets forth the basis for his distinctive point of view among quantum physicists; M. Born, *The Natural Philosophy of Cause and Chance* (London: Oxford University Press, 1949); L. Brunschvicg, *L'Expérience humaine et la causalité physique* (Paris: Alcan, 1922); E. Cassirer, *Determinism and Indeterminism in Modern Physics* (New Haven: Yale University Press, 1956), esp. Chapter 6 on "The General Principle of Causality"; F. Enriques, *Causalité et déterminisme dans la philosophie et l'histoire des sciences* (Paris: Hermann, 1941); P. Frank, *Das Kausalgesetz und seine Grenzen* [Vienna: Springer, 1932 (translated into French by J. du Plessis de Grénedan, as *Le Principe de causalité et ses limites* (Paris: Flammarion, 1937)]. For further discussion by Frank, see his *Philosophy of Science* (Englewood Cliffs, N.J.: Prentice-Hall, 1957), Chapters 11 and 12 ("Causal Laws" and "The Principle of Causality") and his *Modern Science and Its Philosophy* (Cambridge, Mass.: Harvard University Press, 1949), Chapter 9 ("Determinism and Indeterminism in Modern Physics"). See also the monograph by V. Lenzen, *Causality in Natural Science* (Springfield, Ill.: Thomas, 1954). A masterful study of the causal principle in the history of science, and a striking thesis as to its status, is in the important book of É. Meyerson, *Identity and Reality,* tr. K. Loewenberg [London: George Allen and Unwin, 1930 (reprinted, New York: Dover, 1962)], as well as in his other, as yet untranslated, works, *De L'Explication dans les sciences* and *Le Chéminement de la pensée.* See also *E. Nagel's* important discussion in his *The Structure of Science, op. cit.,* Chapter 10; and in his *Freedom and Reason* (New York: The Free Press, 1951), the essay "The Causal Character of Modern Physical Theory" (reprinted in Feigl and Brodbeck, eds., *Readings in the Philosophy of Science* (New York: Appleton-Century-Crofts, 1953); M. Planck, "The Concept of Causality in Physics," in P. Wiener, *Readings in the Philosophy of Science* (New York: Scribner, 1953), [from Planck's *Scientific Autobiography* (New York: Philosophical Library, 1949)]; B. Russell, "On the Notion of Cause, with Applications to the Free Will Problem," in *Mysticism and Logic* [London: George Allen and Unwin, 1954 (reprinted, New York: Doubleday Anchor Books, 1957)]. (For a full analysis of Russell's views on this subject see E. Götlind, *Bertrand Russell's Theory of Causation* (Uppsala, Sweden,

1952); L. Silberstein, *Causality* (London: Macmillan, 1933) and H. Weyl, *Philosophy of Mathematics and Natural Science* (Princeton, N.J.: Princeton University Press, 1949), especially Part II, Chapter iii, Section 23, and Appendix C.

The most sustained full-scale discussion of causality in the contemporary literature of philosophy of science is M. Bunge, *Causality—The Place of the Causal Principle in Modern Science* (Cambridge, Mass.: Harvard University Press, 1959). Among the symposium discussions that have been published recently are S. Hook, ed., *Determinism and Freedom in the Age of Modern Science* (New York: New York University Press, 1959), which includes Brand Blanshard, "The Case for Determinism," Max Black, "Making Something Happen," P. W. Bridgman, "Determinism in Modern Science," A. Landé, "The Case for Indeterminism," and D. W. Sciama, "Determinism and the Cosmos," as well as discussion by Nagel, Hook, Pap, Taylor, and others. See also M. Wartofsky, ed., *Boston Studies in the Philosophy of Science,* Vol. 1. (Dordrecht, Holland: Reidel, 1963), which includes the symposium on "Deterministic Interpretations of the Quantum Theory" (R. Schiller, A. Siegel, and A. Shimony); and S. Körner, ed., *Observation and Interpretation* [London: Butterworth, 1957 (reprinted New York: Dover, n.d.)], which includes J. Vigier, "The concept of probability in the frame of the probabilistic and the causal interpretation of quantum mechanics" and the discussion between D. Bohm and L. Rosenfeld on so-called hidden-variable approaches to causal explanation and their critique.

Again, one of the best introductory discussions of the question of causality and of the logic of causal propositions is in A. Pap, *An Introduction to the Philosophy of Science* (New York: The Free Press, 1962), especially Part 4, Chapters 14–17, on "Causality and Laws of Nature," which includes a discussion of counterfactuals and dispositional statements, and of the determinism-indeterminism issue. The formal or logical analysis of causal propositions is treated in A. W. Burks, "The Logic of Causal Propositions," *Mind,* **60**:363–382 (1951); Dagfinn Follesdal, "Quantification into Causal Contexts" and the comment on Follesdal's paper by Roderick Chisholm, "Query on Substitutivity" in R. S. Cohen and M. Wartofsky, eds., *Boston Studies in the Philosophy of Science,* Vol. II (New York: Humanities Press, 1965); G. P. Henderson, "Causal Implication," *Mind,* **63**:504–518 (1954); J. Watling, "Propositions Asserting Causal Connection," *Analysis,* **14**:31–37 (1953–54). See also K. W. Rankin, "Causal Modalities and Alternative Action," *Philosophical Quarterly,* **7**:289–304 (1957) and the excerpt from R. von Mises, *Positivism: A Study in Human Understanding* (Cambridge, Mass.: Harvard University Press, 1951), reprinted in P. Wiener, *op. cit.,* as "Causality and Probability."

The extensive periodical literature on this topic includes R. D. Bradley, "Must the Future Be What It Is Going to Be?" *Mind,* **68**:193–208 (1959) and "Determinism and Indeterminism in Microphysics," *Brit. J. for the Phil. of Science,* **13**:193–215 (1962); R. B. Braithwaite, "The Idea of Necessary Connection," Parts I and II, *Mind,* **36**:476–477 (1927), **37**:62–72 (1928); R. G. Collingwood, "On the So-called Idea of Causation," *Aristotelian Society Proceedings,* **38**:85–112 (1938); C. J. Ducasse, "On the Nature and Efficacy of Causes," *Phil. Review,* **41**:395–399 (1932) and "On the Analysis of Causality," *Journal of Philosophy,* **4**:422–426 (1957); A. C. Ewing, "A Defence of Causality," *Aristotelian Society Proceedings,* **33**:95–128 (1933); H. Feigl, "Notes on Causality," in Feigl and Brodbeck, *op. cit.;* W. B. Gallie, "An Interpretation of Causal Law," *Mind,* **48**:409–426 (1939); I. J. Good, "A Theory of Causality," *Brit. Journal for the Phil. of Science,* **9**:307–310 (1958); T. A. Goudge, "Causal Explanation in Natural History," *Brit. J. for the Phil. of Science,* **9**:194–202 (1958); M. Grene, "Causes," *Philosophy,* **38**:149–159 (1963); J. C. Gregory "Causal Efficacy," *Aristotelian Society Proceedings,* **44**:1–14 (1944); E. W. Hall, "Time and Causality," *Phil. Rev.,* **43**:333–350 (1934); A. Hofstadter, "Causality and Necessity," *J. Phil.,* **46**:257–270 (1949); and "Power and Causality," *J. Phil.,* **32**:5–19 (1935); D. J. O'Connor, "Determinism and Predictability," *Brit. J. for the Phil. of Science,* **7**:310–315 (1957); D. F. Pears, "The Priority of Causes," *Analysis,* **17**:54–63 (1956–1957); H. C. Plaut, "Condition, Cause, Free Will and the Direction of Time," *Brit. J. for the Phil. of Science,* **11**:212–221 (1961); A. Pap, "A Note on Causation and the Meaning of Event," *J. Phil.,* **54**:155–159 (1957); W. H. Riker, "Causes of Events," *J. Phil.,* **55**:281–291 (1958); H. D. Roelofs, "Second Thoughts on Causality," *Mind,* **56**:60–71 (1947); L. J. Russell, "The Principle of Causality," *Aristotelian Society Proceedings,* **46**:105–126 (1946); R. L. Saw, "An Aspect of Causal Connexion," *Aristotelian Society Proceedings,* **35**:95–112 (1935); F. C. S. Schiller, "Creation, Emergence, Novelty," *Aristotelian Society Proceedings,* **31**:25–36 (1931); M. Schlick, "Causality in Everyday Life and in Recent Science," in Feigl and Sellars, eds., *Readings in Philosophical Analysis* (New York: Appleton-Century-Crofts, 1949); M. Scriven, "Randomness and the Causal Order," *Analysis,* **17**:5–9 (1956–1957); H. A. Simon, "On the Definition of the Causal Relation," *J. Phil.,* **49**:517–528 (1952); the symposium on "Mechanical and Teleological Causation," with C. A. Mace, G. F. Stout, A. C. Ewing and C. D. Broad, *Aristotelian Society Proceedings,* supp. Vol. **14**:22–112 (1935); J. R. Weinberg, "The Idea of Causal Efficacy," *J. Phil.,* **47**:397–407 (1950).

The literature on causality and human action, both in relation to the question of free will and action and to causality in psychology and the social sciences, is listed briefly here, and there is a fuller account of relevant works in the bibliographical note to Chapter 14. William James' essay "The Dilemma of Determinism" states some classical problems and gives a generally voluntarist account (in James' *The Will to Believe and Other*

Essays in Popular Philosophy [New York: Dover, 1956 (reprint)]. L. S. Feuer and E. M. Albert join in a symposium on "Causality in the Social Sciences," *J. Phil.,* **51**:681–706 (1954). See also W. Gruen, "Determinism, Fatalism and Historical Materialism," *J. Phil.,* **33**:617–628 (1936); A. Grünbaum, "Causality and the Science of Human Behavior," *Am. Scientist,* **40**:665–676 (1952) (reprinted in Feigl and Brodbeck, *op. cit.*); H. L. A. Hart, A. M. Honoré, "Causation in the Law," *Mind,* **70**:553–561 (1961); also see the extensive treatment by H. L. A. Hart and A. M. Honoré, *Causation and the Law* (Oxford: Clarendon Press, 1959). See also the symposium volume *Determinism and the Will,* D. F. Pears, ed., (New York: St. Martin's Press, 1963), which includes discussion by Pears, P. F. Strawson, H. L. A. Hart, James Thomson, S. Hampshire, and others; and the review by M. Wartofsky, *J. Phil.,* **61**:308–315 (1964). The classical experimental study in psychology is A. Michotte, *The Perception of Causality* (London: Methuen, 1963). See also G. F. McIntosh, "The Category of Causation in Psychology," *Australasian J. Phil.,* **13**:257–278 (1935).

Teleological, organismic, and emergentist views of causality and the approach of cybernetics and of "retroactive" causality are referred to in the bibliographical note to Chapter 13.

CHAPTER 12

Like the concept of causality, the concepts of space, time, and matter are central throughout the history of science and of natural philosophy, and are cornerstones of metaphysical thought. Thus, the major treatments of these questions range through the works of all major philosophers and philosopher-scientists, and involve central aspects of theological thought as well. No attempt will be made to include these in this bibliographical note, beyond specific mention of Kant's epoch-making formulation of the nature of space-time concepts [in *The Critique of Pure Reason,* tr. N. Kemp Smith (New York: St. Martin's Press, 1961), "Transcendental Aesthetic," pp. 65–91]. Special attention may be called to the views of Maimonides, Thomas Aquinas, Spinoza, Descartes, Leibniz, Boscovic, and Newton. The historical background of contemporary views is given in such works as E. A. Burtt, *The Metaphysical Foundations of Modern Science,* revised edition [New York: Doubleday, Anchor (reprint), n.d.], esp. Chapters III (Section D), IV (Sections B and C), and VII (Section 4, A, B, C, on Newton's philosophy of mass, space, and time); Max Jammer's excellent studies, *Concepts of Space* Cambridge, Mass.: Harvard University Press, 1954), *Concepts of Mass* (Cambridge, Mass.: Harvard University Press, 1961), and *Concepts of Force* (Cambridge, Mass.: Harvard University Press, 1957); M. Čapek, *The Philosophic Impact of Contemporary Physics*

(Princeton, N.J.: Van Nostrand, 1961); A. G. van Melsen, *From Atomos to Atom,* tr. H. J. Koren (Duquesne University Studies, Philosophical Series, 1952); and once again, É. Meyerson, *Identity and Reality* [London: George Allen and Unwin, 1930 (reprinted New York: Dover, 1962)], esp. Chapters iv, vi, and vii. Among the many studies on the history of physics which include discussions of these matters, there are A. D'Abro, *The Evolution of Scientific Thought from Newton to Einstein* [New York: Dover (reprint), 1950] and *The Rise of the New Physics* [New York: Dover (reprint), 1951]; G. Holton, *Concepts and Theories in Physical Science* (Cambridge, Mass.: Addison–Wesley, 1952); A. Einstein and L. Infeld, *The Evolution of Physics* (New York: Simon and Schuster, 1938). M. Munitz, ed., *Theories of the Universe* (New York: The Free Press, 1957) is a collection of cosmological accounts from Babylonian myths to the present, in many of which the concepts of space, time, and matter are central.

For characteristic views of space and time in systematic metaphysical thought, especially in relation to the distinction between the experience of space and time and the construction of "objective" space-time constructs, see G. W. F. Hegel, *Phenomenology of Mind,* tr. by Baillie (London: Allen and Unwin, 1961), especially Part A, Chapter 1, "The Certainty of the Senses," which deals with the concepts of "here" and "now"; the British neo-Hegelian treatment by F. H. Bradley, *Appearance and Reality* (Oxford: Clarendon Press, 1930); Sir Samuel Alexander's compendious discussion in *Space, Time and Deity* (London: Macmillan, 1920), two volumes; J. McTaggart, *Existence and Reality* (Cambridge: Cambridge University Press, 1921–1927), especially the discussion of the "unreality" of time; C. D. Broad, *An Examination of McTaggart's Philosophy* (Cambridge: Cambridge University Press, 1933–1938) and A. N. Whitehead, *Process and Reality* (New York: Harper & Row, 1957) and *Scientific Thought* (London: Kegan Paul, 1923). See also, for a contemporary idealist discussion, W. T. Stace, *Time and Eternity* (Princeton, N.J.: Princeton University Press, 1952). Intuitionist and phenomenological views of time and space are represented in H. Bergson, *Time and Free Will,* tr. F. L. Pogson (London: Allen and Unwin, 1913); *Creative Evolution,* tr. Mitchell (New York: Holt, 1911); *Duration and Simultaneity,* tr. L. Jacobson (Indianapolis, Ind.: Bobbs-Merrill, 1965); and *Matter and Memory,* tr. N. M. Paul and W. S. Palmer (London: Allen and Unwin, 1950); E. Husserl, *The Phenomenology of Internal Time-Consciousness,* tr. J. S. Churchill (The Hague: Martinus Nijhoff, 1964); and M. Merleau-Ponty, *The Phenomenology of Perception,* tr. C. Smith (New York: Humanities Press, 1962).

Some major discussions in philosophy of science include É. Borel, *Space and Time;* N. Bohr, *Atomic Physics and Human Knowledge* (New York: Wiley, 1958), and *Atomic Theory and the Description of Nature* (Cambridge: Cambridge University Press, 1934); M. Born, *The Constitution of Matter,* tr. E. W. Blair and T. S. Wheeler (London: Methuen, 1923); C. D. Broad, *Scientific Thought* (London: Routledge and Kegan Paul, 1923), especially Chapters IX-XII; C. D. Broad, "Is Space Euclidean?" *Mind,* **24**:464–480 (1915); E. Cassirer, *Substance and Function in Einstein's Theory of Relativity* (New York: Dover, 1953); R. G. Collingwood, *The Idea of Nature* (Oxford: Clarendon Press, 1945); F. M. Cornford, "The Invention of Space" in *Essays in Honor of Gilbert Murray* (London: Allen and Unwin, 1936); A. Eddington's *The Nature of the Physical World* [Ann Arbor: University of Michigan Press (reprint), 1958] is an especially good introduction to the newer concepts of space, time, and matter. See especially Chapters III and X. A more advanced account is in Eddington's *Space, Time and Gravitation* (Cambridge: Cambridge University Press, 1935). An introductory account of the new physics is given also in J. Jeans, *The New Background of Science* [Ann Arbor: University of Michigan Press (reprint) 1959)], especially Chapters III–V, and by W. Heisenberg, *Physics and Philosophy* (New York: Harper, 1958) and *The Physicist's Conception of Nature,* tr. A. J. Pomerans (New York: Harcourt, Brace, 1958). See also Philipp Frank's discussion in *Philosophy of Science* (Englewood Cliffs, N. J.: Prentice-Hall, 1957), especially Chapters 6–10, and his "Philosophical Misinterpretations of Quantum Theory," in *Modern Science and Its Philosophy* (Cambridge, Mass.: Harvard University Press, 1949). A full-scale treatment by a contemporary philosopher of physics is A. Grünbaum, *Philosophical Problems of Space and Time* (New York: Knopf, 1963). See also his essays, "The Nature of Time," in *Frontiers of Science and Philosophy,* R. G. Colodny, ed. (Pittsburgh, Pa.: Pittsburgh University Press, 1962); "Geometry, Chronometry and Empiricism," in H. Feigl and G. Maxwell, eds., *Minnesota Studies in Philosophy of Science,* Vol. III (Minneapolis: University of Minnesota Press, 1962) and "The Special Theory of Relativity as a Case Study of the Importance of the Philosophy of Science for the History of Science," in B. Baumrin, ed., *Philosophy of Science—The Delaware Seminar,* Vol. II (New York: Interscience, 1963). In the same volume, see also H. Putnam's critique of Grünbaum, "An Examination of Grünbaum's Philosophy of Geometry," and the essay by D. Shapere, "Space, Time and Language—An Examination of Some Problems and Methods of the Philosophy of Science." Among the classical older treatments are E. Mach *Space and Geometry* (LaSalle, Ill.: Open Court, 1943) and the selection from his *Science of Mechanics* (LaSalle, Ill.: Open Court, 1942) reprinted in H. Feigl and M. Brodbeck, eds., *Readings in the Philosophy of Science* (New York: Appleton-Century-Crofts, 1953), as "Newton's Views of Time, Space and Motion" [and at somewhat greater length in A. Danto and S. Morgenbesser, eds., *Philosophy of Science* (New York: Meridian, 1960)]. This latter collection includes also Newton's *Scholium* to the Definitions in *Principia Mathematica,* as

"Absolute and Relative Space, Time and Motion," and gives Bishop Berkeley's eighteenth-century criticism of Newton, selected from Berkeley's *Principles of Human Knowledge,* as well as a translation of H. Poincaré's "Geometry and Space." H. Poincaré's essays on these questions appear also in his *Science and Method* [New York: Dover (reprint), n.d.], and *The Value of Science* [New York: Dover (reprint) 1958]. Also see M. Planck, *Philosophy of Physics,* tr. W. H. Johnston (London: Allen and Unwin, 1936); and the series of works by H. Reichenbach *Philosophy of Space and Time* (New York: Dover, 1957), *Philosophical Foundations of Quantum Mechanics* (Berkeley, Calif.: University of California Press, 1946), and *The Direction of Time* [Berkeley, Calif.: University of California Press, 1956 (published posthumously and edited by Maria Reichenbach)] and the introductory treatment in *The Rise of Scientific Philosophy* (Berkeley, Calif.: University of California Press, 1951). In 1945–46, Ernest Nagel and Reichenbach engaged in an exchange: E. Nagel, "Reichenbach's *Philosophical Foundations of Quantum Mechanics,*" *J. Phil.,* **42**:437–444 (1945); H. Reichenbach, "Reply to Ernest Nagel's Criticism on My Views on Quantum Mechanics," *J. Phil.,* **43**:239–247 (1946); E. Nagel, "Reichenbach on Quantum Mechanics: A Rejoinder," *J. Phil.,* **43**:247–250 (1946). Nagel's later views are in *The Structure of Science* (New York: Harcourt, Brace, 1961), Chapter 10 ("Causality and Indeterminism in Physical Theory").

The Marxist critique of positivist views of space, time and matter is given in V. I. Lenin, *Materialism and Empirio-Criticism,* tr. D. Kvitko (New York: International Publishers, 1927), esp. Chapters Three and Five. Bertrand Russell deals with these matters in several works. See for example, his *Analysis of Matter* (New York: Harcourt, Brace, 1927), esp. Chapters 1–6 and 27–36; and *Human Knowledge: Its Scope and Limits* (New York: Simon and Schuster, 1948), esp. Part Four, Chapters 5–10. See also, É. Meyerson, *Réel et Déterminisme dans la physique quantique* (Paris: Hermann et Cie., 1933); H. Margenau, *The Nature of Physical Reality* (New York: McGraw-Hill, 1929); C. F. von Weizsäcker, *The World View of Physics* (Chicago: University of Chicago Press, 1949) and *The History of Nature* (Chicago: University of Chicago Press, 1949); H. Weyl, *Space-Time-Matter* (New York: Dover, 1950) and *Philosophy of Mathematics and Natural Science* (Princeton, N.J.: Princeton University Press, 1949), esp. Part II, Chapters i and iii; J. A. Wheeler, "Curved Empty Space-Time as the Building Material of the Physical World: An Assessment" in E. Nagel, P. Suppes and A. Tarski, eds., *Logic, Methodology and Philosophy* [Stanford, Calif.: Stanford University Press, 1962 (a very imaginative view by a leading physicist)]; J. J. Whitrow, *The Natural Philosophy of Time* [London: Nelson, 1961 (a detailed and learned account)]; and the important account of Sir Edmund Whittaker, *From Euclid to Eddington: A Study of the Conceptions of the External World* (Cambridge: Cambridge University Press, 1949). For philosophical and scientific subtlety of the highest order, see the essays by A. N. Whitehead collected in *A. N. Whitehead: The Interpretation of Science—Selected Essays,* A. H. Johnston, ed. (Indianapolis: Ind.; Bobbs-Merrill, 1961), which includes "Time, Space and Material," "Time," "Space, Time and Relativity," "The Philosophical Aspects of the Principle of Relativity," "The Idealistic Implications of Einstein's Theory," "The Problem of Simultaneity" (on the relation of measured time to lived time).

Other important discussions include, J. J. C. Smart, "The River of Time," *Mind,* **58**:483–494 (1949); R. O. Kapp, "Hypotheses About the Origin and Disappearance of Matter," *Brit. J. for the Phil. of Science,* **6**:177–186; H. Mehlberg, "Space, Time, Relativity," in *Proceedings of the 1964 International Congress of Logic, Methodology and Philosophy of Science* (Amsterdam: North-Holland Publishing Co., 1966); and the Symposium volume, *The Concept of Matter,* E. McMullin, ed. (Notre Dame, Ind.: University of Notre Dame Press, 1963), esp. Parts Four and Five. See also E. McMullin, "From Matter to Mass," in R. S. Cohen and M. W. Wartofsky, *Boston Studies in the Philosophy of Science,* Vol. II (New York: Humanities Press, 1965), and the "Comment on McMullin's View" by M. Wartofsky.

For a delightful introduction to Relativity Theory, see the work by two leading Soviet scientists, L. D. Landau and G. B. Rumer, *What Is Relativity?* tr. N. Kemmer, with an introduction by R. S. Cohen [Greenwich, Conn.: Fawcett Publications (reprint), 1966]. The excellent popular accounts by the founder of relativity theory and his colleague are A. Einstein, *Sidelights of Relativity* (New York: Dutton, 1923) and Philipp Frank, *Relativity—A Richer Truth* (Boston: Beacon Press, 1950). See also P. Bridgman, *A Primer of Relativity* (Middletown, Conn.: Wesleyan University Press, 1962), and D. Bohm, *The Special Theory of Relativity* (New York: Benjamin, 1965).

CHAPTER 13

Among the works which deal with the distinctiveness of biological systems are W. B. Cannon, *The Wisdom of the Human Body* (New York: W. W. Norton, 1939) which deals with the self-regulating homeostatic mechanisms of the organism, hence the "wisdom" [an excerpt appears in P. Wiener, *Readings in the Philosophy of Science* (New York: Scribner, 1953), under the title "The Self-Regulation of the Human Body"]; H. Driesch, *The Science and Philosophy of the Organism* (London: A. C. Black, 1908), and E. Rignano, *The Nature of Life* (New York: Harcourt,

Brace, 1930). (Driesch is the foremost proponent of the view of life as self-directed activity, in terms of some innate *entelechy,* irreducible to physical mechanism. Rignano too supports the view of life as exhibiting "vital" properties which are irreducible and distinctive of organisms.) C. J. Herrick, *The Evolution of Human Nature* [New York: Harper Torchbooks (reprint), 1961]; R. S. Lillie, *General Biology and Philosophy of Organism* (Chicago: University of Chicago Press, 1945); [see also his articles "Types of Physical Determination and the Activities of Living Organisms," *J. Phil.,* **28**:561–573 (1931)]; E. Mayr, *Animal Species and Evolution* (Cambridge, Mass.: Harvard University Press, 1965) (see also his article "Cause and Effect in Biology," *Science,* **134**:1501–1506 (1961); J. Loeb, *The Mechanistic Conception of Life* (Chicago: University of Chicago Press, 1912); P. B. Medawar, *The Uniqueness of the Individual* (London: Methuen, 1957) and *The Future of Man* (London: Methuen, 1960); J. Needham, *Order and Life* (Cambridge: Cambridge University Press, 1936) and *Integrative Levels: A Reevaluation of the Idea of Progress* (The Herbert Spencer Lecture, Oxford, 1937); E. S. Russell, *The Directiveness of Organic Activities* (Cambridge, Mass.: Cambridge University Press, 1945); E. Schrödinger, *What Is Life?* (Garden City, N.Y.: Doubleday, 1956) (an organicist view by a noted physicist); C. Sherrington, *Man on His Nature* (Cambridge, Mass.: Cambridge University Press, 1951); E. W. Sinnott, *Matter, Mind and Man* (New York: Harper & Row, 1957) and *Cell and Psyche* (Chapel Hill, N.C.: University of North Carolina Press, 1950); T. H. Savory, *Mechanistic Biology and Animal Behavior* (London: Watts, 1936); E. C. Tolman, *Purposive Behavior in Animals and Men* (New York: Appleton-Century-Crofts, 1932); L. von Bertalanffy, *Problems of Life—An Evolution of Modern Biological Thought* (New York: Harper & Row, 1952) (a distinctive organicist view in terms of general systems theory); W. M. Wheeler, *Essays in Philosophical Biology* (Cambridge, Mass.: Harvard University Press, 1939); J. H. Woodger, *Biological Principles* (New York: Harcourt, Brace, 1929) (this remains the best discussion of philosophical problems in biology). Other works dealing with the relation of biological to other questions include T. Dobzhansky, *The Biological Basis of Human Freedom* (New York: Columbia University Press, 1956); A. I. Oparin, *The Origin of Life* (New York: Academic Press, 1957) (the theory of an outstanding Soviet scientist about the physico-chemical conditions under which the formation of protein chains and of living cells could have taken place). See also *The Physics and Chemistry of Life* [by the Editors of the *Scientific American* (New York: Simon and Schuster, 1955)] which includes essays on this question by G. Wald ("The Origin of Life"), L. Pauling, R. B. Corey, and R. Hayward ("The Structure of Proteins"), and F. H. C. Crick ("The Structure of the Hereditary Material"). See also Crick's Nobel Prize lecture, "On the Genetic

Code," *Science,* **139**:461–464. On the relation of Marxist philosophy to biology, see M. Prenant, *Biology and Marxism* (London: Lawrence and Wishart, 1938) and on the genetics controversy over Lysenkoism in the 1940's see D. Joravsky, "The Lysenko Affair," *Sci. Am.,* **207**:41–47 (1962).

The periodical literature on mechanism, organicism, emergence and teleology in biological thought is extensive. See, for example, H. F. Blum, "On the Origin and Evolution of Living Machines," *American Scientist,* **49**:474–501 (1961) and "The Origin and Evolution of Human Culture," *American Scientist,* **51**:32–47 (1963) (in which Blum coins the term "mnemotype" for the memory-images transmitted in cultural evolution); C. D. Broad, "Mechanistic Explanation and Its Alternative," *Aristotelian Society Proceedings,* **19**:86–124 (1918–1919); M. R. Cohen, *Reason and Nature* (New York: The Free Press, 1953), Chapter III; C. Ducasse, "Explanation, Mechanism and Teleology," *J. Phil.,* **22**:150–155 (1925); W. Köhler, "Direction of Processes in Living Systems," in P. Frank, ed., *The Validation of Scientific Theories* [New York: Collier Books (reprint), 1961] (this volume contains also, in the section on "Organism and Machine"—part of a symposium organized by the American Association for the Advancement of Science in 1953—the following articles: N. Rashevsky, "Is the Concept of an Organism as a Machine a Useful One?" and the delightful essay by W. S. McCulloch, "Mysterium Iniquitatis—of Sinful Man Aspiring into the Place of God".) See also A. O. Lovejoy, "The Meanings of 'Emergence' and its Modes," in *Proceedings of the Sixth International Congress of Philosophy* [New York: Longmans, Green, 1927 (reprinted in P. Wiener, *op. cit.*)]; G. W. Gotshalk, "Causality and Emergence," *Phil. Review,* **51**:397–405 (1942); P. Henle, "The Status of Emergence," *J. Phil.,* **39**:486–493 (1942); E. Mayr, "Cause and Effect in Biology," *Science,* **134**:1501–1506. On the questions of reduction and teleological explanation, see A. Pap, *An Introduction to the Philosophy of Science* (New York: The Free Press, 1962), Chapter 19; E. C. Pollard, "Are Life Processes Governed by Physical Laws?" in B. Baumrin, ed., *Philosophy of Science—The Delaware Symposium* (New York: Interscience, 1963), Vol. II; also the important original paper on the notions of cybernetics, A. Rosenblueth, N. Wiener, and J. Bigelow, "Behavior, Purpose and Teleology," *Philosophy of Science,* **10**:18–24 (1943); N. Rashevsky's early article, "Physico-mathematical Methods in Biological and Social Science," *Erkenntnis,* **6**:357–365 (1936); F. A. O. Schmitt, "The Physical Basis of Life and Learning," *Science,* **149**:931–936 (1965); I. Scheffler, "Thoughts on Teleology," *Brit. J. for the Phil. of Science,* **9**:265–284 (1959); M. Schlick, "Philosophy of Organic Life," in H. Feigl and M. Brodbeck, eds., *Readings in the Philosophy of Science* (New York: Appleton-Century-Crofts, 1953) and in the same volume, E. Nagel, "Teleological Explanation and Teleological Systems." See also, W. Seifretz, "A Materialistic Interpretation of Life," *Philosophy of Science,* **6**:266–284 (1939); E. A. Singer, Jr., "Beyond Mechanism and Vitalism," *Philosophy of Science,* **1**:273–295 (1934), "Logico-Historical Study of Mechanism," in *Studies in the History of Science,* University of Pennsylvania Bicentennial Conference, 1941, and "Mechanism, Vitalism, Naturalism," *Philosophy of Science,* **13**:81–99 (1946); W. T. Stace, "Novelty, Indeterminism and Emergence," *Phil. Review,* **48**:296–310 (1939); G. F. Stout, "Mechanical and Teleological Causation," *Aristotelian Society Proceedings Supplement,* **14**:46–65 (1935); J. S. Willkie, "Causation and Explanation in Theoretical Biology," *Brit. J. for the Phil. of Science,* **1**:273–291 (1950). See also E. Yovits and D. Cameron, eds., *Self-Organizing Systems: Proceedings of an Interdisciplinary Conference* (New York: Pergamon Press, 1960), which includes H. von Foerster, "On Self-Organizing Systems and Their Environments," A. M. Uttley, "The Mechanization of Thought Processes," and W. McCulloch, "The Reliability of Biological Systems."

On questions of evolutionary theory and its interpretation, see H. Bergson, *Creative Evolution* (New York: Holt, 1911) which introduces the notion of an *élan vital* or "vital force" which expresses itself in evolution. For earlier views, see esp. A. Schopenhauer, *The World as Will and Idea,* tr. R. B. Haldane and J. Kemp (London: Routledge and Kegan Paul, 1906), and H. Spencer, *First Principles* [New York: DeWitt Revolving Fund (reprint), 1958], and *The Principles of Biology* (New York: Appleton-Century-Crofts, 1899). For contemporary discussion see T. Dobzhansky, *Genetics and the Origin of Species,* 3rd ed. (New York: Columbia University Press, 1951) and *Mankind Evolving—The Evolution of the Human Species* (New Haven: Yale University Press, 1962); T. A. Goudge, "The Concept of Evolution," *Mind,* **63**:16–25 (1954); J. Huxley, *Evolution: The Modern Synthesis* [Ithaca, N.Y.: Cornell University Press (reprint), 1966]; M. Mandelbaum, "The Scientific Background of Evolutionary Theory in Biology" in P. Wiener and A. Noland, eds., *The Roots of Scientific Thought* (New York: Basic Books, 1957). On the history of ideas with respect to this question, see also A. O. Lovejoy's classic study *The Great Chain of Being* (Cambridge, Mass.: Harvard University Press, 1936); B. Rensch, *Evolution Above the Species Level* (New York: Columbia University Press, 1960), esp. Chapter 8, "The Evolution of Life" and Chapter 10, "The Evolution of Consciousness"; G. G. Simpson, *The Meaning of Evolution;* J. C. Willis, *The Course of Evolution* (Cambridge: Cambridge University Press, 1940).

On questions of the methods of the biological sciences see especially the great work of Claude Bernard, *Introduction to Experimental Medicine* (New York: Dover, 1957); [Also the study by J. M. D. Olmsted and E. H. Olmsted, *Claude Bernard and the Experimental Method in Medicine* (New York: Henry Schuman, 1952)]; E. Caspari, "On the Conceptual

Basis of the Biological Sciences," in R. G. Colodny, ed., *Frontiers of Science and Philosophy* (Pittsburgh: Pittsburgh University Press, 1962); G. Sommerhof, *Analytical Biology* (London: Oxford University Press, 1950); and the works of J. H. Woodger, *The Axiomatic Method in Biology* (Cambridge: Cambridge University Press, 1937) and *Biology and Language* (Cambridge: Cambridge University Press, 1952). Relevant discussion on morphology and adaptation is in E. S. Russell, *Form and Function* (London: Murray, 1916), in the great and classic study by D'Arcy Wentworth Thompson, *Growth and Form* (Cambridge: Cambridge University Press, 1917), and in J. Needham, *Biochemistry and Morphogenesis* (Cambridge: Cambridge University Press, 1950).

CHAPTER 14

The dividing line between methodological and substantive questions, and between scientific questions of the behavioral and social sciences and questions of epistemology, social philosophy, and philosophy of mind is often very hard to draw. At the extremes, one may distinguish between hard experimental studies and empirical theories, on the one hand, and philosophical analysis and speculative reflection, on the other. But perhaps nowhere is there such a constant interplay between philosophical and scientific considerations as in the human sciences; nowhere does methodology impinge so directly upon the very character of the subject matter and its epistemological characterization. Perhaps because the subject matter is human consciousness, human action, human purpose, the very instrument of inquiry is caught up in the object of inquiry. Thus, a major emphasis in works dealing with the human sciences is the attempt to refashion the subject matter as an *objective* one, which may be approached in the same way, and with ostensibly the same dispassionateness as the natural sciences boast. Thus, in behaviorist psychology, in empirical sociology and anthropology, as in the craft of the historian, the attempt has been made to eliminate the subjectivity of the observer, to approach the subject matter in a "value-free" way. At the same time, the very problem of the participant observer, of the reflexivity of "mind thinking itself," or of man studying man has become a unique methodological issue in the human sciences. For this reason, which bears on the general question of the continuity of science and philosophy, the literature which could properly be listed here is vast, and cannot always be distinguished as "scientific" or "philosophical." The limitations of a bibliographical note impose severe exclusions therefore. The literature on relevant epistemological questions can only be touched on, as can also the rich lode of experimental psychology, and of empirical studies in the social sciences.

Part 1

On the questions of mind, consciousness, and behavior, and on the mind-body problem, some of the relevant works are A. F. Bentley, *Behavior, Knowledge, Fact* (Bloomington, Ind.: Principia Press, 1935); G. Bergmann, *The Philosophy of Science* (Madison: University of Wisconsin Press, 1957), and among Bergmann's many articles, representing the logical empiricist view, "On Some Methodological Problems of Psychology," *Philosophy of Science,* **7**:205–219 (1940), reprinted in H. Feigl and M. Brodbeck, *Readings in the Philosophy of Science* (New York: Appleton-Century-Crofts, 1953); "The Logic of Psychological Concepts," *Philosophy of Science,* **18**:93–110 (1951), "Theoretical Psychology" *Annual Review of Psychology,* **4**:435–458 (1953); B. Blanshard, "Behaviorism and the Theory of Knowledge," *Philosophical Review,* **37**:328–352 (1928); E. G. Boring, *The Physical Dimensions of Consciousness* (New York: The Century Co., 1933), and also "Mind and Mechanism," *American Journal of Psychology,* **59**:173–192 (1946); C. D. Broad, *The Mind and Its Place in Nature* (London: Kegan Paul, 1925) (a fundamental and systematic work, among the many which Broad has written on perception, consciousness, and the philosophy of mind); H. Driesch, *Mind and Body* (London: Methuen, 1927) (by the vitalist biologist); J. C. Eccles, *The Neurophysiological Basis of Mind* (Oxford: Clarendon, 1953); H. Feigl, "Principles and Problems of Theory-Construction in Psychology," in W. Dennis, ed., *Current Trends of Psychological Theory* (Pittsburgh: University of Pittsburgh Press, 1951); and his "Functionalism, Psychological Theory, and the Uniting Sciences: Some Discussion Remarks," *Psychological Review,* **62**:232–235 (1955); "Physicalism, Unity of Science and the Foundations of Psychology," in P. A. Schilpp, ed., *The Philosophy of Rudolf Carnap* (LaSalle, Ill.: Open Court, 1964); and especially Feigl's long essay, "The 'Mental' and the 'Physical'," in H. Feigl, M. Scriven, and G. Maxwell, *Minnesota Studies in the Philosophy of Science* (Minneapolis: University of Minnesota Press, 1958), Vol. II, which includes a full bibliography as well.

For an evolutionary naturalist thesis on the development of consciousness, see the book by the neuroanatomist, C. J. Herrick, *The Evolution of Human Nature* [Austin: University of Texas Press, 1956 (reprinted, New York: Harper Torchbooks, 1961)]. See also the works of R. W. Sellars, *The Philosophy of Physical Realism* (New York: Macmillan, 1932), and *Evolutionary Naturalism* (LaSalle, Ill.: Open Court, 1922). See also P. Laslett, ed., *The Physical Basis of Mind* (Oxford: Blackwell, 1959); B. Russell, *The Analysis of Mind* (New York: Macmillan, 1921); C. Sherrington, *Man On His Nature* (Cambridge: Cambridge University Press, 1940); E. W. Sinnott, *Matter, Mind and Man* (New York: Harper & Row, 1957).

Further works on or about the science of psychology, and related methodological questions include E. Brunswik, "Psychology as a Science of Objective Relations," *Philosophy of Science,* **4**:227–260 (1937) and also his monograph, "The Conceptual Framework of Psychology," *International Encyclopedia of Unified Science,* Vol. 10 (Chicago: University of Chicago Press, 1952); R. J. Herrnstein and E. G. Boring, eds., *A Source Book in the History of Psychology* (Cambridge, Mass.: Harvard University Press, 1965) (an excellent collection of writings from the history of psychology, most of which bear on conceptual issues. See especially Section XV, "The Nature of Psychology"); E. R. Hilgard, *Theories of Learning* (New York: Appleton-Century-Crofts, 1948); C. L. Hull, *Principles of Behavior* (New York: Appleton-Century-Crofts, 1943) and also his "Knowledge and Purpose as Habit Mechanisms," *Psychological Review,* **37**:511–525 (1930); K. Koffka, *Principles of Gestalt Psychology* (New York: Harcourt, Brace, 1935); W. Köhler, *Gestalt Psychology* (New York: Liveright, 1947) as well as his *The Place of Values in a World of Fact* (New York: Liveright, 1938), and his recent essay criticizing behaviorism, "A Task for Philosophers," in P. K. Feyerabend and G. Maxwell, eds., *Matter, Mind and Method* (Minneapolis, Minn.: University of Minnesota Press, 1966); K. Lewin, *Topological Psychology* (New York: McGraw-Hill, 1936), and "The Conceptual Representation and the Measurement of Psychological Forces," *Contributions to Psychological Theory,* **4**:1–247 (1938); K. MacQuorquodale and P. Meehl, "On a Distinction between Hypothetical Constructs and Intervening Variables," *Psychological Review,* **55**:95–107 (1948), reprinted in H. Feigl and M. Brodbeck, *op. cit.;* E. Madden, "The Nature of Psychological Explanation," *Methodos,* **9**:53–63 (1957), "The Philosophy of Science in Gestalt Psychology," *Philosophy of Science,* **19**:228–238 (1952), and "Science, Philosophy, and Gestalt Theory," *Philosophy of Science,* **20**:329–331 (1953); M. Marx, ed., *Psychological Theory—Contemporary Readings* (New York: Macmillan, 1951); P. Meehl, "Law and Convention in Psychology," in H. Feigl and M. Brodbeck, *op. cit.,* reprinted from "On the Circularity of the Law of Effect," *Psychological Bulletin,* **47**:53–75 (1950); G. Miller, E. Galanter, and K. Pribram, *Plans and the Structure of Behavior* (New York: Holt, 1960); C. C. Pratt, *The Logic of Modern Psychology* (New York: Macmillan, 1939); J. B. Pratt, *Matter and Spirit* (New York: Macmillan, 1922); W. Sellars, *Science, Perception and Reality* (New York: Humanities Press, 1963) (collects a number of relevant essays in philosophy of mind); E. A. Singer, *Mind as Behavior* (Columbus, Ohio: Adams, 1924); K. W. Spence, "The Nature of Theory-Construction in Contemporary Psychology," *Psychological Review,* **51**:47–68 (1944) and "The Postulates and Methods of Behaviorism" in H. Feigl and M. Brodbeck, *op. cit.;* S. S. Stevens, "The Operational Basis of Psychology," *American Journal of Psychology,* **47**:323–330 (1935), "The Operational Definition of Psychological Concepts," *Psychological Review,* **42**:517–525 (1935) and "Psychology and the Science of Science," *Psychological Bulletin,* **36**:221–262 (1939); E. L. Thorndike, *The Psychology of Learning* (New York: Teacher's College, Columbia, 1913); E. C. Tolman, *Purposive Behavior in Animals and Men* (New York: Century, 1932); D. C. Williams, "Scientific Method and the Existence of Consciousness," *Psychological Review,* **41**:461–479 (1934), and more recently, "Mind as a Matter of Fact," *Review of Metaphysics,* **13**:205–225 (1959).

The work of B. F. Skinner, a leading representative of behaviorism, in experimental method and in theory, includes *The Behavior of Organisms* (New York: Appleton-Century-Crofts, 1938), *Science and Human Behavior* (New York: Macmillan, 1953), and such articles as "The Operational Analysis of Scientific Terms," *Psychological Review,* **52**:270–277 (1945), reprinted in H. Feigl and M. Brodbeck, *op. cit.,* "Are Theories of Learning Necessary?" *Psychological Review,* **57**:193–216 (1950), and the recent evaluation, "Behaviorism at Fifty," *Science,* **140**:951–958 (1963), reprinted in T. W. Wann, ed., *Behaviorism and Phenomenology: Contrasting Bases for Modern Psychology* (Chicago: University of Chicago Press, 1964).

The question of minds and machines is dealt with in an extensive recent literature. See, for example, M. Arbib, *Brains, Machines and Mathematics* (New York: McGraw-Hill, 1965), for a summary of contemporary development; W. R. Ashby, *Design for a Brain* (New York: Wiley, 1954); D. V. Blake and A. M. Uttley, eds., *Proceedings of a Symposium on Mechanization of Thought Processes,* two vols. (London: Her Majesty's Stationery Office, 1959); M. Bunge, "Do Computers Think?" *Brit. J. for the Phil. of Science,* **7**:139–149, 212–220 (1956); L. Couffignal, *Les Machines à penser* (Paris: Éditions de Minuit, 1952); J. T. Culbertson, *Consciousness and Behavior* (Dubuque, Iowa: Brown, 1950) and *The Minds of Robots* (Urbana, Ill.: University of Illinois Press, 1963); J. Feldman, "Computer Simulation of Cognitive Processes," in H. Borko, ed., *Computer Applications in the Behavioral Sciences* (Englewood Cliffs, N.J.: Prentice-Hall, 1962); F. H. George, "Machines and the Brain," *Science,* **127**:1269–1274; P. de Latil, *Thinking by Machine* (Boston: Houghton Mifflin, 1957); D. M. Mackay, "Mindlike Behavior in Artifacts," *Brit. J. for the Phil. of Science,* **2**:105–121 (1951); W. Mays, "Can Machines Think?" *Philosophy,* **27**:148–162 (1952); M. Minsky, "Steps Toward Artificial Intelligence," *Proceedings of the I.R.E.,* **49**:8–30 (1961); A. Newell and H. A. Simon, "The Simulation of Human Thought," in *Current Trends in Psychological Theory* (Pittsburgh: University of Pittsburgh Press, 1961); W. Pitts and W. S. McCulloch, "How We Know Universals," *Bulletin for Mathematical Biophysics,* **9**:127–147 (1947); W. Sluckin, *Minds and Machines* (Hammondsworth: Penguin Books, 1954); M. Scriven, "The Mechanical Concept of Mind," *Mind,* **62**:230–240 (1953);

A. M. Turing, "Computing Machines and Intelligence," *Mind,* **59**:433–460 (1950) and "Can a Machine Think?" in J. R. Newman, ed., *The World of Mathematics* (New York: Simon and Schuster, 1956), Vol. IV.

In addition, there are a number of paperback collections which include articles on these questions, notably: V. C. Chappell, ed., *The Philosophy of Mind* (Englewood Cliffs, N.J.: Prentice-Hall, 1962) which contains J. Wisdom, "The Concept of Mind," U. T. Place, "Is Consciousness a Brain Process?" J. J. C. Smart, "Sensations and Brain Processes," and P. Ziff, "About Behaviorism"; also, the volume edited by S. Hook, *Dimensions of Mind* (New York: Collier Books, 1961), which contains a symposium (Part II. The Brain and the Machine) with contributions by N. Wiener, M. Scriven, "The Compleat Robot: A Prolegomena to Androidology," and H. Putnam, "Minds and Machines," and in Part III, S. Toulmin, "Concept Formation in Philosophy and Psychology," and discussion by B. F. Skinner, E. Nagel, N. Hanson, S. Morgenbesser and others. Similarly, the collection edited by A. Anderson, *Minds and Machines* (Englewood Cliffs, N.J.: Prentice-Hall, 1964), includes, in addition to some of the articles already mentioned, P. Ziff, "The Feelings of Robots," J. J. C. Smart, "Professor Ziff on Robots," and N. Smart, "Robots Incorporated." A more recent collection, edited by S. Hampshire, *Philosophy of Mind* (New York: Harper & Row, 1966) contains W. Sellars, "The Identity Approach to the Mind-Body Problem" and H. Putnam, "Robots: Machines, or Artificially Created Life?"

Part 2.

A sustained discussion on the nature of the social sciences and their methodology is in E. Nagel, *The Structure of Science* (New York: Harcourt, Brace, 1961), Chapters 13–15 (pp. 447–606). See also M. R. Cohen, *Reason and Nature* (New York: Harcourt, Brace, 1931), Book III, Chapter One, for an older but still fresh treatment. Many of the introductory texts and collections of readings listed in the bibliographical note for Chapter 1 also have relevant material, notably, the readings edited by Feigl and Brodbeck, by Wiener, and by Madden.

Methodological and general questions are discussed in such works as T. Abel, "The Operation Called *Verstehen,*" *American Journal of Sociology,* **54**:211–218 (1948), reprinted in the *Readings* edited by Feigl and Brodbeck, and also in those edited by Madden; A. F. Bentley, *Inquiry into Inquiries: Essays in Social Theory,* ed. with introduction by S. Ratner (Boston: Beacon Press, 1954); G. Bergmann, "Holism, Historicism and Emergence," *Philosophy of Science,* **11**:209–221 (1944); M. Brodbeck, "On the Philosophy of the Social Sciences," *Philosophy of Science,* **21**:140–156 (1954); R. Brown, "Explanation by Laws in Social Science," *Philosophy of Science* **21**:25–32 (1954); F. Hayek, "The Facts of the

Social Sciences," *Ethics,* **54**:1–13 (1943); G. A. Birks, "Towards a Science of Social Relations," *Brit. J. for the Phil. of Science,* **7**:117–129, 206–212 (1956); H. Blumer, "What Is Wrong with Social Theory," *American Sociological Review,* 19:3–10 (1954); D. Braybrooke, ed., *Philosophical Problems of the Social Science* (New York: Macmillan, 1965); A. Gewirth, "Subjectivism and Objectivism in the Social Sciences," *Philosophy of Science,* **21**:157–163 (1954); Q. Lauer, *The Logic of Social Inquiry* (London: Routledge and Kegan Paul, 1960); M. Ginsburg, "Causality in the Social Sciences," *Aristotelian Society Proceedings,* **35**:253–270 (1935); A. Grünbaum, "Historical Determinism, Social Activism and Prediction in the Social Sciences," *Brit. J. for the Phil. of Science,* **7**:236–240 (1956); A. Gurwitsch, "The Common Sense World as Social Reality: A Discourse on Alfred Schutz," *Social Research,* **29**:50–72 (1962); R. Handy, "Philosophy's Neglect of the Social Sciences," *Philosophy of Science,* **25**:117–124 (1958); F. Hayek, *The Counter-Revolution of Science* (New York: The Free Press, 1952); I. L. Horowitz, *Philosophy, Science and the Sociology of Knowledge* (Springfield, Ill.: Thomas, 1961); A. Kaplan, *The Conduct of Inquiry—Methodology for Behavioral Sciences* (San Francisco: Chandler, 1965); F. Kaufmann, *Methodology in the Social Sciences* (London: Oxford University Press, 1944); P. F. Lazarsfeld, ed., *Mathematical Thinking in the Social Sciences* (New York: The Free Press, 1954), and also his articles, "Problems in Methodology," in R. K. Merton, L. Broom, and L. S. Cottrell, Jr., eds., *Sociology Today: Problems and Prospects* (New York: Basic Books, 1959), and "Philosophy of Science and Empirical Social Research," in E. Nagel, P. Suppes, and A. Tarski, eds., *Logic, Methodology and Philosophy of Science* (Stanford, Calif.: Stanford University Press, 1962). (Lazarsfeld here traces the influence of analyses in the philosophy of science, e.g., Hempel and Oppenheim's work on the concept of "Type," upon empirical research in the social sciences. See, for further discussion, P. F. Lazarsfeld and A. H. Barton, "Qualitative Measurement in the Social Sciences—Classification, Typologies and Indices,," in D. Lerner and H. D. Lasswell, eds., *The Policy Sciences* (Stanford, Calif.: Stanford University Press, 1951). On questions of social scientific measurement and the use of mathematics, see also J. K. Kemeny and J. L. Snell, *Mathematical Models in the Social Sciences* (Boston: Ginn and Co., 1962). On questions of so-called qualitative measurement, see also K. Lewin, *Field Theory in Social Science* (New York: Harper & Row, 1951). See also A. Kaplan, "The Study of Man: Sociology Learns the Language of Mathematics," *Commentary,* **14**:274–284 (1952), and the collection edited by H. Borko, *Computer Applications in the Behavioral Sciences* (Englewood Cliffs, N.J.: Prentice-Hall, 1962).

Further works on general questions are G. A. Lundberg, "The Concept of Law in the Social Sciences," *Philosophy of Science,* **5**:189–203 (1938); R. M. MacIver, *Social Causation* (Boston: Ginn and Co., 1942); M. Mandelbaum, "Societal Facts," *British Journal of Sociology,* **6**:305–317

(1955) and "Societal Laws," *Brit. J. for the Phil. of Science,* **8**:211–224 (1957); J. Mayer, *Social Science Principles in Light of Scientific Method* (Durham, N.C.: Duke University Press, 1941); G. H. Mead, *Mind, Self and Society* (Chicago: University of Chicago Press, 1934); J. S. Mill, "On the Logic of the Moral Sciences," in *A System of Logic* (available in paperback, E. Nagel, ed., *John Stuart Mill's Philosophy of Scientific Method* (New York: Hafner, 1950, Book VI); also reprinted in P. Wiener, *Readings in Philosophy of Science* (New York: Scribner, 1953); L. von Mises, *Human Action* (New Haven: Yale University Press, 1949); E. Nagel and C. Hempel, "Problems of Concepts and Theory in the Social Sciences," Symposium, in *Language, Science and Human Rights, American Philosophical Association Proceedings* (Philadelphia: University of Pennsylvania Press, 1952).

M. Natanson, ed., *Philosophy of the Social Sciences* (New York: Random House, 1963) is an excellent collection of essays, including the Nagel article in the Symposium mentioned above, G. A. Lundberg, "The Postulates of Science and their Implications for Sociology," G. Simmel, "How is Society Possible?" C. G. Hempel, "Typological Methods in the Social Sciences," A. Schutz, "Concepts and Theory Formation in the Social Sciences," M. Natanson, "A Study in Philosophy and the Social Sciences," M. Merleau-Ponty, "The Philosophers and Sociology," L. Goldstein, "The Phenomenological and the Naturalistic Approaches to the Social" and others. The latter essay characterizes the volume, which includes a wide selection of phenomenological approaches not ordinarily found in the current philosophy of science readings, as well as some important naturalistic and analytic treatments. The book also has a good bibliography. Among the classic logical positivist approaches is the monograph by O. Neurath, "Foundations of the Social Sciences," Vol. II, no. 1 of the *Encyclopedia of Unified Science* (Chicago: University of Chicago Press, 1944). B. Phillips, *Social Research* (New York: Macmillan, 1965) is a recent text which emphasizes current methodological techniques and conceptual issues in the social sciences. On the questions of "objectivity" in the social sciences, see the selection from Max Weber (under that title) in P. Wiener, *op. cit.;* J. A. Passmore, "Can the Social Sciences Be Value-Free," reprinted in H. Feigl and M. Brodbeck, *op. cit.;* and E. Bisbee, "Objectivity in the Social Sciences," *Philosophy of Science,* **4**:372–382 (1937). Karl Popper's views on the social theories of Plato, Hegel and Marx, and his critique of "historicism" are in *The Open Society and its Enemies,* rev. ed. (Princeton, N.J.: Princeton University Press, 1950) and *The Poverty of Historicism* (London: Routledge and Kegan Paul, 1961). See also (for a "historicist" view) J. H. Randall, Jr., "History and the Social Sciences," reprinted in P. Wiener, *op. cit.*

Additional readings on general questions include M. Roshwald, "Value Judgments in the Social Sciences," *Brit. J. for the Phil. of Science,* **6**:186–208 (1955); R. Rudner, "Philosophy and Social Science," *Philosophy of*

Science, **21**:164–168 (1954) and also his *Philosophy of Social Science* (Englewood Cliffs, N.J.: Prentice-Hall, 1965); M. Weber, *The Methodology of the Social Sciences* (New York: The Free Press, 1949); P. Winch, *The Idea of a Social Science: and Its Relation to Philosophy* (London: Routledge and Kegan Paul, 1960); B. Wootton, *Testament for Social Science: An Essay in the Application of Scientific Method to Human Problems* (London: Allen and Unwin, 1950); E. Zilsel, "Physics and the Problem of Historico-Sociological Law," in H. Feigl and M. Brodbeck, *op. cit.* The forthcoming major collection, M. Brodbeck, ed., *Readings in the Philosophy of Social Science* (New York: Macmillan, 1967) brings together a large number of essays, on the nature of social action, values, social facts and social laws, explanation, models and measurement, and other related topics in the social sciences.

Works dealing specifically with problems of sociology and anthropology include D. Bidney, *Theoretical Anthropology* (New York: Columbia University Press, 1953); F. S. Chapin, "The Meaning of Measurement in Sociology," *Publications of the American Sociological Society,* no. 24 (1930); E. Durkheim, *Sociology and Philosophy,* tr. D. F. Pocock (New York: The Free Press, 1953); A. Edel, "Some Relations of Philosophy and Anthropology," *American Anthropologist,* **55**:649–660 (1953); R. Firth, "Function," in W. L. Thomas, ed., *Current Anthropology* (Chicago: University of Chicago Press, 1955); and in the same volume, J. S. Huxley, "Evolution, Cultural and Biological"; I. Jarvie, *The Revolution in Anthropology* (New York: Humanities Press, 1964); H. Kelsen, *Society and Nature—A Sociological Inquiry* (London: K. Paul, Trench, Trubner, 1946); A. L. Kroeber, *The Nature of Culture* (Chicago: University of Chicago Press, 1960); and A. L. Kroeber and others, *Anthropology Today—An Encyclopedic Inventory* (Chicago: University of Chicago Press, 1953); B. Malinowski, *A Scientific Theory of Culture, and Other Essays* [Chapel Hill, N.C.: University of North Carolina Press, 1944 (the title essay is reprinted in P. Wiener, *op. cit.*)]; R. K. Merton, *Social Theory and Social Structure* (New York: The Free Press, 1949); C. W. Mills, *The Sociological Imagination* (New York: Oxford University Press, 1959); (a collection of the late C. W. Mills' essays, including one on philosophy of science and its limits); V. Pareto, *The Mind and Society,* tr. A. Bongiorno and A. Livingston (New York: Harcourt, Brace, 1935) four vols.; T. Parsons, *The Structure of Social Action,* 2nd ed., (New York: The Free Press, 1949); T. Parsons and E. A. Shils, *Toward a General Theory of Action* (Cambridge, Mass.: Harvard University Press, 1951); A. Schutz, "The Social World and the Theory of Social Action," *Social Research,* **27**:203–221 (1960). See also R. M. Zaner, "Theory of Intersubjectivity: Alfred Schutz," *Social Research,* **28**:71–93 (1961); L. A. White, *The Science of Culture* (New York: Farrar, Strauss, 1949); A. R. Radcliffe-Brown, *A Natural Science of Society* (New York: The Free Press, 1957), and also his *Structure and Function in Primitive Society* (London: Cohen & West, 1952); N. Timasheff, *Sociological Theory* (Garden City, N.Y.: Doubleday, 1955); K. H. Wolff, "The Unique and the General: Toward a Theory of Sociology," *Philosophy of Science,* **15**:192–210 (1948).

On questions of the theory of history, see H. Ausubel, *Historians and Their Craft* (New York: Russell & Russell, 1950); E. H. Carr, *What Is History?* (New York: Knopf, 1962); M. Chatterji, *History as a Science* (London: Butterworth, 1927); M. R. Cohen, *The Meaning of Human History* (LaSalle, Ill.: Open Court, 1947); R. G. Collingwood, *The Idea of History* (London: Oxford University Press, 1946); A. Danto, "Mere Chronicle and History Proper," *Journal of Philosophy,* **50**:173–182 (1953); also, his "On Explanations in History," *Philosophy of Science,* **23**:15–30 (1956) and the book *Analytic Philosophy of History* (Cambridge: Cambridge University Press, 1965); W. Dilthey, *Selected Readings from his Works,* M. A. Hodges, ed., (London: Routledge and Kegan Paul, 1944); W. Dray, *Laws and Explanation in History* (London: Oxford University Press, 1957); W. B. Gallie, *Philosophy and the Historical Understanding* (London: Chatto and Windus, 1964); P. Gardiner, *The Nature of Historical Explanation* (London: Oxford University Press, 1952); J. B. S. Haldane, *Everything Has a History* (London: Allen and Unwin, 1951); C. Hempel, "The Function of General Laws in History," *Journal of Philosophy,* **39**:35–48 (1942) and also "Explanation in Science and History," in R. G. Colodny, ed., *Frontiers of Science and Philosophy* (Pittsburgh: University of Pittsburgh Press, 1962); S. Hook, ed., *Philosophy and History—A Symposium* (New York: New York University Press, 1963); M. Mandelbaum, *The Problem of Historical Knowledge* (New York: Liveright, 1938); H. Meyerhoff, *The Philosophy of History in Our Time* (New York: Doubleday, Anchor, 1959); G. Salvemini, *Historian and Scientist: An Essay on the Nature of History and the Social Sciences* (Cambridge, Mass.: Harvard University Press, 1939); P. Schrecker, *Work and History* (Princeton, N.J.: Princeton University Press, 1948); E. J. Tapp, "Some Aspects of Causation in History," *Journal of Philosophy,* **49**:67–79 (1952); W. H. Walsh, *An Introduction to Philosophy of History* (London: Hutchinson, 1951); J. W. N. Watkins, "Ideal Types and Historical Explanation," *Brit. J. for the Phil. of Science,* **3**:22–43 (1952), reprinted in H. Feigl and M. Brodbeck, *op. cit.;* see also his "Historical Explanation in the Social Sciences," *Brit. J. for the Phil. of Science,* **8**:104–117 (1957); M. White, *The Foundations of Historical Knowledge* (New York: Harper & Row (1965); Watkins' discussion with L. Goldstein on the question of so-called methodological individualism is in *Journal of Philosophy,* **55**:390–395 (1958), in *Philosophy of Science,* **22**:58–62, and in the *Brit. J. for the Phil. of Science,* **10**:242–244 (1959). Goldstein's discussion is in "The Inadequacy of the Principle of Methodological Individualism," *Journal of Philosophy,* **53**:801–813 (1956) and again in "The

Two Theses of Methodological Individualism," *Brit. J. for the Phil. of Science,* **9**:1–11 (1958). See also his "Evidence and Events in History," *Philosophy of Science,* **29**:175–194 (1962), and also M. Brodbeck, "Methodological Individualism: Definition and Reduction," *Philosophy of Science,* **25**:1–22 (1958). See also, S. Hook, *The Hero in History* (Boston: Beacon Press, 1943).

On the Marxist view of the individual in history, and of historical laws, see F. Engels, *On Historical Materialism* (New York: International Publishers, n.d.); G. Plekhanov, *The Materialist Conception of History* (New York: International Publishers, 1940) and also his essay, *The Role of the Individual in History* (New York: International Publishers, 1940). See also L. Feuer, ed., *Marx and Engels, Basic Writings on Politics and Philosophy* (New York: Doubleday, Anchor, 1959), especially the *Theses on Feuerbach,* the excerpt from *The German Ideology* and the letters on Historical Materialism. On the related question of historical determinism, see E. Nagel, "Determinism in History," *Journal of Philosophy and Phenomenological Research,* **20**:290–317 (1960).

BIBLIOGRAPHICAL NOTE—CHAPTER 15

Among the works dealing with the scientific study of science as a social institution and as a value system, there are: B. Barber, *The Sociology of Science* (New York: Free Press, 1963), and also his *Science and the Social Order* (New York: The Free Press, 1952); J. D. Bernal, *The Social Function of Science* (London: Routledge and Kegan Paul, 1939); R. K. Merton, *Social Theory and Social Structure* (New York: The Free Press, 1957).

See also, in a more general context, J. Bronowski, *Science and Human Values* (New York: Messner, 1958); E. Cassirer, "Implications of Physics for Ethics," in E. Madden, ed., *The Structure of Scientific Thought* (Boston: Houghton-Mifflin, 1960). [Chapter 13 of Cassirer's *Determinism and Indeterminism in Modern Physics* (New Haven: Yale University Press, 1956)]; also, see E. Cassirer, *An Essay on Man—Introduction to a Philosophy of Human Culture* (New Haven: Yale University Press, 1945); A. Einstein, "The Laws of Science and the Laws of Ethics," in H. Feigl and M. Brodbeck, eds., *Readings in the Philosophy of Science* (New York: Appleton-Century-Crofts, 1953) and his "Science, Philosophy and Religion," in P. Wiener, ed., *Readings in Philosophy of Science* (New York: Scribner, 1953); H. Feigl, "The Scientific Outlook: Naturalism and Humanism," in H. Feigl and M. Brodbeck, *op. cit.,* and the brief article, "Models of Man," in *The Humanist,* **25**:260–261 (1965); E. W. Hall, *Modern Science and Human Values* (Princeton, N.J.: Van Nostrand, 1956), and the important later work, *Our Knowledge of Fact and Value*

(Chapel Hill, N.C.: University of North Carolina Press, 1961); J. A. Irving, *Science and Value: Explorations in Philosophy* (Toronto: Ryerson Press, 1952); W. Köhler, *The Place of Value in a World of Fact* (New York: Liveright, 1938); and from an anthropologist's view, R. Linton, "The Problem of Universal Values," in R. F. Spencer, ed., *Method and Perspective in Anthropology* (Minneapolis: University of Minnesota Press, 1954).

The renowned physicist R. B. Lindsay raises the question of whether a science of ethics is possible, in "Physics, Ethics, and the Thermodynamic Imperative," in B. Baumrin, ed., *Philosophy of Science—The Delaware Seminar* Vol. II (New York: Interscience, 1963); and for a point of view critical of rationalist interpretations of science, see the works of M. Polanyi, *Science, Faith and Society,* (London: Oxford University Press, 1946); *The Logic of Liberty* (Chicago: University of Chicago Press, 1951); and *Personal Knowledge* (New York: Harper Torchbooks, 1960).

See also B. Russell, "Science and Values," Chapter XVII of *The Scientific Outlook* [(New York: Norton, 1962), also reprinted in P. Wiener, *op. cit.*], and his *The Impact of Science on Society* (New York: Simon and Schuster, 1953). H. Mehlberg provides a tough-minded analysis in chapters on the social function of science, the intrinsic value of science, and the instrumental value of science, in his *The Reach of Science* (Toronto: University of Toronto Press, 1958). And with usual clarity, M. R. Cohen deals with "The Possibility of Ethical Science," in *Reason and Nature* (New York: Harcourt, Brace, 1931), Book III, Chapter 5.

Fundamental treatments of value theory relevant to the issues raised here are J. Dewey, *Theory of Valuation,* Vol. II, no. 4, *International Encyclopedia of Unified Science* (Chicago: University of Chicago Press, 19) and also his *Philosophy and Civilization* (New York: Minton, Balch & Co., 1931) esp. the essay, "Science and Society," as well as the chapter on Reconstruction in Moral Conceptions, in *Reconstruction in Philosophy* (Boston: Beacon Press, 1948), reprinted in E. Madden, ed., *The Structure of Scientific Thought* (Boston: Houghton Mifflin, 1960); A. Edel, *Science and the Structure of Ethics,* Vol. II, no. 3, *International Encyclopedia of Unified Science* (Chicago: University of Chicago Press, 1961); and R. B. Perry, *Realms of Value* (Cambridge, Mass.: Harvard University Press, 1954).

APPENDIX A

Some of the general histories of science which deal with the development of the concept of motion and related questions are M. Boas, *The Scientific Renaissance, 1450–1630* (New York: Harper & Row, 1962) Chapter vii, "The Uses of Mathematics"; H. Butterfield, *The Origins of*

Modern Science, 1300–1800 (New York: Macmillan, 1961) especially chapter one, which deals with the theory of impetus, and the relation of concepts of motion to the ideas of force and inertia; A. C. Crombie, *Augustine to Galileo—The History of Science, 400–1650* (London: Falcon Educational Books, 1952); A. R. Hall, *From Galileo to Newton, 1630–1720* (New York: Harper & Row, 1963) especially chapters ii and iii, on Galileo's physics and mathematics; and also A. R. Hall, *The Scientific Revolution* (Boston: Beacon Press, 1954) especially Chapter iii; S. F. Mason, *Main Currents in Scientific Thought* (New York: Schuman, 1953); E. Mach, *The Science of Mechanics* (Chicago: Open Court, 1893); G. Sarton's *magnum opus: Introduction to the History of Science,* three volumes (Baltimore: Williams and Wilkins, 1927–1948) which contains exhaustive bibliographies (Volume III is on the fourteenth century); and L. Thorndike's great work, *A History of Magic and Experimental Science,* eight vols. (New York: Macmillan, 1923–1958).

Among the studies that trace the relations of scientific and philosophic thought, E. A. Burtt, *Metaphysical Foundations of Modern Science* (revised edition, 1932) (New York: Doubleday Anchor Books, n.d.) is indispensable. See also, J. H. Randall, Jr., *The Making of the Modern Mind* (New *York*: Houghton Mifflin, 1940). Aristotle's *Physics* is available in the translation of P. H. Wicksteed and F. M. Cornford, *Loeb Classical Library,* two vols., 1929–1934, and in the edition of W. D. Ross, with annotations, *Aristotle's Physics* (Oxford: Oxford University Press, 1936). On the experience of motion and the developmental account of the concept from a psychological point of view, see H. Werner, *The Comparative Psychology of Mental Development* (New York: International University Press, 1948); and in the works of J. Piaget, see for example, *The Child's Conception of the World* (Paterson, N.J.: Littlefield, Adams and Co., 1965); *The Child's Conception of Physical Causality* (Paterson, N.J.: Littlefield, Adams and Co., 1960); *The Child's Conception of Geometry* with B. Inhelder and A. Szeminska (New York: Harper Torchbooks, 1964) especially Chapters 1, 7, and 10; and especially *Les Notions de mouvement et de vitesse chez l'enfant* (Paris: Presses Universitaires de France, 1946).

Among recent collections of articles on the history of science, see R. M. Palter, *Towards Modern Science,* Vol. I: *Studies in Ancient and Medieval Science* (New York: Noonday Press, 1961) which includes P. Duhem, "Medieval Physics," O. Neugebauer, "Exact Science in Antiquity," E. A. Moody, "Laws of Motion in Medieval Physics," and G. Holton, "Kepler's Universe: Its Physics and Metaphysics." See also R. Taton, ed., *History of Science—Ancient and Medieval Science from the Beginnings to 1450,* tr. A. J. Pomerans (New York: Basic Books, 1963) which has a number of very meaty articles.

Special studies on the background of ancient and medieval physics and the concepts of motion (in addition to those listed in the bibliographical note for Chapter 4) include M. Clagett, *Giovanni Marliani and Late Medieval Physics* (New York: Columbia University Press, 1941); L. Cooper, *Aristotle, Galileo and the Tower of Pisa* (Ithaca, N.Y.: Cornell University Press, 1935) a stimulating argument which we refer to in the text, see p.); F. M. Cornford, *The Laws of Motion in Ancient Thought* (Cambridge: Cambridge University Press, 1931); A. C. Crombie, *Oxford's Contribution to the Origins of Modern Science* (Oxford: Blackwell, 1954).

The work which revealed the complexity and sophistication of the development of medieval mechanics is P. Duhem, *Études sur Leonardo da Vinci,* three vols. (Paris, 1906–13). See also C. H. Haskins, *Studies in Medieval Science* (Cambridge, Mass.: Harvard University Press, 1927); T. L. Heath, *Mathematics in Aristotle* (Oxford: 1949); W. A. Heidel, *The Heroic Age of Science* (Baltimore, Md.: Williams and Wilkins, 1933); A. Koyré, *Études Galiléennes,* three vols. (Paris: Hermann & Cie., 1939) —an outstanding analysis, which should be translated into English; De L. O'Leary, *How Greek Science Passed to the Arabs* (London: Routledge, 1949); H. Shapiro, *Motion, Time, and Place According to William of Ockham* (Louvain: *Publications of the Franciscan Institute,* Philosophical Series, no. 13, 1957); J. B. Skemp, *The Theory of Motion in Plato's Later Dialogues* (Cambridge: Cambridge University Press, 1942); E. W. Strong, *Procedures and Metaphysics: A Study in the Philosophy of Mathematical-Physical Science in the Sixteenth and Seventeenth Centuries* (Berkeley: University of California Press, 1936); C. Wilson, *William Heytesbury: Medieval Logic and the Rise of Mathematical Physics* (Madison: University of Wisconsin Press, *Publications in Medieval Science,* No. 3). Many of the important works in this area are available only in German, French and languages other than English. Though these are not listed here in any number, still one should mention such outstanding and relevant works as Anneliese Maier's *Die Vorlaufer Galileis im 14. Jahrhundert,* Rome, 1949; and Ernst Borchert's *Die Lehre von der Bewegung bei Nicolaus Oresme,* Münster, 1934.

The periodical literature contains many special studies such as D. J. Allan, "Medieval Versions of Aristotle, *De Caelo,* and of the Commentary of Simplicius," *Medieval and Renaissance Studies,* **2**:82–120 (1950); F. Cajori, "Falling Bodies in Ancient and Modern Times," *Science and Mathematics,* **21**:638–648 (1921); M. Clagett, "Some General Aspects of Medieval Physics," *Isis,* **39**:29–44 (1948); I. B. Cohen, "Galileo's Rejection of the Possibility of Velocity Changing Uniformly with Respect to Distance," *Isis,* **47**:231–38 (1956); A. Koyré, "A Documentary History of the Problem of Fall from Kepler to Newton," *Transactions of the American Philosophical Society,* New Series, **45**:329–95 (1955); and also Koyré's "Galileo and Plato" in P. Wiener and A. Noland, *Roots of Scientific Thought* (New York: Basic Books, 1957) (in which Koyré distinguishes two platonisms: "mystical arithmetology" and "mathematical science"); E. A. Moody, "Galileo and Avempace: The Dynamics of the Leaning Tower Experiment," *Journal of the History of Ideas,* **12**:163–193, 375–422 (1951) and also his "Laws of Motion in Medieval Physics," *The Scientific Monthly,* **72**:18–23 (1951); J. H. Randall, Jr., "The Development of Scientific Method in the University of Padua," *Journal of the History of Ideas,* **1**:177–206 (1940).

Finally, some of the available primary sources on medieval mechanics and on Galileo are the series of *Publications in Medieval Science,* which includes the sources cited in the text from M. Clagett, *The Science of Mechanics in the Middle Ages;* H. Lamar Crosby, *Thomas of Bradwardine: His "Tractatus de proportionibus." Its Significance for the Development of Mathematical Physics;* I. E. Drabkin and S. Drake, tr., Galileo Galilei: *On Motion* and *On Mechanics* (both in one volume); and E. A. Moody and M. Clagett, *The Medieval Science of Weights.* All these are published at Madison, Wisconsin, University of Wisconsin Press. In an unpublished, mimeographed version, E. A. Moody, *The Rise of Mechanism in Fourteenth Century Natural Philosophy* (New York: Columbia University, circa 1949), contains translations of Jean Buridan and John Dumbleton which are essential to the study of the development of the laws of motion, and it is to be hoped that they will be published sometime soon. Galileo's works are available in several editions, but the central ones of concern here are: the work listed above (*On Motion* and *On Mechanics*), the *Dialogues Concerning Two New Sciences,* tr. H. Crew and A. de Salvio Evanston and Chicago: Northwestern University Press, 1946) and the collection translated and edited by S. Drake, *Discoveries and Opinions of Galileo* (New York: Doubleday, Anchor, 1957) which includes *The Starry Messenger* and excerpts from *The Assayer,* among other writings.

INDEX

Index